V. D. KUPRADZE

POTENTIAL METHODS in the THEORY OF ELASTICITY

Translated from Russian by
H. Gutfreund
Translation edited by
I. Meroz

Israel Program for Scientific Translations
Jerusalem 1965

Published in the U. S. A. by:
DANIEL DAVEY & CO., INC.
257 Park Avenue South, New York, N. Y

This book is a translation of
METODY POTENTSIALA V TEORII UPRUGOSTI

Gosudarstvennoe Izdatel'stvo Fiziko-Matematicheskoi Literatury
Moskva 1963

IPST Cat. No. 2109

Printed and Bound in Israel
Printed by S. Monson, Jerusalem
Binding: K. Wiener

X/10

TABLE OF CONTENTS

PREFACE

This book is devoted to the application of potential methods to the fundamental boundary-value problems of the theory of elasticity. This subject has been treated by the author before /13a, d, f/, but here the investigation is extended for the first time to sectionally, or piecewise-homogeneous bodies, and the associated existence theorems for the solutions of the fundamental boundary value problems are proved.

Another distinctive feature of this book is the development of the entire theory of boundary-value problems on the basis of the theory of singular integral equations. This has enabled us to embrace a wider class of boundary-value problems (contact problems, mixed problems), and also to indicate the new possibilities offered by this method for exact and approximate solution of many problems*. The book also presents the first account of two new methods for approximate solution of boundary-value problems.

Chaps. I–VII and X deal with oscillations and equilibrium of isotropic homogeneous and piecewise-homogeneous three-dimensional bodies; the basic uniqueness theorems are proved in Chap. III. Two-dimensional equilibrium problems for anisotropic homogeneous and piecewise-homogeneous bodies are considered in Chaps. VIII–IX.

The treatment of these problems is based on an extension of the Fredholm method. The latter, in which potential theory is used in conjunction with the theory of linear integral equations, is extended to singular integral equations of boundary value problems of the theory of elasticity. In this manner the existence theorems could be proved for homogeneous bodies in the general case, and for piecewise-homogeneous bodies with minor restrictions of the physical parameters. These results are presented in Chaps. VI-VII.

Several problems important for applications are considered in Chaps. IV and IX, and their solution is either constructed explicitly or by means of successive approximations. Chapter X deals with two methods of approximate solution of boundary-value problems and describes their application in elasticity.

The book is based on lectures given by the author in 1959–1962 in various special courses in the mechanical-mathematical faculty of the University of Tbilisi, and also on results obtained by young colleagues and postgraduate students which have been reported in seminars.

The author wishes to thank L. G. Magnaradze and S. G. Mikhlin, who read the manuscript and made many valuable comments. Individual chapters were also read by participants of the seminars; an especially great effort was made by M. O. Basheleishvili, T. V. Burchuladze and T. G. Gegeliya. The computations and tables of chapter X were carried out by N. Arveladze and L. Khachapuridze of the Computational Center of the Academy of Sciences of the Georgian SSR. The author feels much indebted to his young colleagues and offers them his cordial thanks.

* T. G. Gegeliya /5f/, using the theory of singular integral equations and a somewhat different approach, has recently proved the existence theorems for the fundamental boundary-value problems of statics for homogeneous elastic bodies bounded by surfaces of a more general class than Lyapunov surfaces.

INTRODUCTION

Potential methods and the theory of linear integral equations were first applied to the solution of the first boundary-value problem of elasticity by Fredholm*.

Fredholm's work was followed by many papers, some of them outstanding contributions, on the application of his method to static problems. Notwithstanding, not all problems of the static theory can yet be regarded as satisfactorily settled. This concerns both general issues and the solution of individual problems. One of the reasons for this situation is, in the author's opinion, that the classical Fredholm theory is not sufficient for the investigation of the second fundamental boundary-value problem (stresses prescribed on the boundary) and the third and fourth problems (displacements and stresses each partly prescribed).

The differential equations for the displacements in elastic equilibrium constitutes an elliptic system and their integration for given boundary values of the displacements (first boundary-value problem) is a Dirichlet problem, analogous to the classical Dirichlet problem for harmonic functions. This was shown, following Fredholm, by Lauricella** and Marcolongo***.

For the second boundary-value problem of elasticity, however, we cannot expect a similar analogy with the second boundary-value problem of the theory of harmonic functions (the Neumann problem). The reason for this is that the stress vector given at the boundary in the second problem is expressed by a linear combination of first derivatives of the displacements which does not reduce to the normal derivative. Therefore the second boundary-value problem of elasticity considerably differs from the Neumann problem, in which the data are the values of the normal derivative of the unknown function. The second boundary-value problem of elasticity, unlike the Neumann problem, may not in general be reduced directly to a regular integral Fredholm equation. The same goes for the third and fourth problems. Nevertheless, efforts have been made in all works, old and new, to treat these problems by the Fredholm method by reducing them directly to a regular Fredholm equation. These attempts to avoid singular equations usually fell through because the kernels of the equations turned out not to be regular after all, which made Fredholm's theory inapplicable, or because the obtained equations did not represent the problems properly.

* Fredholm, J. Solution d'un problème fondamental de la théorie de l'élasticité.— Arkiv för Matematik, Astronomi och Fysik, 2(28): 3-8. 1906.

** Lauricella, G. — Atti della Reale Accademia dei Lincei, 15: 426-432. 1906.

*** Marcolongo, R. — Ibid., 16: 742-794. 1907.

Two of the best known old papers of this kind, those of Korn* and Boggio**, were criticized by Weyl***.

In his critique, Weyl mentions two different ways of solution of the first boundary-value problem; one was developed by Fredholm, Lauricella, and Marcolongo; the other by Korn, and Boggio. While the first is analogous to the Neumann-Fredholm method in potential theory, the second, in Weyl's words, "leads to integral equations with complicated, intractable kernels, which Boggio erroneously considers to be regular." This paper of Weyl contains the well-known reduction of the second boundary-value problem of elasticity to regular Fredholm equations by means of the so-called antenna potential † (cf. I, 5). Weyl's equations, however, are not completely equivalent to the considered problem and the uniqueness theorem for the latter does not imply the absence of nontrivial solutions for Weyl's homogeneous integral equations. In order to prove under these conditions the solvability of his inhomogeneous equations, Weyl assumes (this has not been proved in the general case) the possibility of biorthonormalizing the sets of fundamental solutions of a pair of adjoint Fredholm equations of the second kind (cf. VI, 5, 11 (end), 14).

Of the later works concerned with Fredholm's method it is worthwhile to mention Lichtenstein's †† paper. He found it necessary to impose severe restrictions on the boundary surfaces; Lichtenstein's method has not yet been applied to the second, third and fourth fundamental boundary value problems.

We may further mention the comparatively recent work of Kinoshita and Mura †††, who use the potential method to construct integral equations for the first two static boundary-value problems of the three-dimensional theory of elasticity. As should be expected, these equations, which are found to be mutually adjoint, are singular and do not belong to the class of Fredholm equations; despite this, the authors apply to them Fredholm's theorems and alternative and illegitimately obtain conclusions which happen to be correct ‡.

So far we have considered static problems, which run into difficulties that can be only partially overcome by means of Fredholm's method. New difficulties must clearly arise when we pass to dynamic problems, even in the simplest case of forced oscillations‡‡.

These difficulties become more severe if instead of homogeneous bodies one considers composite bodies made up of parts having different elastic properties which are somehow joined together. In the oscillation and equilibrium problems of such piecewise-homogeneous bodies, it is necessary

* Korn, A. Über die Lösung der ersten Randwertaufgabe der Elastizitätstheorie. — Rend. Circ. Mat. Palermo, 30(2). 1910.

** Boggio, T. Nuova risolutione di un problema fondamentale della teoria dell'elasticita. — Atti Reale Accademia dei Lincei, 16(2). 1907.

*** Weyl, H. Das asymptotische Verteilungsgesetz der Eigenschwingungen eines beliebig gestalteten elastischen Körpers. — Rend. Circ. Mat. Palermo, 39(1). 1915.

† [Describes the electrostatic field of a surface bristling with uniformly charged normal filaments, or "antennae." Hence the name.]

†† Lichtenstein, L. Über die erste Randwertaufgabe der Elastizitätstheorie. — Math., 20. 1924.

††† Kinoshita, M. and T. Mura. On Boundary-Value Problem of Elasticity. — Research Reports of the Faculty of Engineering, Meiji University, No. 8: 56-82. 1956.

‡ The integral equations appearing in this work were derived before in a more general form by the author /13d/.

‡‡ The general case may be reduced to this by means of the Laplace transform.

to take into account not only the boundary conditions characteristic of the first, second, third or fourth boundary-value problem, but also the coupling between the separate component parts, i.e., the conditions of contact at the interfaces between different media.

All the boundary-value problems described above, from static problems for homogeneous to dynamic for piecewise-homogeneous elastic bodies, are treated in this book by the methods of potential theory and many-dimensional singular integral equations; the basic existence theorems are proved and an effective method of approximate solution is described.

The Giraud-Mikhlin theory of multiple integral equations with singular kernels of a certain type, mainly for a single equation, was a comparatively late development. But in the theory of elasticity we almost always deal with systems of equations; this has called for an extension of the Giraud-Mikhlin theory to the systems of singular integral equations of elasticity over closed manifolds. This problem, which in the words of Fichera* is "tutt'altro che semplice" [anything but simple] and to which Ch. V of the present book is devoted, turned out to be not quite so difficult after all**.

* Fichera, G. Sull'esistenza e sul calcolo delle soluzioni dei problemi al contorno, relativi all'equilibrio di un corpo elastico. — Annali Sc. norm. super. Pisa, Series III, Vol. IV: 36. 1950. This interesting work contains proofs of the existence theorems of the fundamental boundary-value problems of elastostatics by means of a method different from Fredholm's.

** Note added in proof. Mikhlin's recent book /22c/ gives another presentation of the theory of systems of many-dimensional singular integral equations on closed manifolds.

Chapter I

SOME FUNDAMENTAL EQUATIONS AND RELATIONS OF THE THEORY OF ELASTICITY

§ 1. Basic differential equations. The Betti formulas

In an orthogonal Cartesian coordinate system $(x_1x_2x_3)$ let $\boldsymbol{v}\,(v_1, v_2, v_3)$ stand for the elastic displacement vector, v_{jk} for the components of the strain tensor,

$$v_{jk}=\frac{1}{2}\left(\frac{\partial v_j}{\partial x_k}+\frac{\partial v_k}{\partial x_j}\right) \qquad (j,\ k=1,\ 2,\ 3;),$$

and $\tau_{jk}(\boldsymbol{v})$, or just τ_{jk}, for the components of the stress tensor corresponding to the displacements $\boldsymbol{v}$; Hooke's law relates the τ_{jk} to the v_{jk} through

$$\tau_{jk}=\sum_{m=1}^{3}\sum_{n=1}^{3} c_{jkmn}v_{mn} \qquad (j,\ k=1,\ 2,\ 3).$$

The elastic stiffness constants c_{jkmn} satisfy the relations

$$c_{jkmn}=c_{mnjk}=c_{kjmn},$$

which imply

$$\tau_{jk}=\tau_{kj}.$$

This reduces the number of independent elastic constants to 21; if the body is isotropic, just two of them will actually be independent. For an isotropic homogeneous body the elastic constants are usually expressed in terms of the Lamé constants λ and μ by the relations

$$c_{jjjj}=\lambda+2\mu, \qquad c_{jjkk}=\lambda, \qquad c_{jkjk}=2\mu;$$

the remaining constants c_{jkmn} vanish.

Hooke's law then assumes the form

$$\tau_{jj}=\lambda\operatorname{div}\boldsymbol{v}+2\mu\frac{\partial v_j}{\partial x_j}, \qquad \tau_{jk}=\mu\left(\frac{\partial v_j}{\partial x_k}+\frac{\partial v_k}{\partial x_j}\right) \qquad (j,\ k=1,\ 2,\ 3).$$

The equations of motion of an elastic body under a body force $\boldsymbol{F}$ are

$$\sum_{k=1}^{3}\frac{\partial\tau_{jk}}{\partial x_k}+F_j=\frac{\partial^2 v_j}{\partial t^2} \qquad (j=1,\ 2,\ 3).$$

Inserting here the τ_{jk} as expressed through Hooke's law above, we obtain the basic equation for the displacements in an isotropic homogeneous body

$$\mu\Delta v + (\lambda+\mu)\,\mathrm{grad\,div}\, v + F = \frac{\partial^2 v}{\partial t^2}, \qquad (*)$$

where Δ is the Laplace operator.

If F depends on time as

$$F(x, t) = \Phi^{(1)}(x)\cos\omega t + \Phi^{(2)}(x)\sin\omega t \quad (\omega \text{ constant}),$$

where x is position specified by the coordinates x_1, x_2, x_3, and $\Phi^{(1)}(x)$, $\Phi^{(2)}(x)$ are time-independent, then we may expect the displacement vector $v(x, t)$ to be of the form

$$v(x, t) = v^{(1)}(x)\cos\omega t + v^{(2)}(x)\sin\omega t.$$

Introducing the complex quantities

$$\Phi = \Phi^{(1)} + i\Phi^{(2)}, \quad u = v^{(1)} + iv^{(2)} \quad (i = \sqrt{-1}),$$

u being a vector with the components u_1, u_2, u_3, we have

$$F(x, t) = \mathrm{Re}\,\{\Phi(x)e^{-i\omega t}\}, \quad v(x, t) = \mathrm{Re}\,\{u(x)e^{-i\omega t}\},$$

where Re denotes the real part. Substituting these expressions, the equation of motion (*) becomes

$$\mu\Delta u(x) + (\lambda+\mu)\,\mathrm{grad\,div}\, u(x) + \omega^2 u(x) + \Phi(x) = 0. \qquad (**)$$

The operator

$$\mu\Delta + (\lambda+\mu)\,\mathrm{grad\,div} \equiv (\lambda+2\mu)\,\mathrm{grad\,div} - \mu\,\mathrm{rot\,rot}$$

plays in the theory of elasticity the same part as the Laplace operator in the theory of harmonic functions, and reduces to it for $\mu = 1$, $\lambda = -1$. It is therefore convenient to use the notation

$$\Delta^* \equiv (\lambda+2\mu)\,\mathrm{grad\,div} - \mu\,\mathrm{rot\,rot} = \mu\Delta + (\lambda+\mu)\,\mathrm{grad\,div}$$

in terms of which equation (**) will be written

$$\Delta^* u(x) + \omega^2 u(x) = -\Phi(x). \qquad (1.1)$$

We will occasionally refer to this vector equation simply as the equation of elasticity; it constitutes the basic system of differential equations for sustained elastic vibrations.

In the particular case $\omega = 0$, (1.1) reduces to

$$\Delta^* u(x) = -\Phi(x); \qquad (1.2)$$

which is the basic equilibrium equation for the displacements.

Along with (1.1) and (1.2) we shall also consider the corresponding homogeneous equations

$$\Delta^* u(x) + \omega^2 u = 0 \qquad (1.1^0)$$

and

$$\Delta^* u(x) = 0. \qquad (1.2^0)$$

We shall now derive the Betti formulas. Let B_i be a finite region of three-dimensional space, occupied by an elastic medium; S its boundary surface, to which n is an outward-drawn unit normal vector; dS a surface element; dv a volume element; and let α and β be any two real numbers which satisfy

$$\alpha+\beta=\lambda+\mu. \tag{1.3}$$

Applying the identity

$$(\alpha+\beta)\int\limits_{B_i}\frac{\partial^2 u_k}{\partial x_l\,\partial x_m}\,dv=\alpha\int\limits_S\frac{\partial u_k}{\partial x_l}\cos(\boldsymbol{n},\ \boldsymbol{x}_m)\,dS+\beta\int\limits_S\frac{\partial u_k}{\partial x_m}\cos(\boldsymbol{n},\ \boldsymbol{x}_l)\,dS\quad (l,\ m=1,\ 2,\ 3)$$

where $\boldsymbol{x}_m$ is a unit vector along the x_m-axis, we obtain

$$\int\limits_{B_i}\Delta^*\boldsymbol{u}\,dv=\int\limits_S \mathsf{P}^{(n)}\boldsymbol{u}\,dS,$$

where

$$\mathsf{P}^{(n)}\boldsymbol{u}=\boldsymbol{P}^{(1)}\cos(\boldsymbol{n},\ \boldsymbol{x}_1)+\boldsymbol{P}^{(2)}\cos(\boldsymbol{n},\ \boldsymbol{x}_2)+\boldsymbol{P}^{(3)}\cos(\boldsymbol{n},\ \boldsymbol{x}_3), \tag{1.4}$$

and

$$\boldsymbol{P}^{(k)}=(\pi_{1k},\ \pi_{2k},\ \pi_{3k})\qquad (k=1,\ 2,\ 3)$$

stands for the vector with the components

$$\left.\begin{aligned}\pi_{jk}(\boldsymbol{u})&=\alpha\frac{\partial u_k}{\partial x_j}+\mu\frac{\partial u_j}{\partial x_k}\qquad (j\neq k),\\ \pi_{jj}(\boldsymbol{u})&=\beta\,\mathrm{div}\,\boldsymbol{u}+(\alpha+\mu)\frac{\partial u_j}{\partial x_j}.\end{aligned}\right\} \tag{1.5}$$

The vector $\mathsf{P}^{(n)}\boldsymbol{u}$ will be called the generalized stress vector at the surface element with the normal $\boldsymbol{n}$.

Let $\boldsymbol{u}$ and $\boldsymbol{v}$ be two vector fields which satisfy in B_i and on S the appropriate conditions so that the Gauss-Ostrogradskii theorem holds for them. Denoting the scalar product of two vectors $\boldsymbol{a}$ and $\boldsymbol{b}$ by $\boldsymbol{a}\cdot\boldsymbol{b}$ or $\boldsymbol{ab}$, and their vector product by $\boldsymbol{a}\times\boldsymbol{b}$, we represent the scalar product $\boldsymbol{u}\cdot\mathsf{P}^{(n)}\boldsymbol{v}$ in the form

$$\boldsymbol{u}\cdot\mathsf{P}^{(n)}\boldsymbol{v}=Q_1\cos(\boldsymbol{n},\ \boldsymbol{x}_1)+Q_2\cos(\boldsymbol{n},\ \boldsymbol{x}_2)+Q_3\cos(\boldsymbol{n},\ \boldsymbol{x}_3),$$

where clearly

$$Q_k=\sum_{j=1}^{3}\pi_{jk}(\boldsymbol{v})\,u_j\qquad (k=1,\ 2,\ 3).$$

The divergence of the new vector $\boldsymbol{Q}(Q_1,\ Q_2,\ Q_3)$ thus defined is

$$\mathrm{div}\,\boldsymbol{Q}=\sum_j\sum_k\frac{\partial\pi_{jk}(\boldsymbol{v})}{\partial x_k}u_j+\mathscr{E}(\boldsymbol{u},\ \boldsymbol{v}).$$

Using (1.5) we readily obtain

$$\begin{aligned}\mathscr{E}(\boldsymbol{u},\ \boldsymbol{v})=(\lambda+2\mu)\sum_k\frac{\partial u_k}{\partial x_k}\frac{\partial v_k}{\partial x_k}+\mu\Big[\Big(\frac{\partial u_1}{\partial x_2}\frac{\partial v_1}{\partial x_2}+\frac{\partial u_2}{\partial x_1}\frac{\partial v_2}{\partial x_1}\Big)+\\ +\Big(\frac{\partial u_3}{\partial x_1}\frac{\partial v_3}{\partial x_1}+\frac{\partial u_1}{\partial x_3}\frac{\partial v_1}{\partial x_3}\Big)+\Big(\frac{\partial u_2}{\partial x_3}\frac{\partial v_2}{\partial x_3}+\frac{\partial u_3}{\partial x_2}\frac{\partial v_3}{\partial x_2}\Big)\Big]+\\ +\beta\Big[\Big(\frac{\partial u_1}{\partial x_1}\frac{\partial v_2}{\partial x_2}+\frac{\partial u_2}{\partial x_2}\frac{\partial v_1}{\partial x_1}\Big)+\Big(\frac{\partial u_1}{\partial x_1}\frac{\partial v_3}{\partial x_3}+\frac{\partial u_3}{\partial x_3}\frac{\partial v_1}{\partial x_1}\Big)+\\ +\Big(\frac{\partial u_2}{\partial x_2}\frac{\partial v_3}{\partial x_3}+\frac{\partial u_3}{\partial x_3}\frac{\partial v_2}{\partial x_2}\Big)\Big]+\alpha\Big[\Big(\frac{\partial u_1}{\partial x_2}\frac{\partial v_2}{\partial x_1}+\frac{\partial u_2}{\partial x_1}\frac{\partial v_1}{\partial x_2}\Big)+\\ +\Big(\frac{\partial u_1}{\partial x_3}\frac{\partial v_3}{\partial x_1}+\frac{\partial u_3}{\partial x_1}\frac{\partial v_1}{\partial x_3}\Big)+\Big(\frac{\partial u_2}{\partial x_3}\frac{\partial v_3}{\partial x_2}+\frac{\partial u_3}{\partial x_2}\frac{\partial v_2}{\partial x_3}\Big)\Big].\end{aligned} \tag{1.6}$$

We see that $\mathcal{E}(u, v)$ is a bilinear form in the derivatives $\frac{\partial u_j}{\partial x_k}$ and $\frac{\partial v_l}{\partial x_m}$, obviously symmetric with respect to the vectors u and v.

On the other hand, inserting the $\pi_{jk}(v)$ from (1.5), we find

$$\sum_{k=1}^{3} \frac{\partial \pi_{jk}(v)}{\partial x_k} = \overset{*}{\Delta}_j v \qquad (j=1, 2, 3),$$

where

$$\overset{*}{\Delta}_j v \equiv \mu \Delta v_j + (\lambda + \mu) \frac{\partial}{\partial x_j} \operatorname{div} v,$$

and hence

$$\operatorname{div} Q = u \cdot \Delta^* v + \mathcal{E}(u, v), \tag{1.7}$$

where the vector $\Delta^* v$ has the components

$$\overset{*}{\Delta}_j v = \mu \Delta v_j + (\lambda + \mu) \frac{\partial}{\partial x_j} \operatorname{div} v \qquad (j=1, 2, 3).$$

Applying the Gauss-Ostrogradskii formula to (1.7),

$$\int_{B_i} u \cdot \Delta^* v \, dv = \int_S u \cdot \mathrm{P}^{(n)} v \, dS - \int_{B_i} \mathcal{E}(u, v) \, dv. \tag{1.8}$$

Setting here $u = v$,

$$\int_{B_i} u \cdot \Delta^* u \, dv = \int_S u \cdot \mathrm{P}^{(n)} u \, dS - \int_{B_i} \mathcal{E}(u, u) \, dv. \tag{1.9}$$

Interchanging u and v in (1.8) and subtracting the two equations we obtain by virtue of the symmetry property $\mathcal{E}(u, v) = \mathcal{E}(v, u)$,

$$\int_{B_i} (u \cdot \Delta^* v - v \cdot \Delta^* u) \, dv = \int_S (u \cdot \mathrm{P}^{(n)} v - v \cdot \mathrm{P}^{(n)} u) \, dS. \tag{1.10}$$

Relations (1.8), (1.9), (1.10) may be called the first, second and third (generalized) Betti formulas. Assigning various values to the constants α and β in conformity with (1.3), we obtain various familiar formulas of the theory of elasticity, in particular the Betti formulas. Thus for

$$\alpha = \mu, \quad \beta = \lambda,$$

straightforward comparison of (1.5) with our initial expressions for the τ_{ik} shows that

$$\pi_{jk} = \tau_{jk} \qquad (j, k = 1, 2, 3),$$

while the generalized stress vector $\mathrm{P}^{(n)} u$ reduces to the stress vector

$$\mathrm{T}^{(n)} u = T^{(1)} \cos(n, x_1) + T^{(2)} \cos(n, x_2) + T^{(3)} \cos(n, x_3), \tag{1.11}$$

where the vectors $T^{(1)}, T^{(2)}, T^{(3)}$ represent tractions across surface elements whose normals parallel the x_1, x_2, x_3-axes, and their components are

$$(\tau_{11}, \tau_{12}, \tau_{13}), \quad (\tau_{21}, \tau_{22}, \tau_{23}), \quad (\tau_{31}, \tau_{32}, \tau_{33}).$$

The relations (1.8), (1.9), (1.10) respectively become the first Betti formula

$$\int_{B_i} u \cdot \Delta v^* \, dv = \int_S u \cdot \mathrm{T}^{(n)} v \, dS - \int_{B_i} W(u, v) \, dv, \tag{1.8'}$$

the second Betti formula

$$\int_{B_i} u \cdot \Delta^* u \, dv = \int_S u \cdot \mathrm{T}^{(n)} u \, dS - \int_{B_i} W(u, u) \, dv \tag{1.9'}$$

and the third Betti formula

$$\int_{B_i} (u \cdot \Delta^* v - v \cdot \Delta^* u) \, dv = \int_S (u \cdot \mathrm{T}^{(n)} v - v \cdot \mathrm{T}^{(n)} u) \, dS, \tag{1.10'}$$

where $W(u, u) \equiv \mathscr{E}(u, v)$ for $v = u$, $\alpha = \mu$ and $\beta = \lambda$, that is

$$W(u, u) = 2\mu \left[2 (u_{12}^2 + u_{23}^2 + u_{31}^2) + \sum_{k=1}^{3} \left(\frac{\partial u_k}{\partial x_k} \right)^2 \right] + \lambda (\operatorname{div} u)^2. \tag{1.12}$$

Equations (1.4) and (1.11), after some manipulation, can be also written in the form

$$\mathrm{P}^{(n)} u = (\alpha + \mu) \frac{\partial u}{\partial n} + \beta n \operatorname{div} u + \alpha (n \times \operatorname{rot} u), \tag{1.13}$$

$$\mathrm{T}^{(n)} u = 2\mu \frac{\partial u}{\partial n} + \lambda n \operatorname{div} u + \mu (n \times \operatorname{rot} u). \tag{1.14}$$

In addition to the identities (1.8'), (1.9'), (1.10'), we shall also use the relations obtained from (1.8), (1.9), (1.10) by assigning to the two disposable parameters the values

$$\alpha = \frac{\mu (\lambda + \mu)}{\lambda + 3\mu}, \qquad \beta = \frac{(\lambda + \mu)(\lambda + 2\mu)}{\lambda + 3\mu}. \tag{1.15}$$

The vector $\mathrm{P}^{(n)} u$ thereby becomes the pseudostress vector, usually denoted by $\mathrm{N}^{(n)} u$:

$$\mathrm{N}^{(n)} u = \frac{2\mu (\lambda + 2\mu)}{\lambda + 3\mu} \frac{\partial u}{\partial n} + \frac{(\lambda + \mu)(\lambda + 2\mu)}{\lambda + 3\mu} n \operatorname{div} u + \frac{\mu (\lambda + \mu)}{\lambda + 3\mu} (n \times \operatorname{rot} u). \tag{1.16}$$

For $v = u$ and the α, β given by (1.15), the bilinear form $\mathscr{E}(u, v)$ assumes the form

$$W_*(u, u) = \frac{\mu (\lambda + \mu)}{\lambda + 3\mu} \left[4 (u_{12}^2 + u_{23}^2 + u_{31}^2) + 2 \sum_{k=1}^{3} u_{kk}^2 \right] + \\ + \frac{2\mu}{\lambda + 3\mu} \sum_{k=1}^{3} (\operatorname{grad} u_k)^2 + \frac{(\lambda + \mu)(\lambda + 2\mu)}{\lambda + 3\mu} (\operatorname{div} u)^2, \tag{1.17}$$

and we obtain three new variants of the Betti formulas

$$\int_{B_i} u \cdot \Delta^* v \, dv = \int_S u \cdot \mathrm{N}^{(n)} v \, dS - \int_{B_i} W_*(u, v) \, dv, \tag{1.8''}$$

$$\int_{B_i} u \cdot \Delta^* u \, dv = \int_S u \cdot N^{(n)} u \, dS - \int_{B_i} W_*(u, u) \, dv, \tag{1.9''}$$

$$\int_{B_i} (u \cdot \Delta^* v - v \cdot \Delta^* u) \, dv = \int_S (u \cdot N^{(n)} v - v \cdot N^{(n)} u) \, dS. \tag{1.10''}$$

In the following we shall simply write P, T, N for $\mathsf{P}^{(n)}$, $\mathsf{T}^{(n)}$, $\mathsf{N}^{(n)}$ and remember that the direction of the normal always specified by that of n. The vector differential operator

$$\mathsf{P} = (\alpha + \mu) \frac{\partial}{\partial n} + \beta n \operatorname{div} + \alpha (n \times \operatorname{rot})$$

will be called the generalized stress operator, and its two particular cases the stress operator

$$\mathsf{T} = 2\mu \frac{\partial}{\partial n} + \lambda n \operatorname{div} + \mu (n \times \operatorname{rot})$$

and the pseudostress operator

$$\mathsf{N} = \frac{2\mu(\lambda + 2\mu)}{\lambda + 3\mu} \frac{\partial}{\partial n} + \frac{(\lambda + \mu)(\lambda + 2\mu)}{\lambda + 3\mu} n \operatorname{div} + \frac{\lambda(\lambda + \mu)}{\lambda + 3\mu} (n \times \operatorname{rot}).$$

The importance of the stress operator in the theory of boundary value problems is due to the mechanical interpretation of the vector $\mathsf{T}u(x)$, which expresses the stress at the point x across a surface element with the normal n; the meaning of the pseudostress operator N will be elucidated in §4.

§ 2. Fundamental solutions

The force $\Phi(x)$ which appears in (1.1) and (1.2) generally differs from zero only in some finite region of the space B. Let us consider the scalar and vector potentials

$$\left.\begin{aligned} \Phi'(x) &= -\frac{1}{4\pi} \int_B \Phi(y) \cdot \operatorname{grad}_x \frac{1}{r(x, y)} \, dv_y, \\ \Psi(x) &= \frac{1}{4\pi} \int_B \Phi(y) \times \operatorname{grad}_x \frac{1}{r(x, y)} \, dv_y, \end{aligned}\right\} \tag{1.18}$$

where $r(x, y)$ is the distance apart of the points $x(x_1, x_2, x_3)$ and $y(y_1, y_2, y_3)$, and dv_y, dS_y are volume and surface elements at y. For $x \in B$ we then have by (1.18)

$$\Phi(x) = \operatorname{grad} \Phi'(x) + \operatorname{rot} \Psi(x).$$

Splitting similarly the displacement vector u into two parts,

$$u(x) = \operatorname{grad} \varphi(x) + \operatorname{rot} \psi(x), \tag{1.19}$$

and substituting the last expressions for $\Phi(x)$ and $u(x)$ into (1.1), we may verify that (1.1) will be fulfilled if the scalar potential $\varphi(x)$ and the vector potential $\psi(x)$ are solutions of the equations

$$\Delta\varphi(x) + k_1^2 \varphi(x) = -\frac{1}{a^2} \Phi'(x)$$

and

$$\Delta\psi(x) + k_2^2 \psi(x) = -\frac{1}{b^2} \Psi(x), \tag{1.20}$$

where

$$a^2=\lambda+2\mu, \quad b^2=\mu, \quad k_1^2=\frac{\omega^2}{a^2}, \quad k_2^2=\frac{\omega^2}{b^2}.$$

The case when the force distribution $\mathbf{\Phi}(x)$ reduces to a constant force concentrated at a point is especially interesting. Let such a concentrated force of magnitude 4π and directed along the x_1-axis be applied at $y(y_1, y_2, y_3)$. We will represent it as the limit approached by the resultant of some system of forces $\mathbf{\Phi}^*(x')$, continuously distributed over the sphere $\sigma(y; \varepsilon)$ of radius ε and centered at y, as ε tends to zero. We stipulate that the x_2- and x_3-components of $\mathbf{\Phi}^*(x')$ are to remain bounded, while the x_1-component, $\Phi_1^*(x')$, increases so that

$$\lim_{\varepsilon\to 0} \int_{\sigma(y;\,\varepsilon)} \Phi_1^*(x')\, d\sigma_x = 4\pi.$$

For the force $\mathbf{\Phi}(x)$ thus defined (1.18) gives

$$\left.\begin{aligned} \Phi'(x) &= -\frac{\partial}{\partial x_1}\frac{1}{r(x, y)}; \quad \Psi_1(x)=0, \\ \Psi_2(x) &= \frac{\partial}{\partial x_3}\frac{1}{r(x, y)}, \quad \Psi_3(x) = -\frac{\partial}{\partial x_2}\frac{1}{r(x, y)}. \end{aligned}\right\} \tag{1.21}$$

Substituting these values of $\Phi'(x)$ and $\mathbf{\Psi}(x)$ in (1.20), we obtain

$$\left.\begin{aligned} \Delta\varphi(x) + k_1^2\varphi(x) &= \frac{1}{a^2}\frac{\partial}{\partial x_1}\frac{1}{r(x, y)}, \\ \Delta\psi_1(x) + k_2^2\psi_1(x) &= 0, \\ \Delta\psi_2(x) + k_2^2\psi_2(x) &= -\frac{1}{b^2}\frac{\partial}{\partial x_3}\frac{1}{r(x, y)}, \\ \Delta\psi_3(x) + k_2^2\psi_3(x) &= \frac{1}{b^2}\frac{\partial}{\partial x_2}\frac{1}{r(x, y)}. \end{aligned}\right\} \tag{1.22}$$

It is easy to verify that the functions

$$\varphi(x; y) = -\frac{1}{\omega^2}\frac{\partial}{\partial x_1}\left(\frac{e^{ik_1 r}}{r} - \frac{1}{r}\right), \tag{1.23}$$

$$\left.\begin{aligned} \psi_1(x; y) &= 0, \quad \psi_2(x; y) = \frac{1}{\omega^2}\frac{\partial}{\partial x_3}\left(\frac{e^{ik_2 r}}{r} - \frac{1}{r}\right), \\ \psi_3(x, y) &= -\frac{1}{\omega^2}\frac{\partial}{\partial x_2}\left(\frac{e^{ik_2 r}}{r} - \frac{1}{r}\right), \end{aligned}\right\} \tag{1.24}$$

respectively solve equations (1.22) for fixed y and $x \neq y$.

Let us introduce the vectors

$$\mathbf{u}_p(x, y) = \operatorname{grad}\varphi(x; y) \text{ and } \mathbf{u}_s(x, y) = \operatorname{rot}\boldsymbol{\psi}(x, y). \tag{1.25}$$

The subscripts p and s will henceforth serve to label lamellar vectors derived from a potential and solenoidal vectors, respectively.

The impressed force concentrated at y has above been assumed to lie parallel to the x_1-axis; such specification will henceforth be indicated by a superscript (in this case 1) appended to $\varphi(x; y)$, $\boldsymbol{\psi}(x; y)$, $\mathbf{u}_p(x, y)$, $\mathbf{u}_s(x, y)$.

From (1.23), (1.24), (1.25) we obtain the following expressions for the components of the vectors $u_p^{(1)}(x, y)$ and $u_s^{(1)}(x, y)$:

$$\left.\begin{aligned} u_{p,j}^{(1)}(x, y) &= -\frac{1}{\omega^2}\frac{\partial^2}{\partial x_j \partial x_1}\left(\frac{e^{ik_1 r}}{r} - \frac{1}{r}\right), \\ u_{s,j}^{(1)}(x, y) &= \frac{1}{\omega^2}\frac{\partial^2}{\partial x_j \partial x_1}\left(\frac{e^{ik_2 r}}{r} - \frac{1}{r}\right) + \frac{1}{b^2}\delta_{1j}\frac{e^{ik_2 r}}{r} \\ & (j = 1, 2, 3), \end{aligned}\right\} \tag{1.26}$$

where

$$\delta_{1j} = \begin{cases} 1, & j = 1, \\ 0, & j \neq 1. \end{cases}$$

The required solution of (1.1) is, by (1.19),

$$u_j^{(1)}(x, y) = u_{p,j}^{(1)}(x, y) + u_{s,j}^{(1)}(x, y) = \\ = \frac{1}{b^2}\delta_{1j}\frac{e^{ik_2 r}}{r} - \frac{1}{\omega^2}\frac{\partial^2}{\partial x_j \partial x_1}\left(\frac{e^{ik_1 r}}{r} - \frac{e^{ik_2 r}}{r}\right) \quad (j = 1, 2, 3). \tag{1.27}$$

The situation for a force applied at y along the x_2- and x_3-axes is analogous, and we can write

$$u_j^{(k)}(x, y) = \frac{1}{b^2}\delta_{kj}\frac{e^{ik_2 r}}{r} - \frac{1}{\omega^2}\frac{\partial^2}{\partial x_k \partial x_j}\left(\frac{e^{ik_1 r}}{r} - \frac{e^{ik_2 r}}{r}\right) \\ (k, j = 1, 2, 3), \tag{1.28}$$

where

$$\delta_{kj} = \begin{cases} 1, & k = j, \\ 0, & k \neq j. \end{cases}$$

It may readily be verified that (1.28) can also be written

$$u^{(k)}(x, y) = \operatorname{rot}\operatorname{rot}\left(\delta^{(k)}\frac{e^{ik_2 r}}{r}\right) - \operatorname{grad}\operatorname{div}\left(\delta^{(k)}\frac{e^{ik_1 r}}{r}\right) \\ (k = 1, 2, 3), \tag{1.28'}$$

where $\delta^{(k)}$ stands for the vector $(\delta_{k1}, \delta_{k2}, \delta_{k3})$.

The vectors $u^{(1)}(x, y)$, $u^{(2)}(x, y)$, $u^{(3)}(x, y)$ with the Cartesian components (1.28) constitute the *fundamental solutions* of equation (1.1^0). By definition (§ 1) they represent in complex form the amplitudes of the even and odd components of the harmonically oscillating displacement vector $v(x, t)$; separating their real and imaginary parts, we can construct solutions of equation (*) of § 1 that will represent the oscillatory displacements called forth in an infinite, isotropic and homogeneous medium by a concentrated periodic force applied at $y(y_1, y_2, y_3)$ and acting parallel to one of the coordinate axes.

Owing to the exceptional status of these solutions, we shall find it convenient to use a special notation for them, viz.,

$$u^{(k)}(x, y) = \Gamma^{(k)}(x, y) \quad (k = 1, 2, 3) \tag{1.29}$$

and for their components

$$u_j^{(k)}(x, y) = \Gamma_j^{(k)}(x, y) \quad (j = 1, 2, 3). \tag{1.29'}$$

It is clear from (1.28) that

$$\Gamma_j^{(k)}(x, y) = \Gamma_k^{(j)}(y, x) = \Gamma_k^{(j)}(x, y). \tag{1.30}$$

The square matrix of order three

$$\begin{Vmatrix} \Gamma_1^{(1)} & \Gamma_1^{(2)} & \Gamma_1^{(3)} \\ \Gamma_2^{(1)} & \Gamma_2^{(2)} & \Gamma_2^{(3)} \\ \Gamma_3^{(1)} & \Gamma_3^{(2)} & \Gamma_3^{(3)} \end{Vmatrix}, \tag{1.31}$$

whose columns are the components of the vectors

$$\Gamma^{(1)}(x, y), \quad \Gamma^{(2)}(x, y), \quad \Gamma^{(3)}(x, y),$$

will be denoted by $\Gamma(x, y)$, or $\{\Gamma^{(1)}, \Gamma^{(2)}, \Gamma^{(3)}\}$, and called the matrix of fundamental solutions of equation (1.1^0). The matrix of fundamental solutions of the static equation (1.2^0) may be obtained from the preceding as a particular case. To this end, one must set $\omega = 0$ in (1.23) and (1.24) and evaluate the ensuing indeterminate expressions by passing to the limit, which is elementary. Doing this for $\varphi(x, y)$ and $\psi^{(k)}(x, y)$ ($k = 1, 2, 3$) and then proceeding as we did for $\omega \neq 0$, we obtain the following static counterpart of (1.28):

$$\overset{0}{u}{}_j^{(k)}(x, y) = \overset{0}{\Gamma}{}_j^{(k)}(x, y) = \\ = \frac{1}{2a^2b^2}\left[(a^2 - b^2)\frac{\partial r}{\partial x_j}\frac{\partial r}{\partial x_k} + (a^2 + b^2)\delta_{jk}\right]\frac{1}{r(x, y)}, \tag{1.32}$$

$$\overset{0}{\Gamma}{}_j^{(k)}(x, y) = \operatorname{grad}\operatorname{div}\left(\delta^{(k)}\frac{r}{2a^2}\right) - \operatorname{rot}\operatorname{rot}\left(\delta^{(k)}\frac{r}{2b^2}\right). \tag{1.32'}$$

We could, naturally, also have derived (1.32) and (1.32') directly from (1.28) and (1.28') in the same way. The matrix

$$\overset{0}{\Gamma}(x, y) = \left\{\overset{0}{\Gamma}{}^{(1)}, \overset{0}{\Gamma}{}^{(2)}, \overset{0}{\Gamma}{}^{(3)}\right\}, \tag{1.31^0}$$

where $\overset{0}{\Gamma}{}^{(k)}(x, y)$ ($k = 1, 2, 3$) are the vectors whose components are defined by (1.32) and (1.32'), will be called the matrix of fundamental solutions of the static equation. The difference

$$\Omega^{(k)}(x, y) = \Gamma^{(k)}(x, y) - \overset{0}{\Gamma}{}^{(k)}(x, y) \qquad (k = 1, 2, 3) \tag{1.33}$$

remains bounded at $r = 0$, while its first derivatives with respect to the coordinates x and y have a first order pole there.

The following simple relations will be needed later on:

$$\operatorname{div}_x \Gamma^{(k)}(x, y) = \frac{1}{a^2}\frac{\partial}{\partial x_k}\frac{e^{ik_1 r}}{r} \qquad (k = 1, 2, 3) \tag{1.34}$$

and

$$\operatorname{div}_x \Gamma(x, y) = \sum_{k=1}^{3}\frac{\partial \Gamma^{(k)}}{\partial x_k} = \operatorname{grad}_x\left(\frac{e^{ik_1 r}}{a^2 r}\right). \tag{1.35}$$

The first follows from (1.19) and (1.23), as may be verified immediately:

$$\operatorname{div}_x \Gamma^{(k)}(x, y) = \Delta\varphi^{(k)}(x, y) = \frac{k_1^2}{\omega^2}\frac{\partial}{\partial x_k}\frac{e^{ik_1 r}}{r} = \frac{1}{a^2}\frac{\partial}{\partial x_k}\frac{e^{ik_1 r}}{r}$$
$$(k = 1, 2, 3).$$

To prove (1.35), note that

$$\frac{\partial \Gamma^{(k)}}{\partial x_k} = \sum_{s=1}^{3} i_s \frac{\partial \Gamma_s^{(k)}}{\partial x_k},$$

where i_1, i_2, i_3 are the unit vectors* along the coordinate axes; but, by definition, the divergence of the matrix $\Gamma(x, y)$ is

$$\sum_{k=1}^{3} \frac{\partial \Gamma^{(k)}}{\partial x_k}.$$

Consequently

$$\operatorname{div}\Gamma(x, y) = \sum_{k, s=1}^{3} i_s \frac{\partial \Gamma_s^{(k)}}{\partial x_k} = \sum_{k, s=1}^{3} i_s \frac{\partial \Gamma_k^{(s)}}{\partial x_k} = \sum_{s=1}^{3} i_s \operatorname{div}\Gamma^{(s)} =$$

$$= \sum_{s=1}^{3} i_s \frac{\partial}{\partial x_s}\left(\frac{e^{ik_1 r}}{a^2 r}\right) = \operatorname{grad}\left(\frac{e^{ik_1 r}}{a^2 r}\right),$$

which proves (1.35).

Finally we give a simple construction for the vectors $\operatorname{rot}\Gamma^{(k)}(x, y)$ which will turn up frequently in the following. Applying the identity

$$\operatorname{rot}\operatorname{rot} = \operatorname{grad}\operatorname{div} - \Delta,$$

we have by (1.19)

$$\operatorname{rot}\Gamma^{(1)}(x, y) = \operatorname{rot}\operatorname{rot}\psi^{(1)} = -\Delta\psi^{(1)}.$$

Inserting (1.24), we obtain

$$\left.\begin{aligned} \operatorname{rot}\Gamma_1^{(1)} &= -\Delta\psi_1^{(1)} = 0, \\ \operatorname{rot}\Gamma_2^{(1)} &= -\Delta\psi_2^{(1)} = \frac{1}{b^2}\frac{\partial}{\partial x_3}\frac{e^{ik_2 r}}{r}, \\ \operatorname{rot}\Gamma_3^{(1)} &= -\frac{1}{b^2}\frac{\partial}{\partial x_2}\frac{e^{ik_2 r}}{r}. \end{aligned}\right\} \qquad (1.34')$$

The expressions for $\operatorname{rot}\Gamma^{(2)}$ and $\operatorname{rot}\Gamma^{(3)}$ are obtained from these by cyclic permutation.

§ 3. Generalized fundamental solutions

Consider the generalized stress vectors $\mathrm{P}\Gamma^{(k)}(x, y)$ $(k = 1, 2, 3)$ corresponding to the displacements of an infinite continuum under the action of concentrated forces; since the operands $\Gamma^{(k)}(x, y)$ are two-point vector functions it is necessary to specify explicitly the one point to which the operation of P refers; this will be indicated by superscripts,

$$\mathrm{P}^{(x)}\Gamma^{(k)}(x, y) \text{ and } \mathrm{P}^{(y)}\Gamma^{(k)}(x, y).$$

The corresponding components will be similarly labeled:

$$\mathrm{P}_s^{(x)}\Gamma^{(k)}(x, y) \text{ and } \mathrm{P}_s^{(y)}\Gamma^{(k)}(x, y) \qquad (s = 1, 2, 3).$$

Let $\boldsymbol{n}_x$ and $\boldsymbol{n}_y$ be unit normals at x and y to surface elements through these

* The basis vectors will sometimes be alternatively denoted by x_m, $m = 1, 2, 3$.

points; then

$$P^{(x)}\Gamma^{(k)}(x, y)=(\alpha+\mu)\frac{\partial\Gamma^{(k)}(x, y)}{\partial n_x}+\beta n_x \operatorname{div}_x \Gamma^{(k)}(x, y)+\alpha(n_x \times \operatorname{rot}_x \Gamma^{(k)}(x, y)), \quad (1.36)$$

$$P^{(y)}\Gamma^{(k)}(x, y)=(\alpha+\mu)\frac{\partial\Gamma^{(k)}(x, y)}{\partial n_y}+\beta n_y \operatorname{div}_y \Gamma^{(k)}(x, y)+\alpha(n_y \times \operatorname{rot}_y \Gamma^{(k)}(x, y)) \quad (1.36')$$

and the components along the axes x_s ($s = 1, 2, 3$) will be

$$P_s^{(x)}\Gamma^{(k)}(x, y)=(\alpha+\mu)\frac{\partial\Gamma_s^{(k)}}{\partial n_x}+ \\ +\beta\cos(n_x, x_s)\operatorname{div}_x \Gamma^{(k)}(x, y)+\alpha(n_x \times \operatorname{rot}_x \Gamma^{(k)}(x, y))_{x_s}. \quad (1.37)$$

$$P_s^{(y)}\Gamma^{(k)}(x, y)=(\alpha+\mu)\frac{\partial\Gamma_s^{(k)}}{\partial n_y}+\beta\cos(n_y, x_s)\operatorname{div}_y \Gamma^{(k)}(x, y)+ \\ +\alpha(n_y \times \operatorname{rot}_y \Gamma^{(k)}(x, y))_{x_s}. \quad (1.37')$$

We now introduce the matrix

$$P^{(x)}\Gamma(x, y)=\left\| \begin{matrix} P_1^{(x)}\Gamma^{(1)} & P_1^{(x)}\Gamma^{(2)} & P_1^{(x)}\Gamma^{(3)} \\ P_2^{(x)}\Gamma^{(1)} & P_2^{(x)}\Gamma^{(2)} & P_2^{(x)}\Gamma^{(3)} \\ P_3^{(x)}\Gamma^{(1)} & P_3^{(x)}\Gamma^{(2)} & P_3^{(x)}\Gamma^{(3)} \end{matrix} \right\|, \quad (1.38)$$

and its associated matrix, obtained by interchanging rows and columns, and also the points x and y,

$$\Pi(x, y)=\left\| \begin{matrix} P_1^{(y)}\Gamma^{(1)} & P_2^{(y)}\Gamma^{(1)} & P_3^{(y)}\Gamma^{(1)} \\ P_1^{(y)}\Gamma^{(2)} & P_2^{(y)}\Gamma^{(2)} & P_3^{(y)}\Gamma^{(2)} \\ P_1^{(y)}\Gamma^{(3)} & P_2^{(y)}\Gamma^{(3)} & P_3^{(y)}\Gamma^{(3)} \end{matrix} \right\| = \{\Pi^{(1)}, \Pi^{(2)}, \Pi^{(3)}\}. \quad (1.38')$$

The column vectors of the associated matrix Π will be denoted by $\Pi^{(1)}\Pi^{(2)}\Pi^{(3)}$, and their components by

$$\Pi_k^{(s)}(x, y)=P_s^{(y)}\Gamma^{(k)}(x, y) \qquad (s, k=1, 2, 3). \quad (1.38'')$$

Theorem 1. The column vectors of the associated matrix considered as functions of $x(x_1, x_2, x_3)$ satisfy equation (1.1⁰).

We have to prove that

$$\mu\Delta_x\Pi_k^{(s)}(x, y)+(\lambda+\mu)\frac{\partial}{\partial x_k}\operatorname{div}_x\Pi^{(s)}(x, y)+\omega^2\Pi_k^{(s)}(x, y)=0 \\ (s, k=1, 2, 3). \quad (1.39)$$

Let us calculate $\operatorname{div}_x\Pi^{(s)}(x, y)$.

By (1.38'')

$$\operatorname{div}\Pi^{(s)}(x, y)=\sum_{k=1}^{3}\frac{\partial}{\partial x_k}(P_s^{(y)}\Gamma^{(k)}(x, y)).$$

Substituting the values of $P_s^{(y)}\Gamma^{(k)}(x, y)$ from (1.37'),

$$\operatorname{div}_x\Pi^{(s)}(x, y)= \\ =\sum_{k=1}^{3}\frac{\partial}{\partial x_k}\left[(\alpha+\mu)\frac{\partial\Gamma_s^{(k)}}{\partial n_y}+\beta\cos(n_y, x_s)\operatorname{div}\Gamma^{(k)}+\alpha(n_y\times\operatorname{rot}_y\Gamma^{(k)})_{x_s}\right].$$

Making use of the symmetry of the matrix $\Gamma(x, y)$ and applying (1.35), we find

$$\operatorname{div}_x \mathrm{II}^{(s)}(x, y) = (\alpha+\mu)\frac{\partial}{\partial n_y}\operatorname{div}_x \Gamma^{(s)} +$$

$$+\beta\cos(n_y, x_s)\operatorname{div}_y\sum_{k=1}^{3}\frac{\partial\Gamma^{(k)}}{\partial x_k}+\alpha\left(n_y\times\operatorname{rot}_y\sum_{1}^{3}\frac{\partial\Gamma^{(k)}}{\partial x_k}\right)_{x_s} =$$

$$= (\alpha+\mu)\frac{\partial}{\partial n_y}\operatorname{div}_x\Gamma^{(s)} - \beta\cos(n_y, x_s)\Delta_x\varphi(x, y).$$

Here $\varphi(x, y)$ stands for the function $\frac{1}{a^2}\frac{e^{ik_1 r}}{r}$.

Substituting in (1.39), expanding according to (1.37'), and using (1.34)*, we obtain

$$\mu\Delta_x(\mathrm{P}_s^{(y)}\Gamma^{(k)}) + (\lambda+\mu)\frac{\partial}{\partial x_k}\left[(\alpha+\mu)\frac{\partial}{\partial n_y}\operatorname{div}_x\Gamma^{(s)} - \beta\cos(n_y, x_s)\Delta_x\varphi\right] +$$

$$+\omega^2 P_s^{(y)}\Gamma^{(k)} = (\alpha+\mu)\frac{\partial}{\partial n_y}\mu\Delta\Gamma_s^{(k)} + \beta\cos(n_y, x_s)\mu\Delta\operatorname{div}_y\Gamma^{(k)} +$$

$$+\alpha(n_y\times\mu\Delta\operatorname{rot}_y\Gamma^{(k)})_{x_s} + (\alpha+\mu)\frac{\partial}{\partial n_y}(\lambda+\mu)\frac{\partial}{\partial x_k}\operatorname{div}_x\Gamma^{(s)} -$$

$$-\beta(\lambda+\mu)\cos(n_y, x_s)\Delta_x\operatorname{div}_x\Gamma^{(k)} + (\alpha+\mu)\frac{\partial}{\partial n_y}\omega^2\Gamma_s^{(k)} +$$

$$+\beta\omega^2\cos(n_y, x_s)\operatorname{div}_y\Gamma^{(k)} + \omega^2\alpha(n_y\times\operatorname{rot}_y\Gamma^{(k)})_{x_s} =$$

$$= (\alpha+\mu)\frac{\partial}{\partial n_y}\left[\mu\Delta\Gamma_k^{(s)} + (\lambda+\mu)\frac{\partial}{\partial x_k}\operatorname{div}_x\Gamma^{(s)} + \omega^2\Gamma_s^{(k)}\right] +$$

$$+\beta\cos(n_y, x_s)[(\lambda+2\mu)\Delta_x\operatorname{div}_y\Gamma^{(k)} + \omega^2\operatorname{div}_y\Gamma^{(k)}] +$$

$$+\alpha[n_y\times(\mu\Delta\operatorname{rot}_y\Gamma^{(k)} + \omega^2\operatorname{rot}_y\Gamma^{(k)})]_{x_s}. \qquad (1.39')$$

Now the relation

$$\mu\Delta\Gamma^{(k)} + (\lambda+\mu)\operatorname{grad}\operatorname{div}\Gamma^{(k)} + \omega^2\Gamma^{(k)} = 0 \qquad (a)$$

implies

$$(\lambda+2\mu)\Delta\operatorname{div}\Gamma^{(k)} + \omega^2\operatorname{div}\Gamma^{(k)} = 0 \qquad (b)$$

and

$$\mu\Delta\operatorname{rot}\Gamma^{(k)} + \omega^2\operatorname{rot}\Gamma^{(k)} = 0. \qquad (c)$$

But the vanishing expressions (a), (b), (c) are precisely those contained in the square brackets in the last member of (1.39'), and annul it. This completes the proof.

§ 4. Fundamental solutions of the first and second kind

It was mentioned in § 1 that the generalized stress vector reduces to the stress vector for

$$\alpha = \mu, \quad \beta = \lambda.$$

Assigning these values to α and β in the associated matrix (1.38') and denoting it in this particular case by

$$\Gamma_{\mathrm{I}}(x, y),$$

* This implies $\frac{\partial}{\partial x_k}\varphi = \operatorname{div}_x \Gamma^{(k)}$.

we have, by Theorem 1 of § 3, that each column of the matrix

$$\Gamma_1(x, y)=\left\|\begin{matrix} T_1^{(y)}\Gamma^{(1)} & T_2^{(y)}\Gamma^{(1)} & T_3^{(y)}\Gamma^{(1)} \\ T_1^{(y)}\Gamma^{(2)} & T_2^{(y)}\Gamma^{(2)} & T_3^{(y)}\Gamma^{(2)} \\ T_1^{(y)}\Gamma^{(3)} & T_2^{(y)}\Gamma^{(3)} & T_3^{(y)}\Gamma^{(3)} \end{matrix}\right\| = \{\Gamma_1^{(1)}, \Gamma_1^{(2)}, \Gamma_1^{(3)}\},$$

as a vector function of $x(x_1, x_2, x_3)$ satisfies equation (1.1°), and each column of

$$\overset{0}{\Gamma}_1(x, y)=\left\{\overset{0}{\Gamma}{}_1^{(1)}, \overset{0}{\Gamma}{}_1^{(2)}, \overset{0}{\Gamma}{}_1^{(3)}\right\},$$

as a vector function of $x(x_1, x_2, x_3)$ satisfies equation (1.2^0). These solutions will be called the fundamental solutions of the first kind of equations (1.1^0) and (1.2^0), respectively. By (1.37'), (1.34), (1.34') we have

$$T_j^{(y)}\Gamma^{(k)}(x, y)=2\mu\frac{\partial\Gamma_j^{(k)}}{\partial n_y}+\frac{\lambda}{\lambda+2\mu}\cos(n_y, x_j)\frac{\partial}{\partial y_k}\frac{e^{ik_1r}}{r(x, y)}+ \\ +\cos(n_y, x_k)\frac{\partial}{\partial y_j}\frac{e^{ik_2r}}{r}-\delta_{jk}\frac{\partial}{\partial n_y}\frac{e^{ik_2r}}{r}, \tag{1.40}$$

$$T_j^{(y)}\overset{0}{\Gamma}{}^{(k)}(x, y)=2\mu\frac{\partial\overset{0}{\Gamma}_j}{\partial n_y}+\frac{\lambda}{\lambda+2\mu}\cos(n_y x_j)\frac{\partial}{\partial y_k}\frac{1}{r(xy)}+ \\ +\cos(n_y x_k)\frac{\partial}{\partial y_j}\frac{1}{r}-\delta_{jk}\frac{\partial}{\partial n_y}\frac{1}{r}. \tag{1.40^0}$$

The associated matrices of $\Gamma_1(x, y)$ and $\overset{0}{\Gamma}_1(x, y)$ are

$$\left.\begin{aligned} T^{(x)}\Gamma(x, y)&=\left\|\begin{matrix} T_1^{(x)}\Gamma^{(1)} & T_1^{(x)}\Gamma^{(2)} & T_1^{(x)}\Gamma^{(3)} \\ T_2^{(x)}\Gamma^{(1)} & T_2^{(x)}\Gamma^{(2)} & T_2^{(x)}\Gamma^{(3)} \\ T_3^{(x)}\Gamma^{(1)} & T_3^{(x)}\Gamma^{(2)} & T_3^{(x)}\Gamma^{(3)} \end{matrix}\right\|, \\ T^{(x)}\overset{0}{\Gamma}(x, y)&=\left\|\begin{matrix} T_1^{(x)}\overset{0}{\Gamma}{}^{(1)} & T_1^{(x)}\overset{0}{\Gamma}{}^{(2)} & T_1^{(x)}\overset{0}{\Gamma}{}^{(3)} \\ T_2^{(x)}\overset{0}{\Gamma}{}^{(1)} & T_2^{(x)}\overset{0}{\Gamma}{}^{(1)} & T_2^{(x)}\overset{0}{\Gamma}{}^{(3)} \\ T_3^{(x)}\overset{0}{\Gamma}{}^{(1)} & T_3^{(x)}\overset{0}{\Gamma}{}^{(1)} & T_3^{(x)}\overset{0}{\Gamma}{}^{(3)} \end{matrix}\right\|, \end{aligned}\right\} \tag{1.41}$$

where

$$T_j^{(x)}\Gamma^{(k)}(x, y)=2\mu\frac{\partial\Gamma_j^{(k)}(x, y)}{\partial n_x}+\frac{\lambda}{\lambda+2\mu}\cos(n_x x_j)\frac{\partial}{\partial x_k}\frac{e^{ik_1r}}{r}+ \\ +\cos(n_x x_k)\frac{\partial}{\partial x_j}\frac{e^{ik_2r}}{r}-\delta_{jk}\frac{\partial}{\partial n_x}\frac{e^{ik_2r}}{r}, \tag{1.42}$$

$$T_j^{(x)}\overset{0}{\Gamma}{}^{(k)}(x, y)=2\mu\frac{\partial\overset{0}{\Gamma}{}_j^{(x)}}{\partial n_x}+\frac{\lambda}{\lambda+2\mu}\cos(n_x x_j)\frac{\partial}{\partial x_k}\frac{1}{r}+ \\ +\cos(n_x x_k)\frac{\partial}{\partial x_j}\frac{1}{r}-\delta_{jk}\frac{\partial}{\partial n_x}\frac{1}{r}. \tag{1.42^0}$$

In the same way as for the stress operator **T** it is obviously possible to derive from the generalized stress operator a set of other operators, by assigning to α and β various values complying with

$$\alpha+\beta=\lambda+\mu.$$

After **T**, the pseudostress operator **N** is of particular importance and plays in the theory of elasticity the same part as the normal derivative operator in the theory of harmonic functions. As we saw in § 1, the operator $\mathbf{N}$ is obtained from $\mathbf{P}$ on setting

$$\alpha=\frac{\mu(\lambda+\mu)}{\lambda+3\mu}, \quad \beta=\frac{(\lambda+\mu)(\lambda+2\mu)}{\lambda+3\mu}.$$

The significance of this choice of α and β will presently be clarified. To this end, let us derive the pseudostress vector in an infinite continuum acted upon by a concentrated force; we start with

$$\mathbf{N}\overset{0}{\Gamma}{}^{(k)}(x, y) \qquad (k=1, 2, 3).$$

By (1.32)

$$\frac{\partial \overset{0}{\Gamma}{}_j^{(k)}(x, y)}{\partial n_x}=\frac{a^2+b^2}{2a^2b^2}\delta_{jk}\frac{\partial}{\partial n_x}\frac{1}{r}+\frac{3(a^2-b^2)}{2a^2b^2}\frac{\partial r}{\partial x_k}\frac{\partial r}{\partial x_j}\frac{\partial}{\partial n_x}\frac{1}{r}-$$
$$-\frac{a^2-b^2}{2a^2b^2}\cos(n_x, x_j)\frac{\partial}{\partial x_k}\frac{1}{r}+\cos(n_x, x_k)\frac{\partial}{\partial x_j}\frac{1}{r}\Big);$$

substituting this expression for the normal derivative in (1.37) and setting $\omega = 0$, we obtain

$$\begin{aligned}\mathbf{P}_j^{(x)}\overset{0}{\Gamma}{}^{(k)}(x, y)=\Big\{\Big[\frac{(\mu+\alpha)(a^2+b^2)}{2a^2b^2}-\frac{\alpha}{b^2}\Big]\delta_{jk}+\\ +\frac{3(\mu+\alpha)(a^2-b^2)}{2a^2b^2}\frac{\partial r}{\partial x_k}\frac{\partial r}{\partial x_j}\Big\}\frac{\partial}{\partial n_x}\frac{1}{r(x, y)}+\\ +\Big[\frac{\beta}{a^2}-\frac{(\mu+\alpha)(a^2-b^2)}{2a^2b^2}\Big]\cos(n_x, x_j)\frac{\partial}{\partial x_k}\frac{1}{r}+\\ +\Big[\frac{\alpha}{b^2}-\frac{(\mu+\alpha)(a^2-b^2)}{2a^2b^2}\Big]\cos(n_x x_k)\frac{\partial}{\partial x_j}\frac{1}{r}.\end{aligned} \qquad (1.43)$$

But

$$\frac{\beta}{a^2}-\frac{(\mu+\alpha)(a^2-b^2)}{2a^2b^2}=-\frac{\alpha}{b^2}+\frac{(\mu+\alpha)(a^2-b^2)}{2a^2b^2},$$

since by (1.3)

$$\frac{\beta}{\lambda+2\mu}+\frac{\alpha}{\mu}=\frac{(\mu+\alpha)(a^2-b^2)}{a^2b^2};$$

accordingly (1.43) becomes

$$\begin{aligned}\mathbf{P}_j^{(x)}\overset{0}{\Gamma}{}^{(k)}(x, y)=\Big\{\Big[\frac{(\mu+\alpha)(a^2+b^2)}{2a^2b^2}-\frac{\alpha}{\mu}\Big]\delta_{jk}+\\ +\frac{3(\mu+\alpha)(a^2-b^2)}{2a^2b^2}\frac{\partial r}{\partial x_k}\frac{\partial r}{\partial x_j}\Big\}\frac{\partial}{\partial n_x}\frac{1}{r}+\\ +\Big[\frac{\alpha}{\mu}-\frac{(\mu+\alpha)(a^2-b^2)}{2a^2b^2}\Big]\Big(\cos(n_x, x_k)\frac{\partial}{\partial x_j}\frac{1}{r}-\cos(n_x, x_j)\frac{\partial}{\partial x_k}\frac{1}{r}\Big).\end{aligned} \qquad (1.44)$$

We now choose the value of the disposable parameter α such that

$$\frac{\alpha}{\mu}-\frac{(\mu+\alpha)(a^2-b^2)}{2a^2b^2}=0$$

that is, in terms of λ and μ,

$$\alpha=\frac{\mu(\lambda+\mu)}{\lambda+3\mu};$$

this fixes β, on account of (1.3), at

$$\beta=\frac{(\lambda+\mu)(\lambda+2\mu)}{\lambda+3\mu}.$$

These are the values of α and β given in § 1; when they are chosen the expression (1.44) for $\mathbf{P}_j^{(x)}\overset{0}{\Gamma}{}^{(k)}(x, y)$ contains none but the normal derivative; all other derivatives drop out, and thus*

$$\mathbf{N}_j^{(x)}\overset{0}{\Gamma}{}^{(k)}(x, y)=\frac{1}{\lambda+3\mu}\left[2\mu\delta_{jk}+3(\lambda+\mu)\frac{\partial r}{\partial x_k}\frac{\partial r}{\partial x_j}\right]\frac{\partial}{\partial n_x}\frac{1}{r(x, y)}. \tag{1.45}$$

It may easily be verified that $\mathbf{N}^{(x)}\Gamma^{(k)}(x, y)$ and $\mathbf{N}^{(x)}\overset{0}{\Gamma}{}^{(k)}(x, y)$ have the same singularities at $r(x, y)=0$; indeed, by (1.33)

$$\mathbf{N}_j^{(x)}\Gamma^{(k)}(x, y)=\mathbf{N}_j^{(x)}\Omega^{(k)}(x, y)+\mathbf{N}_j^{(x)}\overset{0}{\Gamma}{}^{(k)}(x, y), \tag{1.45'}$$

where the first term on the right-hand side has a removable (nonfundamental) singularity. In analogy with

$$\mathbf{T}^{(x)}\dot{\Gamma}(x, y),\quad \Gamma_{\text{I}}(x, y),\quad \mathbf{T}^{(x)}\overset{0}{\Gamma}(x, y),\quad \overset{0}{\Gamma}_{\text{I}}(x, y)$$

we now define four new matrices

$$\mathbf{N}^{(x)}\Gamma(x, y)=\left\|\mathbf{N}_j^{(x)}\Gamma^{(k)}(x, y)\right\|,\quad \mathbf{N}^{(x)}\overset{0}{\Gamma}(x, y)=\left\|\mathbf{N}_j^{(x)}\overset{0}{\Gamma}{}^{(k)}(x, y)\right\| \tag{1.46}$$

and their associated matrices

$$\Gamma_{\text{II}}(x, y)=\begin{Vmatrix}\mathbf{N}_1^{(y)}\Gamma^{(1)} & \mathbf{N}_2^{(y)}\Gamma^{(1)} & \mathbf{N}_3^{(y)}\Gamma^{(1)}\\ \mathbf{N}_1^{(y)}\Gamma^{(2)} & \mathbf{N}_2^{(y)}\Gamma^{(2)} & \mathbf{N}_3^{(y)}\Gamma^{(2)}\\ \mathbf{N}_1^{(y)}\Gamma^{(3)} & \mathbf{N}_2^{(y)}\Gamma^{(3)} & \mathbf{N}_3^{(y)}\Gamma^{(3)}\end{Vmatrix},\quad \overset{0}{\Gamma}_{\text{II}}(x, y)=\left\|\mathbf{N}_j^{(y)}\overset{0}{\Gamma}{}^{(k)}(x, y)\right\|. \tag{1.46'}$$

The quantities $\mathbf{N}_j^{(y)}\Gamma^{(k)}(x, y)$ and $\mathbf{N}_j^{(y)}\overset{0}{\Gamma}{}^{(k)}(x, y)$ are given by (1.45') and (1.45) upon interchanging x and y. The column vectors of $\Gamma_{\text{II}}(x, y)$ and $\overset{0}{\Gamma}_{\text{II}}(x, y)$ which respectively satisfy equations (1.1^0) and (1.2^0) at any point $x(x_1, x_2, x_3)$ will be called the fundamental solutions of the second kind.

§ 5. Fundamental solutions of the third kind

Let S be a closed surface such that none of its outward-drawn normals, endlessly prolonged, ever meets it again. For the point $y(y_1, y_2, y_3)$ on S, and an arbitrary $x(x_1, x_2, x_3)$ consider the function

$$v(x, y)=r\cos(\boldsymbol{r}_0, \boldsymbol{n}_y)\ln[r+r\cos(\boldsymbol{r}_0, \boldsymbol{n}_y)]-r, \tag{1.47}$$

where $\boldsymbol{n}_y$ is the unit inward normal at y, and $\boldsymbol{r}_0$ a unit vector along the segment $r(x, y)$, directed from y to x.

We shall now show that $v(x, y)$ is a harmonic function of the variable x. In fact, since

$$r\cos(\boldsymbol{r}_0, \boldsymbol{n}_y)=r\boldsymbol{n}_y=\sum_1^3(x_k-y_k)(\boldsymbol{n}_y)_k.$$

* This construction of the operator $\mathbf{N}$ was pointed out to the author by M. O. Basheleishvili.

we have

$$\frac{\partial v}{\partial x_k}=(n_y)_k \ln[r+(rn_y)]+(rn_y)\frac{\frac{\partial r}{\partial x_k}+(n_y)_k}{r+(rn_y)}-\frac{\partial r}{\partial x_k},$$

$$\frac{\partial^2 v}{\partial x_k^2}=2(n_y)_k\frac{\frac{\partial r}{\partial x_k}+(n_y)_k}{r+(rn_y)}+$$

$$+(rn_y)\left[\frac{\frac{\partial^2 r}{\partial x_k^2}}{r+(rn_y)}-\frac{\left(\frac{\partial r}{\partial x_k}+(n_y)_k\right)^2}{(r+(rn_y))^2}\right]-\frac{\partial^2 r}{\partial x_k^2},$$

$$\sum_{k=1}^{3}\frac{\partial^2 v}{\partial x_k^2}=2\frac{1+\cos(r_0, n_y)}{r+(rn_y)}+$$

$$+\frac{(rn_y)}{r+(rn_y)}\left[\sum_{k=1}^{3}\frac{\partial^2 r}{\partial x_k^2}-\frac{1}{r+(rn_y)}\sum_{k=1}^{3}\left(\frac{\partial r}{\partial x_k}+(n_y)_k\right)^2\right]-\sum_{k=1}^{3}\frac{\partial^2 r}{\partial x_k^2}.$$

But

$$\sum_{k=1}^{3}\frac{\partial^2 r}{\partial x_k^2}=\frac{2}{r},\quad \sum_{k=1}^{3}\left(\frac{\partial r}{\partial x_k}+(n_y)_k\right)^2=2[1+\cos(r_0, n_y)]=2\frac{r+(rn_y)}{r}.$$

Consequently

$$\sum_{k=1}^{3}\frac{\partial^2 v}{\partial x_k^2}\equiv\Delta_x v(x, y)=0.$$

As $v(x, y)$ does not depend on the origin and orientation of the coordinate system, we may place the origin at y and direct the x_1-axis along the inward normal n_y; then

$$v=x_1\ln(r+x_1)-r. \tag{1.48}$$

By virtue of the assumed property of the surface S – lying clear of its own outward-issuing normals – necessarily $x_1+r\neq 0$ for all its interior points.

Let us construct the matrix

$$Z=\left\|\begin{matrix}\frac{\partial^2 v}{\partial x_1^2} & -\frac{\partial^2 v}{\partial x_2\,\partial x_1} & -\frac{\partial^2 v}{\partial x_3\,\partial x_1}\\ \frac{\partial^2 v}{\partial x_1\,\partial x_2} & \frac{\partial^2 v}{\partial x_1^2}-\frac{\partial^2 v}{\partial x_3} & \frac{\partial^2 v}{\partial x_3\,\partial x_2}\\ \frac{\partial^2 v}{\partial x_1\,\partial x_3} & \frac{\partial^2 v}{\partial x_2\,\partial x_3} & \frac{\partial^2 v}{\partial x_1^2}-\frac{\partial^2 v}{\partial x_2^2}\end{matrix}\right\|=$$

$$=\left\|\begin{matrix}\frac{1}{r} & -\frac{x_2}{r(x_1+r)} & -\frac{x_3}{r(x_1+r)}\\ \frac{x_2}{r(x_1+r)} & \frac{1}{r}+\frac{r(x_1+r)-x_3^2}{r(x_1+r)^2} & \frac{x_2x_3}{r(x_1+r)^2}\\ \frac{x_3}{r(x_1+r)} & \frac{x_2x_3}{r(x_1+r)^2} & \frac{1}{r}+\frac{r(x_1+r)-x_2^2}{r(x_1+r)^2}\end{matrix}\right\|. \tag{1.49}$$

Each column of this matrix is a vector function of $x(x_1, x_2, x_3)$ satisfying

$$\operatorname{div} Z^{(k)}=\operatorname{rot}\operatorname{rot} Z^{(k)}=0 \qquad (k=1,\ 2,\ 3).$$

The matrix $Z(x, y)$ is consequently a matrix of solutions of the equilibrium equation (1.2^0). Let us consider still another matrix, introduced by Weyl /4a/:

$$M(x, y)=\frac{1}{3(\lambda+\mu)}\left[\frac{1}{2}Z(x, y)-(\lambda+2\mu)\overset{0}{\Gamma}(x, y)\right]. \tag{1.50}$$

This matrix, which evidently satisfies equation (1.2^0), will be called a fundamental solution of the third kind (with respect to $x(x_1, x_2, x_3)$) of the equilibrium equation (1.2^0). This solution is defined only for points x contained in the finite domain bounded by the surface S.

We shall now deduce one important property of the matrix $M(x, y)$, which justifies the introduction of solutions of the third kind. Let us construct the stress field corresponding to the displacement field defined by $M(x, y)$, i.e., derive the vectors

$$\mathrm{T}^{(x)}M^{(k)}(x, y) \qquad (k=1, 2, 3).$$

The first step is to obtain the vectors $\mathrm{T}^{(x)}Z^{(k)}(x, y)$. To avoid lengthy calculations, we choose a surface element through x such that its normal n_x is aligned with n_y. Then, by (1.11),

$$\mathrm{T}_1 Z^{(k)} = \lambda \operatorname{div} Z^{(k)} + 2\mu \frac{\partial Z_1^{(k)}}{\partial x_1} = 2\mu \frac{\partial Z_1^{(k)}}{\partial x_1},$$

$$\mathrm{T}_2 Z^{(k)} = \tau_{12} = \mu\left(\frac{\partial Z_1^{(k)}}{\partial x_2} + \frac{\partial Z_2^{(k)}}{\partial x_1}\right),$$

$$\mathrm{T}_3 Z^{(k)} = \tau_{13} = \mu\left(\frac{\partial Z_3^{(k)}}{\partial x_1} + \frac{\partial Z_1^{(k)}}{\partial x_3}\right) \qquad (k=1, 2, 3).$$

Inserting here the columns of the matrix (1.49) in turn, we obtain

$$\mathrm{T}^{(x)}Z = 2\mu I \frac{\partial}{\partial n_x}\frac{1}{r} + 2\mu \begin{Vmatrix} 0 & -\frac{\partial}{\partial x_2} & -\frac{\partial}{\partial x_3} \\ \frac{\partial}{\partial x_2} & 0 & 0 \\ \frac{\partial}{\partial x_3} & 0 & 0 \end{Vmatrix} \frac{1}{r}, \tag{1.51}$$

where I is the unit matrix. To obtain the operator T from P we now set $\alpha=\mu$, $\beta=\lambda$ in (1.44), which gives

$$\mathrm{T}_j^{(x)} \overset{0}{\Gamma}{}^{(k)} = \frac{1}{\lambda+2\mu}\left\{\left[\mu\delta_{jk} + 3(\lambda+\mu)\frac{\partial r}{\partial x_j}\frac{\partial r}{\partial x_k}\right]\frac{\partial}{\partial n_x}\frac{1}{r} + \right.$$
$$\left. + \mu\left(\cos(n_x x_k)\frac{\partial}{\partial x_j}\frac{1}{r} - \cos(n_x, x_j)\frac{\partial}{\partial x_k}\frac{1}{r}\right)\right\}. \tag{1.52}$$

Being free to take n_x parallel to n_y without loss of generality, we finally obtain

$$\mathrm{T}^{(x)}\overset{0}{\Gamma} = \frac{1}{\lambda+2\mu}\left[\mu I \frac{\partial}{\partial n_x}\frac{1}{r} + 3(\lambda+\mu) \times \right.$$
$$\left. \times \begin{Vmatrix} \left(\frac{\partial r}{\partial x_1}\right)^2 & \frac{\partial r}{\partial x_1}\frac{\partial r}{\partial x_2} & \frac{\partial r}{\partial x_1}\frac{\partial r}{\partial x_3} \\ \frac{\partial r}{\partial x_1}\frac{\partial r}{\partial x_2} & \left(\frac{\partial r}{\partial x_2}\right)^2 & \frac{\partial r}{\partial x_2}\frac{\partial r}{\partial x_3} \\ \frac{\partial r}{\partial x_1}\frac{\partial r}{\partial x_3} & \frac{\partial r}{\partial x_2}\frac{\partial r}{\partial x_3} & \left(\frac{\partial r}{\partial x_3}\right)^2 \end{Vmatrix} \frac{\partial}{\partial n_x}\frac{1}{r} + \mu \begin{Vmatrix} 0 & -\frac{\partial}{\partial x_2} & -\frac{\partial}{\partial x_3} \\ \frac{\partial}{\partial x_2} & 0 & 0 \\ \frac{\partial}{\partial x_3} & 0 & 0 \end{Vmatrix} \frac{1}{r}\right]. \tag{1.53}$$

Multiplying (1.51) and (1.53) by the appropriate constants as in (1.50) and adding them together, we obtain the required stress field corresponding to the displacement field M,

$$\mathbf{T}^{(x)}M=\begin{Vmatrix}\left(\frac{\partial r}{\partial x_1}\right)^2 & \frac{\partial r}{\partial x_2}\frac{\partial r}{\partial x_1} & \frac{\partial r}{\partial x_3}\frac{\partial r}{\partial x_1}\\ \frac{\partial r}{\partial x_1}\frac{\partial r}{\partial x_2} & \left(\frac{\partial r}{\partial x_2}\right)^2 & \frac{\partial r}{\partial x_2}\frac{\partial r}{\partial x_3}\\ \frac{\partial r}{\partial x_1}\frac{\partial r}{\partial x_3} & \frac{\partial r}{\partial x_2}\frac{\partial r}{\partial x_3} & \left(\frac{\partial r}{\partial x_3}\right)^2\end{Vmatrix}\frac{\partial}{\partial n_x}\frac{1}{r}. \tag{1.54}$$

The operation of $\mathbf{T}$ on a fundamental solution of the third kind thus gives rise to a singularity of type $\frac{\partial}{\partial n}\frac{1}{r}$ at $x=0$, as the pseudostress operator does when operating on $\overset{0}{\Gamma}$. This property makes solutions of the third kind useful in the theory of boundary-value problems. This was first shown in a particular case by Weyl /4a/, and later generalized and extended to equation (1.1) in /13a, d/.

§ 6. Elastic potentials for an isotropic medium

Let $\tau(x;\varepsilon)$ be a sphere of radius ε centered at x, and let $\sigma(x;\varepsilon)$ be its surface. Let $x\in B_i$, where B_i is a domain bounded by a closed surface S, and let ε be sufficiently small for the sphere to be wholly contained in B_i; applying the generalized Betti formula (1.10) in the domain $B_i-\tau(x;\varepsilon)$ to some regular vector function $\boldsymbol{v}(y)$ and to

$$\boldsymbol{u}(y)=\Gamma^{(k)}(x,y)\qquad (k=1,2,3),$$

we obtain

$$\int\limits_{B_i-\tau(x;\varepsilon)}\Gamma^{(k)}(x,y)\left[\Delta^*\boldsymbol{v}(y)+\omega^2\boldsymbol{v}(y)\right]dv_y=$$
$$=\int\limits_{S+\sigma(x;\varepsilon)}\left[\Gamma^{(k)}(x,y)\mathbf{P}\boldsymbol{v}(y)-\boldsymbol{v}(y)\mathbf{P}^{(y)}\Gamma^{(k)}(x,y)\right]dS_y\ (k=1,2,3). \tag{1.55}$$

Since $\boldsymbol{v}(y)$ is regular in B_i and $\Gamma^{(k)}(x,y)$ has only a first-order pole at $y=x$, the following bound is easily deduced

$$\left|\int\limits_{\sigma(x;\varepsilon)}\Gamma^{(k)}(x,y)\mathbf{P}\boldsymbol{v}(y)\,dS_y\right|<C\varepsilon\qquad (k=1,2,3),$$

where C is a finite constant. Further

$$\int\limits_{\sigma(x;\varepsilon)}\boldsymbol{v}(y)\mathbf{P}\Gamma^{(k)}(x,y)\,dS_y=$$
$$=\int\limits_{\sigma(x;\varepsilon)}\left[\boldsymbol{v}(y)-\boldsymbol{v}(x)\right]\mathbf{P}\Gamma^{(k)}(x,y)\,dS_y+\boldsymbol{v}(x)\int\limits_{\sigma(x;\varepsilon)}\mathbf{P}^{(y)}\Gamma^{(k)}(x,y)\,dS_y, \tag{1.56}$$

and the first integral on the right-hand side approaches zero together with ε; as to the second integral, it may be written in the form

$$\boldsymbol{v}(x)\int\limits_{\sigma(x;\varepsilon)}\mathbf{P}^{(y)}\Gamma^{(k)}(x,y)\,dS_y=$$
$$=\boldsymbol{v}(x)\int\limits_{\sigma(x;\varepsilon)}\mathbf{P}^{(y)}\left(\Gamma^{(k)}-\overset{0}{\Gamma}{}^{(k)}\right)dS_y+\boldsymbol{v}(x)\int\limits_{\sigma(x;\varepsilon)}\mathbf{P}^{(y)}\overset{0}{\Gamma}{}^{(k)}(x,y)\,dS_y$$

2109

while in view of the properties of the difference (1.33) and its first derivatives

$$\lim_{\varepsilon\to 0}\int_{\sigma(x;\varepsilon)} v(y)\,\mathrm{P}\Gamma^{(k)}(x,y)\,dS_y=\lim_{\varepsilon\to 0}\left[v(x)\int_{\sigma(x;\varepsilon)}\mathrm{P}\overset{0}{\Gamma}{}^{(k)}(x,y)\,dS_y\right]=$$

$$=\lim_{\varepsilon\to 0}\sum_{j=1}^{3} v_j(x)\int_{\sigma(x;\varepsilon)}\mathrm{P}_j\overset{0}{\Gamma}{}^{(k)}(x,y)\,dS_y. \qquad (1.57)$$

Substituting here the expressions from (1.43) and using the equality

$$\int_{\sigma(x;\varepsilon)}\cos(n_y,x_j)\frac{\partial}{\partial y_k}\frac{1}{r(x,y)}\,dS_y=\begin{cases}0, & j\neq k,\\ \frac{4}{3}\pi, & j=k,\end{cases} \qquad (1.57')$$

we obtain

$$\lim_{\varepsilon\to 0}\int_{\sigma(x;\varepsilon)} v(y)\,\mathrm{P}\overset{0}{\Gamma}{}^{(k)}(x,y)\,dS_y=$$

$$=\lim_{\varepsilon\to 0}\sum_{j=1}^{3} v_j(x)\int_{\sigma(x;\varepsilon)}\left\{\left[\frac{(\alpha+\mu)(a^2+b^2)}{2a^2b^2}-\frac{\alpha}{b^2}\right]\delta_{jk}+\right.$$

$$\left.+\frac{3(\mu+\alpha)(a^2-b^2)}{2a^2b^2}\frac{\partial r}{\partial x_k}\frac{\partial r}{\partial x_j}\right\}\frac{\partial}{\partial n_y}\frac{1}{r}\,dS_y. \qquad (1.58)$$

The integrals on the right-hand side are easily calculated. Let

$$y_1=x_1+r\sin\theta\cos\varphi,\quad y_2=x_2+r\sin\theta\sin\varphi,\quad y_3=x_3+r\cos\theta.$$

Taking the direction from x to y, and the normals pointing outwards from $B_i-\tau(x;\varepsilon)$ as positive, we obtain for points on the sphere's surface

$$\frac{\partial}{\partial n_y}\frac{1}{r(x,y)}=-\frac{\partial}{\partial r}\frac{1}{r}=\frac{1}{\varepsilon^2}.$$

Hence

$$\left.\begin{aligned}&\int_{\sigma(x;\varepsilon)}\left(\frac{\partial r}{\partial y_k}\right)^2\frac{\partial}{\partial n_y}\frac{1}{r}\,dS_y=\int_0^{\pi}\int_0^{2\pi}\left(\frac{y_k-x_k}{r}\right)^2\sin\theta\,d\theta\,d\varphi=\frac{4}{3}\pi,\\ &\int_{\sigma(x;\varepsilon)}\frac{\partial r}{\partial y_j}\frac{\partial r}{\partial y_k}\frac{\partial}{\partial n_y}\frac{1}{r(x,y)}\,dS_y=\int_0^{\pi}\int_0^{2\pi}\frac{(y_j-x_j)(y_k-x_k)}{r^2}\sin\theta\,d\theta\,d\varphi=\\ &\qquad=0\ (j\neq k),\end{aligned}\right\} \qquad (1.57'')$$

$$\int_{\sigma(x;\varepsilon)}\frac{\partial}{\partial n_y}\frac{1}{r}\,dS_y=4\pi,$$

and, by (1.58),

$$\lim_{\varepsilon\to 0}\int_{\sigma(x;\varepsilon)} v(y)\,\mathrm{P}\overset{0}{\Gamma}{}^{(k)}(x,y)\,dS_y=$$

$$=\left\{\left[\frac{(\mu+\alpha)(a^2+b^2)}{2a^2b^2}-\frac{\alpha}{b^2}\right]4\pi+\frac{3(\mu+\alpha)(a^2-b^2)}{2a^2b^2}\,\frac{4}{3}\pi\right\}v_k(x)=$$

$$=4\pi v_k(x)\qquad (k=1,2,3). \qquad (1.58')$$

Finally, from (1.55) and (1.57) follows

$$v_k(x) = \frac{1}{4\pi}\int\limits_S \Gamma^{(k)}(x, y)\,\mathbf{P}v(y)\,dS_y - \frac{1}{4\pi}\int\limits_S v(y)\,\mathbf{P}\Gamma^{(k)}(x, y)\,dS_y - \\ - \frac{1}{4\pi}\int\limits_{B_i} (\Delta^* v + \omega^2 v)\,\Gamma^{(k)}(x, y)\,dv_y. \qquad (1.59)$$

In particular, if the regular vector function $v(y)$ is chosen such that

$$\Delta^* v(y) + \omega^2 v(y) = 0,$$

then .

$$v_k(x) = \frac{1}{4\pi}\int\limits_S [\Gamma^{(k)}(x, y)\,\mathbf{P}v(y) - v(y)\,\mathbf{P}^{(y)}\Gamma^{(k)}(x, y)\,dS_y \quad (k=1, 2, 3). \qquad (1.60)$$

We have so far considered points x interior to B_i, but all the arguments clearly apply also to $x \in B_a$ or $x \in S$, where B_a is the complement of B_i to make up all infinite space. Consequently, the following general formula holds

$$\delta(x)\,v_k(x) = \frac{1}{4\pi}\int\limits_S [\Gamma^{(k)}(x, y)\,\mathbf{P}v(y) - v(y)\,\mathbf{P}\Gamma^{(k)}(x, y)]\,dS_y \\ (k = 1, 2, 3), \qquad (1.61)$$

where

$$\delta(x) = \begin{cases} 1, & x \in B_i, \\ \frac{1}{2}, & x \in S, \\ 0, & x \in B_a. \end{cases}$$

Let us now set down some rules concerning matrix notation. Right-multiplication of a matrix

$$A(x, y) = \begin{Vmatrix} a_{11}(x, y) & a_{12}(x, y) & a_{13}(x, y) \\ a_{21}(x, y) & a_{22}(x, y) & a_{23}(x, y) \\ a_{31}(x, y) & a_{32}(x, y) & a_{33}(x, y) \end{Vmatrix}$$

by a vector $\varphi(y)$ will signify matrix multiplication of $A(x, y)$ by the one-column matrix

$$\varphi(y) = \begin{Vmatrix} \varphi_1(y) \\ \varphi_2(y) \\ \varphi_3(y) \end{Vmatrix},$$

whose product is the column-vector

$$A(x, y)\,\varphi(y) = \begin{Vmatrix} \sum_1^3 a_{1k}(x, y)\,\varphi_k(y) \\ \sum_1^3 a_{2k}(x, y)\,\varphi_k(y) \\ \sum_1^3 a_{3k}(x\ y)\,\varphi_k(y) \end{Vmatrix}.$$

Similarly, left-multiplication of $A(x, y)$ by the vector $\varphi(x)$ will signify the product of the one-row matrix $\varphi(x) = \|\varphi_1(x), \varphi_2(x), \varphi_3(x)\|$ and $A(x, y)$, that is, the row-vector

$$\varphi(x) A(x, y) = \left\| \sum_1^3 a_{k1}(x, y) \varphi_k(x), \sum_1^3 a_{k2}(x, y) \varphi_k(x), \sum_1^3 a_{k3}(x, y) \varphi_k(x) \right\|.$$

With this definition of multiplication we have the identity

$$A(x, y) \varphi(y) = \varphi(y) A^*(x, y), \tag{1.62}$$

where $A^*(x, y)$ is the transpose of $A(x, y)$, i.e., the matrix obtained by interchanging rows and columns in the original one.

In view of (1.38') and the symmetry of the matrix $\Gamma(x, y)$ (1.61) will be written in vector form as

$$\delta(x) v(x) = \frac{1}{4\pi} \int_S \Gamma(x, y) \mathrm{P} v(y) \, dS_y - \frac{1}{4\pi} \int_S \Pi(x, y) v(y) \, dS_y. \tag{1.61'}$$

Assigning to α and β the values

$$\alpha = \mu, \quad \beta = \lambda,$$

(1.61') becomes

$$\delta(x) v(x) = \frac{1}{4\pi} \int_S \Gamma(x, y) \mathrm{T} v(y) \, dS_y - \frac{1}{4\pi} \int_S \Gamma_{\mathrm{I}}(x, y) v(y) \, dS_y. \tag{1.63}$$

The vector functions

$$V(x) = \frac{1}{2\pi} \int_S \Gamma(x, y) \varphi(y) \, dS_y, \quad W_{\mathrm{I}}(x) = \frac{1}{2\pi} \int_S \Gamma_{\mathrm{I}}(x, y) \varphi(y) \, dS_y, \tag{1.64}$$

where $\varphi(y)$ is a vector function defined on S and satisfying (say) the Hölder condition with respect to points $x(x_1, x_2, x_3)$ not on S, are solutions of the homogeneous equation (1.1^0)*. They will be respectively called the s i n g l e - l a y e r p o t e n t i a l, and the d o u b l e - l a y e r p o t e n t i a l o f t h e f i r s t k i n d.

Similarly, when α and β are taken as

$$\alpha = \frac{\mu(\lambda + \mu)}{\lambda + 3\mu}, \quad \beta = \frac{(\lambda + \mu)(\lambda + 2\mu)}{\lambda + 3\mu}, \quad \alpha + \beta = \lambda + \mu,$$

we obtain, in the notation of § 4, the vector function

$$W_{\mathrm{II}}(x) = \frac{1}{2\pi} \int_S \Gamma_{\mathrm{II}}(x, y) \varphi(y) \, dS_y, \tag{1.65}$$

which will be called the d o u b l e - l a y e r p o t e n t i a l o f t h e s e c o n d k i n d. The fundamental solutions of the third kind can be used to construct the vector function

$$A(x) = \frac{1}{2\pi} \int_S M(x, y) \varphi(y) \, dS_y, \tag{1.65'}$$

* This follows from Theorem 1 of § 3.

which evidently satisfies $\Delta^* u = 0$; it will sometimes be called the antenna potential [following Weyl /4a/]. This potential is defined only for points interior to the finite closed surface S.

Finally, the vector function

$$U(x) = \frac{1}{4\pi} \int_{B_i} \Gamma(x, y) \varphi(y)\, dv_y, \tag{1.66}$$

which appears in the general representation of the regular vector function $v(x)$, will be called the volume potential.

Each of the constructed dynamic potentials reduces to a static equilibrium potential for $\omega = 0$:

$$V(x) = \frac{1}{2\pi} \int_S \overset{0}{\Gamma}(x, y) \varphi(y)\, dS_y \quad W_{\text{I}}(x) = \frac{1}{2\pi} \int_S \overset{0}{\Gamma}_{\text{I}}(x, y) \varphi(y)\, dS_y,$$

$$W_{\text{II}}(x) = \frac{1}{2\pi} \int_S \overset{0}{\Gamma}_{\text{II}}(x, y) \varphi(y)\, dS_y, \quad U(x) = \frac{1}{4\pi} \int_{B_i} \overset{0}{\Gamma}(x, y) \varphi(y)\, dv_y. \tag{1.67}$$

The first three of these potentials are integrals of equation (1.2^0). We shall study in the following stress-fields corresponding to displacements derivable from potentials of the above types. According to our matrix-vector multiplication rule, the operand in the symbol

$$\mathrm{T}^{(x)} [\Gamma(x, y) \varphi(y)]$$

is understood to be

$$\Gamma(x, y) \varphi(y) = \sum_j \sum_k i_j \Gamma_j^{(k)}(x, y) \varphi_k(y), \tag{1.68}$$

while by definition of the operator T

$$\mathrm{T}^{(x)} [\Gamma(x, y) \varphi(y)] = 2\mu \frac{\partial}{\partial n_x} (\Gamma(x, y) \varphi(y)) +$$
$$+ \lambda n_x \operatorname{div}_x (\Gamma(x, y) \varphi(y)) + \mu (n_x \times \operatorname{rot} \Gamma(x, y) \varphi(y)).$$

Substituting the expression (1.68), we obtain

$$\mathrm{T}^{(x)} [\Gamma(x, y) \varphi(y)] = 2\mu \frac{\partial}{\partial n_x} (\Gamma(x, y) \varphi(y)) +$$
$$+ \lambda n_x (\varphi \operatorname{div} \Gamma) + \mu (n_x \times \operatorname{rot} \Gamma\varphi)), \tag{1.69}$$

where $\operatorname{div} \Gamma$ is, by (1.34) and (1.35), a vector with the components

$$\operatorname{div}_x \Gamma^{(1)}, \quad \operatorname{div}_x \Gamma^{(2)}, \quad \operatorname{div}_x \Gamma^{(3)},$$

and $\operatorname{rot}(\Gamma\varphi)$ is the vector

$$\sum_j \sum_k i_j (\operatorname{rot}_x \Gamma^{(k)}(x, y))_{x_j} \varphi_k(y).$$

The x_1-component of the vector $\mathrm{T}^{(x)} (\Gamma(x, y) \varphi(y))$ will be

$$[\mathrm{T}^{(x)} (\Gamma(x, y) \varphi(y))]_{x_1} =$$
$$= 2\mu \frac{\partial}{\partial n_x} [(\Gamma_1^{(1)}(x, y) \varphi_1(y) + \Gamma_1^{(2)}(x, y) \varphi_2(y) + \Gamma_1^{(3)}(x, y) \varphi_3(y))] +$$
$$+ \lambda \cos(n_x, x_1) [\varphi_1(y) \operatorname{div}_x \Gamma^{(1)}(x, y) + \varphi_2(y) \operatorname{div}_x \Gamma^{(2)}(x, y) +$$
$$+ \varphi_3(y) \operatorname{div}_x \Gamma^{(3)}(x, y)] + \mu \{\cos(n_x, x_2) [\varphi_1(y) (\operatorname{rot}_x \Gamma^{(1)})_{x_3} +$$
$$+ \varphi_2(y) (\operatorname{rot}_x \Gamma^{(2)})_{x_3} + \varphi_3(y) (\operatorname{rot}_x \Gamma^{(3)})_{x_3}] - \cos(n_x, x_3) [\varphi_1(y) (\operatorname{rot}_x \Gamma^{(1)})_{x_2} +$$
$$+ \varphi_2(y) (\operatorname{rot}_x \Gamma^{(2)})_{x_2} + \varphi_3(y) (\operatorname{rot}_x \Gamma^{(3)})_{x_2}]\},$$

and since T operates here with respect to the point x, of which $\varphi(y)$ is independent, we may write

$$\{\mathrm{T}^{(x)}[\Gamma(x, y)\varphi(y)]\}_{x_1} =$$
$$= \varphi_1(y)\left[2\mu\frac{\partial\Gamma_1^{(1)}}{\partial n_x} + \lambda\cos(n_x, x_1)\operatorname{div}_x\Gamma^{(1)} + \mu(n_x \times \operatorname{rot}_x\Gamma^{(1)})_{x_1}\right] +$$
$$+ \varphi_2(y)\left[2\mu\frac{\partial\Gamma_1^{(2)}}{\partial n_x} + \lambda\cos(n_x, x_1)\operatorname{div}_x\Gamma^{(2)} + \mu(n_x \times \operatorname{rot}_x\Gamma^{(2)})_{x_1}\right] +$$
$$+ \varphi_3(y)\left[2\mu\frac{\partial\Gamma_1^{(3)}}{\partial n_x} + \lambda\cos(n_x, x_1)\operatorname{div}_x\Gamma^{(3)} + \mu(n_x \times \operatorname{rot}_x\Gamma^{(3)})_{x_1}\right] =$$
$$= \sum_{k=1}^{3}[\mathrm{T}_1^{(x)}\Gamma^{(k)}(x, y)]\varphi_k(y). \qquad (1.70)$$

On the other hand, by (1.41) and our matrix-vector multiplication rule

$$\{(\mathrm{T}^{(x)}\Gamma(x, y))\varphi(y)\}_{x_1} = \sum_{k=1}^{3}\left(\mathrm{T}_1^{(x)}\Gamma^{(k)}(x, y)\right)\varphi_k(y).$$

Comparing with (1.70) and observing that the above considerations remain in force when x_1 is replaced by x_2 or x_3, we obtain

$$\mathrm{T}^{(x)}[\Gamma(x, y)\varphi(y)] = (\mathrm{T}^{(x)}\Gamma(x, y))\varphi(y), \qquad (1.71)$$

and similarly

$$\mathrm{N}^{(x)}[\Gamma(x, y)\varphi(y)] = (\mathrm{N}^{(x)}\Gamma(x, y))\varphi(y). \qquad (1.72)$$

§ 7. The Poisson formula

The volume potential

$$U(x) = \frac{1}{4\pi}\int_{B_i}\varphi(y)\Gamma_{(a)}(x, y)\,dv_y, \qquad (1.73)$$

where $\Gamma_{(a)}(x, y)$ denotes the matrix $\Gamma(x, y)$ for $\lambda = \lambda_a$ and $\mu = \mu_a$, and the vector $\varphi(y)$ is assumed continuous and differentiable in B_i, plays an important part in what follows. We shall be particularly interested for $x \in B_i$ in the expressions

$$(\Delta^*_{(i)} + \omega^2)U(x)$$

and

$$(\Delta^*_{(a)} + \omega^2)U(x),$$

where

$$\Delta^*_{(i)} \equiv \mu_i\Delta + (\lambda_i + \mu_i)\operatorname{grad}\operatorname{div},$$
$$\Delta^*_{(a)} \equiv \mu_a\Delta + (\lambda_a + \mu_a)\operatorname{grad}\operatorname{div}.$$

Let the point $x_0 \in B_i$ be enclosed within the sphere $\tau(x_0; \varepsilon)$ and let $x \in \tau(x_0; \varepsilon)$. We now take

$$U(x) = U^{(1)}(x) + U^{(2)}(x),$$

where

$$U^{(1)}(x) = \frac{1}{4\pi}\int_{B_i - \tau(x_0; \varepsilon)}\varphi(y)\Gamma_{(a)}(x, y)\,dv_y,$$

$$U^{(2)}(x)=\frac{1}{4\pi}\int\limits_{\tau(x_0;\,\varepsilon)}\varphi(y)\,\Gamma_{(a)}(x,\,y)\,dv_y.$$

The components of U along the axes are given by the expressions

$$U_j(x)=\frac{1}{4\pi}\int\limits_{B_l}(\varphi\Gamma_{(a)})_j\,dv_y=\frac{1}{4\pi}\int\limits_{B_l}\sum_{k=1}^{3}\Gamma_k^{(j)}(x,\,y)\,\varphi_k(y)\,dv_y=$$

$$=\frac{1}{4\pi}\int\limits_{B_l}\varphi(y)\,\Gamma_{(a)}^{(j)}\,dv_y\qquad(j=1,\,2,\,3)$$

and similarly for $U_j^{(1)}$ and $U_j^{(2)}$.

The operator $(\overset{*}{\Delta}_{(l)}+\omega^2)$ may be introduced under the integral sign in the expression for $U^{(1)}(x)$; therefore

$$(\overset{*}{\Delta}_{(l)}+\omega^2)\,U(x)=\frac{1}{4\pi}\int\limits_{B_l-\tau(x_0;\,\varepsilon)}(\overset{*}{\Delta}_{(l)}+\omega^2)(\varphi\Gamma_{(a)})\,dv_y+$$

$$+\frac{1}{4\pi}(\overset{*}{\Delta}_{(l)}+\omega^2)\int\limits_{\tau(x_0;\,\varepsilon)}\varphi(y)\,\Gamma_{(a)}(x,\,y)\,dv_y.$$

We shall now work out

$$\Delta U_j^{(2)}(x)\ \text{and}\ \operatorname{grad}\operatorname{div}U^{(2)}(x).$$

Consider the derivatives

$$\frac{\partial U_j^{(2)}(x)}{\partial x_k}=\frac{1}{4\pi}\int\limits_{\tau(x_0,\,\varepsilon)}\varphi(y)\frac{\partial\Gamma_{(a)}^{(j)}}{\partial x_k}\,dv_y=-\frac{1}{4\pi}\int\limits_{\tau(x_0;\,\varepsilon)}\varphi(y)\frac{\partial\Gamma_{(a)}^{(j)}}{\partial y_k}\,dv_y=$$

$$=-\frac{1}{4\pi}\int\limits_{\tau(x_0;\,\varepsilon)}\frac{\partial}{\partial y_k}(\varphi\Gamma_{(a)}^{(j)})\,dv_y+\frac{1}{4\pi}\int\limits_{\tau(x_0;\,\varepsilon)}\left(\Gamma_{(a)}^{(j)}\frac{\partial\varphi}{\partial y_k}\right)dv_y=$$

$$=-\frac{1}{4\pi}\int\limits_{\sigma(x_0;\,\varepsilon)}\varphi\Gamma_{(a)}^{(j)}\cos(n_y,\,x_k)\,dS_y+\frac{1}{4\pi}\int\limits_{\tau(x_0;\,\varepsilon)}\left(\Gamma_{(a)}^{(j)}\frac{\partial\varphi}{\partial y_k}\right)dv_y\qquad(1.74)$$

$$(k=1,\,2,\,3).$$

Here n_y is the unit outward normal to the sphere $\tau(x;\,\varepsilon)$ at y, and the positive direction of the segment

$$r=\sqrt{(y_1-x_{01})^2+(y_2-x_{02})^2+(y_3-x_{03})^2}$$

is taken from x_0 to y, so that on the sphere surface

$$\cos(r,\,x_k)=\cos(n_y,\,x_k)=\frac{y_k-x_{0k}}{r}\qquad(k=1,\,2,\,3).$$

The first integral in the far-right member of (1.74) may be differentiated with respect to x, since x does not lie on $\sigma(x_0;\,\varepsilon)$; so may the second integral, being a volume potential with the continuous density $\frac{\partial\varphi(y)}{\partial y_k}$. Hence the second derivatives

$$\frac{\partial^2 U^{(2)}(x)}{\partial x_k\,\partial x_j}\qquad(j,\,k=1,\,2,\,3)$$

exist, along with

$$\frac{\partial^2 U(x)}{\partial x_k\,\partial x_j},$$

which equal the sum

$$\frac{\partial^2 U^{(1)}(x)}{\partial x_k \partial x_j} + \frac{\partial^2 U^{(2)}(x)}{\partial x_k \partial x_j}$$

and do not depend on ε.

Differentiating (1.74) with respect to x_j, we obtain

$$\frac{\partial^2 U_s^{(2)}(x)}{\partial x_k \partial x_j} = -\frac{1}{4\pi}\int\limits_{\sigma(x_0;\,\varepsilon)} \frac{\partial}{\partial x_j}\left(\varphi \Gamma_{(a)}^{(s)} \cos(n_y,\, x_k)\right) dS_y + \\ + \frac{1}{4\pi}\int\limits_{\tau(x_0;\,\varepsilon)} \frac{\partial}{\partial x_j}\left(\Gamma_{(a)}^{(s)} \frac{\partial \varphi}{\partial y_k}\right) dv_y = -\frac{1}{4\pi}\int\limits_{\tau(x_0;\,\varepsilon)} \frac{\partial}{\partial x_j}\Big[\left(\varphi \Gamma_{(a)}^{(s)}\right) - \\ - \left(\varphi \overset{0}{\Gamma}{}_{(a)}^{(s)}\right)\Big] \cos(n_y,\, x_k)\, dS_y + \frac{1}{4\pi}\int\limits_{\tau(x_0;\,\varepsilon)} \frac{\partial}{\partial x_j}\left(\Gamma_{(a)}^{(s)} \frac{\partial \varphi}{\partial y_k}\right) dv_y - \\ - \frac{1}{4\pi}\int\limits_{\sigma(x_0;\,\varepsilon)} \frac{\partial}{\partial x_j}\left(\varphi \overset{0}{\Gamma}{}_{(a)}^{(s)}\right) \cos(n_y,\, x_k)\, dS_y = I_1 + I_2 + I_3, \qquad (1.75)$$

where I_1, I_2, I_3 concisely denote the respective terms. Now in the limit

$$\lim_{\varepsilon\to 0} I_1 = \lim_{\varepsilon\to 0} I_2 = 0,$$

whence

$$\lim_{\varepsilon\to 0} \frac{\partial^2 U_s^{(2)}(x)}{\partial x_k \partial x_j} = \lim_{\varepsilon\to 0} I_3,$$

where

$$I_3 = -\frac{1}{4\pi}\int\limits_{\sigma(x_0;\,\varepsilon)} \frac{\partial}{\partial x_j}\left(\varphi(y) \overset{0}{\Gamma}{}^{(s)}(x,\, y)\right) \cos(n_y x_k)\, dS_y = \sum_{p=1}^{3} I_s^{(p)},$$

while

$$I_s^{(p)} = -\frac{1}{4\pi}\int\limits_{\sigma(x_0;\,\varepsilon)} \varphi_p(y) \frac{\partial \overset{0}{\Gamma}{}_p^{(s)}}{\partial x_j} \cos(n_y,\, x_k)\, dS_y.$$

Using (1.32), we obtain

$$I_s^{(p)} = -\frac{a^2+b^2}{8\pi a^2 b^2}\int\limits_{\sigma(x_0;\,y)} \delta_{ps}\varphi_p(y) \frac{\cos(n,\, x_k)\cos(r,\, x_j)}{r^2} dS_y - \\ - \frac{a^2-b^2}{8\pi a^2 b^2}\int\limits_{\sigma(x_0;\,\varepsilon)} \varphi_p(y) \frac{\partial}{\partial x_j}\left(\frac{(y_p - x_p)(y_s - x_s)}{r^3}\right) \cos(n_y,\, x_k)\, dS_y = \\ = -\frac{a^2+b^2}{8\pi a^2 b^2} I_{pskj} - \frac{a^2-b^2}{8\pi a^2 b^2} I'_{pskj},$$

where

$$I_{pskj} = \int\limits_{\sigma(x_0;\,\varepsilon)} \delta_{ps}\varphi_p(y) \frac{\cos(n,\, x_k)\cos(r,\, x_j)}{r^2} dS_y,$$

$$I'_{pskj} = \int\limits_{\sigma(x_0;\,\varepsilon)} \varphi_p(y) \frac{\partial}{\partial x_j}\left(\frac{(y_p - x_p)(y_s - x_s)}{r^3}\right) \cos(n_y,\, x_k)\, dS_y.$$

Let $x = x_0$ be the origin of the polar coordinates

$$y_1 = x_1 + r\sin\theta\cos\varphi, \quad y_2 = x_2 + r\sin\theta\sin\varphi, \quad y_3 = x_3 + r\cos\theta;$$

then

$$\cos(\boldsymbol{n}_y, \boldsymbol{x}_1) = \frac{y_1 - x_1}{r} = \sin\theta\cos\varphi, \quad \cos(\boldsymbol{n}_y, \boldsymbol{x}_2) = \sin\theta\sin\varphi,$$
$$\cos(\boldsymbol{n}_y, \boldsymbol{x}_3) = \cos\theta.$$

We obtain

$$\frac{\partial^2 U_1^{(2)}(x)}{\partial x_1^2} = -\frac{a^2+b^2}{8\pi a^2 b^2}\lim_{\varepsilon\to 0}(I_{1111}+I_{2111}+I_{3111}) - \\ -\frac{a^2-b^2}{8\pi a^2 b^2}\lim_{\varepsilon\to 0}(I'_{1111}+I'_{2111}+I'_{3111}),$$

$$I_{1111} = \int_{\sigma(x;\,\varepsilon)} \varphi_1(y)\frac{\cos^2(\boldsymbol{n}_y, \boldsymbol{x}_1)}{r^2}dS_y = \int_{\sigma(x;\,\varepsilon)} (\varphi_1(y)-\varphi_1(x))\frac{\cos^2(\boldsymbol{n}_y, \boldsymbol{x}_1)}{r^2}dS_y + \\ +\varphi_1(x)\int_{\sigma(x;\,\varepsilon)}\frac{\cos^2(\boldsymbol{n}_y, \boldsymbol{x}_1)}{r^2}dS_y,$$

$$\lim_{\varepsilon\to 0} I_{1111} = \varphi_1(x)\lim_{\varepsilon\to 0}\int_{\sigma(x;\,\varepsilon)}\frac{\cos^2(\boldsymbol{n}_y, \boldsymbol{x}_1)}{r^2}dS_y = \\ = \frac{1}{3}\varphi_1(x)\lim_{\varepsilon\to 0}\int_{\sigma(x;\,\varepsilon)}\frac{\cos^2(\boldsymbol{n}, \boldsymbol{x}_1)+\cos^2(\boldsymbol{n}, \boldsymbol{x}_2)+\cos^2(\boldsymbol{n}, \boldsymbol{x}_3)}{r^2}dS_y = \\ = \frac{1}{3}\varphi_1(x)\lim_{\varepsilon\to 0}\int_{\sigma(x;\,\varepsilon)}\frac{dS_y}{r^2} = \frac{4}{3}\pi\varphi_1(x).$$

Since $\delta_{21}=\delta_{31}=0$, we obtain*

$$I_{2111} = I_{3111} = 0,$$

$$I'_{1111} = \int_{\sigma(x;\,\varepsilon)}\varphi_1(y)\left[-\frac{2(y_1-x_1)}{r^3}+\frac{3(y_1-x_1)^3}{r^5}\right]\cos(\boldsymbol{n}_y, \boldsymbol{x}_1)\,dS_y = \\ = -2\int_{\sigma(x;\,\varepsilon)}\varphi_1(y)\frac{\cos^2(\boldsymbol{n}, \boldsymbol{x}_1)}{r^2}dS_y + 3\int_{\sigma(x;\,\varepsilon)}\varphi_1(y)\frac{\cos^4(\boldsymbol{n}, \boldsymbol{x}_1)}{r^2}dS_y,$$

$$\lim_{\varepsilon\to 0} I'_{1111} = -\frac{8}{3}\pi\varphi_1(x) + 3\varphi_1(x)\int_{\sigma(x;\,\varepsilon)}\frac{\cos^4(\boldsymbol{n}, \boldsymbol{x}_1)}{r^2}dS_y = \\ = -\frac{8}{3}\pi\varphi_1(x) + 3\varphi_1(x)\int_0^{\pi}\int_0^{2\pi}\cos^4\theta\sin\theta\,d\theta\,d\varphi = -\frac{4}{15}\pi\varphi_1(x).$$

Eventually we arrive at the expressions

$$\lim_{\varepsilon\to 0}\Delta U_1^{(2)}(x) = -\frac{2\lambda_a+5\mu_a}{3\mu_a(\lambda_a+2\mu_a)}\varphi_1(x)$$

and

$$\lim_{\varepsilon\to 0}\operatorname{grad}_{x_1}\operatorname{div}U^2 = -\frac{1}{3(\lambda_a+2\mu_a)}\varphi_1(x),$$

whence

$$\lim_{\varepsilon\to 0}\left[(\overset{*}{\Delta}_{(i)}+\omega^2)U^{(2)}\right]_{x_1} = -\frac{(\lambda_i\mu_a+2\lambda_a\mu_i)+6\mu_i\mu_a}{3\mu_a(\lambda_a+2\mu_a)}\varphi_1(x).$$

* To calculate the last limit replace $\int_{\sigma(x;\,\varepsilon)}\frac{\cos^4(\boldsymbol{n}, \boldsymbol{x}_1)}{r^2}dS_y$ by the equal integral $\int_{\sigma(x;\,\varepsilon)}\frac{\cos^4(\boldsymbol{n}, \boldsymbol{x}_3)}{r^2}dS_y$.

The same treatment applied to $U_2^{(2)}(x)$ and $U_3^{(2)}(x)$ results in

$$\lim_{\varepsilon\to 0}(\Delta^*_{(i)}+\omega^2)U^{(2)}(x)=-4\pi l\varphi(x),$$

where

$$l=\frac{(\lambda_i\mu_a+2\lambda_a\mu_i)+6\mu_i\mu_a}{3\mu_a(\lambda_a+2\mu_a)}.$$

For $\lambda_i=\lambda_a$, $\mu_i=\mu_a$, we have $l=1$.

We have seen that $\frac{\partial^2 U}{\partial x_k\,\partial x_j}$; exists at every $x\in B_i$; this equals the sum

$$\frac{\partial^2 U^{(1)}}{\partial x_k\,\partial x_j}+\frac{\partial^2 U^{(2)}}{\partial x_k\,\partial x_j}$$

for arbitrary ε; hence

$$\frac{\partial^2 U(x)}{\partial x_k\,\partial x_j}=\lim_{\varepsilon\to 0}\left(\frac{\partial^2 U^{(1)}(x)}{\partial x_k\,\partial x_j}+\frac{\partial^2 U^{(2)}(x)}{\partial x_k\,\partial x_j}\right),$$

where

$$\frac{\partial^2 U^{(1)}(x)}{\partial x_k\,\partial x_j}=\int\limits_{B_i-\tau(x;\,\varepsilon)}\frac{\partial^2}{\partial x_k\,\partial x_j}(\varphi(y)\Gamma_{(a)}(x,\,y))\,dv_y.$$

We have also shown that the limit

$$\lim_{\varepsilon\to 0}\frac{\partial^2 U^{(2)}(x)}{\partial x_k\,\partial x_j}\qquad(k,\ j=1,\,2,\,3),$$

exists, which implies that so does

$$\lim_{\varepsilon\to 0}\int\limits_{B_i-\tau(x;\,\varepsilon)}\frac{\partial^2}{\partial x_k\,\partial x_j}(\varphi(y)\Gamma_{(a)}(x,\,y))\,dv_y\qquad(k,\ j=1,\,2,\,3).$$

The latter integral should be understood in the sense of the Cauchy principal value, as it is obtained by separating-off the singular point by means of the sphere.

Keeping that in mind, we obtain the equality

$$(\Delta^*_{(i)}+\omega^2)\int\limits_{B_i}\varphi(y)\Gamma_{(a)}(x,\,y)\,dv_y=-4\pi l\varphi(x)+\int\limits_{B_i}(\Delta^*_{(i)}+\omega^2)(\varphi\Gamma_{(a)})\,dv_y.\qquad(1.76)$$

This is an analogue of the Poisson formula. We will transform it a little:

$$\begin{aligned}(\Delta^*_{(i)}+\omega^2)(\varphi\Gamma_{(a)})&=\mu_i\left(\Delta+\frac{\lambda_i+\mu_i}{\mu_i}\operatorname{grad}\operatorname{div}+\frac{\omega^2}{\mu_i}\right)(\varphi\Gamma_{(a)})=\\&=\mu_i\left(\Delta+\frac{\lambda_a+\mu_a}{\mu_a}\operatorname{grad}\operatorname{div}+\frac{\omega^2}{\mu_a}\right)(\varphi\Gamma_{(a)})+\frac{m}{\mu_a}\operatorname{grad}\operatorname{div}(\varphi\Gamma_{(a)})+\\&+\omega^2\left(1-\frac{\mu_i}{\mu_a}\right)(\varphi\Gamma_{(a)})=\frac{\mu_i}{\mu_a}(\Delta^*_{(a)}+\omega^2)(\varphi(y)\Gamma_{(a)}(x,\,y))+\\&+\frac{m}{\mu_a}\operatorname{grad}\operatorname{div}(\varphi\Gamma_{(a)})+\omega^2\left(1-\frac{\mu_i}{\mu_{(a)}}\right)(\varphi\Gamma_{(a)})=\\&=\frac{m}{\mu_a}\operatorname{grad}\operatorname{div}(\varphi\Gamma_{(a)})+\omega^2\left(1-\frac{\mu_i}{\mu_a}\right)(\varphi\Gamma_{(a)}),\end{aligned}$$

where

$$m=\lambda_i\mu_a-\lambda_a\mu_i.$$

Thus

$$(\Delta^*_{(l)}+\omega^2)\int_{B_l}\varphi(y)\Gamma_{(a)}(x,\ y)\,dv_y=$$
$$=-4\pi l\varphi(x)+\omega^2\left(1-\frac{\mu_l}{\mu_a}\right)\int_{B_l}\varphi(y)\Gamma_{(a)}(x,\ y)\,dv_y+$$
$$+\frac{m}{\mu_a}\int_{B_l}\varphi(y)\operatorname{grad}\operatorname{div}\Gamma_{(a)}(x,\ y)\,dv_y. \qquad (1.77)$$

If

$$\lambda_l=\lambda_a=\lambda,\quad \mu_l=\mu_a=\mu,$$

then

$$l=1,\ \overset{*}{\Delta}_{(l)}=\overset{*}{\Delta}_{(a)}\equiv\overset{*}{\Delta},\ m=0,$$

and we obtain the Poisson formula for $x\in B_l$

$$(\Delta^*+\omega^2)\int_{B_l}\varphi(y)\Gamma(x,\ y)\,dv_y=-4\pi\varphi(x). \qquad (1.78)$$

Chapter II

INTEGRAL EQUATIONS OF BOUNDARY-VALUE PROBLEMS FOR HOMOGENEOUS BODIES

§ 1. Behavior of potentials at the boundary

The elastic potentials behave near boundaries much like the ordinary harmonic potentials, whose properties have been thoroughly investigated and fully described in many books on potential theory. Therefore we do not give detailed proofs, but for convenience restate the main boundary properties of the elastic potentials as separate theorems. The surface S on which the density distributions giving rise to the various potentials are prescribed is assumed to be a closed Lyapunov surface [for definition see (V, 1)]*, and the surface density function is assumed to be continuous or to satisfy the Hölder condition with exponent $\gamma \leqslant 1$ (that is, to belong to the class $H(\gamma)$). The normal $\boldsymbol{n}$ and the vector $\boldsymbol{r}(x, y)$ are respectively taken positive outwards and from $x(x_1, x_2, x_3)$ to the source-point $y(y_1, y_2, y_3)$.

Theorem 1. For a continuous density $\varphi(y)$ *the single-layer potential*

$$V(x)=\frac{1}{2\pi}\int_S \Gamma(x, y)\varphi(y)\,dS_y$$

is continuous everywhere.

Theorem 2. For a density $\varphi(y)$ *of class* $H(\gamma)$ *the double-layer potential of the first kind*

$$W_{\mathrm{I}}(x)=\frac{1}{2\pi}\int_S \Gamma_{\mathrm{I}}(x, y)\varphi(y)\,dS_y$$

tends to the following finite limits as x *approaches a boundary point* $x_0 \in S$ *from the inside and from the outside:*

$$W_{\mathrm{I},i}(x_0)=-\varphi(x_0)+\frac{1}{2\pi}\int_S \Gamma_{\mathrm{I}}(x_0, y)\varphi(y)\,dS_y,$$

$$W_{\mathrm{I},a}(x_0)=\varphi(x_0)+\frac{1}{2\pi}\int_S \Gamma_{\mathrm{I}}(x_0, y)\varphi(y)\,dS_y. \qquad (2.1)$$

Henceforward, unless the opposite is stated explicitly, the subscripts i and a appended to a variable quantity will indicate its limiting values at

* Cases in which it will be found necessary to narrow down this class will be individually treated.

the boundary when approached respectively from the inside and from the outside.

The integrals in (2.1) stand for their principal values, i.e., limits for $\varepsilon\to 0$ of integrals over $S-S(x_0;\varepsilon)$, where $S(x_0;\varepsilon)$ is a neighborhood of the point $x_0\in S$ with diameter 2ε. We shall examine the notion of principal value at greater length in Ch. V. To prove Theorem 2 we write $W_{\rm I}(x)$ in the form

$$W_{\rm I}(x)=\frac{1}{2\pi}\int_S \Gamma_{\rm I}(x,y)[\varphi(y)-\varphi(x_0)]\,dS_y+$$
$$+\frac{1}{2\pi}\int_S\left[\Gamma_{\rm I}(x,y)-\overset{0}{\Gamma}_{\rm I}(x,y)\right]\varphi(x_0)\,dS_y+\frac{1}{2\pi}\int_S\overset{0}{\Gamma}_{\rm I}(x,y)\varphi(x_0)\,dS_y. \tag{2.2}$$

Here the first two integrals are continuous, since $\varphi(y)\in H(\gamma)$ and the difference $\Gamma_{\rm I}(x,y)-\overset{0}{\Gamma}_{\rm I}(x,y)$ has only a first-order pole at $r=0$; the last integral may be evaluated explicitly by applying (1.63), which for $\omega=0$ becomes

$$\delta(x)\,v(x)=\frac{1}{4\pi}\int_S\left[\overset{0}{\Gamma}(x,y)\,Tv(y)-\overset{0}{\Gamma}_{\rm I}(x,y)\,v(y)\right]dS_y.$$

Setting for $v(x)$ unit vectors along the axes and resolving this identity in turn, we obtain for the diagonal elements of the matrix $\overset{0}{\Gamma}_{\rm I}(x,y)$

$$\int_S\left(\overset{0}{\Gamma}_{\rm I}(x,y)\right)_{kk}dS_y=\begin{cases}-4\pi, & x\in B_i,\\ -2\pi, & x\in S,\\ 0, & x\in B_a\end{cases}\qquad (k=1,2,3) \tag{2.3}$$

and for the off-diagonal elements

$$\int_S\left(\overset{0}{\Gamma}_{\rm I}(x,y)\right)_{kj}dS_y=0\qquad (k\neq j) \tag{2.3'}$$

for any position of x. Let $W_{\rm I}(x_0)$ denote the value of $W_{\rm I}(x)$ at $x_0\in S$. Passing to the limit in (2.2) as x approaches $x_0\in S$ from the inside and from the outside and comparing the limiting expressions with $W_{\rm I}(x_0)$, we obtain in view of (2.3) and the continuity of the first two terms

$$W_{{\rm I},i}(x_0)+2\varphi(x_0)=W_{\rm I}(x_0)+\varphi(x_0)=W_{{\rm I},a}(x_0),$$

which amounts to the relations (2.1).

In a similar way we may prove

Theorem 3*. For a continuous density* $\varphi(y)$ *the double-layer potential of the second kind*

$$W_{\rm II}(x)=\frac{1}{2\pi}\int\Gamma_{\rm II}(x,y)\varphi(y)\,dS_y$$

tends to the following finite limits as x *approaches a boundary point* x_0 *from the inside and from the outside:*

$$\begin{aligned}W_{{\rm II},i}(x_0)&=-\varphi(x_0)+\frac{1}{2\pi}\int_S\Gamma_{\rm II}(x_0,y)\varphi(y)\,dS_y,\\ W_{{\rm II},a}(x_0)&=\varphi(x_0)+\frac{1}{2\pi}\int_S\Gamma_{\rm II}(x_0,y)\varphi(y)\,dS_y.\end{aligned} \tag{2.4}$$

Here it is sufficient to demand that the vector function $\varphi(y)$ be continuous in the ordinary sense, whereas for the proof of (2.1) we stipulated $\varphi(y) \in H(\gamma)$. The reason for this is that the double-layer potential of the second kind arises from the pseudostress operator $\mathbf{N}$, which behaves at $x_0 = y$ as the normal derivative $\frac{1}{r(x_0, y)}$, where r is the length of the chord joining the points x_0 and y on S. The integrals in (2.4) consequently reduce to ordinary improper integrals, while those in (2.1) may be understood only in the sense of principal value.

Theorem 4. *For a density function $\varphi(y)$ of class $H(\gamma)$ the application of the $\mathbf{T}$-operator to the single-layer potential $V(x)$ results in a function which tends to the following finite limits as x approaches the boundary point $x_0 \in S$ from the inside and from the outside:*

$$(\mathbf{T}V)_i = \varphi(x_0) + \frac{1}{2\pi}\int_S \left(\mathbf{T}^{(x_0)}\Gamma(x_0, y)\right)\varphi(y)\,dS_y$$

and

$$(\mathbf{T}V)_a = -\varphi(x_0) + \frac{1}{2\pi}\int_S \left(\mathbf{T}^{(x_0)}\Gamma(x_0, y)\right)\varphi(y)\,dS_y. \tag{2.5}$$

The proof is based on the possibility of representing $\mathbf{T}V(x)$, for x not lying on S, in the form

$$\mathbf{T}V(x) = \frac{1}{2\pi}\int_S (\mathbf{T}^{(x)}\Gamma(x, y))\varphi(y)\,dS_y = \frac{1}{2\pi}\int_S \varphi(y)[\mathbf{T}^{(x)}\Gamma(x, y) + \mathbf{T}^{(y)}\Gamma(x, y)]\,dS_y - \frac{1}{2\pi}\int_S \varphi(y)\mathbf{T}^{(y)}\Gamma(x, y)\,dS_y. \tag{2.6}$$

The last term on the right-hand side is a double-layer potential of the first kind whose behavior at the boundary comes under Theorem 2; the first term will now be shown to be continuous in x. Setting in (1.44)

$$\alpha = \mu, \quad \beta = \lambda,$$

we obtain

$$\mathbf{T}_s\overset{0}{\Gamma}{}^{(k)}(x, y) = \frac{1}{\lambda + 2\mu}\left\{\left[\mu\delta_{sk} + 3(\lambda+\mu)\frac{\partial r}{\partial x_s}\frac{\partial r}{\partial x_k}\right]\frac{\partial}{\partial n_x}\frac{1}{r(x, y)} + \mu\cos(n_x, x_k)\frac{\partial}{\partial x_s}\frac{1}{r} - \cos(n_x, x_s)\frac{\partial}{\partial x_k}\frac{1}{r}\right)\right\}. \tag{2.7}$$

On the other hand

$$\mathbf{T}^{(x)}\Gamma(x, y) + \mathbf{T}^{(y)}\Gamma(x, y) = (\mathbf{T}^{(x)} + \mathbf{T}^{(y)})\overset{0}{\Gamma}(x, y) + L(x, y), \tag{2.8}$$

where $L(x, y)$ is a matrix with a removable singularity. Now

$$r(x, y) = \sum_{k=1}^{3} i_k(y_k - x_k),$$

so that

$$\frac{\partial}{\partial n_x}\frac{1}{r}=-\frac{1}{r^2}\frac{\partial r}{\partial n_x}=\frac{1}{r^2}\cos(r,\,n_x),$$

$$\frac{\partial}{\partial n_y}\frac{1}{r}=-\frac{1}{r^2}\cos(r,\,n_y),\qquad \frac{\partial}{\partial x_k}\frac{1}{r}=-\frac{\partial}{\partial y_k}\frac{1}{r}.\qquad (k=1,\,2,\,3).$$

Substituting in (2.8) $\mathbf{T}^{(x)}\overset{0}{\Gamma}(x,\,y)$ and $\mathbf{T}^{(y)}\overset{0}{\Gamma}(x,\,y)$ from (2.7), we obtain for the sk-element

$$\begin{aligned}(\mathbf{T}^{(x)}\Gamma(x,\,y)+\mathbf{T}^{(y)}\Gamma(x,\,y))_{sk}=&\\ =\frac{1}{\lambda+2\mu}\Big\{\Big[\mu\delta_{sk}+3(\lambda+\mu)\frac{\partial r}{\partial x_s}\frac{\partial r}{\partial x_k}\Big]&\frac{\cos(r,\,n_x)-\cos(r,\,n_y)}{r^2(x,\,y)}+\\ +\mu\Big[(\cos(n_x,\,x_k)-\cos(n_y,\,x_k))&\frac{\partial}{\partial x_s}\frac{1}{r}-\\ -(\cos(n_x,\,x_s)-\cos(n_y,\,x_s))&\frac{\partial}{\partial x_k}\frac{1}{r}\Big]+L_{sk}(x,\,y)\Big\}.\end{aligned}$$

The continuity of the first term on the right-hand side of (2.6), along with the validity of relations (2.5) follow from the last expression by virtue of the properties of a Lyapunov surface.

In a similar manner we may prove

Theorem 5. For a continuous density function $\varphi(y)$ *the application of the* **N**-*operator to the single-layer potential* $V(x)$ *results in a function which tends to the following finite limits as* x *approaches the boundary point* $x_0\in S$ *from the inside and from the outside:*

$$\begin{aligned}(\mathbf{N}V)_i&=\varphi(x_0)+\frac{1}{2\pi}\int_S\left(\mathbf{N}^{(x_0)}\Gamma(x_0y)\right)\varphi(y)\,dS_y,\\ (\mathbf{N}V)_a&=-\varphi(x_0)+\frac{1}{2\pi}\int_S\left(\mathbf{N}^{(x_0)}\Gamma(x_0,\,y)\right)\varphi(y)\,dS_y.\end{aligned}\qquad (2.9)$$

The kernel of an antenna potential (matrix of fundamental solutions of the third kind) was shown in (I, 5) to be of the same type as the kernel of a single-layer potential, and the **T**-operator applied to it yields a kernel of the type of a double-layer potential of the second kind. The two following theorems accordingly hold for antenna potentials.

Theorem 6. For a continuous density function $\varphi(y)$ *the antenna potential (single-layer potential of the second kind)*

$$A(x)=\frac{1}{2\pi}\int_S M(x,\,y)\,\varphi(y)\,dS_y\qquad (2.10)$$

is continuous everywhere in the closed domain B_i.

Theorem 7. For a continuous density function $\varphi(y)$ *the* **T**-*operator applied to an antenna potential results in a function which tends to the following finite limit as* x *approaches the boundary point* $x_0\in S$ *from the inside:*

$$(\mathbf{T}A)_i=-\varphi(x_0)+\frac{1}{2\pi}\int_S\left(\mathbf{T}^{(y)}M(x_0y)\right)\varphi(y)\,dS_y.\qquad (2.11)$$

Note that Theorems 6 and 7 refer only to the internal domain B_i, as the antenna potential is not defined elsewhere.

In addition to the above theorems on the behavior of the elastic potentials near boundaries, results from the theory of harmonic potentials such as the Liapunov-Tauber theorem, and some theorems related to other types of potential play an important part in the theory of boundary-value problems. These will be considered later on.

§ 2. Formulation of the boundary-value problems and the reduction to integral equations

Let the space occupied by the body be divided into two parts, the internal domain B_i and the external domain B_a; we shall always assume that B_i is finite and B_a connected. Their common boundary, S, may consist of one or several closed non-intersecting Lyapunov surfaces, $S^{(k)}$, $k=1, 2, \ldots, n$, with interiors $B_i^{(k)}$, $k=1, 2, \ldots, n$ so that

$$S=\sum_{k=1}^{n} S^{(k)}, \quad B_i=\sum_{k=1}^{n} B_i^{(k)}.$$

In case the external domain B_a does not contain the point at infinity, its finite outer boundary (Figure 2) will be denoted by S_a. Figure 1 shows B_i hatched while B_a is the surrounding blank expanse, while Figure 2 shows B_a hatched with B_i as finite blank enclosures.

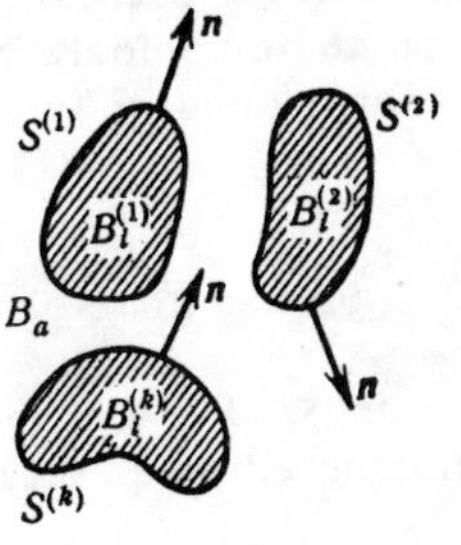

FIGURE 1

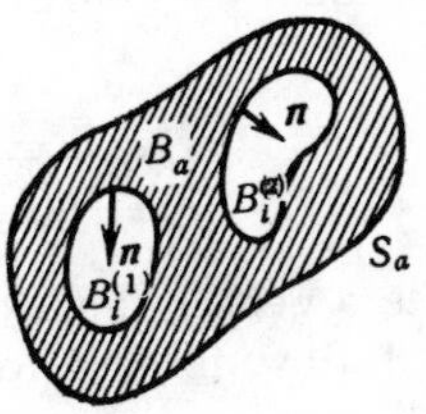

FIGURE 2

When simply referring to a domain we shall always have in mind an open one, without its boundary; a domain B with its boundary added will be called a closed domain and denoted by $\bar{B}$. A vector function $U(x)$ which satisfies equation (1.1^0) in the internal domain B_i and for which the Betti formulas hold in $\bar{B}_i$ will be said to constitute a r e g u l a r s o l u t i o n of (1.1^0) in B_i. Similarly, a vector function $U(x)$ will be called a regular solution of (1.1^0) in the external domain B_a if it satisfies this equation in B_a and fulfils in $\bar{B}_a$ the conditions imposed by the Betti formulas; the last requirement reduces at infinity to a certain attenuation law known as the radiation condition (see III, 1-2).

We shall consider the following principal boundary value problems:

First interior problem. To find a solution of (1.1^0), regular in B_i, such that the inner limiting values of the displacement vector coincide on S with a prescribed vector function of Class $H(\gamma)$.

Second interior problem. To find a solution of (1.1^0), regular in B_i, such that the inner limiting values of the stress vector coincide on S with a prescribed vector function of class $H(\gamma)$.

First exterior problem. To find a solution of (1.1^0), regular in B_a, such that the outer limiting values of the displacement vector coincide on S with a prescribed vector function of class $H(\gamma)$.

Second exterior problem. To find a solution of (1.1^0), regular in B_a, such that the outer limiting values of the stress vector coincide on S with a prescribed vector function of class $H(\gamma)$.

Third interior problem. To find a solution of (1.1^0), regular in B_i, such that the inner limiting values of the expression $\mathbf{T}\boldsymbol{u}(x)+\sigma\boldsymbol{u}(x)$, where $\sigma(x)$, $x\in S$, is a scalar positive function of class $H(\gamma)$, coincide on S with a prescribed vector function of class $H(\gamma)$.

Third exterior problem. To find a solution of (1.1^0), regular in B_a, such that the outer limiting values of the expression $\mathbf{T}\boldsymbol{u}(x)+\sigma_*\boldsymbol{u}(x)$ where $\operatorname{Im}\sigma_*\geqslant 0$ coincide on S with a prescribed vector function of class $H(\gamma)$.

Fourth (mixed) boundary-value problem. To find a solution of the equations of elasticity, regular in a given domain, when the displacements are prescribed over a portion of its boundary, and the surface tractions over the remaining portion.

On setting $\omega = 0$ the foregoing statements become the formulation of the principal boundary-value problems of static equilibrium.

Let us now turn to the derivation of the integral equations.

It is sufficient to look for a solution of the first interior problem in the form of a double-layer potential of the first kind which, by Theorem 2 gives the following integral equation for the unknown density function $\varphi(x_0)$:

$$\varphi(x_0)-\frac{1}{2\pi}\int_S \Gamma_{\mathrm{I}}(x_0, y)\varphi(y)\,dS_y=-f(x_0), \qquad (D_i)$$

where $f(x_0)$ is a vector function of class $H(\gamma)$, given on S. For convenience, this and the following equations will be henceforth denoted by suitable symbols, as indicated.

The solution of the second internal problem is to be sought in the form of a single-layer potential which, by Theorem 4, gives the following integral equation for the unknown density function:

$$\varphi(x_0)+\frac{1}{2\pi}\int_S \left(\mathbf{T}^{(x_0)}\Gamma(x_0 y)\right)\varphi(y)\,dS_y=f(x_0). \qquad (T_i)$$

The solution of the first exterior problem, as with the first interior problem, is again sought in the form of a double-layer potential of the first kind which, by Theorem 2, gives the following integral equation for the unknown density function:

$$\varphi(x_0)+\frac{1}{2\pi}\int_S \Gamma_{\mathrm{I}}(x_0, y)\varphi(y)\,dS_y=f(x_0). \qquad (D_a)$$

The solution of the second exterior problem, as with the second interior problem, is sought in the form of a single-layer potential, and by Theorem 4 we have

$$\varphi(x_0) - \frac{1}{2\pi} \int\limits_S \left(\mathrm{T}^{(x_0)}\Gamma(x_0, y)\right)\varphi(y)\,dS_y = -f(x_0). \qquad (T_a)$$

Solutions for the third interior and exterior problems are sought in the form of a single-layer potential; on account of Theorem 4, we obtain for the density function in the case of the interior problem

$$\varphi(x_0) + \frac{1}{2\pi} \int\limits_S \left[\mathrm{T}^{(x_0)}\Gamma(x, y) + \sigma(x_0)\Gamma(x_0, y)\right]\varphi(y)\,dS_y = f(x_0), \qquad (M_i)$$

and in the case of the exterior problem

$$\varphi(x_0) - \frac{1}{2\pi} \int\limits_S \left[\mathrm{T}^{(x_0)}\Gamma(x_0, y) + \sigma_*(x_0)\Gamma(x_0, y)\right]\varphi(y)\,dS_y = -f(x_0). \qquad (M_a)$$

The integral equations of the fourth problem (mixed boundary conditions) will be derived and studied in Ch. X.

The homogeneous equations associated with equations (D_i), (D_a), (T_i), (T_a), (M_i), (M_a), that is, for $f(x_0)=0$, will be denoted by (D_i^0), (D_a^0), (T_i^0), (T_a^0), (M_i^0), (M_a^0). The same symbols will also be used to designate the corresponding boundary-value problems.

The integral equations introduced here formally resemble Fredholm equations of the second kind. However, they are all *singular*, involving integrals which are only meaningful in the sense of principal value; at that, they are also *two-dimensional*. These two circumstances raise the question of applicability of the Fredholm theory, which requires a special investigation. A second important point is the fact that equations (D_i^0) and (T_a^0), (T_i^0) and (D_a^0) are *pairwise associated* with each other, which follows from the form of their kernels.

The transition to the integral equation of statics is effected by setting $\omega = 0$ in the preceding equations; this is formally equivalent to replacing the matrix $\Gamma(x, y)$ by the matrix $\overset{0}{\Gamma}(x, y)$.

Equations (D_i), (D_a), $(T_i)(T_a)$ may be written in a concise form by using appropriate notation. Let $K(x, y)$ be a third-order square matrix.

$$K(x, y) = \|g_{ik}(x, y)\| \qquad (i, k = 1, 2, 3),$$

and $K^*(x, y)$ its transpose

$$K^*(x, y) = \|g_{ki}(x, y)\|;$$

while $K'(x, y)$ is its associated matrix:

$$K'(x, y) = \|g_{ki}(y, x)\|.$$

Evidently

$$K'(x, y) = K^*(y, x).$$

Now writing

$$\frac{1}{2\pi}\mathrm{T}^{(x)}\Gamma(x, y) = K(x, y),$$

we find that the matrix $\frac{1}{2\pi}\Gamma_1(x, y)$, which is by definition associated with $\frac{1}{2\pi}\mathrm{T}^{(x)}\Gamma(x, y)$, equals $K^*(y, x)$, and equations (D_i) and (D_a), (T_i) and (T_a) may be rewritten, in view of (1.62), as

$$\varphi(x) - \varkappa \int_S \varphi(y) K(y, x)\, dS_y = f'(x) \qquad (2.12),\ (D)$$

and

$$\varphi(x) - \varkappa \int_S K(x, y) \varphi(y)\, dS_y = f'(x), \qquad (2.13),\ (T)$$

which respectively reduce to the pair (D_i) and (T_a) for $\varkappa = +1$ and $f' = -f$, and to the pair (D_a) and (T_i) for $\varkappa = -1$ and $f' = f$.

Chapter III

CONDITIONS AT INFINITY. UNIQUENESS THEOREMS

§ 1. Nonuniqueness of solutions of the wave equation

Whenever a boundary-value problem of mathematical physics refers to a domain which extends to infinity, it is necessary to examine the asymptotic behavior of the solution there. The conditions of the problem generally give no direct clue to that behavior, which must therefore be determined by indirect physical reasoning. It is most important to ascertain that the assumed behavior of the solution at infinity actually warrants its uniqueness. The condition which secures uniqueness will as a rule not be unique itself, and so the problem arises of making the best choice of that condition, which naturally must in the first place admit the existence of solutions with the specified behavior at infinity. Green's and similar formulas (in the theory of elasticity especially the Betti formulas) serve as means for making that choice; in any case, when some asymptotic behavior has been imposed on the solution — whether on physical grounds or as appears to be indicated by arguments evolved from Green's formulas — it is necessary to prove that such a solution actually exists and is unique. Sommerfeld was the first, in 1898, to specify in this manner the asymptotic behavior of the solutions of a boundary-value equation. His condition for solutions of the membrane equation (scalar wave equation), deduced from Green's formula, is known as the r a d i a t i o n c o n d i t i o n; the existence and uniqueness of solutions of the fundamental boundary-value wave equations satisfying the radiation condition were proved by the author in 1933-1934 /13b, c, e/*.

Sommerfeld's "model", and the author's proof of existence and uniqueness will now be extended to the boundary-value problems of elasticity /13d/. We start with the simplest case of an infinite continuum under the action of a concentrated force. We already know that the solution of (1.1^0) is then expressed by the matrix of fundamental solutions $\Gamma(x, y)$. When we constructed this matrix by means of the formulas (1.28), we chose the positive sign for the exponent in

$$\frac{1}{r} e^{\pm icr}, \quad c = \frac{k_1}{k_2}, \tag{3.1}$$

though the negative sign is in principle no less admissible. The reason for this choice is the following. As we saw in (I,1), in order to pass from the vector $\Gamma^{(k)}(x, y)$ to the real displacement vector we must multiply it by $e^{-i\omega t}$,

* C. Müller, who is apparently unacquainted with the author's work, says in his recent book /23a/ that the uniqueness theorem was proved by Rellich in 1943, and the existence theorem by Weyl in 1952 (Cf. /4b/ and /23b/).

and then take the real part. Then we obtain, as can be readily verified, the expression

$$u_j^{(k)}(x, y) = A_j^{(k)}(x, y)\frac{\cos(k_1 r - \omega t)}{r(x, y)} + B_j^{(k)}(x, y)\frac{\cos(k_2 r - \omega t)}{r(x, y)}$$

$$(j, k = 1, 2, 3), \tag{3.2}$$

where*

$$A_j^{(k)}(x, y) = \frac{1}{a^2}\left(\frac{\partial r}{\partial x_k}\frac{\partial r}{\partial x_j}\right) - \left(3\frac{\partial r}{\partial x_j}\frac{\partial r}{\partial x_k} - \delta_{jk}\right)\left(\frac{1}{ia\omega r} + \frac{1}{\omega^2 r^2}\right) + O(r^{-3}),$$

$$B_j^{(k)}(x, y) = \frac{1}{b^2}\left(\delta_{jk} - \frac{\partial r}{\partial x_k}\frac{\partial r}{\partial x_j}\right) + \left(3\frac{\partial r}{\partial x_j}\frac{\partial r}{\partial x_k} - \delta_{jk}\right)\left(\frac{1}{ib\omega r} + \frac{1}{\omega^2 r^2}\right) + O(r^{-3}).$$

Choosing the negative sign in (3.1) gives e^{-icr} instead of e^{+icr} in the expression for $\Gamma^{(k)}(x, y)$, and the expanded expression for the real displacement vector becomes

$$u_j^{(k)}(x, y) = A_j^{(k)}(x, y)\frac{\cos(k_1 r + \omega t)}{r(x, y)} + B_j^{(k)}(x, y)\frac{\cos(k_2 r + \omega t)}{r(x, y)}$$

$$(k, j = 1, 2, 3). \tag{3.3}$$

Thus, both displacement fields, (3.2) and (3.3), satisfy equation (*) (I, 1) in the absence of body forces, and both have a singularity at $r = 0$, which means that a source is located there. These two solutions differ essentially however, in that (3.2) represents two wave trains propagating from the point $y = x$ with velocities $\frac{\omega}{k_1}$ and $\frac{\omega}{k_2}$ respectively, and falling off to zero at infinity, while (3.3) represents two wave trains which originate at infinity and close in with the velocities $-\frac{\omega}{k_1}$ and $-\frac{\omega}{k_2}$. The latter waves and thus solutions of the type (3.3) are in general physically meaningless and must be ruled out because it is assumed that no real sources or reflectors of energy, which could give rise to perturbations, exist at infinity. These arguments dictate the choice of the positive sign in (1.22).**

Let us remark that if solutions of type (3.3) were not excluded, we could construct by linear combinations of (3.2) and (3.3) two other kinds of solution

$$A_j^{(k)}(x, y)\frac{\cos k_1 r}{r}\cos\omega t + B_j^{(k)}(x, y)\frac{\cos k_2 r}{r}\cos\omega t, \tag{3.4}$$

$$(j, k = 1, 2, 3),$$

$$A_j^{(k)}(x, y)\frac{\sin k_1 r}{r}\sin\omega t + B_j^{(k)}(x, y)\frac{\sin k_2 r}{r}\sin\omega t \tag{3.5}$$

which are regular at $r = 0$ and thus could be multiplied by a constant and added to $\Gamma_k^{(s)}(x, y)$, which would violate the uniqueness of solution. Solutions of the type (3.5) represent the so-called proper oscillations of an infinite continuum.

We have so far considered specific solutions, out of which we were able to select the suitable one by making use of the physical principle described above. It is obviously necessary to extend this into an analytic criterion which would serve to make that choice in the general case. This criterion may be obtained in the following way. The function

$$f = \frac{e^{ikr}}{r}, \quad k = \text{const}, \quad r = r(x, y),$$

* The symbols $x = O(y)$ and $x = o(y)$ signify, the first that $\frac{x}{y}$ is bounded, and the second that it tends to zero as $|y|$ increases.

** It is clear that if, in the transition of real vectors, we agreed to multiply by the factor $e^{+i\omega t}$ (which is fully equivalent) the sign of k would be reversed.

satisfies

$$\lim_{r\to\infty} f=0,\quad \lim_{r\to\infty} r\left(\frac{\partial f}{\partial r}-ikf\right)=0; \tag{3.6}$$

and the limits are approached uniformly over all directions of r; similarly, the function

$$f=\frac{e^{-ikr}}{r}$$

satisfies

$$\lim_{r\to\infty} f=0,\quad \lim_{r\to\infty} r\left(\frac{\partial f}{\partial r}+ikf\right)=0. \tag{3.7}$$

It may be shown that the vectors $\Gamma^{(k)}(x, y)$, as well as their potential and solenoidal components, satisfy conditions of type (3.6). To show that, we rewrite (1.26) in the form

$$u^{(k)}_{p,j}(x, y)=\left[\frac{1}{a^2}\left(\frac{\partial r}{\partial x_k}\frac{\partial r}{\partial x_j}\right)-\left(\frac{3}{r}\frac{\partial r}{\partial x_k}\frac{\partial r}{\partial x_j}-\frac{1}{r}\delta_{kj}\right)\left(\frac{1}{\omega^2}+\frac{1}{ia\omega}\right)\right]\frac{e^{ik_1r}}{r}+O(r^{-3}), \tag{3.8}$$

$$u^{(k)}_{s,j}(x, y)=\left[\frac{1}{b^2}\left(\delta_{kj}-\frac{\partial r}{\partial x_k}\frac{\partial r}{\partial x_j}\right)+\right.$$

$$\left.+\left(\frac{3}{r^2}\frac{\partial r}{\partial x_k}\frac{\partial r}{\partial x_j}-\frac{1}{r}\delta_{kj}\right)\left(\frac{1}{\omega^2}+\frac{1}{ib\omega}\right)\right]\frac{e^{ik_2r}}{r}+O(r^{-3})\quad (k, j=1, 2, 3); \tag{3.9}$$

it is easy to verify now that

$$\lim_{r\to\infty} u_p=0,\quad \lim_{r\to\infty} r\left(\frac{\partial u_p}{\partial r}-ik_1u_p\right)=0, \tag{3.10}$$

$$\lim_{r\to\infty} u_s=0,\quad \lim_{r\to\infty} r\left(\frac{\partial u_s}{\partial r}-ik_2u_s\right)=0. \tag{3.11}$$

These conditions may be called the elastic radiation conditions.

Let us now examine the connection between these results and some consequences which follow from the Betti formula.

Let forces $F(x)$ act on the medium within some finite domain of space B, and let us try to find the solution of (1.1) throughout the continuum. We have

$$\Delta^* u(x)+\omega^2 u(x)=F(x), \tag{3.12}$$

where $F(x)$ is a local vector function which differs from zero only in B. A solution of (3.12) is given by

$$u_k(x)=\frac{1}{4\pi}\int_{\Sigma_R}\Gamma^{(k)}(x, y)\,Tu(y)\,dS_y-\frac{1}{4\pi}\int_{\Sigma_R}u(y)\,T\Gamma^{(k)}(x, y)\,dS_y-$$

$$-\frac{1}{4\pi}\int_{B_i}(\Delta^* u+\omega^2 u)\,\Gamma^{(k)}(x, y)\,dv_y, \tag{3.13}$$

which is obtained from (1.59) upon substituting $\alpha=\mu$, $\beta=\lambda$; here B_i is a sphere of (arbitrary) radius R, and Σ_R is its surface.

By definition of $F(x)$ and in view of (3.12), (3.13) becomes

$$u_k(x)=-\frac{1}{4\pi}\int_{B}F(y)\,\Gamma^{(k)}(x, y)\,dv_y+$$

$$+\frac{1}{4\pi}\int_{\Sigma_R}\left[\Gamma^{(k)}(x, y)\,Tu(y)-\Gamma_1^{(k)}(x, y)\,u(y)\right]dS_y. \tag{3.14}$$

Now the field is uniquely specified by $F(x)$, so the sum of the surface integrals in (3.14) must vanish. Since R can be made as large as desired, it is necessary to stipulate that the sought solutions behave at infinity in such a manner as to make these surface integrals vanish.

Later on we shall show that in order to secure this it is sufficient to assume

$$r(\mathrm{T}u_p - ia\omega u_p) = o(1), \quad u_p \cdot \Gamma_s^{(k)} = o(R^{-2}), \tag{3.15}$$

$$r(\mathrm{T}u_s - ib\omega u_s) = o(1), \quad u_s \cdot \Gamma_p^{(k)} = o(R^{-2}); \tag{3.16}$$

it will now be shown that these conditions are implied in the radiation conditions (3.10) and (3.11).

§ 2. Radiation conditions. Asymptotic estimates

Let us first sharpen a little the definition of regular solutions given in (II, 2).

Let $u(x)$ be a solution of

$$\Delta^* u(x) + \omega^2 u(x) = 0 \tag{3.17}$$

in the infinite exterior B_a of a domain bounded by the surface S. For the potential and solenoidal parts of $u(x)$ we have

$$\Delta u_p(x) + k_1^2 u_p(x) = 0, \tag{3.18}$$

$$\operatorname{rot} u_p(x) = 0, \tag{3.19}$$

$$\Delta u_s(x) + k_2^2 u_s(x) = 0, \tag{3.20}$$

$$\operatorname{div} u_s(x) = 0. \tag{3.21}$$

We now define a solution regular in B_a as a $u(x)$ that satisfies the following conditions:

1. $u(x)$ is continuously twice-differentiable and satisfies (3.17) in B_a.
2. $u(x)$ satisfies, at all sufficiently distant points $x(x_1, x_2, x_3)$, the conditions

$$u_p(x) = o(1), \tag{3.22}$$

$$r\left(\frac{\partial u_p}{\partial r} - ik_1 u_p\right) = o(1), \tag{3.23}$$

$$u_s(x) = o(1), \tag{3.24}$$

$$r\left(\frac{\partial u_s}{\partial r} - ik_2 u_s\right) = o(1) \tag{3.25}$$

uniformly over all directions of $r(x, y)$, where y is an arbitrary fixed point.

3. $u(x)$ admits a P-operation in $\bar{B}_a$, complying with the requirements for applicability of the Betti formulas.

We recall that $u_p(x)$ and $u_s(x)$ are determined from a given $u(x)$ by the formulas

$$u_p(x) = -\frac{1}{k_1^2} \operatorname{grad} \operatorname{div} u(x), \quad u_s(x) = \frac{1}{k_1^2} \operatorname{grad} \operatorname{div} u(x) + u(x). \tag{3.26}$$

These expressions obviously fulfill the relations

$$u_p(x) + u_s(x) = u(x)$$

and

$$\operatorname{rot} u_p(x) = 0, \quad \operatorname{div} u_s(x) = 0,$$

seeing that

$$\Delta(\operatorname{div} \boldsymbol{u}) + k_1^2(\operatorname{div} \boldsymbol{u}) = 0. \tag{3.27}$$

Further, since any twice-differentiable vector function satisfies

$$\Delta \boldsymbol{a} = \operatorname{grad} \operatorname{div} \boldsymbol{a} - \operatorname{rot} \operatorname{rot} \boldsymbol{a},$$

we may, on account of (3.27), write

$$\Delta \boldsymbol{u}_p + k_1^2 \boldsymbol{u}_p = -\frac{1}{k_1^2} \operatorname{grad} \Delta(\operatorname{div} \boldsymbol{u}) - \operatorname{grad}(\operatorname{div} \boldsymbol{u}) = 0$$

and

$$\Delta \boldsymbol{u}_s + k_2^2 \boldsymbol{u}_s = \frac{1}{k_1^2} \operatorname{grad} \Delta(\operatorname{div} \boldsymbol{u}) + \operatorname{grad} \operatorname{div} \boldsymbol{u} - \operatorname{rot} \operatorname{rot} \boldsymbol{u} +$$

$$+ \frac{k_2^2}{k_1^2} \operatorname{grad} \operatorname{div} \boldsymbol{u} + k_2^2 \boldsymbol{u} = - \operatorname{grad} \operatorname{div} \boldsymbol{u} + \operatorname{grad} \operatorname{div} \boldsymbol{u} - \operatorname{rot} \operatorname{rot} \boldsymbol{u} +$$

$$+ \frac{k_2^2}{k_1^2} \operatorname{grad} \operatorname{div} \boldsymbol{u} + k_2^2 \boldsymbol{u} = \frac{1}{\mu} [(\lambda + 2\mu) \operatorname{grad} \operatorname{div} \boldsymbol{u} - \mu \operatorname{rot} \operatorname{rot} \boldsymbol{u} + \omega^2 \boldsymbol{u}] = 0.$$

We will now show that the asymptotic relations (3.15), (3.16), follow from the conditions (3.22)–(3.25) and apply uniformly over all directions $\boldsymbol{r}$, along with the relations

$$r(\mathbf{T}\boldsymbol{u}_p - i\omega a \boldsymbol{u}_p) = o(1), \tag{3.28}$$

$$r(\mathbf{T}\boldsymbol{u}_s - i\omega b \boldsymbol{u}_s) = o(1), \tag{3.29}$$

as indicated at the end of the preceding section.

As $\boldsymbol{u}_p(x)$ and $\boldsymbol{u}_s(x)$ are respectively solutions of (3.18) and (3.20) and satisfy conditions (3.22)–(3.25), they may each be represented in B_a by Green's formula (cf. /13a/, also I, 2) as

$$\begin{aligned} \boldsymbol{u}_p(x) &= \frac{1}{4\pi} \int_S \left(\frac{e^{ik_1 r}}{r} \frac{\partial \boldsymbol{u}_p}{\partial n_y} - \boldsymbol{u}_p(y) \frac{\partial}{\partial n_y} \frac{e^{ik_1 r}}{r(x, y)} \right) dS_y, \\ \boldsymbol{u}_s(x) &= \frac{1}{4\pi} \int_S \left(\frac{e^{ik_2 r}}{r} \frac{\partial \boldsymbol{u}_s}{\partial n_y} - \boldsymbol{u}_s(y) \frac{\partial}{\partial n_y} \frac{e^{ik_2 r}}{r(x, y)} \right) dS_y. \end{aligned} \tag{3.30}$$

Here $r = r(x, y)$ is the distance apart of $x(x_1, x_2, x_3)$ and $y(y_1, y_2, y_3) \in S$, and $\frac{\partial}{\partial n_y}$ indicates normal differentiation at y, the positive normal pointing from B_i into B_a. Let R and ρ be the radius-vectors of the points x and y, and $\boldsymbol{R}_0$, $\boldsymbol{\rho}_0$, $\boldsymbol{r}_0$ corresponding unit vectors.

By (3.30) we have

$$\frac{\partial \boldsymbol{u}_p(x)}{\partial x_k} = \frac{\partial \boldsymbol{u}_p(x)}{\partial R} \frac{\partial R}{\partial x_k} + o(R^{-1}), \tag{3.31}$$

$$\frac{\partial \boldsymbol{u}_s(x)}{\partial x_k} = \frac{\partial \boldsymbol{u}_s(x)}{\partial R} \frac{\partial R}{\partial x_k} + o(R^{-1}) \qquad (k = 1, 2, 3). \tag{3.31'}$$

Actually, since the point x is external to S, we may write

$$\frac{\partial \boldsymbol{u}_p(x)}{\partial x_k} = \frac{1}{4\pi} \int_S \frac{\partial}{\partial r} \left(\frac{e^{ik_1 r}}{r(x, y)} \frac{\partial \boldsymbol{u}_p}{\partial n_y} - \boldsymbol{u}_p(y) \frac{\partial}{\partial n_y} \frac{e^{ik_1 r}}{r(x, y)} \right) \frac{\partial r}{\partial x_k} dS_y$$

or

$$\frac{\partial \boldsymbol{u}_p(x)}{\partial x_k} = \frac{1}{4\pi} \int_S \frac{\partial}{\partial R} \left(\frac{e^{ik_1 r}}{r} \frac{\partial \boldsymbol{u}_p}{\partial n_y} - \boldsymbol{u}_p(y) \frac{\partial}{\partial n_y} \frac{e^{ik_1 r}}{r} \right) \frac{\partial R}{\partial r} \frac{\partial r}{\partial x_k} dS_y.$$

But $\frac{\partial R}{\partial r} = \cos \varepsilon$, where ε is the angle between $\boldsymbol{r}_0 r$ and $\boldsymbol{R}_0 R$, so from the triangle

Oxy we have

$$\cos\varepsilon = 1 + O(R^{-2}), \quad \frac{r}{R} = 1 + O(R^{-1}).$$

On the other hand,

$$\frac{\partial R}{\partial x_k} - \frac{\partial r}{\partial x_k} = \frac{x_k}{R} - \frac{x_k - y_k}{r} = x_k\left(\frac{1}{R} - \frac{1}{r}\right) + \frac{y_k}{r} =$$

$$= -2x_k \frac{x_1y_1 + x_2y_2 + x_3y_3 + (y_1^2 + y_2^2 + y_3^2)}{Rr(r+R)} + \frac{y_k}{r}.$$

Now, when x recedes to infinity while y remains on the finite surface S we obviously obtain

$$\frac{\partial R}{\partial x_k} - \frac{\partial r}{\partial x_k} = O(R^{-1}),$$

whence

$$\frac{\partial u_p(x)}{\partial x_k} = \frac{1}{4\pi}\int_S \frac{\partial}{\partial R}\left(\frac{e^{ik_1 r}}{r}\frac{\partial u_p}{\partial n_y} - u_p(y)\frac{\partial}{\partial n_y}\frac{e^{ik_1 r}}{r}\right)[1 + O(R^{-2})]\times$$

$$\times\left[\frac{\partial R}{\partial x_k} + O(R^{-1})\right] dS_y = \frac{\partial u_p(x)}{\partial R}\frac{\partial R}{\partial x_k} + O(R^{-2}) =$$

$$= \frac{\partial u_p(x)}{\partial R}\frac{\partial R}{\partial x_k} + o(R^{-1}).$$

An analogous formula may be obtained for $u_s(x)$. It can now be shown that

$$\left(R_0 \cdot \frac{\partial u_s}{\partial R}\right) = o(R^{-1}) \tag{3.32}$$

$$\left(R_0 \times \frac{\partial u_p}{\partial R}\right) = o(R^{-1}). \tag{3.33}$$

Indeed, the condition $\operatorname{div} u_s(x) = 0$, and the relation (3.31') show that

$$\left(R_0 \cdot \frac{\partial u_s}{\partial R}\right) = \sum_{k=1}^{3}\frac{\partial R}{\partial x_k}\frac{\partial u_{s,k}}{\partial R} =$$

$$= \sum_{k=1}^{3}\frac{\partial u_{s,k}}{\partial x_k} + o(R^{-1}) = \operatorname{div} u_s + o(R^{-1}) = o(R^{-1}).$$

Similarly, by the condition $\operatorname{rot} u_p(x) = 0$ and (3.31),*

$$\left(R_0 \times \frac{\partial u_p}{\partial R}\right)_k = \frac{\partial R}{\partial x_{k+1}}\frac{\partial u_{p,k+2}}{\partial R} - \frac{\partial R}{\partial x_{k+2}}\frac{\partial u_{p,k+1}}{\partial R} =$$

$$= \frac{\partial u_{p,k+2}}{\partial x_{k+1}} - \frac{\partial u_{p,k+1}}{\partial x_{k+2}} + o(R^{-1}) = (\operatorname{rot} u_p)_{x_k} + o(R^{-1}) = o(R^{-1}).$$

We now rewrite the conditions (3.22)–(3.25) in the form

$$u_p(x) = o(1), \quad R\left(\frac{\partial u_p}{\partial R} - ik_1 u_p\right) = o(1), \quad u_s(x) = o(1),$$

$$R\left(\frac{\partial u_s}{\partial R} - ik_2 u_s\right) = o(1). \tag{3.34}$$

Scalar-multiplying R_0 by $\left(\frac{\partial u_s}{\partial R} - ik_2 u_s\right)$ and making use of (3.32) and (3.34), we obtain

$$(R_0 \cdot u_s(x)) = o(R^{-1}). \tag{3.35}$$

* Here always $k = 1, 2, 3 \pmod 3$, so $k = 4$ and $k = 5$ in turn become $k = 1$ and $k = 2$.

Vector-multiplying R_0 by $\left(\frac{\partial u_p}{\partial R} - ik_1 u_p\right)$ and using (3.33) and (3.34), we obtain

$$(R_0 \times u_p(x)) = o(R^{-1}). \tag{3.36}$$

Finally, by (3.31) the scalar product of R_0 and $\left(\frac{\partial u_p}{\partial R} - ik_1 u_p\right)$ gives

$$\left(R_0 \cdot \frac{\partial u_p}{\partial R}\right) - ik_1 (R_0 \cdot u_p) = \operatorname{div} u_p - ik_1 (R_0 \cdot u_p) + o(R^{-1}) = o(R^{-1}),$$

while by (3.31') the vector product of R_0 and $\frac{\partial u_s}{\partial R} - ik_2 u_s$ gives

$$\left(R_0 \times \frac{\partial u_s}{\partial R}\right) - ik_2 (R_0 \times u_s) = \operatorname{rot} u_s - ik_2 (R_0 \times u_s) + o(R^{-1}) = o(R^{-1}).$$

Consequently,

$$u_p(x) = o(1), \quad \operatorname{div} u_p(x) - ik_1 (R_0 \cdot u_p) = o(R^{-1}), \tag{3.32'}$$

$$u_s(x) = o(1), \quad \operatorname{rot} u_s(x) - ik_2 (R_0 \times u_s) = o(R^{-1}). \tag{3.33'}$$

According to expression (1.14) for $Tu(x)$, and the properties (3.19) and (3.21), the stress field corresponding to the potential (irrotational) and the solenoidal displacement field will respectively be

$$Tu_p(x) = 2\mu \frac{\partial u_p}{\partial n} + n\lambda \operatorname{div} u_p, \tag{3.34'}$$

$$Tu_s(x) = 2\mu \frac{\partial u_s}{\partial n} + \mu (n \times \operatorname{rot} u_s). \tag{3.35'}$$

Let the point $x(x_1, x_2, x_3)$ be located on a sphere Σ_R of sufficiently large radius R, centered at the origin. Since $n \equiv R_0$ on Σ_R, we obtain from (3.34) and (3.32')

$$Tu_p(x) = 2\mu i k_1 u_p(x) + \lambda i k_1 R_0 (u_p)_n + o(R^{-1}),$$

$$((u_p)_n = (R_0 \cdot u_p) = (n \cdot u_p));$$

but

$$R_0 (u_p)_n = u_p - t (u_p)_t, \tag{3.36'}$$

where $(u_p)_n$ is the normal component of the vector $u_p(x)$, and $(u_p(x))_t$ is some tangential component along the unit vector t; now $(u_p)_t$ equals the length of the vector $(R_0 \times u_p)$ and hence is of the order of $o(R^{-1})$, so that by (3.36') we have

$$Tu_p(x) = 2\mu i k_1 u_p(x) + \lambda i k_1 u_p(x) + o(R^{-1})$$

or

$$Tu_p(x) - i\omega a u_p(x) = o(R^{-1}). \tag{3.28}$$

In the same way we obtain

$$Tu_s(x) = 2\mu i k_2 u_s(x) + \mu (R_0 \times \operatorname{rot} u_s(x)) + o(R^{-1}).$$

However

$$ik_2 u_s(x) + (R_0 \times \operatorname{rot} u_s(x)) = o(R^{-1}),$$

since in view of (3.35) and the properties of the triple vector product, we obtain from (3.33')

$$(R_0 \times \operatorname{rot} u_s) = ik_2 [R_0 \times (R_0 \times u_s)] + o(R^{-1}) =$$
$$= ik_2 \{R_0 (R_0 \cdot u_s) - u_s (R_0 \cdot R_0)\} + o(R^{-1}) = -ik_2 u_s + o(R^{-1}).$$

Hence, finally

$$\mathsf{T}u_s(x) - i\omega b u_s(x) = o(R^{-1}). \tag{3.29}$$

The potential and solenoidal components $\Gamma_p^{(k)}(x, y)$ and $\Gamma_s^{(k)}(x, y)$ satisfy conditions analogous to (3.28) and (3.29), but stronger. From the explicit expressions (1.26) for the components of these vectors we obtain the estimates

$$\mathsf{T}\Gamma_p^{(k)}(x, y) - i\omega a\Gamma_p^{(k)}(x, y) = O(R^{-2}), \tag{3.37}$$

$$\mathsf{T}\Gamma_s^{(k)}(x, y) - i\omega b\Gamma_s^{(k)}(x, y) = O(R^{-2}) \quad (k = 1, 2, 3). \tag{3.38}$$

From the same expressions it also follows that

$$(R_0 \times \Gamma_p^{(k)}) = O(R^{-2}), \tag{3.39}$$

$$(R_0 \cdot \Gamma_s^{(k)}) = O(R^{-2}) \quad (k = 1, 2, 3). \tag{3.40}$$

From (3.36) and (3.40) we now have

$$-\Gamma_s^{(k)} \times (R_0 \times u_p) - u_p(R_0 \cdot \Gamma_t^{(k)}) = o(R^{-2}). \tag{3.41}$$

Applying the formula for the triple vector product

$$A \times (B \times C) = B(A \cdot C) - C(A \cdot B),$$

we find

$$-R_0(\Gamma_s^{(k)} \cdot u_p) + u_p(\Gamma_s^{(k)} \cdot R_0) - u_p(R_0 \cdot \Gamma_s^{(k)}) = o(R^{-2})$$

and upon scalar multiplication by R_0,

$$\Gamma_s^{(k)} \cdot u_p(x) = o(R^{-2})$$

or

$$R^2(u_p \cdot \Gamma_s^{(k)}) = o(1) \quad (k = 1, 2, 3). \tag{3.42}$$

Similarly, we obtain from the estimates (3.35) and (3.39)

$$R^2(u_s \cdot \Gamma_p^{(k)}) = o(1) \quad (k = 1, 2, 3). \tag{3.43}$$

This completes the derivation of formulas (3.15) and (3.16) from the radiation conditions.

§ 3. The Betti formula for an infinite domain

The estimates obtained in the preceding section allow us to derive the Betti formula for an infinite domain. Let the point $x \in B_a$ be contained within a sphere Σ_R which is made large enough to enclose the domain B_i; the domain bounded by the surfaces S and Σ_R will be denoted by Ω_R. Then if $u(x)$ is a solution, regular in B_a, of the equation of elasticity, we may write

$$u_k(x) = \frac{1}{4\pi} \int\limits_{S+\Sigma_R} \Gamma^{(k)}(x, y)\, \mathsf{T}u(y)\, dS_y - \\ - \frac{1}{4\pi} \int\limits_{S+\Sigma_R} u(y)\, \mathsf{T}^{(y)} \Gamma^{(k)}(x, y)\, dS_y \quad (k = 1, 2, 3). \tag{3.44}$$

We now split $u(x)$ and $\Gamma^{(k)}(x, y)$ into

$$u(x) = u_p(x) + u_s(x) \qquad \Gamma^{(k)}(x, y) = \Gamma_p^{(k)}(x, y) + \Gamma_s^{(k)}(x, y)$$

and rewrite (3.44) as follows

$$4\pi u_k(x) = \int\limits_{S+\Sigma_R} (\Gamma_p^{(k)} T u_p + \Gamma_s^{(k)} T u_s)\, dS_y -$$

$$- \int\limits_{S+\Sigma_R} (u_p T\Gamma_p^{(k)} + u_s T\Gamma_s^{(k)})\, dS_y + \int\limits_{S+\Sigma_R} (\Gamma_p^{(k)} T u_s + \Gamma_s^{(k)} T u_p)\, dS_y -$$

$$- \int\limits_{S+\Sigma_R} (u_p T\Gamma_s^{(k)} + u_s T\Gamma_p^{(k)})\, dS_y.$$

In this relation we now write the first two integrals over Σ_R in the form

$$\int\limits_{\Sigma_R} \Gamma_p^{(k)} (T u_p - ik_1 a^2 u_p)\, dS_y + \int\limits_{\Sigma_R} \Gamma_s^{(k)} (T u_s - ik_2 b^2 u_s)\, dS_y -$$

$$- \int\limits_{\Sigma_R} u_p (T\Gamma_p^{(k)} - ik_1 a^2 \Gamma_p^{(k)})\, dS_y - \int\limits_{\Sigma_R} u_s (T\Gamma_s^{(k)} - ik_2 b^2 \Gamma_s^{(k)})\, dS_y$$

and the last two integrals over Σ_R, in the form

$$\int\limits_{\Sigma_R} \Gamma_p^{(k)} (T u_s - ik_2 b^2 u_s)\, dS_y + \int\limits_{\Sigma_R} \Gamma_s^{(k)} (T u_p - ik_1 a^2 u_p)\, dS_y -$$

$$- \int\limits_{\Sigma_R} u_p (T\Gamma_s^{(k)} - ik_2 b^2 \Gamma_s^{(k)})\, dS_y - \int\limits_{\Sigma_R} u_s (T\Gamma_p^{(k)} - ik_1 a^2 \Gamma_p^{(k)})\, dS_y -$$

$$- ik_1 a^2 \int\limits_{\Sigma_R} (u_s \Gamma_p^{(k)} - u_p \Gamma_s^{(k)})\, dS_y - ik_2 b^2 \int\limits_{\Sigma_R} (u_p \Gamma_s^{(k)} - u_s \Gamma_p^{(k)})\, dS_y.$$

Passing to the limit as $R \to \infty$ and applying the estimates (3.28), (3.29), (3.37), (3.38), (3.42), (3.43), we find that the integrals over Σ_R vanish and obtain the Betti formula for the domain B_a:

$$u_k(x) = \frac{1}{4\pi} \int\limits_S [\Gamma^{(k)}(x, y)\, T u(y) - u(y)\, T^{(y)} \Gamma^{(k)}(x, y)]\, dS_y, \quad x \in B_a$$

$$(k = 1, 2, 3). \qquad (3.45)$$

The Betti formula for an infinite domain gives rise to a series of important corollaries.

Corollary 1. A solution of $\Delta^* u + \omega^2 u = 0$, *regular in* B_a, *possesses the estimate*

$$R u(x) = O(1), \quad R u_p(x) = O(1), \quad R u_s(x) = O(1). \qquad (3.46)$$

Corollary 2. A solution of $\Delta^* u + \omega^2 u = 0$ *which is everywhere regular vanishes identically.*

Corollary 3. A solution of $\Delta^* u + \omega^2 u = 0$, *regular in* B_a *and* B_i, *vanishes identically if it satisfies on* S *the conditions*

$$u_i = u_a, \quad (T u)_i = (T u)_a, \qquad (3.47)$$

The first two corollaries are obvious. To prove the third it is sufficient to write down the Betti formula for the domain B_a (or B_i) which contains the point x, and for the other domain, B_i (or B_a) which does not contain it. In the latter case the left-hand side of the Betti formula (3.45) is zero. Subtracting the two expressions obtained in this way, and taking into account the boundary conditions, we find that $u(x) \equiv 0$ in B_a, and similarly $u(x) \equiv 0$ in B_i.

Let us make one more remark with regard to the physical interpretation of the obtained results. According to (3.46) the potential component $u_p(x)$ falls off at infinity as $\frac{\text{const}}{R}$, while by (3.36) and (3.36') its tangential component $(u_p)t$ decreases as $o(R^{-1})$, i. e., more rapidly. But for the solenoidal component $u_s(x)$ which according to (3.46) falls off as $\frac{\text{const}}{R}$, (3. 35) shows that here it is the normal component that decreases more rapidly, as $o(R^{-1})$. It follows that far off $u_p(x)$ will be normal to the wave front, while $u_s(x)$ will lie in its tangent plane; this means that the first describes longitudinal, and the second transverse oscillations.

We will now derive a few other estimates which will prove useful later on.

Let

$$u(x) = \alpha(x) + i\beta(x) \tag{3.48}$$

and

$$u_p(x) = \alpha^{(1)}(x) + i\beta^1(x), \quad u_s(x) = \alpha^{(2)}(x) + i\beta^{(2)}(x). \tag{3.49}$$

Separating the real and imaginary parts in (3.35) and (3.36), we obtain

$$(R_0 \cdot \alpha^{(2)}) \doteq (R_0 \cdot \beta^{(2)}) = o(R^{-1}), \quad (R_0 \times \alpha^{(1)}) \doteq (R_0 \times \beta^{(1)}) = o(R^{-1}); \tag{3.50}$$

similarly from (3.46)

$$\alpha^{(1)} = O(R^{-1}), \quad \alpha^{(2)} = O(R^{-1}), \quad \beta^{(1)} = O(R^{-1}), \quad \beta^{(2)} = O(R^{-1}). \tag{3.51}$$

From (3.50) and (3.51) follows

$$\alpha^{(2)} \times (R_0 \times \alpha^{(1)}) + \alpha^{(1)}(R_0 \cdot \alpha^{(2)}) = o(R^{-2});$$

Using again the expression for the triple vector product, we obtain

$$R_0(\alpha^{(2)} \cdot \alpha^{(1)}) - \alpha^{(1)}(\alpha^{(2)} \cdot R_0) + \alpha^{(1)}(R_0 \cdot \alpha^{(2)}) = o(R^{-2}),$$

or

$$(\alpha^{(1)} \cdot \alpha^{(2)}) = o(R^{-2}). \tag{3.52}$$

The estimate

$$(\beta^{(1)} \cdot \beta^{(2)}) = o(R^{-2}). \tag{3.53}$$

is obtained in the same way. From (3.50) and (3.51) we obtain

$$\beta^{(2)} \times (R_0 \times \alpha^{(1)}) + \alpha^{(1)}(R_0 \cdot \beta^{(2)}) = o(R^{-2});$$

working out the first term on the left-hand side, we have

$$R_0(\beta^{(2)}\alpha^{(1)}) - \alpha^{(1)}(\beta^{(2)} \cdot R_0) + \alpha^{(1)}(R_0 \cdot \beta^{(2)}) = o(R^{-2}),$$

that is,

$$(\alpha^{(1)} \cdot \beta^{(2)}) = o(R^{-2}). \tag{3.54}$$

Similarly, also

$$(\alpha^{(2)} \cdot \beta^{(1)}) = o(R^{-2}). \tag{3.55}$$

Finally, from (3.52)–(3.55) follows

$$R^2(u_p \cdot u_s) = o(1). \tag{3.55'}$$

§ 4. Uniqueness theorem for homogeneous and nonhomogeneous media

In this section we shall prove several uniqueness theorems, which cover all the cases of boundary-value (including contact) problems to be considered in this book. It is known that the total energy of an elastic body consists of the potential energy, U, plus the kinetic energy, K, where

$$U = \int_B \left\{ \frac{1}{2} \lambda (\operatorname{div} v)^2 + \mu (v_{11}^2 + v_{22}^2 + v_{33}^2 + 2v_{12}^2 + 2v_{13}^2 + 2v_{23}^2) \right\} dv$$

and

$$K=\frac{1}{2}\int_B\sum_{i=1}^{3}\left(\frac{\partial v_i}{\partial t}\right)^2 dv,$$

B being the volume occupied by the elastic isotropic body, v_{ik} the components of the strain tensor, t the time. It should be kept in mind that $\boldsymbol{v}(x, t)$ is here the real displacement vector, which satisfies the equation

$$\mu\Delta\boldsymbol{v}+(\lambda+\mu)\operatorname{grad}\operatorname{div}\boldsymbol{v}=\frac{\partial^2\boldsymbol{v}}{\partial t^2}$$

and is related to the complex displacement vector as indicated in (I, 1). The fundamental energy theorem of the theory of elasticity states that

$$\frac{\partial}{\partial t}(U+K)=-\int_S\left(\mathsf{T}\boldsymbol{v}\cdot\frac{\partial\boldsymbol{v}}{\partial t}\right)dS. \tag{3.56}$$

Since

$$\mathsf{T}_j\boldsymbol{v}=\tau_{j1}\cos(\boldsymbol{n}, \boldsymbol{x}_1)+\tau_{j2}\cos(\boldsymbol{n}, \boldsymbol{x}_2)+\tau_{j3}\cos(\boldsymbol{n}, \boldsymbol{x}_3) \qquad (j=1, 2, 3),$$

we may write the scalar product $\left(\mathsf{T}\boldsymbol{v}\cdot\frac{\partial\boldsymbol{v}}{\partial t}\right)$ as

$$\left(\frac{\partial\boldsymbol{v}}{\partial t}\cdot\mathsf{T}\boldsymbol{v}\right)=\sum_{i=1}^{3}\sum_{j=1}^{3}\tau_{ij}\frac{\partial v_i}{\partial t}\cos(\boldsymbol{n}, \boldsymbol{x}_j).$$

Introducing the vector F with the components

$$F_j=-\sum_{i=1}^{3}\tau_{ij}\frac{\partial v_i}{\partial t} \qquad (j=1, 2, 3), \tag{3.57}$$

we have

$$-\left(\frac{\partial\boldsymbol{v}}{\partial t}\cdot\mathsf{T}\boldsymbol{v}\right)=\sum_{j=1}^{3}F_j\cos(\boldsymbol{n}, \boldsymbol{x}_j)=F_n. \tag{3.58}$$

As defined by (3.57), $\boldsymbol{F}$ is the e n e r g y f l u x v e c t o r, specifying the time rate of energy transfer across unit area per unit time.

Theorem 1. *A solution of $\Delta^*\boldsymbol{u}+\omega^2\boldsymbol{u}=0$ which is regular in B_a vanishes identically if it satisfies on S one of the following boundary conditions:*

(1) $\boldsymbol{u}_a(x)=0,$

(2) $(\mathsf{T}\boldsymbol{u}(x))_a=0,$

(3) $u_a(x)=0$ *on* S_1, $(\mathsf{T}u(x))_a=0$ *on* S_2, *where* $S_1+S_2=S.$

Using the notations Σ_R and Ω_R, introduced in § 3, applying the energy theorem (3.56) in Ω_R, and assuming that either $\boldsymbol{v}$ or $\mathsf{T}\boldsymbol{v}$ vanishes on S, we find

$$\frac{\partial}{\partial t}(U+K)=-\int_{\Sigma R}\left(\frac{\partial\boldsymbol{v}}{\partial t}\cdot\mathsf{T}\boldsymbol{v}\right)dS. \tag{3.56'}$$

Since

$$\boldsymbol{v}(x, t)=\operatorname{Re}(\boldsymbol{u}e^{-i\omega t})$$

and

$$\boldsymbol{u}(x)=\boldsymbol{\alpha}(x)+i\boldsymbol{\beta}(x),$$

we have

$$\boldsymbol{v}(x, t)=\boldsymbol{\alpha}(x)\cos\omega t+\boldsymbol{\beta}(x)\sin\omega t. \tag{3.59}$$

Inserting (3.49) in (3.28) and (3.29) and separating the real and imaginary parts, we obtain

$$\begin{aligned}
&\boldsymbol{\alpha}^{(s)}(x) = o(1), \quad (\mathbf{T}\boldsymbol{\alpha}^{(s)}(x) + k_s c_s \boldsymbol{\beta}^{(s)}) = o(R^{-1}),\\
&\boldsymbol{\beta}^{(s)}(x) = o(1), \quad (\mathbf{T}\boldsymbol{\beta}^{(s)}(x) - k_s c_s \boldsymbol{\alpha}^{(s)}) = o(R^{-1}) \qquad (s = 1, 2)
\end{aligned} \tag{3.60}$$

where

$$c_s = \begin{cases} a^2, & \text{if } s = 1,\\ b^2, & \text{if } s = 2.\end{cases}$$

We also have the estimates (3.46), which now give

$$\boldsymbol{\alpha}^{(s)}(x) = o(R^{-1}), \quad \boldsymbol{\beta}^{(s)}(x) = o(R^{-1}) \qquad (s = 1, 2). \tag{3.61}$$

Representing $\boldsymbol{v}$ as a sum of potential and solenoidal components $\boldsymbol{v}^{(1)}$ and $\boldsymbol{v}^{(2)}$, respectively, we obtain

$$F_n = -\left(\frac{\partial \boldsymbol{v}}{\partial t}\mathbf{T}\boldsymbol{v}\right) = -\sum_{k=1}^{2}\sum_{s=1}^{2}\frac{\partial \boldsymbol{v}^{(k)}}{\partial t}\mathbf{T}\boldsymbol{v}^{(s)}.$$

Inserting (3.59),

$$\begin{aligned}
-\left(\frac{\partial \boldsymbol{v}^{(k)}}{\partial t}T\boldsymbol{v}^{(s)}\right) &= -\omega(\boldsymbol{\beta}^{(k)}\cos\omega t - \boldsymbol{\alpha}^{(k)}\sin\omega t)(\mathbf{T}\boldsymbol{\alpha}^{(s)}\cos\omega t +\\
&+ \mathbf{T}\boldsymbol{\beta}^{(s)}\sin\omega t) = -\omega(\boldsymbol{\beta}^{(k)}\cos\omega t - \boldsymbol{\alpha}^{(k)}\sin\omega t)[(\mathbf{T}\boldsymbol{\alpha}^{(s)} + k_s c_s \boldsymbol{\beta}^{(s)})\cos\omega t +\\
&+ (\mathbf{T}\boldsymbol{\beta}^{(s)} - k_s c_s \boldsymbol{\alpha}^{(s)})\sin\omega t] +\\
&+ k_s c_s \omega(\boldsymbol{\beta}^{(k)}\cos\omega t - \boldsymbol{\alpha}^{(k)}\sin\omega t)(\boldsymbol{\beta}^{(s)}\cos\omega t - \boldsymbol{\alpha}^{(s)}\sin\omega t) \quad (s, k = 1, 2),
\end{aligned}$$

and hence finally, on account of (3.52)–(3.55),

$$F_n = \sum_{s=1}^{2} k_s c_s \omega(\boldsymbol{\beta}^{(s)}\cos\omega t - \boldsymbol{\alpha}^{(s)}\sin\omega t)^2 + o(R^{-2}). \tag{3.62}$$

The fact that the normal component of the energy flux vector, F_n, is positive for large R means that this vector points outwards from the sphere Σ_R, so that energy is leaving the system and going out to infinity, in accordance with the physical interpretation of the radiation condition (§ 1).

Substituting the value of F_n from (3.62) into (3.56'), we obtain

$$\frac{\partial}{\partial t}(U + K) = \sum_{s=1}^{2} k_s c_s \omega \int_{\Sigma_R} (\boldsymbol{\beta}^{(s)}\cos\omega t - \boldsymbol{\alpha}^{(s)}\sin\omega t)^2\, dS + o(1). \tag{3.63}$$

Let us show that this implies that

$$\lim_{R\to\infty}\int_{\Sigma_R}[\boldsymbol{\alpha}^{(s)}(x)]^2\, dS_x = 0 \quad\text{and}\quad \lim_{R\to\infty}\int_{\Sigma_R}[\boldsymbol{\beta}^{(s)}(x)]^2\, dS_x = 0 \quad (s = 1, 2). \tag{3.64}$$

Suppose (3.64) does not hold. Then, for sufficiently large R, the right-hand side of (3.63) will be non-negative; but the left-hand side changes sign, as may be verified easily. Indeed, let α_j and $\beta_j (j = 1, 2, 3)$ be the components of the time-independent vectors $\boldsymbol{\alpha}(x)$ and $\boldsymbol{\beta}(x)$, $\alpha_j^{(1)}$, $\beta_j^{(1)}$ the components of the potential vectors $\boldsymbol{\alpha}^{(1)}(x)$, $\boldsymbol{\beta}^{(1)}(x)$, and $\alpha_j^{(2)}(x)$, $\beta_j^{2}(x)$ those of the solenoidal vectors $\boldsymbol{\alpha}^{(2)}(x)$, $\boldsymbol{\beta}^{(2)}(x)$. Let

$$a(x) = \operatorname{div}\boldsymbol{\alpha}(x), \qquad b(x) = \operatorname{div}\boldsymbol{\beta}(x);$$

$$\alpha_{jk} = \frac{1}{2}\left(\frac{\partial \alpha_j}{\partial x_k} + \frac{\partial \alpha_k}{\partial x_j}\right), \qquad \beta_{jk} = \frac{1}{2}\left(\frac{\partial \beta_j}{\partial x_k} + \frac{\partial \beta_k}{\partial x_j}\right);$$

then

$$\operatorname{div} \boldsymbol{v}(x, t) = a(x) \cos \omega t + b(x) \sin \omega t;$$

$$v_{jk}(x, t) = \alpha_{jk} \cos \omega t + \beta_{jk} \sin \omega t.$$

Substituting these expressions, as well as (3.59), in the right-hand side of

$$U + K = \int_{\mathfrak{L}_R} \left[\frac{1}{2} \lambda (\operatorname{div} \boldsymbol{v})^2 + \mu (v_{11}^2 + \ldots) + \frac{1}{2} \sum_{k=1}^{3} \left(\frac{\partial v_k}{\partial t}\right)^2 \right\} dv,$$

we obtain

$$\frac{\partial}{\partial t}(U + K) = \int_{\mathfrak{L}_R} \Bigg\{ \lambda\omega (a \cos \omega t + b \sin \omega t)(b \cos \omega t - a \sin \omega t) +$$

$$+ 2\mu\omega \sum_{j, k=1}^{3} (\alpha_{jk} \cos \omega t + \beta_{jk} \sin \omega t)(\beta_{jk} \cos \omega t - \alpha_{jk} \sin \omega t) -$$

$$- \omega^2 \sum_{k=1}^{3} (\beta_k \cos \omega t - \alpha_k \sin \omega t)(\beta_k \sin \omega t + \alpha_k \cos \omega t) \Bigg\} dv. \quad (3.65)$$

For the two times $t = 0$ and $t = \frac{\pi}{2\omega}$ this expression becomes

$$\left[\frac{\partial}{\partial t}(U + K)\right]_{t=0} = \int_{\mathfrak{L}_R} \Bigg[\lambda\omega a(x) b(x) + 2\mu\omega \sum_{j, k}^{3} \alpha_{jk}(x) \beta_{ik}(x) -$$

$$- \omega^2 \sum_{k=1}^{3} \alpha_k(x) \beta_k(x) \Bigg] dv, \quad (3.66_1)$$

$$\left[\frac{\partial}{\partial t}(U + K)\right]_{t=\frac{\pi}{2\omega}} = -\int_{\mathfrak{L}_R} \Bigg[\lambda\omega a(x) b(x) + 2\mu\omega \sum_{j, k} \alpha_{jk}(x) \beta_{jk}(x) -$$

$$- \omega^2 \sum_{k=1}^{3} \alpha_k(x) \beta_k(x) \Bigg] dv. \quad (3.66_2)$$

We may assume that

$$A = \int_{\mathfrak{L}_R} \left[\lambda\omega ab + 2\mu\omega \sum_{j, k} \alpha_{jk}\beta_{jk} - \omega^2 \sum_{k} \alpha_k\beta_k \right] dv \neq 0,$$

for otherwise (3.64) follows immediately from (3.63); this proves that $\frac{\partial}{\partial t}(U + K)$ changes sign. Let $A > 0$; then (3.66_2) and (3.63) imply that

$$\lim_{R \to \infty} \int_{\Sigma_R} [\boldsymbol{\alpha}^{(s)}]^2 \, dS = 0 \quad (3.67)$$

uniformly over all directions. But $\boldsymbol{\alpha}^{(s)}(x)$ is a solution of the membrane equation

$$\Delta u + k_s^2 u = 0 \quad (s = 1, 2).$$

Now we have the following theorem /13a/:

Theorem 2. *A solution, $u(x)$, of the membrane equation $\Delta u + k^2 u = 0$ $(k^2 > 0)$ vanishes identically if*

$$\lim_{R \to \infty} \int_{\Sigma_R} |u|^2 \, dS = 0$$

*uniformly over all directions.**

* This theorem is sometimes referred to as Rellich's lemma (cf., e.g., /4b/). Rellich derived it in 1943 /26/, but the theorem had been proved long before that by the author (in 1933, cf. /13b/). See also /13a, 3a/.

By this theorem we have

$$\alpha^{(s)}(x) \equiv 0 \qquad (s=1,\ 2).$$

But then on account of (3.63)

$$\frac{\partial}{\partial t}(U+K) = \sum_{s=1}^{2} k_s c_s \omega \cos^2 \omega t \int_{\Sigma_R} [\beta^{(s)}(x)]^2 dS + o(1)$$

and the change of sign of the left-hand side implies

$$\lim_{R\to\infty} \int_{\Sigma_R} [\beta^{(s)}(x)]^2 dS = 0; \tag{3.68}$$

here $\beta^{(s)}(x)$ is a solution of the membrane equation which vanishes due to (3.68), in view of Theorem 2. It follows that

$$u^{(s)}(x) = \alpha^{(s)}(x) + \beta^{(s)}(x) = 0 \qquad (s=1,\ 2)$$

and consequently

$$u(x) = u^{(1)}(x) + u^{(2)}(x) = 0,$$

which was to be proved.

Theorem 3. *A solution of* $\Delta^* u + \omega^2 u = 0$, *regular in* B_a, *vanishes identically if it satisfies on* S *the boundary condition*

$$(\mathrm{T}u(x) + \sigma(x)u(x))_a = 0, \qquad \mathrm{Im}\,\sigma \geqslant 0$$

A proof of this theorem, based on the estimates (3.50)–(3.55) and Green's formula, was given in /2a/.

Theorem 4. *A regular vector function vanishes identically if for* $x \in B_i$ *it satisfies the equation*

$$\mu_i \Delta u + (\lambda_i + \mu_i)\,\mathrm{grad}\,\mathrm{div}\, u + \omega^2 u = 0$$

and for $x \in B_a$ *the equation*

$$\mu_a \Delta u + (\lambda_a + \mu_a)\,\mathrm{grad}\,\mathrm{div}\, u + \omega^2 u = 0$$

while on S *it satisfies the boundary conditions*

$$C_i u_i = C_a u_a,$$
$$C_i'(\mathrm{T}u)_i = C_a'(\mathrm{T}u)_a,$$

where $C_i,\ C_i',\ C_a,\ C_a'$ *are nonzero constants.*

The proof of this theorem, which will find important applications in Ch. VII, is analogous to the proof of Theorem 1; indeed, let $U_i,\ K_i,\ U_a,\ K_a$ be the potential and kinetic energies in B_i and B_a, respectively. The energy theorem then gives

$$\frac{\partial}{\partial t}(U_i + K_i) = -\int_S \left(\frac{\partial v}{\partial t}\cdot \mathrm{T}v\right) ds,$$

$$\frac{\partial}{\partial t}(U_a + K_a) = -\int_{S+\Sigma_R} \left(\frac{\partial v}{\partial t}\cdot \mathrm{T}v\right) ds.$$

Multiplying the first equality by C_iC_i', the second by C_aC_a', and keeping in mind the reversed direction of the normals to S, we add them together; the integrals over S cancel out due to the boundary conditions, leaving

$$\frac{\partial}{\partial t}\{C_iC_i'(U_i + K_i) + C_aC_a'(U_a + K_a)\} = -C_aC_a' \int_{\Sigma_R} \left(\frac{\partial v}{\partial t}\cdot \mathrm{T}v\right) dS.$$

This corresponds to (3.56'), from which point on the reasoning is the same as before.

The proofs of Theorems 1, 3 and 4 are also valid for $\omega=0$, in which case the regularity conditions at infinity become

$$u(x)=o(1), \quad \frac{\partial u}{\partial R}=o(R^{-1}) \tag{3.69}$$

and we have the following theorem:

Theorem 5. A solution of $\Delta^* u=0$ *which is regular in* B_a *vanishes identically if it satisfies on* S *any of the boundary conditions of Theorems 1, 3, 4.*

Until now we have considered uniqueness theorems for domains containing the point at infinity; these theorems play an essential part in the theory of exterior boundary-value problems. There is no uniqueness theorem for interior oscillation problems of finite domains, owing to the discreteness of the frequency spectrum of proper oscillations (see VI, 8). However, even in the case of finite domains, the following uniqueness theorems are valid for static problems.

Theorem 6. A solution of $\Delta^* u=0$, *which is regular in* B_i *vanishes identically if it satisfies the boundary condition*

$$u_i(x)=0 \quad \text{or} \quad (\mathsf{T}u+\sigma u)_i=0, \quad \sigma>0,$$

Theorem 7. A solution of $\Delta^* u=0$, *which is regular in* B_i *and satisfies the boundary condition*

$$(\mathsf{T}u(x))_i=0,$$

is of the form $A+B(x)$, *where* A *is an arbitrary constant vector, and* $B(x)$ *a vector with the components*

$$qx_3-rx_2, \quad rx_1-px_3, \quad px_2-qx_1,$$

p, q, r *being arbitrary constants.*

Both theorems may be proved easily by making use of the identity (1.9') and formula (1.12). A solution of the form $A+B(x)$ describes a rigid displacement of the body as a whole.

Chapter IV

INTEGRAL EQUATIONS OF BOUNDARY-VALUE PROBLEMS FOR NONHOMOGENEOUS BODIES

§ 1. Formulation of the boundary-value problems

Problem (A). Let an elastic medium B_a, characterized by the constants λ_a, μ_a fill all three-dimensional space, except for a finite number of bounded disjoint domains $B_i^{(k)}$ $(k=1, 2, 3, \ldots, n)$ which are occupied by other elastic media with the constants $\lambda_i^{(k)}$, $\mu_i^{(k)}$ $(k=1, 2, 3, \ldots, n)$ constituting n distinct inclusions embedded within the medium B_a. We shall assume that each such insert is bounded by a closed surface $S^{(k)}(k=1, 2, \ldots, n)$ (see Figure 1, Ch. II) across which some mechanically allowable coupling between the insert and the ambient medium is realized. Let a source of time-periodic oscillations with a given amplitude and a constant frequency ω be applied at some point x_*. It is required to find the stress-strain state which arises due to the source action in the nonhomogeneous composite medium.

Problem (B). We shall also consider the following problem. Suppose the external medium does not extend to infinity but has an external boundary, which is also a closed surface (see Figure 2, Ch. II). Let either (1) the displacements, or (2) the stresses, or (3) a linear combination of both be prescribed on this surface, as well as some mechanically realizable conditions of coupling of the media across the internal boundaries $S^{(k)}$ $(k=1, 2, \ldots, n)$. It is required to work out the state of stress of the system. These problems will be respectively denoted by (B_1), (B_2), (B_3).

Problem (C). There is also the important particular case when S_a is an infinite plane, so that

$$B_a+\sum_{k=1}^{n} B_i^{(k)}$$

is a half-space containing inclusions; these problems are of special interest in theoretical geophysics.

We shall consider two types of coupling as examples of interfacial conditions of contact:

(a) rigid contact, for which the displacements and stresses vary continuously across the interface.

(b) free contact, for which the stresses remain continuous but the displacements change discontinuously across the interface by given increments.

These problems will be considered sufficiently typical, and we shall not be concerned with other modifications of boundary and contact conditions.

For $\omega=0$ all the above oscillation problems reduce to the corresponding static problems, whose solutions may be obtained in case ω is not an eigenvalue from the solutions of the dynamic problems by simply setting $\omega=0$.

The eigenvalue case requires separate treatment but it, too, can be completely solved.

We shall first make a study of Problem (A) and hence proceed to the problems whose treatment will in a sense be modeled on this example. Since there is no essential difference between having one or several inserts, we will for simplicity consider a single internal domain, B_i, bounded by the surface S and occupied by a material with Lamé constants λ_i, μ_i. We shall examine the cases of rigid and free contact at S.

§ 2. Integral equations for Problem (A)

Let the source point x_* belong to domain B_a. Let $E(x, x_*)$, where $x(x_1, x_2, x_3)$ is a field point, be the displacement field to which the given source gives rise throughout the homogeneous infinite continuum characterized by the constants λ_a, μ_a; this field satisfies the equation

$$\overset{*}{\Delta}_{(a)}E+\omega^2 E=0$$

and has a specified singularity at x_*. The vector function $u(x)$ will be called a solution of Problem (A), if it satisfies the following conditions:

1°. For $x \in B_i$

$$\overset{*}{\Delta}_{(i)}u(x)+\omega^2 u(x)\equiv(\lambda_i+2\mu_i)\operatorname{grad}\operatorname{div}u(x)-\mu_i\operatorname{rot}\operatorname{rot}u(x)+\omega^2 u(x)=0.$$

2°. For $x \in B_a$

$$\overset{*}{\Delta}_{(a)}u(x)+\omega^2 u(x)\equiv(\lambda_a+2\mu_a)\operatorname{grad}\operatorname{div}u(x)-\mu_a\operatorname{rot}\operatorname{rot}u(x)+\omega^2 u(x)=0.$$

3°. For $x \in S$

$$u_i(x)=u_a(x), \qquad (\mathrm{T}^{(i)}u(x))_i=(\mathrm{T}^{(a)}u(x))_a,$$

where

$$\mathrm{T}^{(i)}u(x)=2\mu_i\frac{\partial u}{\partial n}+\lambda_i n\operatorname{div}u(x)+\mu_i(n\times\operatorname{rot}u(x)),$$

$$\mathrm{T}^{(a)}u(x)=2\mu_a\frac{\partial u}{\partial n}+\lambda_a\operatorname{div}u(x)+\mu_a(n\times\operatorname{rot}u(x))$$

are stress vectors in B_i and B_a.*

4°. The vector $D(x; x_*)=u(x)-E(x, x_*)$ is regular in B_a (in the sense of III, 2).

To justify our claim that a vector function $u(x)$ which satisfies conditions 1°, 2°, 3°, 4° actually constitutes a unique and stable solution of Problem (A) we now obviously have to prove that such a $u(x)$ exists, is unique, and depends continuously on the parameters of the problem.

Let us introduce some new notations.

The operators, matrices and vectors defined in Ch. I,

$$\Delta^*,\ \mathrm{P},\ \Gamma,\ \mathrm{T},\ \mathrm{N},\ \Gamma^{(k)},\ \Gamma_p^{(k)},\ \Gamma_s^{(k)}\ \text{etc.}$$

depend, as we know, on the parameters λ and μ:

$$\Delta^*=\Delta^*(\lambda, \mu), \quad \mathrm{P}=\mathrm{P}(\lambda, \mu), \quad \Gamma=\Gamma(\lambda, \mu), \quad \mathrm{T}=\mathrm{T}(\lambda, \mu),$$
$$\Gamma^{(k)}=\Gamma^{(k)}(\lambda, \mu), \quad \Gamma_p^{(k)}=\Gamma_p^{(k)}(\lambda, \mu)\ \text{etc.}$$

* To repeat our convention (II, 1) regarding the use of the subscripts i and a: when attached to variable quantities, they denote the limiting values as the argument point approaches the interface from the inside and from the outside, respectively; but when enclosed within brackets or appended to constant parameters, they are simply indices specifying the particular region concerned.

In this chapter we shall also use the symbols

$$\overset{*}{\Delta}_{(i)},\ \overset{*}{\Delta}_{(a)},\ \mathbf{T}^{(i)},\ \mathbf{T}^{(a)},\ \mathbf{P}^{(i)},\ \mathbf{P}^{(a)},\ \Gamma_{(i)},\ \Gamma_{(a)},\ \Gamma^{(k)}_{(i)},\ \Gamma^{(k)}_{(a)},\ \Gamma^{(k)}_{p,(i)},\ \Gamma^{(k)}_{p,(a)}\ \text{etc.},$$

some of which are already familiar from (I, 7) and which are defined as

$$\overset{*}{\Delta}_{(i)} = (\lambda_i + 2\mu_i)\,\text{grad div} - \mu_i \,\text{rot rot} \equiv \mu_i\Delta + (\lambda_i + \mu_i)\,\text{grad div},$$
$$\overset{*}{\Delta}_{(a)} = (\lambda_a + \mu_a)\,\text{grad div} - \mu_a \,\text{rot rot} = \mu_a\Delta + (\lambda_a + \mu_a)\,\text{grad div},$$
$$\mathbf{T}^{(i)} = \mathbf{T}(\lambda_i, \mu_i), \quad \mathbf{T}^{(a)} = \mathbf{T}(\lambda_a, \mu_a), \quad \Gamma^{(k)}_{(i)} = \Gamma^{(k)}(\lambda_i, \mu_i),$$
$$\Gamma^{(k)}_{(a)} = \Gamma^{(k)}(\lambda_a, \mu_a),$$

and similarly for the others.

One cannot derive the integral equations for boundary-value problems concerning nonhomogeneous media in the way this has been done for homogeneous media. We shall now see how to make use of the Betti formulas and their linear combinations in order to get rid of some "undesirable" terms in the obtained expressions, and exemplify the procedure by working it out for Problem (A).

To start with we assume that Problem (A) admits a regular solution, $\boldsymbol{u}(x)$. Let us apply the Betti formula (1.10') to $\boldsymbol{u}(x)$ or $\boldsymbol{D}(x;\, x_*) = \boldsymbol{u}(x) - E$, and to $\Gamma^{(k)}_{(a)}(x,\, y)$ $(k = 1,\, 2,\, 3)$,* considering separately the two cases $x \in B_i$ and $x \in B_a$. Formula (1.10') is applied twice in each of these cases, first in B_a using the operator $\overset{*}{\Delta}_{(a)}$ and then in B_i with the operator $\overset{*}{\Delta}_{(i)}$. Combining the obtained expressions, and making use of the prescribed conditions on the interface between B_i and B_a we may eliminate the terms containing $\mathbf{T}\boldsymbol{u}(x)$. In applying Betti's formula it is obviously necessary to exclude each time the pole of $\Gamma^{(k)}_{(a)}(x,\, y)$ from the region of integration. This may be achieved by enclosing the pole within a small sphere of radius ε centered at it, $\tau(x;\, \varepsilon)$; the sphere surface will be denoted by $\sigma(x;\, \varepsilon)$.

Let $x \in B_i$. Then**

$$\int\limits_{B_i - \tau(x;\,\varepsilon)} \left[\boldsymbol{u}(y) \cdot \overset{*}{\Delta}_{(i)}\Gamma^{(k)}_{(a)}(x,\, y) - \Gamma^{(k)}_{a}(x,\, y) \cdot \overset{*}{\Delta}_{(i)}\boldsymbol{u}(y)\right] dv_y =$$
$$= \int\limits_{S + \sigma(x;\,\varepsilon)} \left[u_i(y) \cdot \mathbf{T}^{(i)}_y \Gamma^{(k)}_{(a)}(x,\, y) - \Gamma^{(k)}_{a}(x,\, y)\left(\mathbf{T}^{(i)}\boldsymbol{u}(y)\right)_i\right] ds_y. \tag{4.1}$$

Since the existence of a solution is assumed, we may write

$$\overset{*}{\Delta}_{(i)}\boldsymbol{u}(y) = -\,\omega^2 \boldsymbol{u}(y), \qquad y \in B_i.$$

Furthermore

$$\overset{*}{\Delta}_{(i)} \cdot \Gamma^{(k)}_{a}(x,\, y) = \mu_i\left(\Delta\Gamma^{(k)}_{(a)} + \frac{\lambda_i + \mu_i}{\mu_i}\,\text{grad div}\,\Gamma^{(k)}_{(a)}\right) =$$
$$= \frac{\mu_i}{\mu_a}\overset{*}{\Delta}_{(a)}\Gamma^{(k)}_{(a)}(x,\, y) + \frac{m}{\mu_a}\,\text{grad div}\,\Gamma^{(k)}_{(a)}(x,\, y) =$$
$$= -\,\omega^2\frac{\mu_i}{\mu_a}\Gamma^{(k)}_{(a)}(x,\, y) + \frac{m}{\mu_a}\,\text{grad div}\,\Gamma^{(k)}_{(a)}(x,\, y), \tag{4.2}$$

where

$$m = \lambda_i\mu_a - \lambda_a\mu_i. \tag{4.3}$$

* If the exciting source is located in B_i we must consider $\Gamma^{(k)}_{(a)}(x,\, y)$ instead of $\Gamma^{(k)}_{(i)}(x,\, y)$.

** $\mathbf{T}^{(i)}_y\Gamma^{(k)}_{(a)}(x,\, y)$ denotes the result of $\mathbf{T}^{(i)}$ operating relative to the point y on the vector function $\Gamma^{(k)}_{(a)}(x,\, y)$; this corresponds to the $\mathbf{T}^{(i)y}\Gamma^{(k)}_{(a)}(x,\, y)$ of Chs. I and II. In the following the arguments and some indices are sometimes omitted for brevity if this can not give rise to misunderstanding.

Equation (4.1) may hence be written

$$\omega^2\left(1-\frac{\mu_l}{\mu_a}\right)\int\limits_{B_l-\tau(x;\varepsilon)} u(y)\cdot\Gamma_{(a)}^{(k)}(x, y)\,dv_y+$$

$$+\frac{m}{\mu_a}\int\limits_{B_l-\tau(x;\varepsilon)} u(y)\,\mathrm{grad\,div}\,\Gamma_{(a)}^{(k)}(x, y)\,dv_y=$$

$$=\int\limits_{S+\sigma(x;\varepsilon)}\left[u_l(y)\cdot \mathrm{T}_y^{(l)}\Gamma_{(a)}^{(k)}(x, y)-\Gamma_{(a)}^{(k)}(x, y)\cdot\left(\mathrm{T}^{(l)}u(y)\right)_l\right]dS_y. \tag{4.4}$$

However

$$\int\limits_{\sigma(x;\varepsilon)} u(y)\cdot \mathrm{T}_y^{(l)}\Gamma_{(a)}^{(k)}(x, y)\,dS_y=\int\limits_{\sigma(x;\varepsilon)}[u(y)-u(x)]\cdot \mathrm{T}_y^{(l)}\Gamma_{(a)}^{(k)}\,dS_y+$$

$$+u(x)\int\limits_{\sigma(x;\varepsilon)} \mathrm{T}_y^{(l)}\left(\Gamma_{(a)}^{(k)}-\overset{0}{\Gamma}{}_{(a)}^{(k)}\right)dS_y+u(x)\int\limits_{\sigma(x;\varepsilon)} \mathrm{T}_y^{(l)}\overset{0}{\Gamma}{}_{(a)}^{(k)}(x, y)\,dS_y.$$

The first two terms on the right-hand side of the last equation tend to zero for $\varepsilon\to 0$, leaving

$$\lim_{\varepsilon\to 0} u(x)\int\limits_{\sigma(x;\varepsilon)} \mathrm{T}_y^{(l)}\overset{0}{\Gamma}{}_{(a)}^{(k)}(x, y)\,dS_y \qquad (k=1,\ 2,\ 3).$$

Substituting the values $\alpha=\mu_l$, $\beta=\lambda_l$ into (1.43), we obtain

$$\left(\mathrm{T}_y^{(l)}\overset{0}{\Gamma}{}_{(a)}^{(k)}(x, y)\right)_j=\left\{\left[\frac{(a^2+b^2)\mu_l}{a^2b^2}-\frac{\mu_l}{b^2}\right]\delta_{jk}+\frac{3(a^2-b^2)\mu_l}{a^2b^2}\frac{\partial r}{\partial y_j}\frac{\partial r}{\partial y_k}\right\}\times$$

$$\times\frac{\partial}{\partial n_y}\frac{1}{r(xy)}+\left[\frac{\lambda_l}{a^2}-\frac{(a^2-b^2)\mu_l}{a^2b^2}\right]+\cos(n_y,\ x_j)\frac{\partial}{\partial y_k}\frac{1}{r}+$$

$$+\left[\frac{\mu_l}{b^2}-\frac{(a^2-b^2)\mu_l}{a^2b^2}\right]\cos(n_y,\ x_k)\frac{\partial}{\partial y_j}\frac{1}{r},$$

whence, on account of (1.57') and (1.57"),

$$\lim_{\varepsilon\to 0} u(x)\int\limits_{\sigma(x;\varepsilon)} \mathrm{T}_y^{(l)}\overset{0}{\Gamma}{}_{(a)}^{(k)}(x, y)\,dS_y=\lim_{\varepsilon\to 0}\sum_{j=1}^{3}u_j(x)\int\limits_{\sigma(x;\varepsilon)}\left(\mathrm{T}_y^{(l)}\overset{0}{\Gamma}{}_{(a)}^{(k)}(x, y)\right)_j dS_y=$$

$$=u_k(x)\left\{4\pi\left[\frac{\mu_l(a^2+b^2)}{a^2b^2}-\frac{\mu_l}{b^2}\right]+4\pi\frac{\mu_l(a^2-b^2)}{a^2b^2}+\right.$$

$$\left.+\frac{4}{3}\pi\left[\frac{\lambda_l}{a^2}+\frac{\mu_l}{b^2}-\frac{2\mu_l(a^2-b^2)}{a^2b^2}\right]\right\}=4\pi l u_k(x) \qquad (k=1,\ 2,\ 3),$$

where

$$l=\frac{1}{3}\left(2\frac{\mu_l}{\mu_a}+\frac{\lambda_l+2\mu_l}{\lambda_a+2\mu_a}\right). \tag{4.5}$$

Passing to the limit as $\varepsilon\to 0$ in (4.4) and seeing that

$$\lim_{\varepsilon\to 0}\int\limits_{B_l-\tau(x;\varepsilon)} u(y)\,\mathrm{grad\,div}\,\Gamma_{(a)}^{(k)}(x, y)\,dv_y=\int\limits_{B_l} u(y)\,\mathrm{grad\,div}\,\Gamma_{(a)}^{(k)}(x, y)\,dv_y$$

holds* in the sense of principal value (cf. I, 7), we obtain

$$4\pi\mu_a l u_k(x)=(\mu_a-\mu_l)\,\omega^2\int\limits_{B_l} u(y)\,\Gamma_{(a)}^{(k)}(x, y)\,dv_y+$$

$$+m\int\limits_{B_l} u(y)\,\mathrm{grad\,div}\,\Gamma_{(a)}^{(k)}(x, y)\,dv_y+$$

$$+\mu_a\int\limits_{S}\left[\Gamma_{(a)}^{(k)}(x, y)\left(\mathrm{T}u^{(l)}\right)_l-u_l(y)\left(\mathrm{T}_y^{(l)}\Gamma_{(a)}^{(k)}\right)\right]dS_y \qquad (k=1,\ 2,\ 3). \tag{4.6}$$

Since the difference $D(x;\ x_*)=u(x)-E(x;\ x_*)$ is by assumption regular in B_a,

* For this it is sufficient to assume that $u(y)\in H(\gamma)$, $0<\gamma\leqslant 1$, for $y\in B_l$ /24/.

we may write for $x \in B_i$

$$\int_{B_a} [D(y; x_*)\Delta^*_{(a)}\Gamma^{(k)}_{(a)}(x, y) - \Gamma^{(k)}_{(a)}(x, y)\Delta^*_{(a)} D]\, dv_y =$$

$$= \int_S [D_a \mathrm{T}^{(a)}_y \Gamma^{(k)}_{(a)}(x, y) - \Gamma^{(k)}_{(a)}(x, y)(\mathrm{T}^{(a)} D)_a]\, dS_y.$$

Now since for $y \in B_a$ the following equality holds in y

$$\Delta^*_{(a)} D + \omega^2 D = \Delta^*_{(a)}\Gamma^{(k)}_{(a)} + \omega^2 \Gamma^{(k)}_{(a)} = 0 \qquad (k = 1, 2, 3),$$

we finally obtain

$$\int_S [D_a \cdot \mathrm{T}^{(a)}_y \Gamma^{(k)}_{(a)} - \Gamma^{(k)}_{(a)}(\mathrm{T}^{(a)} D)_a]\, dS_y = 0. \tag{4.7}$$

Here and in (4.6) the normal to S points from B_i into B_a.

Adding (4.6) and (4.7) together and taking into account the boundary conditions on S

$$u_i = u_a, \quad (\mathrm{T}^{(i)} u)_i = (\mathrm{T}^{(a)} u)_a,$$

we obtain

$$4\pi\mu_a l u_k(x) = (\mu_a - \mu_i)\, \omega^2 \int_{B_i} u(y)\Gamma^{(k)}_{(a)}(x, y)\, dv_y +$$

$$+ m \int_{B_i} u(y) \operatorname{grad} \operatorname{div} \Gamma^{(k)}_{(a)}\, dv_y +$$

$$+ \mu_a \int_S u_i(y)\, \mathrm{T}^*_y \Gamma^{(k)}_{(a)}(x, y)\, dS_y + 4\pi\mu_a F_k(x; x_*), \tag{4.8}$$

where

$$\mathrm{T}^* = \mathrm{T}^{(a)} - \mathrm{T}^{(i)}$$

and

$$F_k(x; x_*) = -\int_S E(y; x_*)\, \mathrm{T}^{(a)}_y \Gamma^{(k)}_{(a)}(x, y)\, dS_y + \int_S \Gamma^{(k)}_{(a)}(x; y)(\mathrm{T}^{(a)} E)\, dS_y. \tag{4.9}$$

Since

$$x_* \in B_a, \quad x \in B_i$$

and

$$\Delta^*_{(a)} E + \omega^2 E = 0, \quad \Delta^*_{(a)}\Gamma^{(k)}_{(a)} + \omega^2 \Gamma^{(k)}_{(a)} = 0,$$

we find from (1.60)

$$E_k(x; x_*) = \frac{1}{4\pi} \int_S [\Gamma^{(k)}_{(a)}(x, y)(\mathrm{T}^{(a)} E) - E(y; x_*)\, \mathrm{T}^{(a)}_y \Gamma^{(k)}_{(a)}]\, dS_y.$$

Thus (4.8) becomes

$$l\mu_a u_k(x) = \frac{1}{4\pi}\, \omega^2 (\mu_a - \mu_i) \int_{B_i} u(y)\Gamma^{(k)}_{(a)}(x, y)\, dv_y +$$

$$+ \frac{m}{4\pi} \int_{B_i} u(y) \operatorname{grad} \operatorname{div} \Gamma^{(k)}_{(a)}(x, y)\, dv_y +$$

$$+ \frac{\mu_a}{4\pi} \int_S u_i(y)\, \mathrm{T}^*_y \Gamma^{(k)}_{(a)}(x, y)\, dS_y + \mu_a E_k(x; x_*). \tag{4.10$_i$}$$

Let now $x \in B_a$. We observe that in the same way as before one arrives instead of (4.4) at

$$\omega^2\left(1-\frac{\mu_i}{\mu_a}\right)\int\limits_{B_i} u(y)\Gamma^{(k)}_{(a)}(x, y)\,dv_y+\frac{m}{\mu_a}\int\limits_{B_i} u(y)\,\mathrm{grad\,div}\,\Gamma^{(k)}_{(a)}(x, y)\,dv_y-$$
$$-\int\limits_S \left[u_i(y)\,\mathrm{T}^{(i)}_y\Gamma^{(k)}_{(a)}-\Gamma^{(k)}_{(a)}(x, y)(\mathrm{T}^{(i)}u)_i\right]dS_y=0. \qquad (4.4')$$

Applying (1.10') in B_a to $\Gamma^{(k)}_{(a)}(x, y)$ and $D(x; x_*)=u(x)-E(x, x_*)$, and keeping in mind that in B_a

$$\Delta^*_{(a)}D+\omega^2 D=0, \quad \Delta^*_{(a)}\Gamma^{(k)}_{(a)}+\omega^2\Gamma^{(k)}_{(a)}=0,$$

we find

$$4\pi D_k(x)=\int\limits_S \left[D_a\mathrm{T}^{(a)}_y\Gamma^{(k)}_{(a)}(x, y)-\Gamma^{(k)}_{(a)}(x, y)(\mathrm{T}^{(a)}D)_a\right]dS_y, \qquad (4.4'')$$

where the normal points from B_i into B_a.

Adding (4.4') and (4.4") together and taking into account the conditions on S, we obtain

$$\mu_a u_k(x)=\frac{1}{4\pi}\omega^2(\mu_a-\mu_i)\int\limits_{B_i} u(y)\Gamma^{(k)}_{(a)}(x, y)\,dv_y+$$
$$+\frac{m}{4\pi}\int\limits_{B_i} u(y)\,\mathrm{grad\,div}\,\Gamma^{(k)}_{(a)}(x, y)\,dv_y+\frac{\mu_a}{4\pi}\int\limits_S u_i(y)\,\mathrm{T}^*_y\,\Gamma^{(k)}_{(a)}(x, y)\,dS_y+$$
$$+\mu_a E_k(x, x_*)-\frac{\mu_a}{4\pi}\int\limits_S \left[E(y; x_*)\,\mathrm{T}^{(a)}_y\Gamma^{(k)}_{(a)}-\Gamma^{(k)}_{(a)}(x, y)(\mathrm{T}^{(a)}E)\right]dS_y.$$

But the last term on the right-hand side vanishes, since for $x\in B_a$

$$\int\limits_S \left[E(y; x_*)\,\mathrm{T}^{(a)}_y\Gamma^{(k)}_{(a)}-\Gamma^{(k)}_{(a)}(x, y)(\mathrm{T}^{(a)}E)\right]dS_y=$$
$$=\int\limits_{B_i}\left[E(y; x_*)\,\Delta^*_{(a)}\Gamma^{(k)}_{(a)}(x, y)-\Gamma^{(k)}_{(a)}(x, y)\,\Delta^*_{(a)}E(y; x_*)\right]dv_y=0;$$

hence we have for $x\in B_a$

$$4\pi\mu_a u_k(x)=\omega^2(\mu_a-\mu_i)\int\limits_{B_i} u(y)\,\Gamma^{(k)}_{(a)}(x, y)\,dv_y+$$
$$+m\int\limits_{B_i} u(y)\,\mathrm{grad\,div}\,\Gamma^{(k)}_{(a)}(x, y)\,dv_y+$$
$$+\mu_a\int\limits_S u_i(y)\,\mathrm{T}^*_y\Gamma^{(k)}_a\,dS_y+4\pi\mu_a E_k(x; x_*). \qquad (4.10_a)$$

Using our vector-matrix multiplication rule and the definition

$$\mathrm{grad\,div}\,A=\begin{Vmatrix} \frac{\partial}{\partial x_1}\mathrm{div}\,A^{(1)} & \frac{\partial}{\partial x_1}\mathrm{div}\,A^{(2)} & \frac{\partial}{\partial x_1}\mathrm{div}\,A^{(3)} \\ \frac{\partial}{\partial x_2}\mathrm{div}\,A^{(1)} & \frac{\partial}{\partial x_2}\mathrm{div}\,A^{(2)} & \frac{\partial}{\partial x_2}\mathrm{div}\,A^{(3)} \\ \frac{\partial}{\partial x_3}\mathrm{div}\,A^{(1)} & \frac{\partial}{\partial x_3}\mathrm{div}\,A^{(2)} & \frac{\partial}{\partial x_3}\mathrm{div}\,A^{(3)} \end{Vmatrix},$$

where $A^{(1)}, A^{(2)}, A^{(3)}$ are the column-vectors of the matrix A, we are now able to write (4.10_i) and (4.10_a) in the form

$$4\pi\mu_a l u(x)=\omega^2(\mu_a-\mu_i)\int\limits_{B_i} u(y)\,\Gamma_{(a)}(x, y)\,dv_y+$$
$$+m\int\limits_{B_i} u(y)\,\mathrm{grad\,div}\,\Gamma_{(a)}\,dv_y+\mu_a\int\limits_S u_i(y)\,\mathrm{T}^*_y\Gamma_{(a)}\,dS_y+4\pi\mu_a E(x; x_*),$$
$$x\in B_i \qquad (4.10_i)$$

$$4\pi\mu_a u(x) = \omega^2(\mu_a - \mu_i)\int_{B_i} u(y)\Gamma_{(a)}(x, y)\,dv_y + \\ + m\int_{B_i} u(y)\,\mathrm{grad\,div}\,\Gamma_{(a)}\,dv_y + \\ + \mu_a\int_S u_i(y)\,T_y^*\Gamma_{(a)}\,dS_y + 4\pi\mu_a E(x;\, x_*),\quad x\in B_a. \tag{4.10$_a$}$$

We have thus proved the following theorem:

Theorem 1. A regular solution of Problem (A) solves the functional equations (4.10$_i$), (4.10$_a$).

The inverse theorem (equivalence theorem) will be proved in (VII, 7), and the existence theorem for solutions of the system (4.10$_i$), (4.10$_a$) in (VII, 4).

§ 3. Integral equations for Problems (B_1) and (B_2)

Problems (B_1) and (B_2) differ from (A) in that the external domain does not extend to infinity, but is bounded by a finite closed surface S_a. Thus all the conditions of Problem (A) remain except the conditions at infinity, which are replaced by the requirement that in (B_1) the displacements, and in (B_2) the stresses take on prescribed values on S_a. This is also the reason for another difference – instead of the matrix of fundamental solutions $\Gamma_{(a)}(x, y)$ it now becomes necessary to use the matrices of the (first and second) Green's tensors.

Let B_a be a domain bounded by the surfaces S and S_a, $B = \bar{B}_i + B_a$ the domain bounded by S_a, and B_a' the domain complementing B to make up all space.

The first dynamic Green's tensor for the domain B is given by the third-order square matrix

$$G(x, y) = \{G^{(1)}(x, y),\, G^{(2)}(x, y),\, G^{(3)}(x, y) = \begin{Vmatrix} G_1^{(1)} & G_1^{(2)} & G_1^{(3)} \\ G_2^{(1)} & G_2^{(2)} & G_2^{(3)} \\ G_3^{(1)} & G_3^{(2)} & G_3^{(3)} \end{Vmatrix},$$

which depends on the positions of x and y, and satisfies the following conditions

(a) for $x\in B$ and $x\neq y$

$$\Delta_{(a)}^* G(x, y) + \omega^2 G(x, y) = 0;*$$

(b) for $x, y\in B$

$$\lim_{x\to x_0} G^{(k)}(x, y) = 0,\quad x_0\in S_a\qquad (k = 1, 2, 3);$$

(c) for $x, y\in B$ $G(x, y)$ admits the representation

$$G(x, y) = \Gamma_{(a)}(x, y) - v(x, y),$$

where $v(x, y)$ is some matrix of solutions of $\Delta_a^* v + \omega^2 v = 0$, regular in B.

The existence of the first Green's tensor is implied by the existence of solutions of (D_i) (cf. II, 2) for values of ω other than the discrete set of proper frequencies, or eigenfrequencies, of (D_i^0) in B; the existence theorem for such solutions will be proved in (VI, 8). Making use of the properties

* Meaning that each column-vector $G^{(k)}(x, y)$ $(k = 1, 2, 3)$ satisfies the equation.

of Green's tensor, and repeating the steps which have led to (4.10_i) and (4.10_a), we obtain the following theorem:

Theorem 2. If ω *is not an eigenfrequency of* (D_i^0) *for the domain* B*, then a regular solution of Problem* (B_1) *solves the functional equation*

$$4\pi\varkappa(x)\,u(x)=\omega^2(\mu_a-\mu_i)\int_{B_i}u(y)\,G(x,y)\,dv_y+$$

$$+m\int_{B_i}u(y)\,\mathrm{grad\,div}\,G\,dv_y+$$

$$+\mu_a\int_S u_i(y)\,\mathrm{T}_y^*G\,dS_y+\mu_a\int_{S_a}f(y)\,\mathrm{T}_y^{(a)}G\,dS_y, \tag{4.11}$$

where $f(x)$ *is a vector function prescribing the boundary values of* $u(x)$ *on* S_a*, and*

$$\varkappa(x)=\begin{cases} l\mu_a, & x\in B_i,\\ \mu_a, & x\in B_a.\end{cases} \tag{4.12}$$

The second dynamic Green's tensor is given by the third-order matrix $H(x,y)=\{H^{(1)},H^{(2)},H^{(3)}\}$, a two-point function satisfying the following conditions:

(a) For $x\in B$ and $x\neq y$

$$\Delta_{(a)}^*H(x,y)+\omega^2H(x,y)=0;$$

(b) for $x,y\in B$

$$\lim_{x\to x_0}\mathrm{T}_x^{(a)}H(x,y)=0,\quad x_0\in S_a\quad (k=1,2,3);$$

(c) for $x,y\in B$ $H(x,y)$ admits the representation

$$H(x,y)=\Gamma_{(a)}(x,y)-w(x,y),$$

where $w(x,y)$ is some matrix of solutions of $\Delta_{(a)}^*w+\omega^2w=0$, regular in B.

The existence of the second Green's tensor is implied by the existence of solutions of (T_i) for values of ω which do not coincide with the eigenfrequencies of the second homogeneous problem (T_i^0) for B; the existence theorem for those solutions will be proved in (VI, 8).

Repeating the steps which have led to (4.10_i) and (4.10_a), we obtain the following theorem:

Theorem 3. If ω *is not an eigenfrequency of* (T_i^0) *for the domain* B*, then a regular solution of Problem* (B_2) *solves the functional equation* ·

$$4\pi\varkappa(x)\,u(x)=\omega^2(\mu_a-\mu_i)\int_{B_i}u(y)\,H(x,y)\,dv_y+$$

$$+m\int_{B_i}u(y)\,\mathrm{grad\,div}\,H(x,y)\,dv_y+$$

$$+\mu_a\int_S u_i(y)\,\mathrm{T}_y^*H\,dS_y-\mu_a\int_{S_a}f(y)\,H(x,y)\,dS_y, \tag{4.13}$$

where $f(x)$ *prescribes the boundary values of* $\mathrm{T}u(x)$ *on* S_a.

§ 4. Integral equations for the static Problems (B_1) and (B_2)

These arise from dynamic problems when $\omega=0$. However, in order that equations (4.11) and (4.13) remain meaningful it is necessary to ascertain that $\omega=0$ is not an eigenfrequency of the homogeneous problem (D_i^0) and (T_i^0), since the dynamic Green's tensors were defined above on that assumption. The uniqueness Theorems 5, 6 (III, 4) resolve this question as follows.

For $\omega=0$, the dynamic problems (D_i) and (T_i) reduce to the corresponding static problems; by Theorem 5, the homogeneous static equation (D_i^0) admits only a trivial solution, and therefore $\omega=0$ is not an eigenvalue of the dynamic problem (D_i). Theorem 6 implies that the homogeneous static problem (T_i^0) admits nonzero solutions of the type

$$a+qx_3-rx_2, \quad b+rx_1-px_3, \quad c+px_2-qx_1,$$

where a, b, c, p, q, r are arbitrary constants; these solutions describe rigid displacements of the body as a whole. Consequently $\omega=0$ is an eigenvalue of the dynamic problem (T_i) and thus the Green's tensor in (4.13) becomes meaningless.

The functional equations of the static Problem (B_1) thus result from (4.11) upon setting $\omega=0$, and have the form

$$4\pi\varkappa(x)\,u(x)=m\int_{B_i} u(y)\,\mathrm{grad\,div}\,\overset{0}{G}(x, y)\,dv_y+$$
$$+\mu_a\int_S u_i(y)\,\mathrm{T}_y^*\overset{0}{G}(x, y)\,dS_y+\mu_a\int_{S_a} f(y)\,\mathrm{T}_y^{(a)}\overset{0}{G}(x, y)\,dS_y, \tag{4.14}$$

where $\overset{0}{G}(x, y)=G(x, y;\omega)|_{\omega=0}=\overset{0}{\Gamma}_a(x, y)-\overset{0}{v}(x, y)$ is the static Green's tensor.

The integral equations for the static Problem (B_2) can not be obtained from (4.13) by setting $\omega=0$. The second static Green's tensor, which we denote by $\overset{0}{H}(x, y)$, must be derived independently. This will be done in (VI, 6). Here we only give its definition and some main properties, and then go on to derive the functional equations of the static Problem (B_2).

Let $\overset{0}{H}{}^{(k)}(x, y)$, for a fixed k, denote the k-th column-vector of the matrix $\overset{0}{H}(x, y)$, and let $\overset{0}{H}{}_1^{(k)}(x, y), \overset{0}{H}{}_2^{(k)}(x, y), \overset{0}{H}{}_3^{(k)}(x, y)$ be its Cartesian components. Similarly, let $\overset{0}{H}_{(k)}(x, y)$ stand for the k-th row-vector of the matrix $\overset{0}{H}(x, y)$, and $\overset{0}{H}{}^1_{(k)}(x, y), \overset{0}{H}{}^2_{(k)}(x, y), \overset{0}{H}{}^3_{(k)}(x, y)$ for its components.

The second static Green's tensor for the domain B is defined as a third-order matrix which depends on the two points x and y and satisfies the following conditions:

(a) For $x, y\in B$,

$$\Delta^*_{(a)}\overset{0}{H}{}^{(k)}(x, y)=4\pi\sum_{s=1}^{6}\mathfrak{B}^{s(k)}(x, y) \qquad (k=1, 2, 3) \tag{4.15$_a$}$$

holds with respect to x for a fixed $y\neq x$, and

$$\Delta^*_{(a)}\overset{0}{H}_{(k)}(x, y)=4\pi\sum_{s=1}^{6}\mathfrak{B}^s_{(k)}(x, y); \tag{4.15$_b$}$$

holds with respect to y for a fixed $x\neq y$; the vector $\mathfrak{B}^{s(k)}(x, y)$ is the k-th column, and the vector $\mathfrak{B}^s_{(k)}(x, y)$ the k-th row of the matrix

$$\mathfrak{A}^{(s)}(x)*\mathfrak{A}^{(s)}(y)=\begin{Vmatrix}\mathfrak{A}_1^{(s)}(x)\,\mathfrak{A}_1^{s}(y) & \mathfrak{A}_1^{(s)}(x)\,\mathfrak{A}_2^{(s)}(y) & \mathfrak{A}_1^{(s)}(x)\,\mathfrak{A}_3^{(s)}(y)\\ \mathfrak{A}_2^{(s)}(x)\,\mathfrak{A}_1^{(s)}(y) & \mathfrak{A}_2^{(s)}(x)\,\mathfrak{A}_2^{(s)}(y) & \mathfrak{A}_2^{(s)}(x)\,\mathfrak{A}_3^{(s)}(y)\\ \mathfrak{A}_3^{(s)}(x)\,\mathfrak{A}_1^{(s)}(y) & \mathfrak{A}_3^{(s)}(x)\,\mathfrak{A}_2^{(s)}(y) & \mathfrak{A}_3^{(s)}(x)\,\mathfrak{A}_3^{(s)}(y)\end{Vmatrix}$$
$$s=1, 2, \ldots, 6, \tag{4.16}$$

where

$$\mathfrak{A}^{(1)}=\left(\frac{1}{M}, 0, 0\right), \quad \mathfrak{A}^{(2)}=\left(0, \frac{1}{M}, 0\right) \quad \mathfrak{A}^{(3)}=\left(0, 0, \frac{1}{M}\right),$$

$$\mathfrak{A}^{(4)}(x)=\left(-\frac{x_3}{S},\ 0,\ \frac{x_1}{S}\right),\ \mathfrak{A}^{(5)}(x)=\left(\frac{x_2}{T},\ -\frac{x_1}{T},\ 0\right),$$
$$\mathfrak{A}^{(6)}(x)=\left(0,\ \frac{x_3}{R},\ -\frac{x_2}{R}\right), \tag{4.17}$$

M^2 being the volume of the body B, or its mass for unit density throughout, and R^2, S^2, T^2 the principal moments of inertia, i.e., the moments about the principal axes of inertia with origin at the center of gravity;

(b) for boundary points $x_0 \in S_a$, with $x,\ y \in B$

$$\lim_{x\to x_0} \mathrm{T}_x \overset{0}{H}{}^{(k)}(x,\ y)=0 \qquad (k=1,\ 2,\ 3); \tag{4.18}$$

(c) for $x,\ y \in B$, the following representation is possible

$$\overset{0}{H}(x,\ y)=\overset{*}{\Gamma}(x,\ y)-\overset{0}{v}(x,\ y),$$

where $\overset{0}{v}(x,\ y)$ is some matrix of solutions, regular in B, of the equation

$$\Delta^*_{(a)}u(x)\equiv\mu_a\Delta u(x)+(\lambda_a+\mu_a)\operatorname{grad}\operatorname{div}u(x)=0$$

and

$$\overset{*}{\Gamma}(x,\ y)=\overset{0}{\Gamma}_{(a)}(x,\ y)-\sum_{s=1}^{6}\mathfrak{A}^{(s)}(x)*\int_B\overset{0}{\Gamma}(y,\ \xi)\,\mathfrak{A}^{(s)}(\xi)\,dv_\xi-$$
$$-\sum_{s=1}^{6}\int_B\overset{0}{\Gamma}(x,\ \eta)\,\mathfrak{A}^{(s)}(\eta)\,dv_\eta*\mathfrak{A}^{(s)}(y)+$$
$$+\sum_{s=1}^{6}\sum_{r=1}^{6}\mathfrak{A}^{(s)}(x)*\mathfrak{A}^{(r)}(y)\int_B\int_B\mathfrak{A}^{(s)}(\xi)\,\overset{0}{\Gamma}(\xi,\ \eta)\,\mathfrak{A}^{(r)}(\eta)\,dv_\xi\,dv_\eta. \tag{4.19}$$

The second static Green's tensor possesses the symmetry property

$$\overset{0}{H}(x,\ y)=\overset{0}{H}{}^*(y,\ x),$$

where $\overset{0}{H}{}^*(x,\ y)$ is the transpose of $\overset{0}{H}(x,\ y)$.

Let us now derive the required functional equations. Let $u(x)$ be a regular solution of Problem (B_2) for $\omega=0$. Applying the Betti formula (1.10') to $u(x)$ and $\overset{0}{H}_{(k)}(x,\ y)$ $(k=1,\ 2,\ 3)$ in B_l for $x\in B_l$, we obtain

$$\int_{B_l-\tau(x;\,\varepsilon)}\left[u(y)\,\Delta^*_{(l)}\overset{0}{H}_{(k)}(x,\ y)-\overset{0}{H}_{(k)}(x,\ y)\,\Delta^*_{(l)}u(y)\right]dv_y=$$
$$=\int_{S+\sigma(x;\,\varepsilon)}\left[u_i(y)\left(\mathrm{T}_y^{(i)}\overset{0}{H}_{(k)}\right)-\overset{0}{H}_{(k)}(x,\ y)\left(\mathrm{T}^{(i)}u(y)\right)_i\right]dS_y, \tag{4.20}$$

when all the differential operations under the integral signs are applied to the point y.

However

$$\Delta^*_{(l)}\overset{0}{H}_{(k)}(x,\ y)=\mu_l\left(\Delta+\frac{\lambda_l+\mu_l}{\mu_l}\operatorname{grad}\operatorname{div}\right)\overset{0}{H}_{(k)}(x,\ y)=$$
$$=\mu_l\left(\Delta+\frac{\lambda_a+\mu_a}{\mu_a}\operatorname{grad}\operatorname{div}\right)\overset{0}{H}_{(k)}(x,\ y)-$$
$$-\mu_l\left(\frac{\lambda_a+\mu_a}{\mu_a}-\frac{\lambda_l+\mu_l}{\mu_l}\right)\operatorname{grad}\operatorname{div}\overset{0}{H}_{(k)}(x,\ y)=$$
$$=4\pi\frac{\mu_l}{\mu_a}\sum_{s=1}^{6}\mathfrak{B}^s_{(k)}(x,\ y)+\frac{m}{\mu_a}\operatorname{grad}\operatorname{div}\overset{0}{H}_{(k)}(x,\ y). \tag{4.21}$$

Accordingly (4.20) becomes

$$4\pi \frac{\mu_l}{\mu_a} \sum_{s=1}^{6} \int\limits_{B_l - \tau(x;\varepsilon)} u(y)\, \mathfrak{B}^{s}_{(k)}(x, y)\, dv_y + $$

$$+ \frac{m}{\mu_a} \int\limits_{B_l - \tau(x;\varepsilon)} u(y)\, \operatorname{grad} \operatorname{div} \overset{0}{H}_{(k)}(x, y)\, dv_y =$$

$$= \int\limits_{S + \sigma(x;\varepsilon)} \left[u_l(y) \left(\mathrm{T}^{(l)}_y \overset{0}{H}_{(k)} \right)_l - \overset{0}{H}_{(k)}(x, y)\, \mathrm{T}^{(l)} u(y)_l \right] dS_y. \tag{4.22}$$

The passage to the limit in (4.22) is carried out as in (4.6) of § 2 (because $\overset{0}{H}_{(k)}(x, y)$ differs from $\overset{0}{\Gamma}_{(a)}(x, y)$ only by an additive regular vector function, and, since here $\omega = 0$, we obtain on account of (4.15_b)

$$4\pi\mu_a l u_k(x) = m \int\limits_{B_l} u(y)\, \operatorname{grad} \operatorname{div} \overset{0}{H}_{(k)}(x, y)\, dv_y +$$

$$+ \mu_a \int\limits_{S} \overset{0}{H}_{(k)}(x, y) \left[(\mathrm{T}^{(l)} u(y))_l - u_l(y) \left(\mathrm{T}^{(l)}_y \overset{0}{H}_{(k)} \right) \right] dS_y + \sum_{s=1}^{6} C'_s \mathfrak{A}^{(s)}_k(x), \tag{4.23}$$

where the constants C'_s are given by

$$C'_s = 4\pi\mu_l \int\limits_{B_l} \sum_{j=1}^{3} u_j(y)\, \mathfrak{A}^{(s)}_j(y)\, dv_y \qquad (s = 1, 2, 3, \ldots, 6). \tag{4.24}$$

Keeping to the assumption that $x \in B_l$, we may write on account of property (b) of the Green's tensor

$$\int\limits_{B_a} \left[u(y)\, \overset{*}{\Delta}_{(a)} \overset{0}{H}_{(k)}(x, y) - \overset{0}{H}_{(k)}(x, y)\, \overset{*}{\Delta}_{(a)} u(y) \right] dv_y =$$

$$= \int\limits_{S} \left[u_a(y) \left(\mathrm{T}^{(a)}_y \overset{0}{H}_k \right) - \overset{0}{H}_{(k)}(x, y) \left(\mathrm{T}^{(a)} u \right)_a \right] dS_y - \int\limits_{S_a} f(y)\, \overset{0}{H}_{(k)}(x, y)\, dS_y,$$

where $f(x)$ is the value of $\mathrm{T}u(x)$ on S_a.

Since $\overset{*}{\Delta}_{(a)} u = 0$ in B_a, we obtain in virtue of (4.15_b)

$$4\pi \int\limits_{B_a} u(y) \sum_{s=1}^{6} \mathfrak{B}^{(s)}_{(k)}(x, y)\, dv_y =$$

$$= \int\limits_{S} \left[u_a(y) \left(\mathrm{T}^{(a)}_y \overset{0}{H}_k \right) - \overset{0}{H}_k(x, y) \left(\mathrm{T}^{(a)} u(y) \right)_a \right] dS_y - \int\limits_{S_a} f(y)\, \overset{0}{H}_{(k)}(x, y)\, dS_y$$

whence, again reversing the direction of the normal,

$$0 = \int\limits_{S} \left[u_a(y) \left(\mathrm{T}^{(a)}_y \overset{0}{H}_{(k)} \right) - \overset{0}{H}_{(k)}(x, y) \left(\mathrm{T}^{a} u(y) \right)_a \right] dS_y -$$

$$- \int\limits_{S_a} f(y)\, \overset{0}{H}_{(k)}(x, y)\, dS_y + \sum_{s=1}^{6} C''_s \mathfrak{A}^{(s)}_k(x), \tag{4.25}$$

where the constants C''_s are given by the relations

$$C''_s = \frac{\mu_a}{\mu_l} C'_s \qquad (s = 1, 2, \ldots, 6). \tag{4.26}$$

Adding (4.23) and (4.25) together after first multiplying the latter by μ_a, and applying the boundary conditions on S, we obtain

$$4\pi\mu_a l u_k(x) = m\int_{B_l} u(y)\operatorname{grad}\operatorname{div}\overset{0}{H}_{(k)}(x, y)\,dv_y +$$

$$+\mu_a\int_S u_l(y)\,\mathrm{T}^*_y\overset{0}{H}_{(k)}(x, y)\,dS_y - \mu_a\int_{S_a} f(y)\cdot\overset{0}{H}_{(k)}(x, y)\,dS_y + \sum_{s=1}^{6} C_s\mathfrak{A}_k^{(s)}(x), \tag{4.27}$$

where

$$C_s = C'_s + C''_s \quad (s = 1, 2, \ldots, 6).$$

Let now $x \in B_a$. Then instead of (4.23) we obviously obtain by the same method

$$0 = m\int_{B_l} u(y)\operatorname{grad}\operatorname{div}\overset{0}{H}_{(k)}(x, y)\,dv_y +$$

$$+\mu_a\int_S\left[\overset{0}{H}_{(k)}(x, y)\left(\mathrm{T}^{(l)}u(y)\right)_l - u_l(y)\left(\mathrm{T}^{(l)}_y\overset{0}{H}_{(k)}\right)\right]dS_y + \sum_{s=1}^{6} C'_s\mathfrak{A}_k^{(s)}(x). \tag{4.28}$$

Further, applying the Betti formula to $u(y)$ and $\overset{0}{H}_{(k)}(x, y)$ in B_a, with $x \in B_a$,

$$0 = -4\pi u_k(x) + \int_S\left[u_a(y)\left(\mathrm{T}^{(a)}_y\overset{0}{H}_{(k)}(x, y)\right) - \overset{0}{H}_{(k)}(x, y)\left(\mathrm{T}^{(a)}u(y)\right)_a\right]dS_y -$$

$$-\int_{S_a} f(y)\,\overset{0}{H}_{(k)}(x, y)\,dS_y + \sum_{s=1}^{6} C''_s\mathfrak{A}_k^{(s)}(x) \tag{4.29}$$

where the normal points from B_l into B_a.

Adding (4.28) and (4.29) together after first multiplying the latter by μ_a, and applying the conditions on S, we obtain

$$4\pi\mu_a u_k(x) = m\int_{B_l} u(y)\operatorname{grad}\operatorname{div}\overset{0}{H}_{(k)}(x, y)\,dv_y +$$

$$+\mu_a\int_S u_l(y)\,\mathrm{T}^*_y\overset{0}{H}_{(k)}(x, y)\,dS_y - \mu_a\int_{S_a} f(y)\,\overset{0}{H}_{(k)}(x, y)\,dS_y +$$

$$+\sum_{s=1}^{6} C^*_s\mathfrak{A}_k^{(s)}(y), \tag{4.30}$$

$$C^*_s = C'_s + \frac{1}{\mu_a}C''_s.$$

Any solution of Problem (B_2) is only determined up to an additive linear combination of the vectors

$$\mathfrak{A}^{(s)}(x) \quad (s = 1, 2, \ldots, 6) \tag{4.31}$$

since $\mathfrak{A}^{(s)}(x)$, being a rigid displacement, is everywhere continuous and

$$\mathrm{T}\mathfrak{A}^{(s)}(x) = 0, \quad \overset{*}{\Delta}_{(l)}\mathfrak{A}^{(s)}(x) = 0, \quad \overset{*}{\Delta}_{(a)}\mathfrak{A}^{(s)}(x) = 0. \tag{4.32}$$

The solution of Problem (B_2) is thus determined apart from rigid displacements, and the terms

$$\sum_{s=1}^{3} C_s\mathfrak{A}_k^{(s)}(x), \quad \sum_{s=1}^{6} C^*_s\mathfrak{A}_k^{(s)}(x) \tag{4.33}$$

may be neglected in (4.27) and (4.30).

Thus we proved the following theorem:

Theorem 4. A regular solution of the static Problem (B_1) *solves the equation*

$$4\pi\varkappa(x)\,u_k(x)=m\int_{B_i} u(y)\,\mathrm{grad\,div}\,\overset{0}{G}{}^{(k)}(x,\,y)\,dv_y+$$

$$+\mu_a\int_S u_i(y)\,\overset{*}{\mathrm{T}}_y\overset{0}{G}{}^{(k)}(x,\,y)\,dS_y+\mu_a\int_{S_a} f(y)\,\mathrm{T}_y^{(a)}\overset{0}{G}{}^{(k)}\,dS_y. \tag{4.34}$$

and a regular solution of the static Problem (B_2) *solves the equation*

$$4\pi\varkappa(x)\,u_k(x)=m\int_{B_i} u(y)\,\mathrm{grad\,div}\,\overset{0}{H}_{(k)}(x,\,y)\,dv_y+$$

$$+\mu_a\int_S u_i(y)\,\overset{*}{\mathrm{T}}_y\overset{0}{H}_{(k)}(x,\,y)\,dS_y-\mu_a\int_S f(y)\,\overset{0}{H}_{(k)}(x,\,y)\,dS_y$$

$$(k=1,\,2,\,3), \tag{4.35}$$

and is determined apart from a rigid displacement.

§ 5. Integral equations for the static Problems (C_1) and (C_2)

Problems (C) differ from (B) in that the surface S_a is at infinity and B_a is a half-space with the inclusion B_i. Equations (4.34) and (4.35) remain meaningful, with the conditions at infinity mentioned before (cf. (3.69)), provided the Green's tensors $\overset{0}{G}(x,\,y)$ and $\overset{0}{H}(x,\,y)$ are replaced by the analogous tensors for the half-space. The fact that the Green's tensor for the half-space can be obtained in closed form results in a considerable simplification as compared with equations (4.34) and (4.35).

The first (static) Green's tensor for the half-space has the form

$$\overset{0}{G}(x,\,y)=\left\{\overset{0}{G}{}^{(1)}(x,\,y),\ \overset{0}{G}{}^{(2)}(x,\,y),\ \overset{0}{G}{}^{(3)}(x,\,y)\right\},$$

where

$$\overset{0}{G}{}^{(k)}(x,\,y)=\overset{0}{\Gamma}{}^{(k)}_{(a)}(x,\,y)+\frac{1}{2\pi}\int_{-\infty}^{+\infty}\Gamma_{\mathrm{II}\,(a)}(x;\,x')\,\overset{0}{\Gamma}{}^{(k)}_{(a)}(x'\,;\,y)\,dS_{x'}$$

$$(k=1,\,2,\,3), \tag{4.36}$$

$\overset{0}{\Gamma}_{\mathrm{II}}$ being the kernel of a double-layer potential of the second kind for the domain B_a (cf. I, 6), which may be verified as follows. The above expression for $\overset{0}{G}(x,\,y)$ is a solution of $\overset{*}{\Delta}_{(a)}u=0$, because the integral

$$v(x,\,y)=\frac{1}{2\pi}\int_{-\infty}^{+\infty}\overset{0}{\Gamma}_{\mathrm{II}\,(a)}(x;\,x')\,\overset{0}{\Gamma}{}^{(k)}_{(a)}(x';\,y)\,dS_{x'}$$

exists and, being a double-layer potential of the second kind, satisfies the same equation. The boundary condition

$$\lim_{x\to x_0}\overset{0}{G}{}^{(k)}(x,\,y)=0\qquad(k=1,\,2,\,3),$$

is satisfied for $x_0\in S_a$; indeed, (2.4) implies

$$v_i(x_0,\,y)=-\overset{0}{\Gamma}{}^{(k)}_{(a)}(x_0,\,y)+\frac{1}{2\pi}\int_{-\infty}^{+\infty}\overset{0}{\Gamma}_{\mathrm{II}\,(a)}(x_0,\,x')\,\overset{0}{\Gamma}{}^{(k)}_{a}(x'\ \,y)\,dS_{x'},$$

while (1.45) shows that if the two points x_0 and x' are on a plane boundary (as in the present case), then

$$\overset{0}{\Gamma}_{II}(x_0, x') = 0.$$

The second (static) Green's tensor for the half-space is the third-order square matrix

$$\overset{0}{H}(x, y) = \left\{ \overset{0}{H}{}^{(1)}(x, y), \overset{0}{H}{}^{(2)}(x, y), \overset{0}{H}{}^{(3)}(x, y) \right\},$$

where

$$\overset{0}{H}{}^{(k)}(x, y) = \overset{0}{\Gamma}{}^{(k)}_{(a)}(x, y) + \frac{1}{2\pi} \int_{-\infty}^{+\infty} M_{(a)}(x, x') \left(\mathrm{T}_{x'} \overset{0}{\Gamma}{}^{(k)}_{(a)}(x; y) \right) dS_x$$

$$(k = 1, 2, 3), \tag{4.37}$$

$M(x, y)$ being a matrix of fundamental solutions of the third kind, as defined by (1.50).*

Since according to (1.65') the antenna potential

$$\frac{1}{2\pi} \int_{-\infty}^{+\infty} M_{(a)}(x; x') \left(\mathrm{T}_{x'} \overset{0}{\Gamma}{}^{(k)}_{(a)}(x'; y) \right) dS_{x'} \qquad (k = 1, 2, 3),$$

satisfies $\overset{*}{\Delta}_a u(x) = 0$, this equation will also be satisfied by (4.37). The boundary condition

$$\lim_{x \to x_0} \mathrm{T}_x \overset{0}{H}{}^{(k)}(x, y) = 0 \qquad (k = 1, 2, 3), \quad x_0 \in S_a,$$

follows from the property of the antenna potential expressed by (2.11), and from the fact, made plain by (1.54), that whenever the two points x_0 and x' lie on the boundary plane $\mathrm{T}_{x_0} M(x_0; x') = 0$.

§ 6. Case of equal Poisson's ratios

In one particular, but practically important case the integral equations of §§ 2-5 are considerably simplified. This is the case of equal Poisson's ratios for the media B_i and B_a; these are given by the expressions

$$\sigma_i = \frac{1}{2} \frac{\lambda_i}{\lambda_i + \mu_i} \text{ and } \sigma_a = \frac{1}{2} \frac{\lambda_a}{\mu_a + \lambda_a}. \tag{4.38}$$

They express the ratio of the relative longitudinal extension to the relative lateral contraction (more accurately, for two perpendicular directions, which for most elastic bodies are fixed). Measurements indicate that the Poisson's ratios of technological materials fall between 0.25 (glass) and 0.45 (lead); they vary even less for geological rocks contiguously deposited in the earth crust under natural conditions, the differences there amounting to only a few percent. Poisson's ratio was for these reasons long considered as a universal constant for all elastic bodies (Cauchy). Adopting Cauchy's assumption, we may write

$$m = \lambda_i \mu_a - \lambda_a \mu_i = 0; \tag{4.39}$$

* This simplification in the definition of the second static Green's tensor as compared with that of § 4 is due to the fact that the unique solution of $\Delta^* u = 0$ which is regular in an infinite domain vanishes identically.

then

$$l=\frac{1}{3}\left(2\frac{\mu_i}{\mu_a}+\frac{\mu_i}{\mu_a}\frac{\frac{\lambda_i}{\mu_i}+2}{\frac{\lambda_a}{\mu_a}+2}\right)=\frac{\mu_i}{\mu_a},$$

while (4.10_i) and (4.10_a) become

$$4\pi\mu_i u(x)=\omega^2(\mu_a-\mu_i)\int_{B_i} u(y)\Gamma_{(a)}(x;\ y)\,dv_y+$$
$$+\mu_a\int_S u_i(y)\,\mathrm{T}_y^*\Gamma_{(a)}(x,\ y)\,dS_y+4\pi\mu_a E(x;\ x),\qquad x\in B_i,$$
$$4\pi\mu_a u(x)=\omega^2(\mu_a-\mu_i)\int_{B_i} u(y)\Gamma_{(a)}(x,\ y)\,dv_y+$$
$$+\mu_a\int_S u_i(y)\,\mathrm{T}^*\Gamma_{(a)}(x,\ y)\,dS_y+4\pi\mu_a E(x;\ x),\qquad x\in B_a,$$

or

$$4\pi\varkappa(x)\,u(x)=\omega^2(\mu_a-\mu_i)\int_{B_i} u(y)\Gamma_{(a)}(x,\ y)\,dv_y+$$
$$+\mu_a\int_S u_i(y)\,\mathrm{T}^*\Gamma_{(a)}\,dS_y+4\pi\mu_a E(x;\ x_*),\tag{4.40}$$

where

$$\varkappa(x)=\begin{cases}\mu_i, & x\in B_i,\\ \mu_a, & x\in B_a.\end{cases}$$

In accordance with (4.39) we may write

$$\mathrm{T}^*=(\mu_a-\mu_i)\left[2\frac{\partial}{\partial n}+n\frac{\lambda_a-\lambda_i}{\mu_a-\mu_i}\operatorname{div}+(n\times\operatorname{rot})\right]=$$
$$=(\mu_a-\mu_i)\left[2\frac{\partial}{\partial n}+n\frac{\lambda a}{\mu_a}\operatorname{div}+(n\times\operatorname{rot})\right],$$

whence

$$\mathrm{T}^*=\frac{\mu_a-\mu_i}{\mu_a}\mathrm{T}^{(a)},$$

and (4.40) becomes

$$4\pi\varkappa(x)\,u(x)=\omega^2(\mu_a-\mu_i)\int_{B_i} u(y)\Gamma_{(a)}(x,\ y)\,dv_y+$$
$$+(\mu_a-\mu_i)\int_S u_i(y)\,\mathrm{T}_y^{(a)}\Gamma_{(a)}(x,\ y)\,dS_y+4\pi\mu_a E(x;\ x_*).\tag{4.41}$$

Hence we obtain, in particular, for $\mu_i=\mu_a$ and $\lambda_i=\lambda_a$ the relation

$$u(x)=E(x;\ x_*).$$

We will now determine the value of the discontinuity coefficient $\varkappa(x)$ at boundary points. Passing to the limit in (4.41) as x approaches the boundary point x_0 from the inside and the outside, and in view of the boundary conditions

$$u_i=u_a \text{ on } S$$

and the discontinuity formulas for a double-layer potential of the first kind (2.1), we obtain

$$4\pi\mu_i u_i(x_0)=\omega^2(\mu_a-\mu_i)\int_{B_i} u(y)\Gamma_{(a)}\,dv_y-2\pi(\mu_a-\mu_i)\,u_i(x_0)+$$
$$+(\mu_a-\mu_i)\int_S u_i(y)\,\mathrm{T}^{(a)}\Gamma_{(a)}\,dS_y+4\pi\mu_a E(x_0;\ x_*)\tag{4.41'}$$

and

$$4\pi\mu_a u_a(x_0) = \omega\ (\mu_a - \mu_i) \int_{B_i} u(y)\Gamma_{(a)}\, dv_y + 2\pi(\mu_a - \mu_i)\, u_i(x_0) +$$

$$+ (\mu_a - \mu_i) \int_S u_i(y)\, T^{(a)}\Gamma_{(a)}\, dS_y + 4\pi\mu_a E(x_0;\ x_*). \qquad (4.41'')$$

Inspection of the values of (4.41) at x_0, and application of (4.41') and (4.41") shows, in view of the continuity of $u(x)$, that

$$\varkappa(x) = \begin{cases} \mu_i, & x \in B_i, \\ \frac{1}{2}(\mu_i + \mu_a), & x \in S, \\ \mu_a, & x \in B_a. \end{cases}$$

We have thereby proved the following theorem:

Theorem 5. If Problem (A) admits a solution in case Cauchy's assumption is fulfilled, this will also solve the system of functional equations (4.41).

The inverse theorem and the existence theorem for solutions of (4.41) will be proved in Ch. VII.

In a similar manner the integral equations of other problems (§§ 3–5) may also be simplified by adopting Cauchy's assumption, but we shall not go into that.

§ 7. Some other conditions of contact

We have studied the case of rigid coupling of media. In the same way equations for other modes of contact may also be obtained.

Let us turn once more to Problem (A) and assume that instead of the inclusion B_i, we first have in B_a a cavity bounded by the surface S, into which an insert of the same shape as S but slightly bigger is forcibly fitted. This may be realized, e.g., by filling the cavity with some molten substance under pressure, which in the free state would upon hardening normally occupy a volume slight larger than B_i. The problems of a freezing enclosed liquid and of shrink and press fitting are cases in point. In these problems the following contact conditions may be assumed to be realized on S:

$$u_a - u_i = g(x), \qquad (T^{(i)}u(x))_i = (T^{(a)}u(x))_a, \qquad (4.42)$$

where $g(x)$ is a given vector function. Repeating the steps which have led to (4.10_i) and (4.10_a), we now obtain

$$4\pi\varkappa(x)\, u(x) = \omega^2(\mu_a - \mu_i) \int_{B_i} u(y)\Gamma_{(a)}(x;\ y)\, dv_y +$$

$$+ m \int_{B_i} u(y) \operatorname{grad} \operatorname{div} \Gamma_a(x,\ y)\, dv_y + \mu_a \int_S u_i(y)\, T^*_y\Gamma_{(a)}(x,\ y)\, dS_y +$$

$$+ \mu_a \int_S g(y)\, T^{(a)}\Gamma_{(a)}(x,\ y)\, dS_y + 4\pi\mu_a E(x;\ x_*). \qquad (4.43)$$

For static problems ($\omega = 0$), when the insert is made of the same material as its matrix,

$$\lambda_i = \lambda_a = \lambda, \quad \mu_i = \mu_a = \mu, \quad m = 0, \quad l = 1, \quad \varkappa = 4\pi\mu_a = 4\pi\mu,$$

$$T^* = T^{(a)} - T^{(i)} = 0, \quad \overset{0}{\Gamma}_{(a)}(x,\ y) = \overset{0}{\Gamma}(x,\ y),$$

and the explicit solution is

$$u(x)=\frac{1}{4\pi}\int_S g(y)\,T_y\overset{0}{\Gamma}(x,\ y)\,dS_y+\overset{0}{E}(x;\ x_0). \tag{4.44}$$

This will be demonstrated in detail in (IX, 11), where it will be shown, in particular, that (4.44) remains a solution of that problem even when $\omega\neq 0$, provided that $\overset{0}{\Gamma}(x,\ y)$ is replaced by $\Gamma(x,\ y)$.

Let us consider also the problem of pressed components. Let B_a be a finite body, bounded by the closed surface S_a, and having n inner cavities bounded by nonintersecting surfaces $S^{(k)}$ $(k=1,\ 2,\ \ldots,\ n)$, each being press-fitted, as above, with inserts of the same material as B_a. The conditions on $S^{(k)}$ will be

$$u_a-u_i=g_k(x),\quad (Tu(x))_i=(Tu(x))_a,\quad x\in S^{(k)},$$

where $g_k(x)$ $(k=1,\ \ldots,\ n)$ are given vector functions; in addition, the boundary values of the displacements $u(x)$ or the stresses $Tu(x)$, which will be denoted by $f(x)$, are known on S_a.

In the same way by which (4.34) and (4.35) have been obtained we now find

$$u(x)=\frac{1}{4\pi}\sum_{k=1}^{n}\int_{S^{(k)}} g_k(y)\,T_y\overset{0}{G}(x,\ y)\,dS_y+\frac{1}{4\pi}\int_{S_a} f(y)\,T_y\overset{0}{G}(x,\ y)\,dS_y \tag{4.45}$$

$$u(x)=\frac{1}{4\pi}\sum_{k=1}^{n}\int_{S^k} g_k(y)\,T_y\overset{0}{H}(x,\ y)\,dS_y-\frac{1}{4\pi}\int_{S_a} f(y)\,\overset{0}{H}{}^{*}(x,\ y)\,dS_y. \tag{4.46}$$

If, in particular, the Green's tensors for the whole (simply connected) domain bounded by S_a (without inclusions) are given, then (4.45) and (4.46) provide explicit solutions of the (first and second) problems of pressed components.

It is known that in the plane theory of elasticity the Green's tensors may be derived explicitly for many of the closed contours encountered in technology /24/. The equations of §§ 1-6 for nonhomogeneous media remain in force for plane problems, and can be carried over without any change; formulas (4.45), (4.46) give explicit solutions of the problems of flat pressed components, in all the cases mentioned above (cf. Ch. IX).

As for three-dimensional problems, let S_a coincide with the plane $x_3=0$; then, as shown in § 5, the first and second Green's tensors are given by formulas (4.36) and (4.37), and in this case both problems are solvable in closed form.

It will be shown in (IX, 11) that the expressions (4.45) and (4.46) actually give solutions of the first and second problems of pressed components.

It is of interest to study by this method other problems which admit explicit solution. Some such problems will be discussed in (IX, 11).

Chapter V

ELEMENTS OF THE THEORY OF SYSTEMS OF MANY-DIMENSIONAL SINGULAR INTEGRAL EQUATIONS

The integral equations for boundary-value problems given in Ch. II constitute a particular case of systems of two-dimensional singular integral equations of the type

$$a(x^0)\varphi(x^0)+\int_S \frac{F(x^0, x)}{r^2(x^0, x)}\varphi(x)\,dS_x=g(x^0), \tag{5.1}$$

where S is a closed Liapunov surface, $r(x^0, x)$ the distance between the points x^0 and x, $a(x^0)$ and $F(x^0, x)$ given matrices, and $g(x^0)$ a given vector function satisfying the Hölder condition; the vector function $\varphi(x)$ will also be sought within that class of functions.

It will be shown in Ch. VII that the functional equations for anisotropic media, obtained in Ch. IV, are also reducible to integral equations of type (5.1). It is therefore very important for our purpose to carry out a detailed investigation of the solvability conditions for such equations, and to this the present chapter is devoted.

The kernel of the considered equation has a second-order pole at the point $x \equiv x^0$, and the surface integral which appears in the equation may be understood only in the sense of the Cauchy principal value. Equations of type (5.1) are accordingly called singular, as opposed to regular equations containing improper integrals which converge in the ordinary sense. One of the main differences between the two types of equations lies in that the usual iteration method, which for regular equations reduces unbounded kernels to bounded ones, fails to do so in the case of singular equations.

It turned out, however, that a generalized iteration method could be indicated by means of which it is in many cases possible to prove the fundamental Fredholm theorems and alternative for equation (5.1).

The usual approach to equations of type (5.1) consists in the following: the equation is written in operator form,

$$\mathrm{A}\varphi=g, \tag{5.1'}$$

and one considers the problem of finding an operator B of the same type as A, such that the classical Fredholm theory will apply to the equation

$$\mathrm{BA}\varphi=\mathrm{B}g. \tag{5.2}$$

The operator B is called a regularizing operator, or simply a regularizer. We shall see that, generally speaking, it is possible to construct an infinite set of such operators, and the next problem is that of picking out from among them one which effects an equivalent regularization (i. e., a regularization which produces an equation (5.2) equivalent to the initial one (5.1')).

Both problems were stated and solved by Giraud /10a, b/. The global regularizer, i. e., the B operator which effects regularization over the whole surface S, is derived by Giraud by "cementing", or piecing together a finite number of partial regularizers, each effective in a small neighborbood of some arbitrarily specified point on S. Such operators will be called local regularizers. When applied to systems of equations, however, Giraud's method for constructing local regularizers encounters fundamental difficulties which so far have not been overcome. S. G. Mikhlin /22a, b/, on the other hand, evolved a method for regularizing n-dimensional singular equations for which the integration region extends over all the n-dimensional Euclidean space.*

I. A. Itskovich /9/ showed that with the aid of a succession of mappings the regularization problem can be reduced to Mikhlin's problem for equations of type (5.1) on a closed surface homeomorphic to a sphere (and some other cases). To carry out an equivalent regularization for systems of equations of type (5.1) on a closed Liapunov surface we shall proceed as follows. On the surface S we arbitrarily single out some element S_0 with a sufficiently small diameter. Using essentially the Itskovich procedure, we first map S_0 onto a disk γ lying in a plane tangent to S_0 and then map γ onto the whole Euclidean plane Π. The original equation (5.1) with the region of integration S_0 is thereby transformed into an equivalent equation with the integration region Π. We then construct the regularizer for the latter equation by Mikhlin's method, and finally obtain the regularizer for equation (5.1) by inverse mapping. The global regularizer for equation (5.1) is obtained by constructing local regularizers for each of a finite number of sections of the surface S, exactly as for S_0, and using what amounts to the Giraud "cementing" method. Finally, generalizing Giraud's theory of the resolvent for a system of equations, we obtain a method for equivalent regularization and prove the Fredholm theorems and alternative for our equations.

§ 1. Lyapunov surfaces. The principal value of a singular integral

A finite, closed surface S will be called a Lyapunov surface if it satisfies the following conditions:

1. The surface possesses a continuous tangent plane at every point.
2. If ϑ is the acute angle between the normals at points x and y on S, and $r(x, y)$ is the distance between x and y, then

$$\vartheta < Cr^{\delta}(x, y), \quad 0 < \delta \leqslant 1,$$

where C and δ are constants.

3. There exists a sufficiently small positive number ε_0, fixed for all points of S, such that no straight line parallel to the normal $\boldsymbol{n}_x$ intersects more than once the neighborhood of x on S which is cut out by the cylinder $C(x; \varepsilon_0)$ of radius ε_0 with its axis along $\boldsymbol{n}_x$.

That part of S will be denoted by $S(x; \varepsilon_0)$ and its complement (the rest of S) by $S'(x; \varepsilon_0)$. We similarly define $S(x; \varepsilon)$ and $S'(x; \varepsilon)$ for any ε, $0 < \varepsilon < \varepsilon_0$.

Let us specify a fixed point x^0 on S and consider the coordinate system $\xi_1\xi_2\xi_3$, with origin at x^0, the ξ_3-axis along the inward normal to S at x^0, and the

$\xi_1\xi_2$-plane coinciding with the tangent plane to S at x^0. Let

$$\xi_3 = \xi_0(\xi_1, \xi_2)$$

be the equation of the surface $S(x^0; \varepsilon)$ (for $\varepsilon < \varepsilon_0$); it will be denoted for brevity by S_0. The function $\xi_0(\xi_1, \xi_2)$ is continuous and has continuous partial derivatives satisfying the Hölder condition in the domain $\gamma: \xi_1^2 + \xi_2^2 < a^2$ (for $\varepsilon \leqslant a < \varepsilon_0$), which is the projection of S_0 upon the $\xi_1\xi_2$-plane.

It is clear that

$$\xi_0(0, 0) = 0, \quad \frac{\partial \xi_0(0, 0)}{\partial \xi_1} = 0, \quad \frac{\partial \xi_0(0, 0)}{\partial \xi_2} = 0.$$

If x and y are two points of S_0, with coordinates ξ_1, ξ_2, ξ_3 and η_1, η_2, η_3, respectively, then the quantities

$$p(x) = \frac{\partial \xi_0(\xi_1, \xi_2)}{\partial \xi_1}, \quad q(x) = \frac{\partial \xi_0(\xi_1, \xi_2)}{\partial \xi_2}, \quad p(y) = \frac{\partial \xi_0(\eta_1, \eta_2)}{\partial \xi_1},$$
$$q(y) = \frac{\partial \xi_0(\eta_1, \eta_2)}{\partial \xi_2}$$

can be made small as desired by choosing a sufficiently small diameter of the domain. The properties 1, 2, 3 further imply that for a sufficiently small ε

$$|\xi_3| \leqslant 6C\rho^{1+\delta}, \quad \left|\frac{\partial \xi_0}{\partial \xi_1}\right| \leqslant 3C\rho^{\delta}, \quad \left|\frac{\partial \xi_0}{\partial \xi_2}\right| \leqslant 3C\rho^{\delta}, \tag{5.3}$$

where $\rho^2 = \xi_1^2 + \xi_2^2$.

These properties of a Liapunov surface enable us to define the principal value of a singular integral on such a surface as follows:

$$\int_S \frac{F(x^0, x)}{r^2(x^0, x)} \varphi(x)\, dS_x = \lim_{\varepsilon \to 0} \int_{S'(x^0; \varepsilon)} \frac{F(x^0, x)}{r^2(x^0, x)} \varphi(x)\, dS_x, \tag{5.4}$$

provided that the limit on the right-hand side exists. For this it is evidently necessary to know the behavior of $F(x^0, x)$ as $x \to x^0$, i. e., the value of the limit

$$\lim_{x \to x^0} F(x^0, x).$$

If this limit exists it will depend, generally speaking, on the path along which the point x approaches x^0 as $\varepsilon \to 0$. In a sufficiently narrow neighborhood of x^0 this path is determined by the dihedral angle θ_0 between the plane through the normal n_{x^0} and the point x, and some fixed reference plane, that is, the azimuth angle in the tangent plane at x^0. Let

$$\lim_{x \to x^0} F(x^0, x) = f(x^0; \theta_0).$$

We further assume that

$$|F(x^0, x) - f(x^0; \theta_0)| \leqslant C' r^{\alpha}(x^0, x), \quad 0 < \alpha \leqslant 1, \quad C' \quad \text{constant}.$$

A function or matrix $f(x^0, \theta_0)$ which satisfies the last two conditions will be called the characteristic of the singular integral or the integral equation (5.1). We now split our integral

$$\int_S \frac{F(x^0, x)}{r^2(x^0, x)} \varphi(x)\, dS_x = \int_S \frac{f(x^0, \theta_0)}{r^2(x^0, x)} \varphi(x)\, dS_x + \int_S \frac{F(x^0, x) - f(x^0; \theta_0)}{r^2(x^0, x)} \varphi(x)\, dS_x.$$

The second integral on the right-hand side is an ordinary improper integral, while the first is singular. Let us represent it as a sum of three terms

$$\int\limits_S \frac{f(x^0, \theta_0)}{r^2(x^0, x)} \varphi(x)\, dS_x = \int\limits_{S'(x^0;\, \varepsilon)} \frac{f(x^0; \theta_0)}{r^2(x^0, x)} \varphi(x)\, dS_x + $$
$$+ \int\limits_{S(x^0;\, \varepsilon)} \frac{f(x^0; \theta_0)}{r^2(x^0, x)} [\varphi(x) - \varphi(x^0)]\, dS_x + \int\limits_{S(x^0;\, \varepsilon)} \frac{f(x^0; \theta_0)}{r^2(x^0, x)} \varphi(x_0)\, dS_x. \qquad (5.4')$$

Let $\varphi(x) \in H(\alpha')$, i. e.,

$$|\varphi(x') - \varphi(x'')| < M|x' - x''|^{\alpha'}, \quad 0 < \alpha' \leqslant 1, \quad M = \text{const},$$
$$x', x'' \in S.$$

Now the first two terms in (5.4') are ordinary integrals and it remains to clarify the conditions of convergence of the third term. The (orthogonal) projection ξ of the point x upon γ has the polar coordinates ρ and θ_0, and thus

$$\int\limits_{S_0} \frac{f(x^0; \theta_0)}{r^2(x^0, x)} dS_x = \int\limits_{\gamma} \frac{f(x^0; \theta_0)}{\rho^2(x^0, \xi)} \frac{\rho^2}{r^2} \sqrt{1 + p^2(\xi) + q^2(\xi)}\, d\xi_1\, d\xi_2,$$

where

$$p(\xi) = \frac{\partial \xi_0}{\partial \xi_1}, \quad q(\xi) = \frac{\partial \xi_0}{\partial \xi_2}.$$

It follows from (5.3) that

$$\frac{\rho^2(x^0, \xi)}{r^2(x^0, x)} = 1 + O(\rho^{2\delta}) \text{ and } \sqrt{1 + p^2(\xi) + q^2(\xi)} = 1 + O(\rho^{2\delta}).$$

Therefore

$$\int\limits_{S_0} \frac{f(x^0; \theta_0)}{r^2(x^0, x)} dS_x = \int\limits_{\gamma} \frac{f(x^0; \theta_0)}{\rho^2(x^0, \xi)} d\xi_1\, d\xi_2 + \int\limits_{\gamma} \frac{f(x^0; \theta_0)}{\rho^2(x^0, \xi)} O(\rho^{2\delta})\, d\xi_1\, d\xi_2.$$

The last integral vanishes in the limit as $\varepsilon \to 0$. For the first integral

$$\int\limits_{\gamma} \frac{f(x^0; \theta_0)}{\rho^2(x^0, \xi)} d\xi_1\, d\xi_2 = \lim_{\varepsilon' \to 0} \int\limits_{\varepsilon' < \rho < a} \frac{f(x^0; \theta_0)}{\rho^2(x^0, \xi)} d\xi_1\, d\xi_2 =$$
$$= \lim_{\varepsilon' \to 0} \int\limits_0^{2\pi} f(x^0; \theta_0)\, d\theta_0 \int\limits_{\varepsilon'}^{a} \frac{d\rho}{\rho} = \lim_{\varepsilon' \to 0} \ln \frac{a}{\varepsilon'} \int\limits_0^{2\pi} f(x^0; \theta_0)\, d\theta_0.$$

The last limit exists if and only if

$$\int\limits_0^{2\pi} f(x^0; \theta_0)\, d\theta_0 = 0. \qquad (5.5)$$

This is a necessary and sufficient condition for the existence of (5.4), the principal value of the singular integral

$$\int\limits_S \frac{F(x^0; x)}{r^2(x^0, x)} \varphi(x)\, dS_x.$$

§ 2. Classification of kernels

Let x and y be points in three-dimensional Euclidean space, E_3. The function $F(x, y)$ will be said to be of class $N^{(\alpha)}$, in symbols $F(x, y) \in N^{(\alpha)}$, if the following conditions are satisfied:

1°. $F(x, y)$ is continuous for all pairs (x, y), $x \neq y$, which belong to a bounded and closed set $\mathfrak{E} \subset E_3$.

2°. There exists a number α such that $F(x, y) = O[r^{\alpha-3}(x, y)]$ uniformly in $\mathfrak{E}$ if $0 \leqslant \alpha < 3$, and $F(x, y) = O\left[\ln \frac{C}{r(x, y)}\right]$ (C constant) if $\alpha = 3$.

The function $F(x, y)$ will be said to be of class $N^{(\alpha, \lambda)}$, in symbols $F(x, y) \in N^{(\alpha, \lambda)}$, if the following conditions are satisfied:

1°. $F(x, y) \in N^{(\alpha)}$.

2°. There exists a positive number λ, $0 < \lambda \leqslant 1$, $\lambda \leqslant \alpha$, such that

$$F(x', y) - F(x'', y) = O\left[r^{\lambda}(x', x'')\, l_y^{\alpha-\lambda-3}(x', x'')\right], \tag{*}$$

where x', x'', y are points in E_3, and $l_y(x'\ x'') \equiv l_y$ is the distance from y to the segment $x'x''$.

If condition (*) is satisfied for the first and second argument simultaneously, $F(x, y)$ will be said to be of class $N_*^{(\alpha, \lambda)}$, in symbols $F(x, y) \in N_*^{(\alpha, \lambda)}$.

Theorem 1. *The function*

$$F(x, y) = \frac{1}{r(x, y)}$$

is of class $N_*^{(2, 1)}$, *and the function*

$$F_k(x, y) = \frac{\partial}{\partial x_k} \frac{1}{r(x, y)} \qquad (k = 1, 2, 3)$$

is of class $N_*^{(1, 1)}$.

Proof. The function

$$F(x, y) = \frac{1}{r(x, y)}$$

is evidently of class $N^{(2)}$, while

$$F_k(x, y) = -\frac{x_k - y_k}{r(x, y)} \cdot \frac{1}{r^2(x, y)}$$

is of class $N^{(1)}$; hence follows the first statement of the theorem. If x is shifted along some direction t from the position x' to x'' with fixed y, we obtain by virtue of the mean value theorem

$$F(x'', y) - F(x', y) = \sum_{k=1}^{3} \frac{\partial F(\xi, y)}{\partial x_k} \cos(x_k, t)\, r(x', x''),$$

where ξ is a point on the segment $x'x''$. Whence

$$|F(x'', y) - F(x', y)| \leqslant \text{const} \frac{r(x', x'')}{r^2(\xi, y)},$$

but since

$$r(\xi, y) \geqslant l_y(x', x''),$$

we have

$$|F(x'', y) - F(x', y)| \leqslant \text{const} \frac{r(x', x'')}{l_y^2(x', x'')}.$$

In view of (*) this also means

$$F(x, y) \in N_*^{(2, 1)}.$$

As to the functions

$$F_{ik}(x, y) = \frac{\partial^2}{\partial x_i \partial x_k} \frac{1}{r(x, y)} = \frac{3(x_i - y_i)(x_k - y_k)}{r^5(x, y)} - \frac{\delta_{ik}}{r^3(x, y)}$$

we have

$$F_{ik}(x, y) \in N^{(0)} \qquad (i, k = 1, 2, 3);$$

applying now to $F_k(x, y)$ the same argument used above for $F(x, y)$, we obtain

$$F_k(x, y) \in N^{(1, 1)}$$

and, owing to the symmetry with respect to x and y,

$$F_k(x, y) \in N_*^{(1, 1)}.$$

From Theorem 1 now follows /24/.

Corollary. *If $f(x, y)$ is of class $H(\lambda)$ with respect to x, then*

$$F(x, y) = \frac{f(x, y)}{r^{3-\alpha}(x, y)}$$

is of class $N^{(\alpha, \mu)}$, $\mu = \min(\alpha, \lambda)$.

Concerning integrals over the surface S of the form

$$\int_S \varphi(y) F(x, y)\, dS_y,$$

where $\varphi(y)$ is of Hölder's class, and $F(x, y) \in N^{(\alpha)}$ we shall say, if $\alpha > 1$, that the kernel $F(x, y)$ has a removable singularity, and if $\alpha = 1$ that it is singular.

§ 3. Theorems of Giraud

In this section we will cite a few of Giraud's theorems to which we shall have recourse later on.

Theorem 2. *If $F_1(x, y)$ and $F_2(x, y)$ are kernels with removable singularities of classes $N^{(\alpha, \lambda)}$ and $N^{(\beta)}$ respectively, then*

$$F_3(x, y) = \int_S F_1(x, \xi) F_2(\xi, y)\, dS_\xi$$

is of class $N^{(\alpha+\beta-1, \mu)}$, where μ is positive, does not exceed λ, and is smaller than $(\alpha - 1)$ if $\alpha + \beta \leqslant 4$; but if $\alpha + \beta > 4$ and $\beta \leqslant 3$, $F_3(x, y)$ is of class $H(\mu)$ with respect to x, and $\mu \leqslant \lambda$, $\mu \leqslant \alpha + \beta - 4$.

Theorem 3. *If $F(x, y)$ is a kernel with removable singularity of class $N^{(\alpha, \lambda)}$, and $\varphi(x)$ is a continuous function, then*

$$\int_S F(x, y) \varphi(y)\, dS_y$$

is of class $H(\mu)$, $\mu < (\alpha - 1)$, $\mu \leqslant \lambda$.

Theorem 4. *If* $F(x, y) = F_1(x, y) + F_2(x, y)$, *and*

(a) $F_2(x, y) \in N^{(\alpha, \lambda)}$, $\alpha > 1$,

(b) $F_1(x, y) = f(x_1 - y_1, x_2 - y_2, x_3 - y_3; \nu(x))$, $\nu(x) \in H(\lambda)$, $0 < \lambda \leqslant 1$;

(c) $f(\omega_1, \omega_2, \omega_3; \nu)$ *and* $\frac{\partial f}{\partial \nu}$ *are positive-definite homogeneous quadratic forms in* $\omega_1, \omega_2, \omega_3$,

(d) $\frac{\partial f}{\partial \omega_i}$ $(i = 1, 2, 3)$ *are positive-definite homogeneous cubic forms in* $\omega_1, \omega_2, \omega_3$,

(e) *the following integral possesses a principal value:*

$$\int_S F_1(x, y)\, dS_y,$$

(f) $\varphi(x) \in H(\mu)$, $\mu \leqslant \lambda$, $\mu < \alpha$,

then the function defined by

$$D(x) = \int_S F(x, y)\, \varphi(y)\, dS_y,$$

is of Hölder's class with exponent μ.

Theorem 5. *If* $F(x, y)$ *is a function as in Theorem 4, and*

(a) $H(x, y) \in N_*^{(\alpha, \lambda)}$, $\alpha > 1$,

(b) $\varphi(x) \in H(\mu)$,

then

$$\int_S H(x, y)\, dS_y \int_S F(y, \xi)\, \varphi(\xi)\, dS_\xi = \int_S \varphi(\xi)\, dS_\xi \int_S H(x, y)\, F(y, \xi)\, dS_y$$

and the function

$$L(x, y) = \int_S H(x, \xi)\, F(\xi, y)\, dS_\xi$$

is of class $N^{(\alpha', \lambda')}$, $\alpha' > 1$.

Theorem 6. *If* $F(x, y)$ *is a function as in Theorem 4, and*

(a) $H(x, y) \in N^{(\alpha, \lambda)}$, $\alpha > 1$,

(b) $\varphi(x)$ *is continuous,*

then

$$\int_S F(x, y)\, dS_y \int_S H(y, \xi)\, \varphi(\xi)\, dS_\xi = \int_S \varphi(\xi)\, dS_\xi \int_S F(x, y)\, H(y, \xi)\, dS_y$$

and the function

$$L'(x, y) = \int_S F(x, \xi)\, H(\xi, y)\, dS_\xi$$

is of class $N^{(\alpha'', \lambda'')}$, $\alpha'' > 1$.

Theorem 7. *If* $F(x, y) = F_1(x, y) + F_2(x, y)$ *and* $H(x, y) = H\ (x, y) + H_2(x, y)$, *and*

(a) $F_1(x, y)$ *is as in Theorem 4,*

(b) $F_2(x, y) \in N_*^{(\alpha, \lambda)}$, $\alpha > 1$,

(c) $H_1(x, y)$ *is analogous to* $F_1(x, y)$,

(d) $H_2(x, y) \in N^{(\alpha, \lambda)}$, $\alpha > 1$,

(e) the principal value of the integral $\int\limits_S H_1(x, y)\, dS_y$ *exists, then the function defined by the integral*

$$\int\limits_S F(x, \xi) H(\xi, y)\, dS_\xi,$$

is of class $N^{(1)}$.

Theorem 8. *If* $F(x, y)$ *and* $H(x, y)$ *satisfy the conditions of Theorem 7, and if the following integral possesses a principal value:*

$$\int\limits_S L(x, y)\, dS_y,$$

where

$$L(x, y) = \int\limits_S F(x, \xi) H(\xi, y)\, dS_\xi,$$

then

$$\int\limits_S F(x, y)\, dS_y \int\limits_S H(y, \xi) \varphi(\xi)\, dS_\xi = -\Phi(x) \varphi(x) + \int\limits_S L(x, \xi) \varphi(\xi)\, dS_\xi$$

where

$$\Phi(x) = \lim_{\varepsilon \to 0} \int\limits_S \int\limits_{S(x;\, \varepsilon)} F(x, \xi) H(\xi, y)\, dS_\xi\, dS_y.$$

The proofs of these theorems are to be found in Giraud's paper /10a/.

Giraud's arguments are occasionally very concise. More general theorems, from which Giraud's theorems follow as corollaries, have been recently proved by T. Gegeliya /5a, b, c, d/.

§ 4. Transformation to local coordinates

In this section we return to the equations of Ch. II (D_i), (T_a), (D_a), (T_i) and consider the transformation of their kernels.

According to (1.52) the matrix

$$K(x, y) = \frac{1}{2\pi} \mathrm{T}_x \overset{0}{\Gamma}(x, y) + \frac{1}{2\pi} \mathrm{T}_x \left[\Gamma(x, y) - \overset{0}{\Gamma}(x, y)\right]$$

has elements of the form

$$(K(x, y))_{jk} = \frac{\mu}{2\pi(\lambda + 2\mu)} \left[\cos(\boldsymbol{n}_x, \boldsymbol{x}_k) \frac{\partial}{\partial x_j} \frac{1}{r(x, y)} - \cos(\boldsymbol{n}_x, \boldsymbol{x}_j) \frac{\partial}{\partial x_k} \frac{1}{r}\right] +$$
$$+ \frac{1}{2\pi(\lambda + 2\mu)} \left[\mu \delta_{jk} + 3(\lambda + \mu) \frac{\partial r}{\partial x_j} \frac{\partial r}{\partial x_k}\right] \frac{\partial}{\partial n_x} \frac{1}{r(x, y)} +$$
$$+ \frac{1}{2\pi} (\mathrm{T}_x \Omega(x, y))_{jk} \qquad (j, k = 1, 2, 3),$$

where $(\mathrm{T}_x \Omega(x, y))_{jk}$ are the elements of the matrix

$$\mathrm{T}_x \left[\Gamma(x, y) - \overset{0}{\Gamma}(x, y)\right],$$

which has a removable singularity at $x = y$.

Let us set

$$K(x, y) = K_1(x, y) + K_2(x, y),$$

where

$$K_1(x, y) = \frac{\mu}{2\pi(\lambda+2\mu)} \cdot \frac{1}{r^3(x, y)} \begin{Vmatrix} 0 & \sigma_{12} & \sigma_{13} \\ -\sigma_{12} & 0 & \sigma_{23} \\ -\sigma_{13} & -\sigma_{23} & 0 \end{Vmatrix}, \tag{5.6}$$

$$\sigma_{12} = (x_1 - y_1)\cos(n_x, x_2) - (x_2 - y_2)\cos(n_x, x_1),$$
$$\sigma_{13} = (x_1 - y_1)\cos(n_x, x_3) - (x_3 - y_3)\cos(n_x, x_1),$$
$$\sigma_{23} = (x_2 - y_2)\cos(n_x, x_3) - (x_3 - y_3)\cos(n_x, x_2)$$

and

$$K_2(x, y) = \frac{1}{2\pi(\lambda+2\mu)} \left\| \left[\mu\delta_{jk} + 3(\lambda+\mu)\frac{\partial r}{\partial x_j}\frac{\partial r}{\partial x_k}\right] \frac{\partial}{\partial n_x}\frac{1}{r(x, y)} \right\| + \frac{1}{2\pi} T_x \Omega(x, y). \tag{5.7}$$

On account of Theorem 1 of § 2

$$K_1(x, y) \in N^{(1, 1)}_* \text{ and } K_2(x, y) \in N^{(\alpha')}, \quad \alpha' > 1.$$

The singular integral which appears in the singular equations under study is of the form

$$\int_S K_1(x, y)\varphi(y)\,dS_y, \quad \varphi(y) \in H(\gamma), \quad 0 \leqslant \gamma < 1.$$

and will now be rewritten by means of the characteristic (cf. § 1) as

$$\int_S \frac{f(x; \theta)}{r^2(x, y)}\varphi(y)\,dS_y + \int_S \frac{r^2(x, y)K_1(x, y) - f(x; \theta)}{r^2(x, y)}\varphi(y)\,dS_y,$$

where θ is the dihedral angle between some fixed plane and the plane through n_x and y. The first operator in the last expression is singular, and the necessary and sufficient condition for its existence

$$\int_0^{2\pi} f(x; \theta)\,d\theta = 0$$

is satisfied, as one may easily verify. The second is a Fredholm operator (or F. O. for short).

Let the surface S be completely covered by a finite number of regions $S_1, S_2, \ldots, S_m$, which may each partly overlap with those next to it. They may for instance be taken as the neighborhoods $S(x^0; \varepsilon)$, $0 < \varepsilon < \varepsilon_0$ (cf. § 1) of a set of points x^0 on S, ε being the radius of the cylinder $C(x^0; \varepsilon)$ with its axis along n_{x^0}. Let the points x and y lie in one of these regions, say S_1; we will now derive an expression for the kernel $K(x, y)$ in the coordinate system ξ_1, ξ_2, ξ_3 with origin at $x^0 \in S_1$ and the ξ_3-axis pointing along n_{x^0}. Let ξ and η be the projections of x and y on the tangent plane (at point x^0), while ξ_1, ξ_2, ξ_3 and η_1, η_2, η_3 are their coordinates in the local system. According to the transformation formulas

$$x_i - y_i = a_{1i}(x^0)(\xi_1 - \eta_1) + a_{2i}(x^0)(\xi_2 - \eta_2) + a_{3i}(x^0)(\xi_3 - \eta_3) \quad (i = 1, 2, 3),$$

where $a_{ij}(x^0)$, $i, j = 1, 2, 3$ are the direction cosines of the old axes (x_i) relative to the new axes (ξ_i), which depend on the position of x^0 and satisfy the orthonormality conditions

$$\sum_{s=1}^{3} a_{si}a_{sj} = \delta_{ij} = \begin{cases} 1, & i = j, \\ 0, & i \neq j. \end{cases}$$

In the new coordinates

$$\sigma_{12} = \sum_{k=1}^{3} [(a_{k1}\cos(n_x, x_2) - a_{k2}\cos(n_x, x_1)](\xi_k - \eta_k), \tag{5.8}$$

$$\left.\begin{aligned}\sigma_{13} &= \sum_{k=1}^{3} [(a_{k1}\cos(n_x, x_3) - a_{k3}\cos(n_x, x_1)](\xi_k - \eta_k),\\ \sigma_{23} &= \sum_{k=1}^{3} [(a_{k2}\cos(n_x, x_3) - a_{k3}\cos(n_x, x_2)](\xi_k - \eta_k).\end{aligned}\right\} \tag{5.8}$$

Introducing the notation

$$\left.\begin{aligned}A_1(x) &= a_{11}(x^0)\cos(n_x, x_2) - a_{12}(x^0)\cos(n_x, x_1),\\ A_2(x) &= a_{21}(x^0)\cos(n_x, x_2) - a_{22}(x^0)\cos(n_x, x_1),\\ A(x) &= a_{31}(x^0)\cos(n_x, x_2) - a_{32}(x^0)\cos(n_x, x_1),\\ A_3(x) &= a_{11}(x^0)\cos(n_x, x_3) - a_{13}(x^0)\cos(n_x, x_1),\\ A_4(x) &= a_{21}(x^0)\cos(n_x, x_3) - a_{23}(x^0)\cos(n_x, x_1),\\ B(x) &= a_{31}(x^0)\cos(n_x, x_3) - a_{33}(x^0)\cos(n_x, x_1),\\ A_5(x) &= a_{12}(x^0)\cos(n_x, x_3) - a_{13}(x^0)\cos(n_x, x_2),\\ A_6(x) &= a_{22}(x^0)\cos(n_x, x_3) - a_{23}(x^0)\cos(n_x, x_2),\\ C(x) &= a_{32}(x^0)\cos(n_x, x_3) - a_{33}(x^0)\cos(n_x, x_2),\end{aligned}\right\} \tag{5.9}$$

and in particular for $x = x^0$

$$\begin{aligned}A_1(x^0) &= a_{11}(x^0)\,a_{32}(x^0) - a_{12}(x^0)\,a_{31}(x^0);\\ A_2(x^0) &= a_{21}(x^0)\,a_{32}(x^0) - a_{22}(x^0)\,a_{31}(x^0);\\ A_3(x^0) &= a_{11}(x^0)\,a_{33}(x^0) - a_{13}(x^0)\,a_{31}(x^0);\\ A_4(x^0) &= a_{21}(x^0)\,a_{33}(x^0) - a_{23}(x^0)\,a_{31}(x^0);\\ A_5(x^0) &= a_{12}(x^0)\,a_{33}(x^0) - a_{13}(x^0)\,a_{32}(x^0);\\ A_6(x^0) &= a_{22}(x^0)\,a_{33}(x^0) - a_{23}(x^0)\,a_{32}(x^0);\\ A(x^0) &= B(x^0) = C(x^0) = 0,\end{aligned}$$

and writing

$$\rho(\xi, \eta) = \sqrt{(\xi_1 - \eta_1)^2 + (\xi_2 - \eta_2)^2}, \qquad r(x, y) = \sqrt{\rho^2 + (\xi_3 - \eta_3)^2},$$

$$l = \frac{\mu}{2\pi(\lambda + 2\mu)},$$

we find that the kernel $K_1(x, y)$ may be written in the form

$$\frac{l}{\rho^2(\xi, \eta)}\frac{\rho^2}{r^2}\begin{Vmatrix} 0 & A^* & A^{**}\\ -A^* & 0 & A^{***}\\ -A^{**} & -A^{***} & 0\end{Vmatrix},$$

where

$$\begin{aligned}A^* &= \frac{\rho}{r}\left[A_1(x)\frac{\xi_1 - \eta_1}{\rho} + A_2(x)\frac{\xi_2 - \eta_2}{\rho} + A(x)\frac{\xi_3 - \eta_3}{\rho}\right],\\ A^{**} &= \frac{\rho}{r}\left[A_3(x)\frac{\xi_1 - \eta_1}{\rho} + A_4(x)\frac{\xi_2 - \eta_2}{\rho} + B(x)\frac{\xi_3 - \eta_3}{\rho}\right],\\ A^{***} &= \frac{\rho}{r}\left[A_5(x)\frac{\xi_1 - \eta_1}{\rho} + A_6(x)\frac{\xi_2 - \eta_2}{\rho} + C(x)\frac{\xi_3 - \eta_3}{\rho}\right].\end{aligned}$$

It can be shown that (cf. p. 87)

$$\lim_{\eta \to \xi}\frac{\rho^2}{r^2} = \frac{1}{1 + [p(\xi)\cos\theta_1 + q(\xi)\sin\theta_1]^2},$$

where

$$\frac{\xi_1 - \eta_1}{\rho} = \cos\theta_1, \qquad \frac{\xi_2 - \eta_2}{\rho} = \sin\theta_1.$$

But $p(\xi)$ and $q(\xi)$ may be made as small as desired together with ε_0; therefore

$$\frac{\rho^2}{r^2} = 1 + \mu_{\varepsilon_0}(\xi, \eta), \qquad \frac{\rho}{r} = 1 + \lambda_{\varepsilon_0}(\xi, \eta),$$

where $\mu_{\varepsilon_0}(\xi, \eta)$ and $\lambda_{\varepsilon_0}(\varepsilon, \eta)$ are well-defined functions which tend to zero with ε_0. Consequently we have

$$K_1(x, y) = \frac{l(1+\mu_{\varepsilon_0})(1+\lambda_{\varepsilon_0})}{\rho^2(\xi, \eta)} \times$$
$$\times \begin{Vmatrix} 0 & A_1(x)\cos\theta_1 + A_2(x)\sin\theta_1 & A_3(x)\cos\theta_1 + A_4(x)\sin\theta_1 \\ -[A_1(x)\cos\theta_1 + A_2(x)\sin\theta_1] & 0 & A_5(x)\cos\theta_1 + A_6(x)\sin\theta_1 \\ -[A_3(x)\cos\theta_1 + A_4(x)\sin\theta_1] & -[A_5(x)\cos\theta_1 + A_6(x)\sin\theta_1] & 0 \end{Vmatrix} +$$
$$+ \frac{l}{\rho^2}\cdot\frac{\rho^3}{r^3}\begin{Vmatrix} 0 & A(x)\frac{\xi_3-\eta_3}{\rho} & B(x)\frac{\xi_3-\eta_3}{\rho} \\ -A(x)\frac{\xi_3-\eta_3}{\rho} & 0 & C(x)\frac{\xi_3-\eta_3}{\rho} \\ -B(x)\frac{\xi_3-\eta_3}{\rho} & -C(x)\frac{\xi_3-\eta_3}{\rho} & 0 \end{Vmatrix},$$

where $A(x)$, $B(x)$, $C(x)$ tend to zero with ε_0. Then, writing

$$f_1'(x;\theta_1) = l\begin{Vmatrix} 0 & A_1(x)\cos\theta_1 + A_2(x)\sin\theta_1 & A_3(x)\cos\theta_1 + A_4(x)\sin\theta_1 \\ -[A_1(x)\cos\theta_1 + A_2(x)\sin\theta_1] & 0 & A_5(x)\cos\theta_1 + A_6(x)\sin\theta_1 \\ -[A_3(x)\cos\theta_1 + A_4(x)\sin\theta_1] & -[A_5(x)\cos\theta_1 + A_6(x)\sin\theta_1] & 0 \end{Vmatrix} \quad (5.10)$$

and in view of the above remarks concerning μ_{ε_0} and λ_{ε_0}, we finally obtain

$$K_1(x, y) = \frac{f_1'(x;\theta_1)}{\rho^2(\xi, \eta)} + \frac{f^*(x;\theta_1)}{\rho^2(\xi, \eta)}, \quad (5.11)$$

where $f^*(x; \theta_1)$ is a well-defined matrix, whose modulus may be made as small as desired by decreasing ε_0.

If we write

$$f_1(\xi;\theta_1) = f_1'(x;\theta_1) + f^*(x;\theta_1),$$

then

$$f_1(\xi;\theta_1) = f(x;\theta). \quad (5.11')$$

§ 5. The regularization problem

We shall now be concerned with the investigation of equation (2.13), corresponding to problems (T_i) and (T_a). Other equations may be treated analogously. We write equation (2.13) in the form

$$\varphi(x) - \varkappa\int_S K(x, y)\varphi(y)\,dS_y = f(x) \quad (5.12)$$

which in operator form becomes

$$(I - \varkappa K)\varphi = f, \quad (5.12')$$

where I is the identity operator, and K the operator defined in § 4.

Upon setting $\varkappa = -1$ equation (5.12) reduces to (T_i) (II, 2).

The problem of regularizing the system of equations (5.12) is now stated as follows. It is required to find an integral operator

$$H\varphi = \int_S H(x, y; \varkappa)\varphi(y)\,dS_y$$

whose singular kernel $H(x, y; \varkappa)$ depends, beside the points x and y, on the parameter $\varkappa$, such that the transformed equations

$$(I+\varkappa H)(I-\varkappa K)\varphi=(I+\varkappa H)f$$

will be Fredholm equations of the second kind.

If such an operator exists then, since by Theorem 8 of § 4

$$-\varkappa^2 HK\varphi=-\varkappa^2\int_S H(x,\ y;\ \varkappa)\,dS_y\int_S K(y,\ \xi)\,\varphi(\xi)\,dS_\xi=$$

$$=+\varkappa^2\Phi(x;\ \varkappa)\,\varphi(x)-\varkappa^2\int_S\int_S H(x,\ y;\ \varkappa)\,K(y,\ \xi)\,\varphi(\xi)\,dS_y\,dS_\xi,$$

we obtain

$$[I+\varkappa^2\Phi(x;\ \varkappa)]\,\varphi(x)+\varkappa\int_S\Big[H(x,\ y;\ \varkappa)-K(x,\ y)-$$

$$-\varkappa\int_S H(x,\ \xi;\ \varkappa)\,K(\xi,\ y)\,dS_\xi\Big]\varphi(y)\,dS_y=If(x)+\varkappa\int_S H(x,\ y;\ \varkappa)\,f(y)\,dS_y$$

or

$$[I+\varkappa^2\Phi(x;\ \varkappa)]\,\varphi(x)+\varkappa\int_S F(x,\ y;\ \varkappa)\,\varphi(y)\,dS_y=X(x), \tag{5.13}$$

where

$$\left.\begin{aligned} F(x,y;\varkappa)&=H(x,y;\varkappa)-K(x,y)-\varkappa\int_S H(x,\ \xi;\ \varkappa)\,K(\xi,\ y)\,dS_\xi,\\ X(x)&=If(x)+\varkappa\int_S H(x,\ y;\ \varkappa)\,f(y)\,dS_y \end{aligned}\right\} \tag{5.14}$$

and $\Phi(x;\ \varkappa)$ is the matrix introduced in § 3 (Theorem 8).

For the system (5.13) to consist of Fredholm equations, it is sufficient that

1°. $F(x,\ y;\ \varkappa)=O\,[r^{-2+\delta'}(x,\ y)],\ \delta'>0,$

2°. $\det\|(I+\varkappa^2\Phi(x;\ \varkappa)\|\neq 0,\ x\in S.$

We stipulate that the matrix $H(x,\ y;\ \varkappa)$ be of the form

$$H(x,\ y;\ \varkappa)=\frac{1}{\rho^2(\xi,\ \eta)}\,\Omega(x,\ \theta;\ \varkappa)+O\,(\rho^{\delta'-2}(\xi,\ \eta)),$$

where the matrix $\Omega(x,\ \theta;\ \varkappa)=\|\omega_{ik}(x,\ \theta;\ \varkappa)\|,\ i,\ k=1,\ 2,\ 3$ and the unknown functions $\omega_{ik}(x,\ \theta;\ \varkappa)$ satisfy the conditions

$$\int_0^{2\pi}\omega_{ik}(x,\ \theta;\ \varkappa)\,d\theta=0\qquad(i,\ k=1,\ 2,\ 3). \tag{5.15}$$

These conditions, by (5.5), are necessary and sufficient for the existence of a singular integral with its kernel equal to $H(x,\ y;\ \varkappa)$.

Let us rewrite the left-hand side of (5.13) in the form

$$[I+\varkappa^2\Phi(x;\ \varkappa)]\,\varphi(x)+\varkappa\int_{S(x^0;\ \varepsilon_0)}\Big[H(x,\ y;\ \varkappa)-K(x,\ y)-$$

$$-\varkappa\int_{S(x^0;\ \varepsilon_0)}H(x,\xi;\varkappa)\,K(\xi,\ y)\,dS_\xi-\varkappa\int_{S'(x^0;\ \varepsilon_0)}H(x,\xi;\varkappa)\,K(\xi,\ y)\,dS_\xi\Big]\times$$

$$\times\varphi(y)\,dS_y+\varkappa\int_{S'(x^0;\ \varepsilon_0)}\Big[H(x,\ y,\ \varkappa)-K(x,\ y)-\varkappa\int_{S'(x^0;\ \varepsilon_0)}H(x,\xi;\varkappa)\times$$

$$\times K(\xi,\ y)\,dS_\xi-\varkappa\int_{S(x^0;\ \varepsilon_0)}H(x,\ \xi;\ \varkappa)\,K(\xi,\ y)\,dS_\xi\Big]\varphi(y)\,dS_y$$

and investigate various compositions of the integrals occurring here for

$x \in S(x^0; \varepsilon)$ $(0 < \varepsilon < \varepsilon_0)$. The integrals

$$\int\limits_{S(x^0;\, \varepsilon_0)} H(x, y; \varkappa)\varphi(y)\, dS_y, \qquad \int\limits_{S(x^0;\, \varepsilon_0)} K(x, y)\varphi(y)\, dS_y,$$

evidently represent singular operators. Next, consider the integrals

$$\int\limits_{S(x^0;\, \varepsilon_0)} \int\limits_{S(x^0;\, \varepsilon_0)} H(x, \xi; \varkappa) K(\xi, y)\varphi(y)\, dS_\xi dS_y;$$

$$\int\limits_{S'(x^0;\, \varepsilon_0)} \int\limits_{S(x^0;\, \varepsilon_0)} H(x, \xi; \varkappa) K(\xi, y)\varphi(y)\, dS_\xi dS_y.$$

The internal integral in the first, being by Theorem 7* of § 3 of the order of $O[r^{-2}(x, y)]$, is a singular operator. The second operator, in view of Theorem 4, turns out to be a Fredholm operator (FO), since the integrand is of the order of $O(r^{-2+\delta}(x, y))$. Finally, the integrals

$$\int\limits_{S(x^0;\, \varepsilon_0)} \left(\int\limits_{S'(x^0;\, \varepsilon_0)} H(x, \xi; \varkappa) K(\xi, y)\, dS_\xi \right) \varphi(y)\, dS_y,$$

$$\int\limits_{S'(x^0;\, \varepsilon_0)} \left(\int\limits_{S'(x^0;\, \varepsilon_0)} H(x, \xi; \varkappa) K(\xi, y)\, dS_\xi \right) \varphi(y)\, dS_y,$$

also represent Fredholm operators.

It is clear from the preceding that (5.13) may be written in the form

$$[I + \varkappa^2 \Phi(x; \varkappa)]\varphi(x) + \varkappa \int\limits_{S(x^0;\, \varepsilon_0)} \Bigg[H(x, y; \varkappa) - K(x, y) - \\ - \varkappa \int\limits_{S(x^0;\, \varepsilon_0)} H(x, \xi; \varkappa) K(\xi, y)\, dS_\xi \Bigg] \varphi(y)\, dS_y + \mathrm{FO} = X(x), \tag{5.16}$$

where FO stands for a Fredholm operator in the above sense. We represent the left-hand side of this equation as a composition of operators

$$L^{(1)}_{\varepsilon_0}\varphi \equiv \varphi(x) - \varkappa \int\limits_{S(x^0;\, \varepsilon_0)} K(x, y)\varphi(y)\, dS_y + \mathrm{FO},$$

$$L^{(2)}_{\varepsilon_0}\varphi \equiv \varphi(x) + \varkappa \int\limits_{S(x^0;\, \varepsilon_0)} H(x, y; \varkappa)\varphi(y)\, dS_y + \mathrm{FO}.$$

Since here $x \in S(x^0; \varepsilon)$, $y \in S(x^0; \varepsilon_0)$, $\varepsilon < \varepsilon_0$, one may still use for the representation of the left-hand side of (5.16) the composition of the operators

$$L^{(1)}_{\varepsilon}\varphi \equiv \varphi(x) - \varkappa \int\limits_{S(x^0;\, \varepsilon)} K(x, y)\varphi(y)\, dS_y + \mathrm{FO}, \tag{5.17$_1$}$$

$$L^{(2)}_{\varepsilon}\varphi \equiv \varphi(x) + \varkappa \int\limits_{S(x^0;\, \varepsilon)} H(x, y; \varkappa)\varphi(y)\, dS_y + \mathrm{FO}, \tag{5.17$_2$}$$

where x and y vary within the domain $S(x^0; \varepsilon) \equiv S_0$. We project S_0 orthogonally upon the circular disk γ: $\xi_1^2 + \xi_2^2 < a$; the projections of x and y will be denoted by ξ and η, respectively, and the projection of $r(x, y)$ by $\rho(\xi, \eta)$. Writing

$$K'(\xi, \eta) = \sqrt{1 + p^2(\eta) + q^2(\eta)}\, K(x, y) \quad \text{and} \quad \varphi'(\xi) = \varphi(x), \tag{5.18}$$

the operator $L^{(1)}_{\varepsilon}\varphi$ becomes

$$L^{(1)}_{\varepsilon}\varphi = \varphi'(\xi) - \varkappa \overset{*}{\int\limits_{\gamma}} K'(\xi, \eta)\varphi'(\eta)\, d\eta_1\, d\eta_2 + \mathrm{FO},$$

* That the functions $\omega_{ik}(x, \theta, \varkappa)$ actually admit the application of Theorems 7 and 8 will be shown in § 7.

where the starred integral, which equals

$$\int_{S_0} K(x, y)\varphi(y)\,dS_y,$$

should be understood in the following sense: the projection which maps S_0 onto γ transforms a circle of sufficiently small radius $\nu_1 < \varepsilon$, lying in the tangent plane at x and centered there, into the ellipse

$$\rho_1 = \rho_1(\theta_1; \nu_1) = \frac{\nu_1}{\sqrt{1+[p(\xi)\cos\theta_1 + q(\xi)\sin\theta_1]^2}}, \tag{5.19}$$

where the angle θ_1 at $\xi(\xi_1, \xi_2)$ is reckoned counterclockwise from the straight line $\xi_2 = \text{const.}$ Hence

$$\overset{*}{\int_{\gamma}} K'(\xi, \eta)\varphi'(\eta)\,d\eta_1\,d\eta_2 = \lim_{\nu_1\to 0} \int_{\gamma - e(\xi;\nu_1)} K'(\xi, \varphi)\varphi'(\eta)\,d\eta_1\,d\eta_2,$$

where $e(\xi; \nu_1)$ is the interior of the ellipse $\rho_1 = \rho_1(\theta_1; \nu_1)$. Let us write the last equality in the form

$$\overset{*}{\int} \ldots = \lim_{\nu_1\to 0}\left\{ \int_{\gamma-\gamma_1} \ldots + \int_{\gamma_1 - e(\xi;\nu_1)} \right\}, \tag{5.20}$$

where γ_1 is a circular disk of radius ν_1 centered at ξ. On account of (5.18) and (5.10)–(5.11') we have

$$J = \lim_{\nu_1\to 0} \int_{\gamma_1 - e(\xi;\nu_1)} K'(\xi, \eta)\varphi'(\eta)\,d\eta_1\,d\eta_2 =$$

$$= \lim_{\nu_1\to 0} \int_0^{2\pi} d\theta_1 \int_{\rho_1(\xi;\nu_1)}^{\nu_1} K'(\xi, \eta)\varphi'(\eta)\rho(\xi, \eta)\,d\rho =$$

$$= \lim_{\nu_1\to 0} \int_0^{2\pi} d\theta_1 \int_{\rho_1}^{\nu_1} \sqrt{1+p^2(\eta)+q^2(\eta)}\,K(x, y)\varphi'(\eta)\rho\,d\rho =$$

$$= \lim_{\nu_1\to 0} \int_0^{2\pi} d\theta_1 \int_{\rho_1}^{\nu_1} \frac{f_1(\xi; \theta_1)}{\rho^2(\xi, \eta)} \sqrt{1+p^2(\eta)+q^2(\eta)}\,\varphi'(\eta)\rho\,d\rho,$$

where

$$f_1(\xi; \theta_1) \equiv f(x; \theta). \tag{5.21}$$

Seeing that

$$\sqrt{1+p^2(\eta)+q^2(\eta)}\,\varphi'(\eta) \in H(\alpha') \qquad (0 < \alpha' \leqslant 1),$$

we may write

$$J = \varphi'(\xi)\sqrt{1+p^2(\xi)+q^2(\xi)} \int_0^{2\pi} f_1(\xi; \theta_1) \times$$
$$\times \log\sqrt{1+[p(\xi)\cos\theta_1 + q(\xi)\sin\theta_1]^2}\,d\theta_1. \tag{5.22}$$

By (5.20), it now follows that the limit

$$\lim_{\nu_1\to 0} \int_{\gamma-\gamma_1} K'(\xi, \eta)\varphi'(\eta)\,d\eta_1\,d\eta_2 = \int_{\gamma} K'(\xi, \eta)\varphi'(\eta)\,d\eta_1\,d\eta_2,$$

exists, where the integral on the right-hand side should be understood in the sense of the Cauchy principal value. Therefore, in view of (5.19)–(5.22),

2109

the operator $L_s^{(1)} f$ may be rewritten as

$$L_s^{(1)}\varphi \equiv a'(\xi)\varphi'(\xi) - \varkappa \int_\gamma K'(\xi, \eta)\varphi'(\eta)\, d\eta_1\, d\eta_2 + \mathrm{FO}, \tag{5.23}$$

where

$$a'(\xi) = I + \sqrt{1 + p^2(\xi) + q^2(\xi)} \int_0^{2\pi} f_1(\xi;\ \theta_1) \times$$
$$\times \log \sqrt{1 + [p(\xi)\cos\theta_1 + q(\xi)\sin\theta_1]^2}\, d\theta_1. \tag{5.24}$$

By choosing a sufficiently small diameter for the domain S_0, $p(\xi)$ and $q(\xi)$ can be made as small as desired, so that $a'(\xi)$ will only slightly differ from the identity operator I.

Let us now derive the characteristic of the singular integral in (5.23). By (5.18)

$$\lim_{\eta \to \xi} \{\rho^2(\xi, \eta) K'(\xi, \eta)\} = \lim_{y \to x} \left\{ \sqrt{1 + p^2(\eta) + q^2(\eta)}\, \frac{\rho^2(\xi, \eta)}{r^2(x, y)} f_1(\xi;\ \theta_1) \right\}.$$

The ratio

$$\frac{\rho^2(\xi, \eta)}{r^2(x, y)}$$

equals in the limit the ratio of the first ground forms of the plane and the surface S_0 at x; this gives /9/

$$\lim_{\eta \to \xi} \frac{\rho^2}{r^2} = \frac{1}{1 + [p(\xi)\cos\theta_1 + q(\xi)\sin\theta_1]^2}.$$

Hence the required characteristic is of the form

$$f_2(\xi;\ \theta_1) = f_1(\xi;\ \theta_1) \frac{\sqrt{1 + p^2(\xi) + q^2(\xi)}}{1 + [p(\xi)\cos\theta_1 + q(\xi)\sin\theta_1]^2}, \tag{5.25}$$

the angles θ and θ_1 being related by

$$\frac{d\theta}{d\theta_1} = \frac{\sqrt{1 + p^2(\xi) + q^2(\xi)}}{1 + [p(\xi)\cos\theta_1 + q(\xi)\sin\theta_1]^2}.$$

This relation affords a check on our necessary and sufficient condition for the existence of the singular integral in (5.23). Indeed we find

$$\int_0^{2\pi} f_2(\xi;\ \theta_1)\, d\theta_1 = \int_0^{2\pi} f_1(\xi;\ \theta_1) \frac{\sqrt{1 + p^2(\xi) + q^2(\xi)}}{1 + [p(\xi)\cos\theta_1 + q(\xi)\sin\theta_1]^2}\, d\theta_1 =$$
$$= \int_0^{2\pi} f_1(\xi;\ \theta_1)\, d\theta = \int_0^{2\pi} f(x;\ \theta)\, d\theta = 0. \tag{5.25'}$$

We now map the disk γ onto the infinite Euclidean plane Π by means of the transformation

$$u_1 = \frac{a\xi_1}{\sqrt{a^2 - \xi_1^2 - \xi_2^2}}, \qquad u_2 = \frac{a\xi_2}{\sqrt{a^2 - \xi_1^2 - \xi_2^2}},$$

whose Jacobian is

$$\frac{\partial(\xi_1, \xi_2)}{\partial(u_1, u_2)} = \frac{a^4}{(a^2 + u_1^2 + u_2^2)^2}.$$

The points $\xi(\xi_1, \xi_2)$ and $\eta(\eta_1, \eta_2)$ are carried over to $u(u_1, u_2)$ and $v(v_1, v_2)$ respectively. The distance between the points u and v will be denoted by $\rho(u, v)$.

Writing

$$a_1'(u)=a'(\xi),\qquad \varphi''(u)=\varphi'(\xi),\qquad K''(u,\,v)=\frac{a^4K'(\xi,\,\eta)}{(a^2+v_1^2+v_2^2)^2},\tag{5.26}$$

we obtain from (5.23)

$$L_\epsilon^{(1)}\varphi\equiv a_1'(u)\varphi''(u)-\varkappa\int\limits_{\Pi}^{*}K''(u,\,v)\,\varphi''(v)\,dv_1\,dv_2+\text{FO},\tag{5.26'}$$

where the integral over Π, which equals the one in (5.23) taken over γ in the sense of the Cauchy principal value, is to be interpreted as follows. The mapping of γ onto Π transforms a circle around ξ, of sufficiently small radius ν_2 to be contained in γ, into the quartic curve

$$\rho_2=\rho_2(\theta_2;\,\nu_2)=\frac{\nu_2}{\sqrt{A\cos^2\theta_2+2B\cos\theta_2\sin\theta_2+C\sin^2\theta_2}}+O(\nu_2^2),\tag{5.26''}$$

where

$$A=\frac{a^6}{(a^2+u_1^2+u_2^2)\left[(a^2+u_1^2)^2+u_1^2u_2^2\right]},$$

$$B=-\frac{a^4u_1u_2(2a^2+u_1^2+u_2^2)}{(a^2+u_1^2+u_2^2)^2\left[(a^2+u_1^2)^2+u_1^2u_2^2\right]},$$

$$C=\frac{a^2\left\{\left[(a^2+u_1^2)^2+u_1^2u_2^2\right]^2+u_1^2u_2^2(2a^2+u_1^2+u_2^2)\right\}}{(a^2+u_1^2+u_2^2)^3\left[(a^2+u_1^2)^2+u_1^2u_2^2\right]},$$

and where θ_2 denotes the image of the angle θ_1 at $u(u_1,\,u_2)$, reckoned (counterclockwise) from the fixed tangent Λ_0 to the quartic curve, which is the image of the line $\xi_2=\text{const}$. Let θ_0 be the angle between Λ_0 and the u_1-axis, reckoned counterclockwise from the latter. We set $\theta_3=\theta_0+\theta_2$. It may be shown /9/ that the angles θ_1 and θ_2 are related by

$$\frac{d\theta_1}{d\theta_2}=\frac{a^4}{(a^2+u_1^2+u_2^2)^2(A\cos^2\theta_2+2B\cos\theta_2\sin\theta_2+C\sin^2\theta_2)}.\tag{5.27}$$

The integral in (5.26') has the following meaning:

$$\int\limits_{\Pi}^{*}K''(u,\,v)\,\varphi''(v)\,dv_1\,dv_2=\lim_{\nu_2\to 0}\int\limits_{\Pi-D(u;\,\nu_2)}K''(u,\,v)\,\varphi''(v)\,dv_1\,dv_2,$$

where $D(u;\,\nu_2)$ denotes the interior of the curve $\rho_2=\rho_2(\theta_2;\,\nu_2)$. It follows that

$$\int\limits_{\Pi}^{*}=\lim_{\nu_2\to 0}\left[\int\limits_{\Pi-\gamma_1}-\int\limits_{D(u;\,\nu_2)-\gamma_1}\right],\tag{5.27'}$$

where γ_1 is a circular disk of radius ν_2 centered at u. But on account of (5.26) and (5.26")

$$\lim_{\nu_2\to 0}\int\limits_{D(u;\,\nu_2)-\gamma_1}K''(u,\,v)\,\varphi''(v)\,dv_1\,dv_2=$$

$$=\lim_{\nu_2\to 0}\int\limits_0^{2\pi}d\theta_3\int\limits_{\nu_2}^{\rho_2}K''(u,\,v)\,\varphi''(v)\,\rho\,d\rho=-\frac{a^4}{(a^2+u_1^2+u_2^2)^2}\int\limits_0^{2\pi}f_3(u;\,\theta_3)\times$$

$$\times\log\sqrt{A\cos^2\theta_3+2B\cos\theta_3\sin\theta_3+C\sin^2\theta_3}\,d\theta_3,\tag{5.27''}$$

where

$$f_3(u;\,\theta_3)=f_2(\xi;\,\theta_1)\ldots\tag{5.28}$$

In view of (5.27') it is now clear that the limit

$$\lim\int\limits_{\Pi-\gamma_1}=\int\limits_{\Pi},$$

exists, where the integral over Π is understood in the sense of the Cauchy principal value. Therefore, by (5.26)–(5.27'), the operator $L_e^{(1)}\varphi$ may be represented as

$$L_e^{(1)}\varphi \equiv a_2(u)\varphi''(u) - \varkappa \int_{\Pi} K''(u, v)\varphi''(v)\,dv_1\,dv_2 + \mathrm{FO}, \tag{5.29}$$

where

$$a_2(u) = a_1'(u) - \frac{\varkappa a^4}{(a^2+u_1^2+u_2^2)^2} \times$$
$$\times \int_0^{2\pi} f_3(u;\ \theta_3) \times \log \sqrt{A\cos^2\theta_3 + 2B\cos\theta_3\sin\theta_3 + C\sin^2\theta_3}\,d\theta_3.$$

It may easily be verified that $a_2(u)$ only slightly differs from $a_1'(u) = a'(\xi)$, and thus from the unit matrix, because the diameter of the domain S_0 can be made sufficiently small. We will now derive the characteristic of the singular integral in (5.29). We have

$$f_4(u;\ \theta_3) = \lim_{\rho(u,v)\to 0} \rho^2(u, v)K''(u, v) =$$
$$= f_3(u;\ \theta_2)\frac{a^4}{(a^2+u_1^2+u_2^2)^2\left(A\cos^2\theta_2 + 2B\cos\theta_2\sin\theta_2 + C\sin^2\theta_2\right)}. \tag{5.30}$$

The relation (5.27) affords a verification of the necessary and sufficient condition for the existence of the singular integral in (5.29). Actually, (5.30) and (5.25') give

$$\int_0^{2\pi} f_4(u;\ \theta_3)\,d\theta_3 = \int_0^{2\pi} f_4(u;\ \theta_2)\,d\theta_2 =$$
$$= \int_0^{2\pi} f_3(u;\ \theta_3)\,d\theta_1 = \int_0^{2\pi} f_2(\xi;\ \theta_1)\,d\theta_1 = \int_0^{2\pi} f(\xi;\ \theta)\,d\theta = 0. \tag{5.30'}$$

Upon setting

$$a_2(u) = \alpha(u), \qquad \varphi''(u) = \psi(u), \qquad K''(u, v) = \mathscr{L}(u, v),$$

(5. 29) becomes

$$L_e^{(1)}\varphi \equiv \alpha(u)\psi(u) - \varkappa \int_{\Pi} \mathscr{L}(u, v)\psi(v)\,dv_1\,dv_2 + \mathrm{FO}. \tag{5.31}$$

In view of (5.30), (5. 28), (5.25) and (5.21) the characteristic of the singular integral in the last expression is

$$f_4(u;\ \theta_2) = a^4\sqrt{1+p^2(\xi)+q^2(\xi)}\,f_1(\xi;\ \theta_1)\Big\{\{1 + [p(\xi)\cos\theta_1 +$$
$$+ q(\xi)\sin\theta_1]^2\}(a^2+u_1^2+u_2^2)^2(A\cos^2\theta_2 + 2B\cos\theta_2\sin\theta_2 + C\sin^2\theta_2)\Big\}^{-1} \tag{5.32}$$

and by (5.30') it satisfies the condition

$$\int_0^{2\pi} f_4(u;\ \theta_3)\,d\theta_3 = 0,$$

which is thus verified as being necessary and sufficient for the existence of the singular integral in (5.13).

Considering the values of the quantities appearing on the right-hand side of (5.32), we immediately see that $f_4(u;\ \theta_2)$ may be made arbitrarily close to $f_1(\xi;\ \theta_1)$, and $\alpha(u)$ to I, by contracting the domain S_0. This remark will prove to be essential in § 7.

It is by now clear that given a regularizing operator for the singular operator (5.31), one may apply the mapping inverse to that which carries (5. 17_1) into (5.31) so as to obtain an operator which regularizes the former. It may be remarked that instead of actually mapping the disk γ onto the plane Π, the operator (5.23) could also be brought to the form (5.31) by extending all the elements of the operator (5.23) from γ throughout Π, subject to the necessary conditions of continuity and the conditions at infinity. The above mapping is only one of the possible realizations of such continuous extension.

§ 6. Integral operator symbols and their properties

A procedure based on a symbolic calculus of singular integrals has been developed by S. G. Mikhlin for the regularization of operators of type (5.31). Some of Mikhlin's theorems /22a/ will be now presented (with certain modifications). Consider the integral

$$J = \frac{1}{2\pi} \int_{\Pi} \frac{e^{in\theta}}{\rho^2(x, y)} \varphi(y)\, d\sigma_y,$$

where n is an integer, Π the infinite plane in which $x, y, y', \ldots$ points and $d\sigma_x$ an area element at x, θ the angle between the line xy and some fixed direction, and $\varphi(y)$ is a function of class H, vanishing sufficiently rapidly at infinity. Writing $J = h_n\varphi$, it may be shown that

$$h_n\varphi = \frac{1}{n} h^n\varphi, \quad h_{-n}\varphi = (-1)^n \frac{1}{n} h^{-n}\varphi, \quad n > 0.$$

Consider the operator

$$L\varphi = a_0(x)\varphi(x) + \int_{\Pi} \frac{f(x;\,\theta)}{\rho^2(x, y)} \varphi(y)\, d\sigma_y + \mathrm{FO},$$

where $a_0(x)$ and $f(x;\,\theta)$ are functions of class H. Let

$$f(x;\,\theta) = \sum_{-\infty}^{\infty} \alpha_n(x) e^{in\theta},$$

where

$$\alpha_0(x) = \frac{1}{2\pi} \int_0^{2\pi} f(x;\,\theta)\, d\theta = 0.$$

We have, formally

$$L\varphi = a_0(x)\varphi(x) + \sum_{-\infty}^{\infty} \alpha_n(x) \int_{\Pi} \frac{e^{in\theta}}{\rho^2(x, y)} \varphi(y)\, d\sigma_y + \mathrm{FO} =$$

$$= a_0(x)\varphi(x) + 2\pi \sum_{-\infty}^{\infty} \alpha_n(x)\, h_n\varphi + \mathrm{FO}.$$

Setting for positive n

$$a_n(x) = \frac{2\pi}{n} \alpha_n(x), \quad a_{-n}(x) = (-1)^n \frac{2\pi}{n} \alpha_{-n}(x),$$

we have

$$L\varphi = \sum_{-\infty}^{\infty} a_n(x)\, h^n\varphi + \mathrm{FO}.$$

The function

$$\Psi(x;\,\theta) = \sum_{-\infty}^{\infty} a_n(x)\, e^{in\left(\theta + \frac{\pi}{2}\right)},$$

if it exists, will be called the symbol of the operator L. Consider the two operators

$$L^{(1)}\varphi=\sum_{-\infty}^{\infty} a_n(x)\,h^n\varphi+\text{FO},\quad L^{(2)}\varphi=\sum_{-\infty}^{\infty} b_n(x)\,h^n\varphi+\text{FO}$$

and their symbols

$$\Psi^{(1)}(x;\,\theta)=\sum_{-\infty}^{\infty} a_n(x)\,e^{in\left(\theta+\frac{\pi}{2}\right)},\quad \Psi^{(2)}(x;\,\theta)=\sum_{-\infty}^{\infty} b_n(x)\,e^{in\left(\theta+\frac{\pi}{2}\right)}.$$

The following theorem is valid (by definition).

Theorem 9. The symbol of a sum of operators equals the sum of the symbols of the summands.

Consider the composition of the singular operators

$$L^{(1)}L^{(2)}\varphi \text{ and } L^{(2)}L^{(1)}\varphi.$$

We have

$$L^{(1)}L^{(2)}\varphi=\sum_{-\infty}^{\infty} a_n(x)\,h^n\sum_{k=-\infty}^{\infty} b_k(x)\,h^k\varphi+\text{FO}=$$

$$=\sum_{n=-\infty}^{\infty} a_n(x)\,h^n\sum_{k=-\infty}^{\infty} b_k(y)\frac{k}{2\pi}\int_{\Pi}\frac{e^{ik\theta'}}{\rho^2(y,y')}\varphi(y')\,d\sigma_{y'}+\text{FO}=$$

$$=\sum_{n=-\infty}^{\infty}\frac{n}{2\pi}a_n(x)\int_{\Pi}\frac{e^{in\theta}}{\rho^2(x,y)}\left(\sum_{k=-\infty}^{\infty}\frac{k}{2\pi}b_k(y)\int_{\Pi}\frac{e^{ik\theta'}}{\rho^2(y,y')}\varphi(y')\,d\sigma_{y'}\right)d\sigma_y+\text{FO}=$$

$$=\sum_{n=-\infty}^{\infty}\frac{n}{2\pi}a_n(x)\int_{\Pi}\frac{e^{in\theta}}{\rho^2(x,y)}\left\{\sum_{k=-\infty}^{\infty}\frac{k}{2\pi}(b_k(y)-b_k(x))\times\right.$$

$$\times\int_{\Pi}\frac{e^{ik\theta'}}{\rho^2(y,y')}\varphi(y')\,d\sigma_{y'}+$$

$$\left.+\sum_{k=-\infty}^{\infty}\frac{k}{2\pi}b_k(x)\int\frac{e^{ik\theta'}}{\rho^2(y,y')}\varphi(y')\,d\sigma_{y'}\right\}d\sigma_y+\text{FO}.$$

Since $b_n(y)\in H$, the first term on the right-hand side, being a composition of a kernel with a removable singularity and a singular kernel, is by Theorems 5 and 3 of § 4 a Fredholm operator. The second term contains the powers h^{n+k}, and we finally obtain

$$L^{(1)}L^{(2)}\varphi=\sum_{-\infty}^{\infty} a_n(x)\sum_{-\infty}^{\infty} b_n(x)\,h^{n+k}\varphi+\text{FO}=$$

$$=\sum_{n=-\infty}^{\infty}\sum_{m=-\infty}^{\infty} a_{m-k}(x)\,b_k(x)\,h_{\varphi}^{m}+\text{FO}.$$

In the same way we can show that

$$L^{(1)}L^{(2)}\varphi=\sum_{-\infty}^{\infty} b_n(x)\sum_{-\infty}^{\infty} a_k(x)\,h^{n+k}\varphi+\text{FO}.$$

Writing $k=m-n$, we obtain

$$L^{(2)}L^{(1)}\varphi=\sum_{k=-\infty}^{\infty}\sum_{m=-\infty}^{\infty} a_{m-k}(x)\,b_k(x)\,h^m\varphi+\text{FO}.$$

Hence we have the following theorem.

Theorem 10. The composition of singular integrals is commutative up to an additive FO. This composition is strictly commutative if there are no FO to start with and the coefficients $a_n(x)$ and $b_n(x)$ are constant.

The symbol of the composition $L^{(1,2)}\equiv L^{(1)}L^{(2}$ or of $L^{(2,1)}\equiv L^{(2)}L^{(1)}$ is, by definition, the function

$$\Psi(x;\ \theta)=\sum_{-\infty}^{\infty}\left(\sum_{k=-\infty}^{\infty} a_{m-k}(x)\, b_k(x)\right) e^{im\left(\theta+\frac{\pi}{2}\right)}=$$

$$=\sum_{-\infty}^{\infty} a_n(x)\, e^{in\left(\theta+\frac{\pi}{2}\right)} \sum_{-\infty}^{\infty} b_n(x)\, e^{in\left(\theta+\frac{\pi}{2}\right)}=\Psi^{(1)}(x;\ \theta)\,\Psi^{(2)}(x;\ \theta),$$

which proves the following theorem:

Theorem 11. The symbol of a composition of operators is the product of the symbols of the component operators.

Giraud /10b/ gives a formula through which it is possible to obtain the symbol $\Psi(x,\ \theta)$ directly from the characteristic $f(x;\ \theta)$, without resorting to series expansion. The derivation of this formula,

$$\Psi(x;\ \theta)=\int_{\theta-\pi}^{\theta} \ln\frac{1}{\sin(\theta-\varphi)}\,[f(x;\ \varphi)+f(x;\ \pi+\varphi)]\, d\varphi+$$

$$+\frac{i\pi}{2}\int_{\theta-\pi}^{\theta} [f(x;\ \varphi)-f(x;\ \pi+\varphi)]\, d\varphi \qquad (*)$$

was given by I. A. Itskovich /9/.

The above theorems about symbols may be extended to systems of operators. Consider the system of singular equations

$$\sum_{k=1}^{n} L^{(1)}_{jk}\varphi_k=F_j \qquad (j=1,\ 2,\ \ldots,\ n),$$

where

$$L^{(1)}_{jk}\varphi_k=a_0^{(jk)}(x)\,\varphi_k(x)+\int_{\Pi}\frac{f^{(1)}_{jk}(x;\ \theta)}{\rho^2(x,\ y)}\,\varphi_k(y)\, d\sigma_y+\text{FO}.$$

Let

$$L^{(1)}=\left\|\begin{matrix} L^{(1)}_{11} & L^{(1)}_{12} & \ldots & L^{(1)}_{1n}\\ L^{(1)}_{21} & L^{(1)}_{22} & \ldots & L^{(1)}_{2n}\\ \cdot & \cdot & \cdot & \cdot\\ L^{(1)}_{n1} & L^{(1)}_{n2} & \ldots & L^{(1)}_{nn}\end{matrix}\right\|$$

and

$$\varphi\equiv(\varphi_1,\ \varphi_2,\ \ldots,\ \varphi_n),\qquad F\equiv(F_1,\ F_2,\ \ldots,\ F_n);$$

then the system of equations may be written in the form

$$L^{(1)}\varphi=F.$$

But $L^{(1)}_{jk}\varphi_k=\sum_{-\infty}^{\infty} a_n^{(jk)}(x)\, h^n\varphi_k+\text{FO}$ and its symbol is $\Psi^{(1)}_{jk}(x;\ \theta)=\sum_{-\infty}^{\infty} a_n^{(jk)}(x)\, e^{in\left(\theta+\frac{\pi}{2}\right)}$ (the notation $a_n^{(jk)}(x)$ is self-explanatory). Therefore the matrix

$$\Psi^{(1)}(x;\ \theta)=\left\|\begin{matrix} \Psi^{(1)}_{11}(x;\ \theta) & \Psi^{(1)}_{12}(x;\ \theta) & \ldots & \Psi^{(1)}_{1n}(x;\ \theta)\\ \cdot & \cdot & \cdot & \cdot\\ \Psi^{(1)}_{n1}(x;\ \theta) & \Psi^{(1)}_{n2}(x;\ \theta) & \ldots & \Psi^{(1)}_{nn}(x;\ \theta)\end{matrix}\right\|$$

may be called the symbol (or symbolic matrix) of the matrix operator $L^{(1)}$.

Let $L^{(2)}$ be another matrix operator of the same type as $L^{(1)}$ with the elements

$$L^{(2)}_{jk}\varphi_k=b_0^{(jk)}(x)\,\varphi_k(x)+\int_{\Pi}\frac{f^{(2)}_{jk}(x;\ \theta)}{\rho^2(x,\ y)}\,\varphi_k(y)\, d\sigma_y+\text{FO}$$

and the symbolic matrix

$$\Psi^{(2)}(x;\ \theta)=\begin{Vmatrix} \Psi_{11}^{(2)}(x;\ \theta) & \Psi_{12}^{(2)}(x;\ \theta) & \dots & \Psi_{1n}^{(2)}(x;\ \theta) \\ \cdot & \cdot & \cdot & \cdot \\ \Psi_{n1}^{(2)}(x;\ \theta) & \Psi_{n2}^{(2)}(x;\ \theta) & \dots & \Psi_{nn}^{(2)}(x;\ \theta) \end{Vmatrix},$$

where $\Psi_{jk}^{(2)}(x;\ \theta)$ is the symbol of the operator $L_{jk}^{(2)}\varphi_k$.

Consider the composition

$$L^{(21)}\varphi=L^{(2)}(L^{(1)}\varphi)=(L^{(2)}L^{(1)})\varphi=\begin{Vmatrix} \sum_j L_{1j}^{(2)}L_{j1}^{(1)} & \sum_j L_{1j}^{(2)}L_{j2}^{(1)} & \dots & \sum_j L_{1j}^{(2)}L_{jn}^{(1)} \\ \cdot & \cdot & \cdot & \cdot \\ \sum_j L_{nj}^{(2)}L_{j1}^{(1)} & \sum_j L_{nj}^{(2)}L_{j2}^{(1)} & \dots & \sum_j L_{nj}^{(2)}L_{jn}^{(1)} \end{Vmatrix}\varphi;$$

by definition and in virtue of Theorems 9 and 11, its symbolic matrix is

$$\Psi^{(2,\ 1)}(x;\ \theta)=\begin{Vmatrix} \sum_j \Psi_{1j}^{(2)}\Psi_{j1}^{(1)} & \dots & \sum_j \Psi_{1j}^{(2)}\Psi_{jn}^{(1)} \\ \cdot & \cdot & \cdot \\ \sum_j \Psi_{nj}^{(2)}\Psi_{j1}^{(1)} & \dots & \sum_j \Psi_{nj}^{(2)}\Psi_{jn}^{(1)} \end{Vmatrix}=\Psi^{(2)}(x;\ \theta)\,\Psi^{(1)}(x;\ \theta);$$

whence:

Theorem 12. The symbolic matrix of the composition $L^{(2,\ 1)}$ *is the product of the symbolic matrices of the operators* $L^{(2)}$ *and* $L^{(1)}$.

Theorem 13. The matrix $L^{(2,\ 1)}$ *coincides with its transpose,* $(L^{(2,\ 1)})^*$, *up to an additive FO, that is,*

$$L^{(2)}L^{(1)}\varphi=L^{(1)*}L^{(2)*}\varphi+\text{FO},$$

where $L^{(1)*}$ *and* $L^{(2)*}$ *are the transpose of* $L^{(1)}$ *and* $L^{(2)}$.

This follows from the fact that on account of Theorem 10

$$L^{(2,\ 1)}\varphi=L^{(2)}(L^{(1)}\varphi)=(L^{(2)}L^{(1)})\varphi=$$

$$=\begin{Vmatrix} \sum_j L_{1j}^{(2)}L_{j1}^{(1)} & \dots & \sum L_{1j}^{(2)}L_{jn}^{(1)} \\ \cdot & \cdot & \cdot \\ \sum_j L_{nj}^{(2)}L_{j1}^{(1)} & \dots & \sum_j L_{nj}^{(2)}L_{jn}^{(1)} \end{Vmatrix}\varphi=\begin{Vmatrix} \sum_j L_{j1}^{(1)}L_{1j}^{(2)} & \dots & \sum_j L_{jn}^{(1)}L_{1j}^{(2)} \\ \cdot & \cdot & \cdot \\ \sum L_{j1}^{(1)}L_{nj}^{(2)} & \dots & \sum L_{jn}^{(1)}L_{nj}^{(2)} \end{Vmatrix}\varphi+$$

$$+\text{FO}=(L^{(1)*}L^{(2)*})\varphi+\text{FO}=L^{(1)*}(L^{(2)*}\varphi)+\text{FO}=L^{(2,\ 1)*}\varphi+\text{FO}.$$

Theorem 14. A symbolic matrix determines its corresponding singular operator up to an additive FO.

This theorem follows immediately from the preceding. Let it now be required to find an operator $L^{(2)}$ such that the composition $L^{(2)}L^{(1)}$ will be a Fredholm operator. The characteristic of the last operator is zero and all the $c_n^{(jk)}(x)=0$ $(n\neq 0)$ vanish identically, because no singular integral is involved; therefore the symbolic matrix of a Fredholm operator is, by definition,

$$C_0(x)=\begin{Vmatrix} c_0^{(11)} & c_0^{(12)} & \dots & c_0^{(1n)} \\ \cdot & \cdot & \cdot & \cdot \\ c_0^{(n1)} & c_0^{(n2)} & \dots & c_0^{(nn)} \end{Vmatrix}.$$

The condition

$$\det A_0(x)\neq 0,\qquad x\in\Pi.$$

suffices for the validity of the Fredholm theorems and alternative. In particular it is sufficient to demand that the symbolic matrix be the unit matrix.

Since by Theorem 12 the symbolic matrix of the composition $L^{(2)}L^{(1)}$ is the product $\Psi^{(2)}(x;\theta)\Psi^{(1)}(x;\theta)$, we have in that case

$$\Psi^{(2)}(x;\theta)=[\Psi^{(1)}(x;\theta)]^{-1},$$

or

$$\Psi^{(2)}(x;\theta)=\frac{1}{\det\Psi^{(1)}(x;\theta)}\left\|\begin{matrix}\Psi^*_{11}(x;\theta) & \Psi^*_{12}(x;\theta) & \dots & \Psi^*_{1n}(x;\theta)\\ \Psi^*_{21}(x;\theta) & \Psi^*_{22}(x;\theta) & \dots & \Psi^*_{2n}(x;\theta)\\ \dots & \dots & \dots & \dots\\ \Psi^*_{n1}(x;\theta) & \Psi^*_{n2}(x;\theta) & \dots & \Psi^*_{nn}(x;\theta)\end{matrix}\right\|,$$

where $\Psi^*_{jk}(x;\theta)$, $j, k=1, 2, \dots, n$, is the cofactor of the element $\Psi_{kj}(x;\theta)$ in the determinant

$$\det\Psi^{(1)}(x;\theta)=\left|\begin{matrix}\Psi^{(1)}_{11}(x;\theta) & \Psi^{(1)}_{12}(x;\theta) & \dots & \Psi^{(1)}_{1n}(x;\theta)\\ \dots & \dots & \dots & \dots\\ \Psi^{(1)}_{n1}(x;\theta) & \Psi^{(1)}_{n2}(x;\theta) & \dots & \Psi^{(1)}_{nn}(x;\theta)\end{matrix}\right|.$$

Hence follows the theorem:

Theorem 15. *If $\Psi^*_{jk}(x;\theta)$ satisfies Hölder's condition in x and is infinitely differentiable with respect to θ, then the inequality*

$$\det\Psi^{(1)}(x,\theta)\neq 0$$

for any $x\in\Pi$, is a necessary and sufficient condition for the existence of the regularizer symbolic matrix $\Psi^{(2)}(x,\theta)$.

§ 7. The local regularization operator

According to § 5 the construction of the regularizing operator reduces to constructing a regularizer for the operator

$$\alpha(u)\psi(u)-\varkappa\int\limits_{\Pi}\frac{f_4(u;\theta_2)}{\rho^2(u,v)}\psi(v)\,dv_\sigma+\mathrm{FO}.$$

As we already know, this in turn may be reduced to proving that the determinant of the symbolic matrix of that operator does not vanish. However, we shall not construct that determinant but another one, which may be made to differ as little as desired from the first by choosing ε_0 sufficiently small. In fact, we know that by reducing ε_0 the characteristic $f_4(u;\theta_2)$ can be made as close as desired to the matrix $f_1(\xi;\theta_1)$, defined on the circular disk γ, while the latter will at the same time closely approximate to the matrix $f_1'(\xi;\theta_1)$, defined by (5.10). Therefore also their Fourier coefficients will be as close as desired, and hence the symbolic determinant of the matrix $f_4(u;\theta_2)$ will be arbitrarily close to the one obtained by the formal construction of § 6 from $f_1'(\xi;\theta_1)$. The symbol, we note, depends also on the coefficient of the free (unintegrated) term, which may be made as close as desired to the unit matrix. The problem thus amounts to a formal construction by means of the formulas of § 6 of the symbolic determinant for the operator

$$L^{(1)}\psi\equiv I\psi(\xi)-\varkappa\int\limits_{\gamma}\frac{f_1'(\xi;\theta_1)}{\rho^2(\xi,\eta)}\psi(\eta)\,d\eta+\mathrm{FO}.$$

Denoting the elements of the matrix $L^{(1)}_{ij}$ by $L^{(1)}$ as before, and calculating the symbols for each of these operators by the formulas of § 6, we obtain

$$\Psi_{11}^{(1)}(x;\ \theta_1)=1,\quad \Psi_{12}^{(1)}(x;\ \theta_1)=-2\pi i\varkappa l\,[A_1(x)\cos\theta_1+A_2(x)\sin\theta_1],$$
$$\Psi_{13}^{(1)}(x;\ \theta_1)=-2\pi i\varkappa l\,[A_3(x)\cos\theta_1+A_4(x)\sin\theta_1],$$
$$\Psi_{22}^{(1)}(x;\ \theta_1)=1,\quad \Psi_{21}^{(1)}(x;\ \theta_1)=2\pi i\varkappa l\,[A_1(x)\cos\theta_1+A_2(x)\sin\theta_1],$$
$$\Psi_{23}^{(1)}(x;\ \theta_1)=-2\pi i\varkappa l\,[A_5(x)\cos\theta_1+A_6(x)\sin\theta_1],$$
$$\Psi_{33}^{(1)}(x;\ \theta_1)=1,\quad \Psi_{31}^{(1)}(x,\ \theta_1)=2\pi i\varkappa l\,[A_3(x)\cos\theta_1+A_4(x)\sin\theta_1],$$
$$\Psi_{32}^{(1)}(x;\ \theta_1)=2\pi i\varkappa l\,[A_5(x)\cos\theta_1+A_6(x)\sin\theta_1].$$

Constructing the symbolic matrix $\Psi^{(1)}(x;\ \theta_1)$ and computing its determinant, we obtain

$$\det\Psi^{(1)}(x;\ \theta_1)=1-4\pi^2\varkappa^2l^2(\mu_{12}^2+\mu_{34}^2+\mu_{56}^2),$$

where

$$\mu_{12}=A_1(x)\cos\theta_1+A_2(x)\sin\theta_1,\quad \mu_{34}=A_3(x)\cos\theta_1+A_4(x)\sin\theta_1,$$
$$\mu_{56}=A_5(x)\cos\theta_1+A_6(x)\sin\theta_1.$$

On setting

$$\eta_j(x,\ x^0)=\cos(\boldsymbol{n}_x,\ \boldsymbol{x}_j)-\cos(\boldsymbol{n}_{x^0},\ \boldsymbol{x}_j)\qquad (j=1,\ 2,\ 3),$$

(5. 9) may be written

$$A_1(x)=A_1(x^0)+[a_{11}(x^0)\eta_2(x,\ x^0)-a_{12}(x^0)\eta_1(x,\ x^0)],$$
$$A_2(x)=A_2(x^0)+[a_{21}(x^0)\eta_2(x,\ x^0)-a_{22}(x^0)\eta_1(x,\ x^0)],$$
$$A_3(x)=A_3(x^0)+[a_{11}(x^0)\eta_3(x,\ x^0)-a_{13}(x^0)\eta_1(x,\ x^0)],$$
$$A_4(x)=A_4(x^0)+[a_{21}(x^0)\eta_3(x^0,\ x)-a_{23}(x^0)\eta_1(x^0,\ x)],$$
$$A_5(x)=A_5(x^0)+[a_{12}(x^0)\eta_3(x^0,\ x)-a_{13}(x^0)\eta_2(x,\ x^0)],$$
$$A_6(x)=A_6(x^0)+[a_{22}(x^0)\eta_3(x,\ x^0)-a_{23}(x^0)\eta_2(x,\ x^0)].$$

In these expressions for $A_k(x)$ $(k=1,\ 2,\ \ldots,\ 6)$ the terms depending on $\eta_j(x,\ x^0)$ will be denoted by

$$\zeta_k(x,\ x^0)\qquad (k=1,\ 2,\ \ldots,\ 6).$$

By the definition of a Liapunov surface

$$|\eta_j(x,\ x^0)|\leqslant Cr^{\delta}(x,\ x^0)\qquad (j=1,\ 2,\ 3).$$

Hence by choosing a sufficiently small ε_0 the absolute values of all $\zeta_k(x,\ x^0)$ $(k=1,\ 2,\ \ldots,\ 6)$ can be made smaller than any given positive number, and we have

$$\mu_{12}^2=(A_1(x^0)\cos\theta_1+A_2(x^0)\sin\theta_1)^2+g_1(x,\ x^0),$$
$$\mu_{34}^2=(A_3(x^0)\cos\theta_1+A_4(x^0)\sin\theta_1)^2+g_2(x,\ x^0),$$
$$\mu_{56}^2=(A_5(x^0)\cos\theta_1+A_6(x^0)\sin\theta_1)^2+g_3(x,\ x^0),$$

where $g_1(x,\ x^0)$, $g_2(x,\ x^0)$, $g_3(x,\ x^0)$ are certain functions of $x,\ x^0$ on S_1, whose absolute values may be made arbitrary small with ε_0. On the other hand, using the direction cosines $a_{ij}(x_0)$ $(i,\ j=1,\ 2,\ 3)$ expressed in terms of the Euler angles:

$$a_{11}(x^0)=\cos\varphi\cos\psi-\sin\varphi\sin\psi\cos\vartheta,$$
$$a_{21}(x^0)=-\sin\varphi\cos\psi-\cos\varphi\sin\psi\cos\vartheta,\quad a_{31}=\sin\psi\sin\vartheta,$$
$$a_{12}(x^0)=\cos\varphi\sin\psi+\sin\varphi\cos\psi\cos\vartheta,$$
$$a_{22}(x^0)=-\sin\varphi\sin\psi+\cos\varphi\cos\psi\cos\vartheta,\quad a_{32}=-\cos\varphi\sin\vartheta,$$
$$a_{13}(x^0)=\sin\varphi\sin\vartheta,$$
$$a_{23}(x^0)=\cos\varphi\sin\vartheta,\qquad a_{33}=\cos\vartheta;$$

we may readily verify that

$$(A_1(x^0)\cos\theta_1+A_2(x^0)\sin\theta_1)^2+(A_3(x^0)\cos\theta_1+A_4(x^0)\sin\theta_1)^2+ \\ +(A_5(x^0)\cos\theta_1+A_6(x^0)\sin\theta_1)^2=1.$$

Consequently

$$\det\Psi^{(1)}(x;\ \theta_1)=1-4\pi^2\varkappa^2 l^2(1+\nu(x,\ x^0)),$$

where

$$\nu(x,\ x^0)=g_1(x,\ x^0)+g_2(x,\ x^0)+g_3(x,\ x^0).$$

It now follows that for appropriately small ε_0 the roots of the equation

$$1-4\pi^2\varkappa^2 l^2(1+\nu(x,\ x^0))=0$$

which are

$$\varkappa=\pm\frac{1}{2\pi l\sqrt{1+\nu(x,\ x^0)}},$$

can be made arbitrarily close to

$$\varkappa=\pm\frac{1}{2\pi l}. \qquad (5.31')$$

The symbolic matrix $\Psi^{(2)}(x;\ \theta_1)$ can thus be constructed and used to derive the regularizing operator for $\varkappa$-values which differ from the above roots but lie sufficiently close to the points (5.31').

Let us now construct the matrix $\Psi^{(2)}(x;\ \theta_1)$ by means of the formulas of § 6, assuming that $\varkappa$ satisfies the last condition; the calculation of the $\Psi^*_{jk}(x;\ \theta_1)$ gives

$$\Psi^*_{11}(x;\ \theta_1)=\Psi^{(1)}_{22}\Psi^{(1)}_{33}-\Psi^{(1)}_{23}\Psi^{(1)}_{32}=1-4\pi^2\varkappa^2 l^2\,[A_5(x)\cos\theta_1+A_6(x)\sin\theta_1]^2,$$

$$\Psi^*_{12}(x;\ \theta_1)=\Psi^{(1)}_{13}\Psi^{(1)}_{32}-\Psi^{(1)}_{12}\Psi^{(1)}_{33}=2\pi i\varkappa l\,[A_1(x)\cos\theta_1+A_2(x)\sin\theta_1]+ \\ +4\pi^2\varkappa^2 l^2\,[A_3(x)\cos\theta_1+A_4(x)\sin\theta_1]\,[A_5(x)\cos\theta_1+A_6(x)\sin\theta_1],$$

$$\Psi^*_{13}(x;\ \theta_1)=\Psi^{(1)}_{12}\Psi^{(1)}_{23}-\Psi^{(1)}_{13}\Psi^{(1)}_{22}=2\pi i\varkappa l\,[A_3(x)\cos\theta_1+A_4(x)\sin\theta_1]- \\ -4\pi^2\varkappa^2 l^2\,[A_1(x)\cos\theta_1+A_2(x)\sin\theta_1]\,[A_5(x)\cos\theta_1+A_6(x)\sin\theta_1],$$

$$\Psi^*_{21}(x;\ \theta_1)=\Psi^{(1)}_{23}\Psi^{(1)}_{31}-\Psi^{(1)}_{21}\Psi^{(1)}_{33}=-2\pi i\varkappa l\,[A_1(x)\cos\theta_1+A_2(x)\sin\theta_1]+ \\ +4\pi^2\varkappa^2 l^2\,[A_3(x)\cos\theta_1+A_4(x)\sin\theta_1]\,[A_5(x)\cos\theta_1+A_6(x)\sin\theta_1],$$

$$\Psi^*_{22}(x;\ \theta_1)=\Psi^{(1)}_{11}\Psi^{(1)}_{33}-\Psi^{(1)}_{13}\Psi^{(1)}_{31}=1-4\pi^2\varkappa^2 l^2\,[A_3(x)\cos\theta_1+A_4(x)\sin\theta_1]^2,$$

$$\Psi^*_{23}(x;\ \theta_1)=\Psi^{(1)}_{13}\Psi^{(1)}_{21}-\Psi^{(1)}_{11}\Psi^{(1)}_{23}=2\pi i\varkappa l\,[A_5(x)\cos\theta_1+A_6(x)\sin\theta_1]+ \\ +4\pi^2\varkappa^2 l^2\,[A_1(x)\cos\theta_1+A_2(x)\sin\theta_1]\,[A_3(x)\cos\theta_1+A_4(x)\sin\theta_1],$$

$$\Psi^*_{31}(x;\ \theta_1)=\Psi^{(1)}_{21}\Psi^{(1)}_{32}-\Psi^{(1)}_{22}\Psi^{(1)}_{31}=-2\pi i\varkappa l\,[A_3(x)\cos\theta_1+A_4(x)\sin\theta_1]- \\ -4\pi^2\varkappa^2 l^2\,[A_1(x)\cos\theta_1+A_2(x)\sin\theta_1]\,[A_5(x)\cos\theta_1+A_6(x)\sin\theta_1],$$

$$\Psi^*_{32}(x;\ \theta_1)=\Psi^{(1)}_{12}\Psi^{(1)}_{31}-\Psi^{(1)}_{11}\Psi^{(1)}_{32}=-2\pi i\varkappa l\,[A_5(x)\cos\theta_1+A_6(x)\sin\theta_1]+ \\ +4\pi^2\varkappa^2 l^2\,[A_1(x)\cos\theta_1+A_2(x)\sin\theta_1]\,[A_3(x)\cos\theta_1+A_4(x)\sin\theta_1],$$

$$\Psi^*_{33}(x;\ \theta_1)=\Psi^{(1)}_{11}\Psi^{(1)}_{22}-\Psi^{(1)}_{12}\Psi^{(1)}_{21}=1-4\pi^2\varkappa^2 l^2\,[A_1(x)\cos\theta_1+A_2(x)\sin\theta_1]^2$$

and

$$\Psi^{(2)}(x;\ \theta_1)=\frac{1}{1-4\pi^2\varkappa^2 l_*^2}\,\|\Psi^*_{ik}(x;\ \theta_1)\|_{i,\,k=1,\,2,\,3},$$

where

$$l_*^2=l^2[1+\nu(x,\ x^0)].$$

Applying Theorem 14 of § 6 and writing

$$\Delta=1-4\pi^2\varkappa^2 l_*^2,\quad \Delta'=2\pi^2\varkappa^2 l^2,$$

we obtain the regularizing operator with the elements

$$L^{(2)}_{jk}\omega_k=b_0^{(jk)}(\xi)\,\omega_k(\xi)+\int\frac{f^{(2)}_{jk}(\xi;\ \theta_1)}{\rho^2(\xi,\ \eta)}\,\omega_k(\eta)\,d\sigma+\mathrm{FO}\ (j,\ k=1,\ 2,\ 3),$$

where

$$b_0^{(11)}(\xi)=\frac{1}{\Delta}\{1-2\pi^2\varkappa^2l^2[A_5^2(x)+A_6^2(x)]\},$$

$$f_{11}^{(2)}(\xi;\ \theta_1)=-\frac{\Delta'}{\Delta}\{[A_6^2(x)-A_5^2(x)]\cos 2\theta_1-2A_5A_6\sin 2\theta_1\};$$

$$b_0^{(12)}=\frac{\Delta'}{\Delta}(A_3A_5+A_4A_6);$$

$$f_{12}^{(2)}(\xi;\ \theta_1)=\frac{\varkappa l}{\Delta}(A_1\cos\theta_1+A_2\sin\theta_1)-$$
$$-\frac{\Delta'}{\Delta}[(A_3A_6+A_4A_5)\sin 2\theta_1+(A_3A_5-A_4A_5)\cos 2\theta_1];$$

$$b_0^{(13)}=-\frac{\Delta'}{\Delta}(A_1A_5+A_2A_6);$$

$$f_{13}^{(2)}(\xi;\ \theta_1)=\frac{\varkappa l}{\Delta}(A_3\cos\theta_1+A_4\sin\theta_1)+$$
$$+\frac{\Delta'}{\Delta}[(A_1A_6+A_2A_5)\sin 2\theta_1+(A_1A_5-A_2A_6)\cos 2\theta_1];$$

$$b_0^{(21)}=\frac{\Delta'}{\Delta}(A_3A_5+A_4A_6);$$

$$f_{21}^{(2)}(\xi;\ \theta_1)=-\frac{\varkappa l}{\Delta}(A_1\cos\theta_1+A_2\sin\theta_1)-$$
$$-\frac{\Delta'}{\Delta}[(A_3A_6+A_4A_5)\sin 2\theta_1+(A_3A_5-A_4A_5)\cos 2\theta_1]:$$

$$b_0^{(22)}=\frac{1}{\Delta}[1-2\pi^2\varkappa^2l^2(A_3^2+A_4^2)];$$

$$f_{22}^{(2)}(\xi;\ \theta_1)=-\frac{\Delta'}{\Delta}[(A_4^2-A_3^2)\cos 2\theta_1-2A_3A_4\sin 2\theta_1];$$

$$b_0^{(23)}=\frac{\Delta'}{\Delta}(A_1A_3+A_2A_4);$$

$$f_{23}^{(2)}(\xi;\ \theta_1)=\frac{\varkappa l}{\Delta}(A_5\cos\theta_1+A_6\sin\theta_1)-$$
$$-\frac{\Delta'}{\Delta}[(A_1A_4+A_2A_5)\sin 2\theta_1+(A_1A_3-A_2A_4)\cos 2\theta_1];$$

$$b_0^{(31)}=-\frac{\Delta'}{\Delta}(A_1A_5+A_2A_6);$$

$$f_{31}^{(2)}(\xi;\ \theta_1)=-\frac{\varkappa l}{\Delta}(A_3\cos\theta_1+A_4\sin\theta_1)+$$
$$+\frac{\Delta'}{\Delta}[(A_1A_6+A_2A_5)\sin 2\theta_1+(A_1A_5-A_2A_6)\cos 2\theta_1];$$

$$b_0^{(32)}=\frac{\Delta'}{\Delta}(A_1A_3+A_2A_4);$$

$$f_{32}^{(2)}(\xi;\ \theta_1)=-\frac{\varkappa l}{\Delta}(A_5\cos\theta_1+A_6\sin\theta_1)-$$
$$-\frac{\Delta'}{\Delta}[(A_1A_4+A_2A_3)\sin 2\theta_1+(A_1A_3-A_2A_4)\cos 2\theta_1];$$

$$b_0^{(33)}=\frac{1}{\Delta}[1-2\pi^2\varkappa^2l^2(A_1^2+A_2^2)];$$

$$f_{33}^{(2)}(\xi;\ \theta_1)=-\frac{\Delta'}{\Delta}[(A_2^2-A_1^2)\cos 2\theta_1-2A_1A_2\sin 2\theta_1].$$

Incidentally, in order to work out these expressions we only need to calculate one diagonal and one off-diagonal element; the other elements are all obtained by formal rearrangement of the coefficients according to a self-evident scheme.

Let

$$B(\xi;\ \varkappa)=\|b_0^{(jk)}(\xi;\ \varkappa)\|=\frac{1}{\Delta}\begin{Vmatrix}1-\Delta'(A_5^2+A_6^2) & \Delta'(A_3A_5+A_4A_6) & -\Delta'(A_1A_5+A_2A_6)\\ \Delta'(A_3A_5+A_4A_6) & 1-\Delta'(A_3^2+A_4^2) & \Delta'(A_1A_3+A_2A_4)\\ -\Delta'(A_1A_5+A_2A_6) & \Delta'(A_1A_3+A_2A_4) & 1-\Delta'(A_1^2+A_2^2)\end{Vmatrix} \quad (5.32')$$

$$D(\xi,\ \eta;\ \varkappa)=\frac{1}{\varkappa\rho^2(\xi,\ \eta)}\begin{Vmatrix}f_{11}^{(2)}(\xi;\ \theta_1) & f_{12}^{(2)}(\xi;\ \theta_1) & f_{13}^{(2)}(\xi;\ \theta_1)\\ f_{21}^{(2)}(\xi;\ \theta_1) & f_{22}^{(2)}(\xi;\ \theta_1) & f_{23}^{(2)}(\xi;\ \theta_1)\\ f_{31}^{(2)}(\xi;\ \theta_1) & f_{32}^{(2)}(\xi;\ \theta_1) & f_{33}^{(2)}(\xi;\ \theta_1)\end{Vmatrix} \quad (5.33)$$

It is necessary to find those values of $\varkappa$, which satisfy the equation $\det B(\xi;\ \varkappa)=0$. The form of the expressions for $A_k(x)$, $A_k(x^0)$ and $B(\xi;\ \varkappa)$ indicate that

$$\det B(\xi;\ \varkappa)=\det B(x^0;\ \varkappa)+\eta(x,\ x^0),$$

where $\eta(x,\ x^0)$ is a certain function whose absolute value may be made smaller than any positive number by reducing ε_0. The required values of $\varkappa$ must be arbitrarily close to the roots of the equation

$$\det B(x^0;\ \varkappa)=0.$$

Let us derive the latter. Substituting the values of $A_k(x^0)$, we obtain

$$\det B(x^0;\ \varkappa)=\frac{1}{\Delta}\begin{vmatrix} 1-\Delta'(1-\sin^2\vartheta\sin^2\psi) & \Delta'\sin^2\vartheta\sin\psi\cos\psi & \Delta'\sin\psi\sin\vartheta\cos\vartheta \\ \Delta'\sin^2\vartheta\sin\psi\cos\psi & 1-\Delta'(1-\sin^2\vartheta\cos^2\psi) & \Delta'\cos\psi\sin\vartheta\cos\vartheta \\ \Delta'\sin\psi\sin\vartheta\cos\vartheta & \Delta'\cos\psi\sin\vartheta\cos\vartheta & 1-\Delta'\sin^2\vartheta \end{vmatrix}=$$

$$=\frac{1}{\Delta}\left[-\Delta'^3\sin^4\vartheta+\Delta'^2(1+\sin^2\vartheta+\sin^4\vartheta)-\Delta'(2+\sin^2\vartheta)+1\right].$$

The equation

$$\det B(x^0;\ \varkappa)=0$$

has three real positive roots:

$$\Delta_1'=1,\quad \Delta_{2,3}'=\frac{(1+\sin^2\vartheta)\pm\sqrt{1+2\sin^2\vartheta-3\sin^4\vartheta}}{2\sin^4\vartheta}.$$

Their reality follows from the inequality

$$1+2\sin^2\vartheta\geqslant 3\sin^4\vartheta,$$

while their positiveness is evident from

$$1+\sin^2\vartheta\geqslant\sqrt{1+2\sin^2\vartheta-3\sin^4\vartheta}.$$

Moreover, the inequality

$$(1+\sin^2\vartheta)\pm\sqrt{1+2\sin^2\vartheta-3\sin^4\vartheta}\geqslant 2\sin^4\vartheta$$

shows that the minimum absolute value of the roots Δ_2' and Δ_3' cannot be smaller than unity:

$$\min(\Delta_2',\ \Delta_3')\geqslant 1;$$

but the maximum values, obtained for $\vartheta=0$, are infinite.

Evidently, the zeros of $B(x^0;\ \varkappa)$ are

$$\varkappa_{1,2}=\pm\frac{1}{\sqrt{2\pi l}},$$

$$\varkappa_{3,4}=\pm\frac{1}{\sqrt{2\pi l}}\sqrt{\Delta_2'(\vartheta)},$$

$$\varkappa_{5,6}=\pm\frac{1}{\sqrt{2\pi l}}\sqrt{\Delta_3'(\vartheta)}.$$

Let us slit the complex $\varkappa$-plane along the real-axis intervals $\left(\pm\frac{1}{4\pi l},\ \pm\infty\right)$, and denote the slit plane by Π'.

It is clear that the points $\varkappa_{1,2}$, $\varkappa_{3,4}$, $\varkappa_{5,6}$ as well as $\varkappa=\pm\frac{1}{2\pi l}$ are thereby removed, as they should be in view of (5.31').

The inverse matrix

$$B^{-1}(\xi,\ \varkappa),$$

defined for any $\xi \in \gamma$ and $\varkappa \in \Pi'$, exists, since in Π'

$$\det B(\xi;\ \varkappa) \neq 0.$$

Along with the operator

$$M\varphi = B(\xi;\ \varkappa)\,\varphi(x) + \varkappa \int D(\xi,\ \eta,\ \varkappa)\,\varphi(\eta)\,d\sigma_\eta + \mathrm{FO},$$

just constructed, the operator

$$L_\varphi^{(2)} = I\varphi(\xi) + \varkappa \int B^{-1}(\xi;\ \varkappa)\,D(\xi,\ \eta;\ \varkappa)\,\varphi(\eta)\,d\sigma_\eta + \mathrm{FO}$$

too, is obviously a regularizer. To return to what was said at the beginning of this section, we observe that while $B^{-1}(\xi;\ \varkappa)\,D(\xi,\ \eta;\ \varkappa)$ is not the matrix which serves to regularize the equation

$$\alpha(u)\,\psi(u) - \varkappa \int\limits_{\Pi} \frac{f_4(u;\ \theta_2)}{\rho^2(u,\ v)}\,\psi(v)\,d\sigma_v + \mathrm{FO}, \tag{5.34}$$

its existence implies the existence of the desired regularizing matrix. Furthermore, if the latter matrix is $H'(u,\ v;\ \varkappa)$, we have

$$H'(u,\ v;\ \varkappa) = B^{-1}(\xi;\ \varkappa)\,D(\xi,\ \eta;\ \varkappa) + R_{\varepsilon_0}(u,\ v;\ \varkappa),$$

where $R_{\varepsilon_0}(u,\ v;\ \varkappa)$ is a matrix which tends to zero together with ε_0. By mappings inverse to those which were applied in § 5 to obtain (5.34) or (5.31) from (5. 12), we now transform $H'(u,\ v;\ \varkappa)$ into a matrix, $H(x,\ y;\ \varkappa)$, defined on S_0, which will serve to regularize (5.12) on S_0. The operator

$$L^{(2)}\varphi = (I + \varkappa H)\,\varphi, \tag{5.35}$$

where H is an integral operator with the kernel $H(x,\ y;\ \varkappa)$, will be said to effect local regularization. It may be shown that this operator has the properties stated in Theorems 7 and 8 of § 3 /6a, b/.

We shall now derive an expression for the matrix $\Phi(x;\ \varkappa)$ introduced in § 5. We already know (cf. § 3) that

$$\Phi(x;\ \varkappa) = \lim_{\varepsilon \to 0} \int\limits_S \Bigl(\int\limits_{S(x;\,\varepsilon)} H(x,\ \xi;\ \varkappa)\,K(\xi,\ y)\,dS_\xi \Bigr)\,dS_y, \tag{5.36}$$

but there exists a simpler and more explicit expression. Obviously

$$ML^{(1)}\varphi = (B + \varkappa D)(I - \varkappa K)\,\varphi = B\varphi + \varkappa(D - BK - \varkappa DK)\,\varphi.$$

Now by Theorem 8 of § 3

$$DK\varphi = -\Phi_*(x;\ \varkappa)\,\varphi(x) + \int\limits_S \varphi(y)\,dS_y \int\limits_S D(x,\ \xi;\ \varkappa)\,K(\xi,\ y)\,dS_\xi,$$

and hence

$$ML^{(1)}\varphi = [B + \varkappa^2\Phi_*(x;\ \varkappa)]\,\varphi(x) + \varkappa \int\limits_S K_*(x,\ \xi;\ \varkappa)\,\varphi(\xi)\,dS_\xi,$$

where $K_*(x,\ \xi;\ \varkappa)$ is a certain matrix which may easily be calculated. Since M is a regularizer, $K_*(x,\ \xi;\ \varkappa)$ is a Fredholm kernel and the symbol of $ML^{(1)}$, equal to $B + \varkappa^2\Phi_*(x;\ \varkappa)$, may be equated with the unit matrix I, which gives

$$\Phi_*(x;\ \varkappa) = \frac{1}{\varkappa^2}(I - B).$$

On the other hand

$$L^{(2)}L^{(1)}\varphi = (I + \varkappa B^{-1}D)(I - \varkappa K)\,\varphi = \Bigl[I + \varkappa^2 \frac{1}{\varkappa^2} B^{-1}(I - B)\Bigr]\varphi(x) + \varkappa \int\limits_S F(x,\ y;\ \varkappa)\,\varphi(y)\,dS_y.$$

where $F(x, y; \varkappa)$ is a Fredholm kernel. Comparing this with the left-hand side of (5.13), we obtain

$$\Phi(x; \varkappa) = \frac{1}{\varkappa^2} B^{-1}(x; \varkappa)[I - B(x; \varkappa)]. \tag{5.37}$$

The condition 2° of § 5:

$$\det[I + \varkappa^2 \Phi(x; \varkappa)] \neq 0,$$

is satisfied as well, since in II′

$$\det[I + \varkappa^2 \Phi(x; \varkappa)] = \det\left[I + B^{-1}(I - B)\right] = \det B^{-1}(x; \varkappa) \neq 0.$$

§ 8. The global regularization operator

Consider n fixed points $x^{(k)}$, $k = 1, 2, \ldots, n$ on a given closed Lyapunov surface S. Let E_k be the neighborhood of $x^{(k)}$ on S which falls within a sphere of radius δ centered there, i. e., containing all points x for which $r(x, x^{(k)}) < \delta$, where $0 < \delta < \varepsilon_0$. It is clear that for sufficiently large n the points $x^{(k)}$ can be chosen so that the union of all E_k completely covers S, thus making every $x \in S$ an interior point of at least one E_k; clearly $E_k \subset S(x^{(k)}; \varepsilon_0)$. Using the above method we now construct in each $S(x^{(k)}; \varepsilon_0)$ the matrix $H^{(k)}(x, y; \varkappa)$, from which the local regularizer for $x, y \in S(x^{(k)}; \varepsilon_0)$ is derived. The matrix $H^{(k)}(x, y; \varkappa)$ is now defined on $S - S(x^{(k)}; \varepsilon_0)$ so that it be finite as a function of x, $x \neq y$, while as a function of y, $y \neq x$, it satisfies the Hölder condition throughout the surface S. Each $H^{(k)}(x, y; \varkappa)$ is then defined on the whole of S. Our next task is to derive a matrix from which to construct the global regularizer for $x, y \in S$. To that end we will make use of a brief outline by Giraud /10a/ and of a certain method often used in similar situations.*

Let

$$F_k(x) = \begin{cases} [\delta^2 - r^2(x, x^{(k)})]^2 & \text{for } x \in E_k, \\ 0 & \text{for } x \in S - E_k. \end{cases}$$

The $F_k(x)$, $k = 1, 2, \ldots, n$ are obviously continuous and continuously differentiable at any $x \in S$. Further,

$$F(x) = \sum_{k=1}^{n} F_k(x) > 0, \quad x \in S,$$

each $x \in S$ being by construction an interior point of at least one domain E_k, $k = 1, 2, \ldots, n$, in which the corresponding $F_k(x) > 0$. We now put

$$e_k(x) = \frac{F_k(x)}{F(x)} \quad (k = 1, 2, \ldots, n).$$

Clearly

$$\sum_{k=1}^{n} e_k(x) = 1. \tag{e}$$

We shall now prove that the matrix

$$H(x, y; \varkappa) = \sum_{k=1}^{n} e_k(x) H^{(k)}(x, y; \varkappa) \tag{H}$$

is in fact the desired one.

* In the author's opinion Giraud's reasoning is not quite adequate; his final result is obtained here in a slightly different way.

The function $H^{(k)}(x, y; \varkappa)$ has in the neighborhood of $y=x$ the fundamental part $\frac{1}{r^2(x, y)} \mathfrak{Q}^{(k)}(x, \theta; \varkappa)$, with $(x, y) \in S(x^{(k)}; \varepsilon_0)$, $k=1, 2, \ldots, n$. Further, $\mathfrak{Q}^{(k)}(x, \theta; \varkappa) = \mathfrak{Q}^{(j)}(x, \theta; \varkappa)$ when x is common to $S(x^{(k)}; \varepsilon_0)$ and $S(x^{(j)}, \varepsilon_0)$.

The function $H(x, y; \varkappa)$ satisfies all the conditions stated in §§ 5 and 7.

§ 9. Functional equation for the resolvent. First Fredholm theorem

Now that we have indicated a method for regularizing a system of equations, the problem arises of proving that Fredholm's fundamental theorems and alternative remain valid for this system. In our proof we follow Giraud, modifying and supplementing his arguments as needed in order to adapt his theory of the single equation to a system of equations.

We have transformed equation (5.12) to the Fredholm equation (5.13)

$$[I + \varkappa^2 \Phi(x; \varkappa)] \varphi(x) + \varkappa \int_S F(x, y; \varkappa) \varphi(y) \, dS_y = X(x),$$

where $F(x, y; \varkappa)$ and $X(x)$ are defined by (5.14), and $\Phi(x; \varkappa)$ by (5.37). Upon setting

$$[I + \varkappa^2 \Phi(x; \varkappa)]^{-1} F(x, y; \varkappa) = F_*(x, y; \varkappa),$$
$$[I + \varkappa^2 \Phi(x; \varkappa)]^{-1} X(x) = X_*(x),$$

equation (5.13) becomes

$$(I + \varkappa F_*) \varphi = X_*. \tag{5.38}$$

It is known that a finite number of iterations reduces this equation to

$$(I + \varkappa^{p+1} F_*^{(p)}) \varphi = X_* + \sum_{n=1}^{p} \varkappa^n F_*^{(n-1)} X_*,$$

where $F_*^{(p)}$ is the p-th iterated matrix, defined by

$$F_*^{(0)} = F_*, \quad F_*^{(n)} = F_*^{(n-1)} F_*.$$

It is known that for any finite p, $F_*^{(p)}(x, y; \varkappa)$ is a continuous function of x and y for $\varkappa \in \Pi'$, and a solution $\varphi(x)$ of (5.13) is representable as

$$\varphi(x) = \psi(x) + \sum_{n=1}^{p} \varkappa^n F_*^{(n-1)} \psi, \tag{5.38'}$$

where $\psi(x)$ is a solution of the equation with a continuous kernel

$$(I + \varkappa^{p+1} F_*^{(p)}) \psi = X_*. \tag{5.39}$$

For any finite value of $\varkappa$ which is not a pole of the resolvent of (5.39), according to the first Fredholm theorem, a solution of (5.13) may be represented as

$$\varphi(x) = [I + \varkappa^2 \Phi(x; \varkappa)]^{-1} f(x) + \varkappa \int_S N_1(x, y; \varkappa) f(y) \, dS_y, \tag{5.40}$$

where the matrix $N_1(x, y; \varkappa)$ may be readily shown to be of the form

$$N_1(x, y; \varkappa) = [I + \varkappa^2 \Phi(x; \varkappa)]^{-1} H(x, y; \varkappa) + O[r^{-2+h}(x, y)] \quad (h > 0) \tag{5.41}$$

and represents a meromorphic function of $\varkappa$ on Π' with poles independent of x and y. If the vector function $f(x)$ belongs to Hölder's class then, by

Theorem 4 of § 3, (5.40) implies that so does $\varphi(x)$, which consequently may be inserted into equation (5.12) whose solution is sought in class H. Even though (5.12) cannot have any solution unless it is (5.40), we cannot decide a priori that this actually is one. A closer examination will reveal that, provided $\varkappa \in \Pi'$ does not coincide with any of the poles of the matrix $N_1(x, y; \varkappa)$, (5.40) is indeed a (unique) solution of the system.

We will first derive one important relation for $N_1(x, y; \varkappa)$.

Let $\varphi(x)$ in (5.12) be an arbitrary vector function of class H, and $f(x)$ the corresponding value of the right-hand side. Inserting this $f(x)$ into (5.40) and applying Theorem 8 of § 3, we obtain

$$\varphi(x) = [I + \varkappa^2\Phi(x; \varkappa)]^{-1}[I + \varkappa^2\Phi(x; \varkappa)]\varphi(x) + \\ + \varkappa \int_S \Big\{ N_1(x, y; \varkappa) - [I + \varkappa^2\Phi(x; \varkappa)]^{-1} K(x, y) - \\ - \varkappa \int_S N_1(x, \xi; \varkappa) K(\xi, y)\, dS_\xi \Big\} \varphi(y)\, dS_y.$$

Whence, $\varphi(x)$ being arbitrary,

$$N_1(x, y; \varkappa) - [I + \varkappa^2\Phi(x; \varkappa)]^{-1} K(x, y) - \varkappa \int_S N_1(x, \xi; \varkappa) K(\xi, y)\, dS_\xi = 0. \tag{5.42}$$

Let us show that for all values of $\varkappa$ in Π' apart from a discrete set, equation (5.12) actually has a solution of class H.

We write the solution as

$$\varphi(x) = \sigma(x) - \varkappa \int_S H^*(x, y; \varkappa)\sigma(y)\, dS_y, \tag{5.43}$$

where $\sigma(y)$ is an unknown vector function of class H, and $H^*(x, y; \varkappa)$ is the transpose of the matrix $H(x, y; \varkappa)$. Substituting (5.43) in (5.12) we obtain in virtue of Theorem 8 of § 3

$$[I - \varkappa^2\Psi(x; \varkappa)]\sigma(x) - \varkappa \int_S \Big[H^*(x, y; \varkappa) + K(x, y) - \\ - \varkappa \int_S K(x, \xi) H^*(\xi, y; \varkappa)\, dS_\xi \Big] \sigma(y)\, dS_y = f(x) \tag{5.44}$$

or in operator notation

$$(I - \varkappa K)(I - \varkappa H^*)\sigma = f, \tag{5.44'}$$

where

$$H^*\sigma = \int_S H^*(x, y; \varkappa)\sigma(y)\, dS_y.$$

Equation (5.44) is a Fredholm equation, because

$$L^{(2,1)}\varphi = L^{(2)}L^{(1)}\varphi = (I + \varkappa H)(I - \varkappa K)\varphi$$

is a Fredholm operator for $\varkappa \in \Pi'$, and so must be

$$\tilde{L}^{(2)}\tilde{L}^{(1)}\varphi = (I - \varkappa H)(I + \varkappa K)\varphi,$$

since either both $\varkappa$ and $-\varkappa$ or neither belong to the plane Π'.

By virtue of Theorem 13 of § 6

$$\tilde{L}^{(2)}\tilde{L}^{(1)}\varphi = \tilde{L}^{(1)*}\tilde{L}^{(2)*}\varphi + \mathrm{FO},$$

where the asterisk indicates matrix transposition.

On the other hand

$$\tilde{L}^{(1)*}\varphi=(I+\varkappa K_1)^*\varphi+\mathrm{FO}.$$

The form of the matrix $K_1(x, y)$ given by (5.6) implies that

$$(I+\varkappa K_1)^*\equiv(I-\varkappa K_1).$$

Consequently

$$\tilde{L}^{(1)*}\varphi=(I-\varkappa K_1)\varphi+\mathrm{FO}$$

and

$$\tilde{L}^{(2)}\tilde{L}^{(1)}\varphi=\tilde{L}^{(1)*}\tilde{L}^{(2)*}\varphi=(I-\varkappa K_1)(I-\varkappa H^*)\varphi+\mathrm{FO}.$$

Since the left-hand side here is a Fredholm operator, such must also be

$$(I-\varkappa K_1)(I-\varkappa H^*)\varphi.$$

Equation (5.44) may now be rewritten as

$$(I-\varkappa K_1)(I-\varkappa H^*)\sigma+\mathrm{FO}=f$$

which in view of the foregoing shows it to be a Fredholm equation.

Consider the matrix $\Psi(x, \varkappa)$ which appears in (5.44). By Theorem 8 of § 3

$$\Psi(x;\ \varkappa)=\lim_{\varepsilon\to 0}\int_S\Bigl(\int_{S(x;\ \varepsilon)}K(x;\ \xi)H^*(\xi,\ y;\ \varkappa)\,dS_\xi\Bigr)dS_y, \tag{5.44''}$$

or

$$\Psi(x;\ \varkappa)=\lim_{\varepsilon\to 0}\int_S\Bigl(\int_{S(x;\ \varepsilon)}K_1(x,\ \xi)H^*(\xi,\ y;\ \varkappa)\,dS_\xi\Bigr)dS_y;$$

which gives for the transposed matrix

$$\begin{aligned}\Psi^*(x;\ \varkappa)&=\lim_{\varepsilon\to 0}\int_S\Bigl(\int_{S(x;\ \varepsilon)}H(\xi,\ y;\ \varkappa)K_1^*(x,\ \xi)\,dS_\xi\Bigr)dS_y=\\&=-\lim_{\varepsilon\to 0}\int_S\Bigl(\int_{S(x;\ \varepsilon)}H(\xi,\ y;\ \varkappa)K_1(x,\ \xi)\,dS_\xi\Bigr)dS_y=\\&=-\lim_{\varepsilon\to 0}\int_S dS_y\int_{S(x;\ \varepsilon)}H(x,\ \xi;\ \varkappa)K_1(\xi,\ y)\,dS_\xi+\\&+\lim_{\varepsilon\to 0}\int_S dS_y\Bigl\{\int_{S(x;\ \varepsilon)}[H(x,\ \xi;\ \varkappa)K_1(\xi,\ y)-H(\xi,\ y;\ \varkappa)K_1(x,\ \xi)]\,dS_\xi\Bigr\}.\end{aligned}$$

Giraud has shown /10a, b (pp. 290-291 and 323-324)/ that

$$\begin{aligned}\int_S H(x,\ \xi;\ \varkappa)K_1(\xi,\ y)\,dS_y-\int_S H(\xi,\ y;\ \varkappa)K_1(x,\ \xi)\,dS_y=&\\=O\,[r^{-2+h'}(x,\ \xi)]\qquad(h'>0).&\end{aligned}$$

whence, in view of (5.36),

$$\Psi^*(x;\ \varkappa)=-\Phi(x,\ \varkappa),$$

but since by (5.37)

$$\varkappa^2\Phi(x;\ \varkappa)=B^{-1}(x;\ \varkappa)-I,$$

which shows $\Phi(x;\ \varkappa)$ to be a symmetric matrix, we obtain

$$\Psi^*\equiv\Psi\quad\text{or}\quad\Psi(x;\ \varkappa)=-\Phi(x;\ \varkappa). \tag{5.44''}$$

This result could also be obtained by working out $\Psi(x;\ \varkappa)$ directly, using (5. 44').

Returning to equation (5.44), we may write

$$[I+\varkappa^2\Phi(x;\varkappa)]\sigma(x)-$$
$$-\varkappa\int_S\left[H^*(x,y;\varkappa)+K(x,y)-\varkappa\int_S K(x,\xi)H^*(\xi,y;\varkappa)\,dS_\xi\right]\times$$
$$\times\sigma(y)\,dS_y=f(x). \tag{5.45}$$

For values of $\varkappa$ in Π' other than the poles of the resolvent of this equation, Fredholm's first theorem gives

$$\sigma(x)=[I+\varkappa^2\Phi(x;\varkappa)]^{-1}f(x)+\varkappa\int_S R^*(x,y;\varkappa)[I+\varkappa^2\Phi(x;\varkappa)]^{-1}f(y)\,dS_y,$$

where $R^*(x,y;\varkappa)$ is the Fredholm resolvent.

Substituting this expression for $\sigma(x)$ into (5.43),

$$\varphi(x)=[I+\varkappa^2\Phi(x;\varkappa)]^{-1}f(x)+$$
$$+\varkappa\int_S R^*(x,y;\varkappa)[I+\varkappa^2\Phi(x;\varkappa)]^{-1}f(y)\,dS_y-$$
$$-\varkappa\int_S H^*(x,y;\varkappa)\Big\{[I+\varkappa^2\Phi(y;\varkappa)]^{-1}f(y)+$$
$$+\varkappa\int_S R^*(y,\xi;\varkappa)[I+\varkappa^2\Phi(\xi;\varkappa)]^{-1}f(\xi)\,dS_\xi\Big\}dS_y;$$

whence, by Theorems 5 and 6 of § 3,

$$\varphi(x)=[I+\varkappa^2\Phi(x;\varkappa)]^{-1}f(x)-\varkappa\int_S\{H^*(x,y;\varkappa)[I+\varkappa^2\Phi(y;\varkappa)]^{-1}+$$
$$+O[r^{-2+h''}(x,y)]\}f(y)\,dS_y$$

and, writing

$$N_2(x,y;\varkappa)=-H^*(x,y;\varkappa)[I+\varkappa^2\Phi(y;\varkappa)]^{-1}+O(r^{-2+h''}(x,y)), \tag{5.46}$$

we finally obtain

$$\varphi(x)=[I+\varkappa^2\Phi(x;\varkappa)]^{-1}f(x)+\varkappa\int_S N_2(x,y;\varkappa)f(y)\,dS_y. \tag{5.47}$$

The manner of derivation of the $\varphi(x)$ given by (5.47) shows that it satisfies equation (5.12); hence

$$N_2(x,y;\varkappa)-K(x,y)[I+\varkappa^2\Phi(y;\varkappa)]^{-1}-\varkappa\int_S K(x,\xi)N_2(\xi,y;\varkappa)\,dS_\xi=0. \tag{5.48}$$

Our analysis is summed up in the following conclusions:

(a) For all $\varkappa$ in Π' except the discrete set of poles of a certain meromorphic function, equation (5.12) may only have solutions of the form (5.40).

(b) For all $\varkappa$ in Π' except the discrete set of poles of a certain meromorphic function, equation (5.12) actually has a unique solution expressed by (5.47).

It follows that for all $\varkappa$ apart from a discrete set of values, equation (5.12) has a unique solution which is simultaneously expressed by (5.40) and (5.47); taking the difference of these expressions and keeping in mind the arbitrariness of $f(x)$, we obtain

$$N_1(x,y;\varkappa)=N_2(x,y;\varkappa) \tag{5.49}$$

identically with respect to x and y, for any $\varkappa$ apart from some isolated values. The identity (5.49) expresses equivalence of meromorphic functions, which means that $N_1(x,y;\varkappa)$ and $N_2(x,y;\varkappa)$ must have common poles, and (5.49) holds for all $\varkappa$ which do not coincide with them. Denoting the common value of $N_1(x, y; \varkappa)$ and $N_2(x, y; \varkappa)$ by $N(x, y; \varkappa)$, we rewrite (5.42) and (5.48) as

$$N(x, y; \varkappa) - [I + \varkappa^2\Phi(x, \varkappa)]^{-1} K(x, y) - \varkappa \int_S N(x, \xi; \varkappa) K(\xi, y) dS_\xi = 0, \quad (5.50)$$

$$N(x, y; \varkappa) - K(x, y) [I + \varkappa^2\Phi(y; \varkappa)]^{-1} - \varkappa \int_S K(x, \xi) N(\xi, y; \varkappa) dS_\xi = 0, \quad (5.51)$$

We have thereby proved the following theorem:

There exists a matrix resolvent $N(x, y; \varkappa)$ *satisfying (5.50) and (5.51), which is a meromorphic function of* $\varkappa$ *on the plane* Π' *such that for any* $\varkappa$ *distinct from its poles equation (5.12) has a unique solution expressed by*

$$\varphi(x) = [I + \varkappa^2\Phi(x; \varkappa)]^{-1} f(x) + \varkappa \int_S N(x, \xi; \varkappa) f(\xi) dS_\xi. \quad (5.52)$$

This result obviously constitutes the first Fredholm theorem for the system (5.12).

Equations (5.50) and (5.51) are the functional equations for the resolvent.

§ 10. Consequences of the functional equations for the resolvent

We replace in (5.50) y by η, multiply on the right by $\nu N(\eta, y; \nu)$ and integrate over S with respect to η, obtaining

$$\nu \int_S N(x, \eta; \varkappa) N(\eta, y; \nu) dS_\eta - \nu [I + \varkappa^2\Phi(x; \varkappa)]^{-1} \int_S K(x, \eta) N(\eta, y; \nu) dS_\eta -$$
$$- \nu\varkappa \int_S dS_\eta \int_S N(x, \xi; \varkappa) K(\xi, \eta) N(\eta, y; \nu) dS_\xi = 0. \quad (5.53)$$

Replacing in (5.51) x by η and $\varkappa$ by ν, multiplying on the left by $\varkappa N(x, \eta; \varkappa)$ and integrating with respect to η, we obtain

$$\varkappa \int_S N(x, \eta; \varkappa) N(\eta, y; \nu) dS_\eta - \varkappa \int_S N(x, \eta; \varkappa) K(\eta, y) [I + \nu^2\Phi(y; \nu)]^{-1} dS_\eta -$$
$$- \nu\varkappa \int_S N(x, \eta; \varkappa) dS_\eta \int_S K(\eta, \xi) N(\xi, y; \nu) dS_\xi = 0. \quad (5.54)$$

Consider the differences

$$A = \nu [I + \varkappa^2\Phi(x; \varkappa)]^{-1} \int_S K(x, \eta) N(\eta, y; \nu) dS_\eta - \varkappa \int_S N(x, \eta; \varkappa) \times$$
$$\times K(\eta, y) [I + \nu^2\Phi(y; \nu)]^{-1} dS_\eta$$

and

$$B = \int_S dS_\eta \int_S N(x, \xi; \varkappa) K(\xi, \eta) N(\eta, y; \nu) dS_\xi -$$
$$- \int_S N(x, \eta; \varkappa) dS_\eta \int_S K(\eta, \xi) N(\xi, y; \nu) dS_\xi.$$

We now replace the integrals in the expression for A by their values from (5.50) and (5.51) and obtain

$$A = [I + \varkappa^2\Phi(x, \varkappa)]^{-1} \{N(x, y; \nu) - K(x, y) [I + \nu^2\Phi(y; \varkappa)]^{-1}\} -$$
$$- \{N(x, y; \varkappa) - [I + \varkappa^2\Phi(x; \varkappa)]^{-1} K(x, y)\} [I + \nu^2\Phi(y; \nu)]^{-1} =$$
$$= [I + \varkappa^2\Phi(x; \varkappa)]^{-1} N(x, y; \varkappa) - N(x, y; \varkappa) [I + \nu^2\Phi(y; \nu)]^{-1}.$$

Interchanging the designations ξ and η for the integration variables in the second term of the expression for B, we obtain

$$B=\int_S dS_\eta \int_S N(x,\ \xi;\ \varkappa)\, K(\xi,\ \eta)\, N(\eta,\ y;\ \nu)\, dS_\xi -$$
$$-\int_S N(x,\ \xi;\ \varkappa)\, dS_\xi \int_S K(\xi,\ \eta)\, N(\eta,\ y;\ \nu)\, dS_\eta.$$

We now separate the surface S into two parts, S_x and S_y, which contain respectively the points x and y. Then B can be represented as

$$B=\int_{S_y} dS_\eta \int_{S_y} \dots dS_\xi+\int_{S_y} dS_\eta \int_{S_x} \dots dS_\xi+\int_{S_x} dS_\eta \int_{S_y} \dots dS_\xi+\int_{S_x} dS_\eta \int_{S_x} \dots dS_\xi-$$
$$-\int_{S_y} \dots dS_\xi \int_{S_y} \dots dS_\eta-\int_{S_y} \dots dS_\xi \int_{S_x} \dots dS_\eta-\int_{S_x} \dots dS_\xi \int_{S_y} \dots dS_\eta-$$
$$-\int_{S_x} \dots dS_\xi \int_{S_x} \dots dS_\eta=\left(\int_{S_y} dS_\eta \int_{S_y} \dots dS_\xi-\int_{S_y} \dots dS_\xi \int_{S_y} \dots dS_\eta\right)+$$
$$+\left(\int_{S_y} dS_\eta \int_{S_x} \dots dS_\xi-\int_{S_x} \dots dS_\xi \int_{S_y} \dots dS_\eta\right)+\left(\int_{S_x} dS_\eta \int_{S_y} \dots dS_\xi-\right.$$
$$\left.-\int_{S_y} \dots dS_\xi \int_{S_x} \dots dS_\eta\right)+\left(\int_{S_x} dS_\eta \int_{S_x} \dots dS_\xi-\int_{S_x} \dots dS_\xi \int_{S_x} \dots dS_\eta\right).$$

Both variables in the first bracket assume values in S_y, and the matrix $N(x,\ \xi;\ \varkappa)$ in the integral

$$\int_{S_y} dS_\eta \int_{S_y} N(x,\ \xi;\ \varkappa)\, K(\xi,\ \eta)\, N(\eta,\ y;\ \nu)\, dS_\xi$$

obviously remains continuous; applying Theorem 8 of § 3, and in view of (5.46) and (5.44"), we find that this integral equals

$$-N(x,\ y;\ \varkappa)\, \Phi(y;\ \nu)\, [I+\nu^2\Phi(y;\ \nu)]^{-1}.$$

The integration in the second bracket extends over S_y with respect to η, and over S_x with respect to ξ; hence ξ and η may coincide only on the common boundary of S_x and S_y. We isolate this boundary within a belt girding the surface S; while this belt contains the boundary, x and y remain clear of it, not even lying on its edges. Integration over this belt, where the matrices $N(x,\ \xi;\ \varkappa)$ and $N(\eta,\ y;\ \nu)$ are continuous, contributes nothing to the difference in question. The remaining part of the surface (S less the belt, indicated by a prime), in which the kernel $K(\xi,\ \eta)$ is continuous, contributes to the second bracket

$$\int_{S'_y} dS_\eta \int_{S'_x} N(x,\ \xi;\ \varkappa)\, [K(\xi,\ \eta)-K(x,\ y)]\, N(\eta,\ y;\ \nu)\, dS_\xi-$$
$$-\int_{S'_x} N(x,\ \xi;\ \varkappa)\, dS_\xi \int_{S'_y} [K(\xi,\ \eta)-K(x,\ y)]\, N(\eta,\ y;\ \nu)\, dS_\eta+$$
$$+\int_{S'_y} dS_\eta \int_{S'_x} N(x,\ \xi;\ \varkappa)\, K(x,\ y)\, N(\eta,\ y;\ \nu)\, dS_\xi-$$
$$-\int_{S'_x} N(x,\ \xi;\ \varkappa)\, dS_\xi \int_{S'_y} K(x,\ y)\, N(\eta,\ y;\ \nu)\, dS_\eta.$$

Since the integration variables are separated in the last two terms, we conclude that the whole expression vanishes.

In the third bracket integration extends over S_x with respect to η and over S_y with respect to ξ; the matrices $N(x, \xi; \varkappa)$ and $N(\eta, y; \nu)$ are there still continuous, so that the third bracket vanishes too.

Finally, in the fourth bracket both variables assume values in S_x, and the matrix $N(\eta, y; \nu)$ is continuous in the integral

$$-\int_{S_x} \ldots dS_\xi \int_{S_x} \ldots dS_\eta;$$

applying Theorem 8 of § 3 and using (5.41), we obtain for that bracket

$$[I + \varkappa^2 \Phi(x; \varkappa)]^{-1} \Phi(x; \varkappa) N(x, y; \nu).$$

Collecting all results and subtracting (5.53) from (5.54), we obtain

$$(\varkappa - \nu) \int_S N(x, \eta; \varkappa) N(\eta, y; \nu) dS_\eta + [I + \varkappa^2 \Phi(x; \varkappa)]^{-1} N(x, y; \nu) -$$
$$- N(x, y; \varkappa)[I + \nu^2 \Phi(y; \nu)]^{-1} - \varkappa\nu N(x, y; \varkappa)\Phi(y; \nu)[I + \nu^2 \Phi(y; \nu)]^{-1} +$$
$$+ [I + \varkappa^2 \Phi(x; \varkappa)]^{-1} \varkappa\nu \Phi(x; \varkappa) N(x, y; \nu) = 0,$$

or

$$(\varkappa - \nu) \int_S N(x, \eta; \varkappa) N(\eta, y; \nu) dS_\eta = N(x, y; \varkappa)[I + \varkappa\nu \Phi(y; \nu)] \times$$
$$\times [I + \nu^2 \Phi(y; \nu)]^{-1} - [I + \varkappa^2 \Phi(x; \varkappa)]^{-1} [I + \varkappa\nu \Phi(x; \varkappa)] N(x, y; \nu). \tag{5.55}$$

The last relation may again be rewritten as

$$\int_S N(x, \eta; \varkappa) N(\eta, y, \nu) dS_\eta = \frac{1}{\varkappa - \nu} [N(x, y; \varkappa) - N(x, y; \nu)] +$$
$$+ \nu N(x, y; \varkappa) \Phi(y; \nu) [I + \nu^2 \Phi(y; \nu)]^{-1} +$$
$$+ \varkappa [I + \varkappa^2 \Phi(x; \varkappa)]^{-1} \Phi(x; \varkappa) N(x, y; \nu), \ldots, \tag{5.56}$$

as may be verified by multiplying (5.56) by $(\varkappa - \nu)$ to obtain

$$(\varkappa - \nu) \int_S N(x, \eta; \varkappa) N(\eta, y; \nu) dS_\eta = N(x, y; \varkappa)[I + \nu^2 \Phi(y; \nu)] \times$$
$$\times [I + \nu^2 \Phi(y; \nu)]^{-1} - [I + \varkappa^2 \Phi(x; \varkappa)]^{-1} [I + \varkappa^2 \Phi(x, \varkappa)] N(x, y; \nu) +$$
$$+ (\varkappa - \nu) \nu N(x, y; \varkappa) \Phi(y; \nu) [I + \nu^2 \Phi(y; \nu)]^{-1} +$$
$$+ (\varkappa - \nu) \varkappa [I + \varkappa^2 \Phi(x; \varkappa)]^{-1} \Phi(x; \varkappa) N(x, y; \nu),$$

from which (5.55) is readily recovered.

From (5.50) we find that for $\varkappa = 0$

$$N(x, y; 0) = K(x, y); \tag{5.57}$$

therefore, setting $\nu = 0$ in (5.55),

$$\varkappa \int_S N(x, \eta; \varkappa) K(\eta, y) dS_\eta + [I + \varkappa^2 \Phi(x; \varkappa)]^{-1} K(x, y) - N(x, y; \varkappa) = 0;$$

which is the same as (5.50); for $\varkappa = 0$ (5.55) similarly reduces to (5.51).

§ 11. Second Fredholm theorem

Let $\varkappa_0$ be a pole of the resolvent $N(x, y; \varkappa)$. For $\varkappa$ close to $\varkappa_0$ we have

$$N(x, y; \varkappa) = \sum_{\alpha=1}^{p} B^{(\alpha)}(x, y)(\varkappa - \varkappa_0)^{-\alpha} + \sum_{\beta=0}^{\infty} A^{(\beta)}(x, y)(\varkappa - \varkappa_0)^{\beta}; \tag{5.58}$$

where $B^{(\alpha)}(x, y)$ and $A^{(\beta)}(x, y)$ are well-defined matrices.

Let

$$B^{(\alpha)}(x, y) = \begin{Vmatrix} B_{11}^{(\alpha)}(x, y) & B_{12}^{(\alpha)}(x, y) & B_{13}^{(\alpha)}(x, y) \\ B_{21}^{(\alpha)}(x, y) & B_{22}^{(\alpha)}(x, y) & B_{23}^{(\alpha)}(x, y) \\ B_{31}^{(\alpha)}(x, y) & B_{32}^{(\alpha)}(x, y) & B_{33}^{(\alpha)}(x, y) \end{Vmatrix}.$$

The column-vectors of $B^{(\alpha)}(x, y)$ and its transpose $B^{(\alpha)*}(x, y)$ will be denoted by $B_k^{(\alpha)}(x, y)$, $B_k^{(\alpha)*}(x, y)$, $k=1, 2, 3$. Let us show that the $B_{jk}^{(\alpha)}(x, y)$, $j=1, 2, 3$ are continuous functions of x, and the $A_{jk}^{(\beta)}(x, y)$ have a second-order pole at $x=y$. As we know (§ 9), a solution of (5.12) has the form

$$\varphi(x) = \psi(x) + \sum_{n=1}^{p} \varkappa^n F_*^{(n-1)}\psi,$$

where $\psi(x)$ is a solution of (5.39) with the kernel $F_*^{(p)}(x, y)$, which is continuous in the sense of Hölder. It may be easily verified that

$$\psi(x) = [I + \varkappa^2\Phi(x; \varkappa)]^{-1} f(x) + \varkappa \int_S \Big\{ [I + \varkappa^2\Phi(x; \varkappa)]^{-1} H(x, y; \varkappa) -$$

$$- \varkappa^p R(x, y; \varkappa) [I + \varkappa^2\Phi(y; \varkappa)]^{-1} -$$

$$- \varkappa^{p+1} \int_S R(x, \xi; \varkappa) [I + \varkappa^2\Phi(\xi; \varkappa)]^{-1} H(\xi, y; \varkappa)\, dS_\xi \Big\} f(y)\, dS_y,$$

where $R(x, y; \varkappa)$, the resolvent of the kernel $F_*^{(p)}(x, y)$, is continuous in the sense of belonging to $H(\gamma)$ and meromorphic in $\varkappa$; the sum

$$\sum_{n=1}^{p} \varkappa^n F^{(n-1)}\psi,$$

obtained by multiplying $\psi(y)$ by kernels holomorphic in $\varkappa$ and having removable singularities and subsequent integration, is by Theorem 4 of § 3 of class $H(\gamma)$ and meromorphic in $\varkappa$.

We finally have

$$\varphi(x) = [I + \varkappa^2\Phi(x; \varkappa)]^{-1} f(x) +$$

$$+ \varkappa \int_S \{[I + \varkappa^2\Phi(x; \varkappa)]^{-1} H(x, y; \varkappa) + P(x, y; \varkappa)\} f(y)\, dS_y,$$

where the matrix $P(x, y; \varkappa)$ is again of class $H(\gamma)$ and meromorphic in $\varkappa$. Combining the last expression with (5.40) we obtain

$$N(x, y; \varkappa) = [I + \varkappa^2\Phi(x; \varkappa)]^{-1} H(x, y; \varkappa) + P(x, y; \varkappa). \tag{5.59}$$

Thus the first term of the right-hand side of (5.59) is a holomorphic, and the second a meromorphic function of $\varkappa$ on Π'. Hence it is clear that in the expansion in powers of $(\varkappa - \varkappa_0)$ negative powers may come only from the last term, and thus $B^{(\alpha)}(x, y)$ must be continuous. Similarly, positive powers of $(\varkappa - \varkappa_0)$ appear in the expansion of the first term, so that $A^{(\beta)}(x, y)$ must have a second-order pole at $x=y$.

Substituting the expansion (5.58) in (5.50), (5.51), and equating coefficients of the powers $(\varkappa - \varkappa_0)^{-p}$, $(\varkappa - \varkappa_0)^{1-p}$, $(\varkappa - \varkappa_0)^0$, we obtain

$$B^{(p)}(x, y) - \varkappa_0 \int_S B^{(p)}(x, \xi) K(\xi, y)\, dS_\xi = 0, \tag{5.60$_1$}$$

$$B^{(p-1)}(x, y) - \int_S B^{(p)}(x, \xi) K(\xi, y)\, dS_\xi -$$

$$- \varkappa_0 \int_S B^{(p-1)}(x, \xi) K(\xi, \eta)\, dS_\xi = 0, \qquad (5.60_2)$$

$$A^{(0)}(x, y) - \left[I + \varkappa_0^2 \Phi(x; \varkappa_0)\right]^{-1} K(x, y) -$$

$$- \int_S B^{(1)}(x, \xi) K(\xi, y)\, dS_\xi - \varkappa_0 \int_S A^0(x, \xi) K(\xi, y)\, dS_\xi = 0 \qquad (5.60_3)$$

and

$$B^{(p)}(x, y) - \varkappa_0 \int_S K(x, \xi) B^{(p)}(\xi, y)\, dS_\xi = 0, \qquad (5.61_1)$$

$$B^{(p-1)}(x, y) - \int_S K(x, \xi) B^{(p)}(\xi, y)\, dS_\xi -$$

$$- \varkappa_0 \int_S K(x, \xi) B^{(p-1)}(\xi, y)\, dS_\xi = 0, \qquad (5.61_2)$$

$$A^{(0)}(x, y) - K(x, y)\left[I + \varkappa_0^2 \Phi(y; \varkappa_0)\right]^{-1} - \int_S K(x, \xi) B^{(1)}(\xi, y)\, dS_\xi -$$

$$- \varkappa_0 \int_S K(x, \xi) A^{(0)}(\xi, y)\, dS_\xi = 0. \qquad (5.61_3)$$

We divide the nine equalities (5.61_1) into three groups of three as follows

$$B_k^{(p)}(x, y) - \varkappa_0 \int_S K(x, \xi) B_k^{(p)}(\xi, y)\, dS_\xi = 0 \quad (k = 1, 2, 3). \qquad (5.62)$$

Treating y as a parameter, we notice that (5.62) is nothing else but the homogeneous system corresponding to (5.12) for $\varkappa = \varkappa_0$:

$$\varphi(x) - \varkappa_0 \int_S K(x, \xi) \varphi(\xi)\, dS_\xi = 0. \qquad (5.12^0)$$

Consequently, the homogeneous system (5.12^0) is satisfied by each of the three vector functions $B_k^{(p)}(x, y)$, $k = 1, 2, 3$ for any value of the parameter y. At least one of these vectors does not vanish identically, because $B^{(p)}(x, y)$ does not. Further, any solution of (5.12^0) is simultaneously also a solution of the homogeneous Fredholm equation (5.13^0), and since the latter has only a finite number of linearly independent solutions the same goes for (5.12^0), so that out of the infinite manifold of solutions $B_k^{(p)}(x, y)$, $k = 1, 2, 3$ generated by having the parameter y range over its all admissible values, only a finite number are linearly independent.

Let these independent solutions be

$$\varphi_1(x), \varphi_2(x), \ldots, \varphi_r(x),$$

then $B_k^{(p)}(x, y)$ may be represented as a linear combination of them with coefficients depending on y:

$$B_k^{(p)}(x, y) = \sum_{j=1}^{r} \psi_{jk}(y) \varphi_j(x) \quad (k = 1, 2, 3). \qquad (5.63)$$

Note that while $\varphi_j(x)$, $j = 1, 2, \ldots, r$ are vectors, their multipliers $\psi_{jk}(y)$, j, $k = 1, 2, \ldots, r$ are scalars.

It follows from (5.63) that the $\psi_{jk}(y)$ are continuous functions of y. We project the vector equation (5.63), keeping $k = 1, 2, 3$ fixed, on the coordinate axes x_s, $s = 1, 2, 3$. The projection of $B_k^{(p)}(x, y)$ on the x_s-axis is labeled by the subscript s written to the left of the subscript k:

$$B_{sk}^{(p)}(x, y) = \sum_{j=1}^{r} \varphi_{sj}(x)\,\psi_{jk}(y) \qquad (k, s = 1, 2, 3). \tag{5.64}$$

We assign r different positions to the point x on S so that

$$\begin{vmatrix} \varphi_{s1}(x^{(1)}) & \varphi_{s2}(x^{(1)}) \dots & \varphi_{sr}(x^{(1)}) \\ \varphi_{s1}(x^{(2)}) & \varphi_{s2}(x^{(2)}) \dots & \varphi_{sr}(x^{(2)}) \\ \dots & \dots & \dots \\ \varphi_{s1}(x^{(r)}) & \varphi_{s2}(x^{(r)}) \dots & \varphi_{sr}(x^{(r)}) \end{vmatrix} \neq 0;$$

this may be done, since if the determinant were to vanish identically for any $s = 1, 2, 3$, the functions $\varphi_{s1}, \varphi_{s2}, \dots, \varphi_{sr}$ would be linearly dependent, which would imply the same for the vectors $\boldsymbol{\varphi}_1(x), \boldsymbol{\varphi}_2(x), \dots, \boldsymbol{\varphi}_r(x)$. Solving the system (5.64) for $\psi_{jk}(y)$, $j = 1, 2, \dots, r$, and thus expressing them as a linear combination of the functions $B_{sk}^{(p)}(x^{(i)}, y)$, $i = 1, 2, \dots, r$, we infer the continuity of

$$\psi_{jk}(y) \qquad (k = 1, 2, 3; \quad j = 1, 2, \dots, r).$$

We now return to the equations (5.60_1), and arrange them in three groups:

$$B_k^{(p)*}(x, y) - \varkappa_0 \int_S B_k^{(p)*}(x, \xi)\,K(\xi, y)\,dS_\xi = 0, \tag{5.65}$$

where $B_k^{(p)*}(x, y)$ is the k-th column-vector* of the transpose of $B^{(p)*}(x, y)$. Treating x as a parameter, we notice that (5.65) is the homogeneous system associated with (5.12^0):

$$\boldsymbol{\psi}(y) - \varkappa_0 \int_S \boldsymbol{\psi}(\xi)\,K(\xi, y)\,dS_\xi = 0. \tag{5.66}$$

Consequently, the associated homogeneous system (5.66) is satisfied by each of the three vectors $B_k^{(p)*}(x, y)$ for any value of the parameter x. We conclude as before that at least one of these vectors does not vanish identically. On the other hand the solutions of (5.66) also satisfy a certain homogeneous system of Fredholm equations, and therefore only a finite number of solutions of the associated system (5.66) are linearly independent.

Let us introduce the vectors $\boldsymbol{\psi}_j(y)$, $j = 1, 2, \dots, r$ whose projections on the x_k-axis, $k = 1, 2, 3$ will be denoted by $\psi_{jk}(y)$, $k = 1, 2, 3$. Then (5.64) may be considered as the projection on the x_k-axis of the vector equation

$$B_s^{(p)*}(x, y) = \sum_{j=1}^{r} \varphi_{sj}(x)\,\boldsymbol{\psi}_j(y), \tag{5.67}$$

where $B_s^{(p)*}$ is the s-th row of the matrix $B^{(p)}(x, y)$. But the $\boldsymbol{\psi}_j(y)$, $j = 1, 2, \dots, r$, turn out to be solutions of equations (5.65), since the $B_s^{(p)*}(x, y)$ considered as vector functions of y are solutions of these equations, and the $\varphi_{sj}(x)$ linearly independent. Thus the number, r_*, of linearly independent solutions of (5.66), which we have seen must be finite, cannot be smaller than r:

$$r_* \geqslant r.$$

Changing the places of (5.61_1) and (5.60_1) and repeating the arguments that have led up to the last inequality, we clearly obtain

$$r \geqslant r_*,$$

* Its projection on the x_s-axis is $B_{ks}^{(p)*}$, i.e., the projection subscript is here on the right of the subscript k indicating the vector's ordinal number as a matrix column; actually, $B_{ks}^{(p)*}$ is the projection of the k-th row-vector of the matrix $B^{(P)}(x, y)$ on the x_s-axis.

whence

$$r = r_*,$$

which completes the proof of the second Fredholm theorem for the singular system of equations (5.12).

§ 12. Elements of resolvent theory

The results established in the preceding sections allow us to develop a theory of canonical kernels and dominant functions [fonctions principales] for the resolvent of the singular system (5.12), in analogy with the Goursat theory for the Fredholm resolvent. This was shown for a single equation by Giraud /10a, b/.

We write

$$N(x, y; \varkappa) = \gamma(x, y; \varkappa) + A(x, y; \varkappa), \tag{5.58}$$

where

$$\gamma(x, y; \varkappa) = \sum_{\alpha=1}^{p} B^{(\alpha)}(x, y)(\varkappa - \varkappa_0)^{-\alpha},$$

$$A(x, y; \varkappa) = \sum_{\beta=0}^{\infty} A^{(\beta)}(x, y)(\varkappa - \varkappa_0)^{\beta},$$

and set

$$\varkappa - \varkappa_0 = u, \quad \nu - \varkappa_0 = v.$$

Substituting this in (5.56) and equating coefficients of negative powers of u and v, we obtain

$$(\varkappa - \nu)\int_S \gamma(x, \eta; \varkappa)\gamma(\eta, y; \nu)\, dS_\eta = \gamma(x, y; \varkappa) - \gamma(x, y; \nu), \tag{5.68}$$

while equating coefficients of the positive and zero powers of u and v gives

$$\int_S A(x, \eta; \varkappa) A(\eta, y; \nu)\, dS_\eta = (\varkappa - \nu)^{-1}[A(x, y; \varkappa) -$$
$$- A(x, y; \nu)] + \nu A(x, y; \varkappa)\Phi(y; \nu)[I + \nu^2\Phi(y; \nu)]^{-1} +$$
$$+ \varkappa[I + \varkappa^2\Phi(x; \varkappa)]^{-1}\Phi(x; \varkappa) A(x, y; \nu). \tag{5.69}$$

Therefore $A(x, y; \varkappa)$ is a resolvent of the kernel $A(x, y; 0)$, as may be verified by setting $\nu = 0$ in the last expression and comparing the result with (5.50). It also follows from (5.57) that

$$K(x, y) = \gamma(x, y; 0) + A(x, y; 0), \tag{5.70}$$

where, as we know, $\gamma(x, y; 0)$ is a continuous function of x and y. Again equating coefficients, we obtain from those of the positive and zero powers of u that

$$\int_S A(x, \eta; \varkappa)\gamma(\eta, y; \nu)\, dS_\eta = \varkappa\Phi(x; \varkappa)\left[I + \varkappa^2\Phi(x, \varkappa)^{-1}\right]\gamma(x, y; \nu), \tag{5.71}$$

while the remaining terms give

$$\int_S \gamma(x, \eta; \varkappa) A(\eta, y; \nu)\, dS_\eta = \gamma(x, y; \nu)\nu\Phi(y; \nu)[I + \nu^2\Phi(y; \nu)]^{-1}. \tag{5.72}$$

Setting $\varkappa = 0$ in (5.71) and $\nu = 0$ in (5.72), we have

$$\int_S A(x, \eta; 0)\gamma(\eta, y; \nu)\, dS_\eta = \int_S \gamma(x, \eta; \varkappa) A(\eta, y; 0)\, dS_\eta = 0 \tag{5.73}$$

and hence for $\nu=0$, $\varkappa=0$

$$\int_S A(x, \eta; 0)\,\gamma(\eta, y; 0)\,dS_\eta=\int_S \gamma(x, \eta; 0)\,A(\eta, y; 0)\,dS_\eta=0. \tag{5.74}$$

It is possible to derive from the foregoing relations a theory of dominant functions and canonical kernels for our singular equations in the same manner as this is done for ordinary Fredholm equations. We will not do that in the general case when $\varkappa=\varkappa_0$ is a multiple pole of the resolvent, but confine ourselves to a detailed treatment of the case of a simple pole. This case is most important for applications in the theory of elasticity; it will be shown in (VI, 1–2) that the problems of the theory of elasticity lead to equations which admit only simple poles in the resolvents.

Accordingly, we set $p=1$; then, by (5.58),

$$-\varkappa_0\gamma(x, y; 0)=B^{(1)}(x, y); \tag{5.75}$$

and so (5.61_1) may be rewritten as

$$\gamma(x, y; 0)-\varkappa_0\int_S K(x, \xi)\,\gamma(\xi, y; 0)\,dS_\xi=0.$$

Substituting here the value of $\gamma(x, y; 0)$ from (5.70) and applying the orthogonality property (5.74) of the matrices $A(x, y; 0)$ and $\gamma(x, y; 0)$, we obtain

$$\gamma(x, y; 0)-\varkappa_0\int_S \gamma(x, \xi; 0)\,\gamma(\xi, y; 0)\,dS_\xi=0. \tag{5.76}$$

Inserting the value of $\gamma(x, y; 0)$ from (5.75), we have

$$B^{(1)}(x, y)+\int_S B^{(1)}(x, \xi)\,B^{(1)}(\xi, y)\,dS_\xi=0$$

or in terms of the elements

$$B^{(1)}_{sk}(x, y)+\int_S\sum_{q=1}^{3} B^{(1)}_{sq}(x, \xi)\,B^{(1)}_{qk}(\xi, y)\,dS_\xi=0.$$

Replacing here $B^{(1)}_{sk}(x, y)$, $B^{(1)}_{sq}(x, \xi)$, $B^{(1)}_{qk}(\xi, y)$ by their values from (5.64), we obtain

$$\sum_{j=1}^{r}\varphi_{sj}(x)\,\psi_{jk}(y)+\int_S\sum_{q=1}^{3}\sum_{j=1}^{r}\varphi_{sj}(x)\,\psi_{jq}(\xi)\sum_{t=1}^{r}\varphi_{qt}(\xi)\,\psi_{tk}(y)\,dS_\xi=0$$
$$(s, k=1, 2, 3); \tag{5.77}$$

term-by-term multiplication of the sums over t and j under the integral sign gives*

$$\begin{aligned}(\varphi^0_{s1}\psi^1_{1q}+\varphi^0_{s2}\psi^1_{2q}+\dots+\varphi^0_{sr}\psi^1_{rq})(\varphi^1_{q1}\psi_{1k}+\varphi^1_{q2}\psi_{2k}+\dots+\varphi^1_{qr}\psi_{rk})=\\ =\varphi^0_{s1}\psi_{1k}\psi^1_{1q}\varphi^1_{q1}+\varphi^0_{s1}\psi_{2k}\psi^1_{1q}\varphi^1_{q2}+\dots+\varphi^0_{s1}\psi_{rk}\psi^1_{1q}\varphi^1_{qr}+\varphi^0_{s2}\psi_{1k}\psi^1_{2q}\varphi^1_{q1}+\\ +\varphi^0_{s2}\psi_{2k}\psi^1_{2q}\varphi^1_{q2}+\dots+\varphi^0_{s2}\psi_{rk}\psi^1_{2q}\varphi^1_{qr}+\dots+\varphi^0_{sr}\psi_{1k}\psi^1_{rq}\varphi^1_{q1}+\\ +\varphi^0_{sr}\psi_{rk}\psi^1_{rq}\varphi^1_{q2}+\dots+\varphi^0_{sr}\psi_{rk}\psi^1_{rq}\varphi^1_{qr},\end{aligned}$$

and after summing over q we obtain

$$\begin{aligned}\varphi^0_{s1}\psi_{1k}(\psi_1(\xi)\,\varphi_1(\xi))+\varphi^0_{s1}\psi_{2k}(\psi^1_1\varphi^1_2)+\dots+\varphi^0_{s1}\psi_{rk}(\psi^1_1\varphi^1_r)+\\ +\varphi^0_{s2}\psi_{1k}(\psi^1_2\varphi^1_1)+\varphi^0_{s2}\psi_{2k}(\psi^1_2\varphi^1_2)+\dots+\varphi^0_{s2}\psi_{rk}(\psi^1_2\varphi^1_r)+\\ \dots\dots\dots\dots\dots\dots\dots\dots\dots\\ +\varphi^0_{sr}\psi_{1k}(\psi^1_r\varphi^1_1)+\varphi^0_{sr}\psi_{2k}(\psi^1_r\varphi^1_r)+\dots+\varphi^0_{sr}\psi_{rk}(\psi^1_r\varphi^1_r).\end{aligned}$$

* The superscripts 0 and 1 respecitvely indicate that the argument is x or ξ; no superscript means argument y.

The unintegrated sum is

$$\varphi_{s1}^{0}\psi_{1k}+\varphi_{s2}^{0}\psi_{2k}+\ldots+\varphi_{sr}^{0}\psi_{rk}.$$

Inserting these expressions for the sums into (5.77) and collecting terms, we obtain

$$\int\limits_{S}\varphi_m(x)\psi_n(x)\,dS_x=\begin{cases}-1, & m=n,\\ 0, & m\neq n,\end{cases} \tag{5.78}$$

where $\varphi_m(x)\psi_n(x)$ is a scalar product.

§ 13. Third Fredholm theorem

Let $\varkappa=\varkappa_0$ be a pole of the resolvent and an eigenvalue of the homogeneous equation (5.12^0). We assume from the outset that the equation

$$\varphi(x)-\varkappa_0\int\limits_{S}K(x,\xi)\varphi(\xi)\,dS_\xi=f(x) \tag{5.79}$$

has a solution. Multiplying it by $\psi_j(x)\,dS_x$, where

$$\psi_1(x),\ \psi_2(x),\ \ldots,\ \psi_r(x) \tag{5.80}$$

is a complete system of solutions of the associated equation, and integrating over S, we obtain

$$\int\limits_{S}\psi_j(x)f(x)\,dS_x=0\qquad (j=1,2,\ldots,r). \tag{5.81}$$

This proves that for a solution to exist it is necessary that the vector $f(x)$ be orthogonal to a complete system of fundamental solutions of the homogeneous associated equation.

To demonstrate the sufficiency of this condition, we first prove an auxiliary proposition.*

Let $\omega(x)$ and $\sigma(x)$ be solutions of the equations

$$\omega(x)-\varkappa_0\int\limits_{S}\gamma(x,y;0)\,\omega(y)\,dS_y=f(x), \tag{5.82}$$

$$\sigma(x)-\varkappa_0\int\limits_{S}A(x,y;0)\,\sigma(y)\,dS_y=f(x), \tag{5.83}$$

whose kernels are orthogonal in virtue of (5.74).

Equation (5.83) has the singular kernel $A(x,y;0)$; by (5.69) its resolvent is $A(x,y;\varkappa)$, and therefore $\varkappa=\varkappa_0$ is not an eigenvalue of (5.83), and its solution may be obtained by Fredholm's first theorem, which we have demonstrated for singular equations in § 9.

Let us show that if $\omega(x)$ is given by (5.82), then the expression

$$\varphi(x)=\omega(x)+\sigma(x)-f(x) \tag{5.84}$$

is a solution of (5.12). In fact, using (5.70), we can write (5.12) in the form

$$\varphi(x)-\varkappa_0\int\limits_{S}[\gamma(x,y;0)+A(x,y;0)]\,\varphi(y)\,dS_y=f(x).$$

Inserting here (5.84) and in view of (5.82) and (5.83), we obtain

$$\int\limits_{S}\gamma(x,y;0)\,[\sigma(y)-f(y)]\,dS_y+\int\limits_{S}A(x,y;0)\,[\omega(y)-f(y)]\,dS_y=0. \tag{5.85}$$

* This proposition is significant in itself, since it indicates a method of actually solving equation (5.12) when $\varkappa=\varkappa_0$ is a pole of the resolvent.

Replacing x by y, and y by ξ in (5.82) and (5.83), we multiply on the left the first equation by $A(x, y; 0)\,dS_y$, the second by $\gamma(x, y; 0)\,dS_y$ and integrate over S. Then, changing the order of integration (this is allowed here) and taking into account the orthogonality relations (5.74), we deduce that each of the integrals in (5.85) vanishes and consequently (5.84) actually is a solution of (5.12).

As has been said before, $\sigma(x)$ may be obtained directly from (5.83); the vector function $\omega(x)$ may be constructed only in the case when $f(x)$ fulfills some additional conditions. In fact, equation (5.82) with the continuous kernel $\gamma(x, y; 0)$ is of the Fredholm type, while the equation (5.68),

$$\gamma(x, y; \varkappa)-\gamma(x, y; \nu)=(\varkappa-\nu)\int_S \gamma(x, \xi; \varkappa)\,\gamma(\xi, y; \nu)\,dS_\xi,$$

indicates, as we know (cf. Goursat /7/), that $\gamma(x, y; \varkappa)$ is the resolvent of the kernel $\gamma(x, y; 0)$; consequently $\varkappa=\varkappa_0$, being a pole of $\gamma(x, y; \varkappa)$, is an eigenvalue of (5.82), and the necessary and sufficient conditions for the solvability of this equation are by the third Fredholm theorem

$$\int_S f(x)\,\omega_j^*(x)\,dS_x=0, \tag{5.86}$$

where $\omega_j^*(x)$, $j=1, 2, \ldots, l$, are l linearly independent solutions of the homogeneous associated equation

$$\omega^*(x)-\varkappa_0\int_S \gamma^*(y, x; 0)\,\omega^*(y)\,dS_y=0,$$

which may also be written

$$\omega^*(y)-\varkappa_0\int_S \omega^*(\xi)\,\gamma(\xi, y; 0)\,dS_\xi=0. \tag{5.87}$$

It remains to show that $l=r$, and that the set of vectors $\omega_j^*(x)$ is a system of fundamental solutions of equation (5.66). To this end we compare (5.87) with (5.76):

$$\gamma(x, y; 0)-\varkappa_0\int_S \gamma(x, \xi; 0)\,\gamma(\xi, y; 0)\,dS_\xi=0.$$

Using the same grouping as in the derivation of (5.65), we may write

$$\gamma_k^*(x, y; 0)-\varkappa_0\int_S \gamma_k^*(x, \xi; 0)\,\gamma(\xi, y; 0)\,dS_\xi=0 \qquad (k=1, 2, 3).$$

Treating x here as a parameter and comparing with (5.87), we obtain

$$\omega^*(y)=\gamma_k^*(x, y; 0).$$

But (5.75) and (5.67) imply

$$\omega^*(y)=-\frac{1}{\varkappa_0}B_k^{(1)*}(x, y)=-\frac{1}{\varkappa_0}\sum_{j=1}^{r}\varphi_{kj}(x)\,\psi_j(y).$$

Thus, any solution of (5.87) is a linear combination of the linearly independent vectors $\psi_1(x), \psi_2(x), \ldots, \psi_r(x)$, and consequently the latter constitute a complete system of fundamental solutions of (5.87), while the conditions (5.86) reduce to (5.81'); this proves the sufficiency of the conditions (5.81), and therefore also the third Fredholm theorem for the system of singular integral equations (5.12).

Chapter VI

EXISTENCE THEOREMS. HOMOGENEOUS MEDIA

§ 1. Properties of the resolvent

We have seen (II, 2) that the integral equations associated with the first two fundamental boundary-value problems of elasticity — the first interior and exterior problems (D_i) and (D_a), and the second interior and exterior problems (T_i) and (T_a) — are of the following form:

$$\varphi(x)-\varkappa\int_S \varphi(y)K(y,x)\,dS_y=f'(x), \tag{6.1}$$

$$\varphi(x)-\varkappa\int_S K(x,y)\varphi(y)\,dS_y=f'(x). \tag{6.2}$$

The first equation corresponds to problem (D_i) for $\varkappa=+1$ and $f'=-f$, and to problem (D_a) for $\varkappa=-1$ and $f'=f$, while the second corresponds to problem (T_i) for $\varkappa=-1$ and $f'=f$, and to problem (T_a) for $\varkappa=+1$, $f'=-f$.

It was shown in Ch. V that the fundamental Fredholm theorems and alternative are valid for the systems of singular equations (6.1) and (6.2) only if the parameter $\varkappa$ takes on values in the Π'-plane which is symmetrically slit along the real-axis intervals

$$\left(\pm\frac{1}{4\pi l},\ \pm\infty\right).$$

For the following discussion it is obviously essential that the values $\varkappa=\pm 1$, corresponding to problems (D) and (T), should not fall on these slits; this condition is fulfilled, as

$$l=\frac{\mu}{2\pi(\lambda+2\mu)}$$

gives

$$\frac{1}{4\pi l}=1+\frac{\lambda}{2\mu}>1 \qquad (\lambda,\ \mu>0).$$

In virtue of (2.1) and (2.5)

$$\frac{1}{2}(1-\varkappa)W_a-\frac{1}{2}(1+\varkappa)W_i=\varphi(x)-\varkappa\int_S\frac{1}{2\pi}\Gamma_{\mathrm{I}}(x,y)\varphi(y)\,dS_y,$$

$$\frac{1}{2}(1-\varkappa)(\mathbf{T}V)_i-\frac{1}{2}(1+\varkappa)(\mathbf{T}V)_a=\varphi(x)-\varkappa\int_S\frac{1}{2\pi}(\mathbf{T}_x\Gamma(x,y))\varphi(y)\,dS_y.$$

Using the previous notation (II, 2), viz.

$$\frac{1}{2\pi}\mathbf{T}_x\Gamma(x,y)=K(x,y),$$

$$\frac{1}{2\pi}\Gamma_{\mathrm{I}}(x,y)=K^*(y,x),$$

we obtain

$$\frac{1}{2}(1-\varkappa)W_a-\frac{1}{2}(1+\varkappa)W_i=\varphi(x)-\varkappa\int_S \varphi(y)K(y,x)\,dS_y, \tag{6.3}$$

$$\frac{1}{2}(1-\varkappa)(TV)_i-\frac{1}{2}(1+\varkappa)(TV)_a=\varphi(x)-\varkappa\int_S K(x,y)\varphi(y)\,dS_y. \tag{6.4}$$

In addition to these formulas we have the homogeneous integral equations associated with the homogeneous problems

$$\varphi(x)-\varkappa\int_S \varphi(y)K(y,x)\,dS_y=0, \tag{6.5}$$

$$\varphi(x)-\varkappa\int_S K(x,y)\varphi(y)\,dS_y=0. \tag{6.6}$$

We will now prove a few theorems about properties of the resolvents of these equations. These properties are analogous to the well-known properties of resolvents of the integral equations of the Dirichlet and Neumann problems in the theory of harmonic functions, and the proof also resembles the classic one for that case (cf., e. g., /12/).

We shall consider the static and dynamic cases separately. In this section we consider the integral equations (6.1), (6.2), (6.5), (6.6) for $\omega=0$ i. e., the static problems.

Theorem 1. All eigenvalues of the kernel $K(x,y)$ *are real.*

Let us assume the opposite and let $\varkappa=\alpha+\beta i$, where α and β are real and nonvanishing, be an eigenvalue of $K(x,y)$. Equation (6.6) admits for this $\varkappa$ a nontrivial solution $\varphi_1+i\varphi_2$. Constructing the corresponding single-layer potential $V(x)=V_1(x)+iV_2(x)$, one may verify that its first derivatives are continuous in B_i and B_a (notation of (II, 2)). Inserting the values of $V(x)$ into (6.4) and separating the real and imaginary parts, we obtain

$$(1-\alpha)(TV_1)_i-(1+\alpha)(TV_1)_a+\beta(TV_2)_i+\beta(TV_2)_a=0, \tag{6.7}$$

$$(1-\alpha)(TV_2)_i-(1+\alpha)(TV_2)_a-\beta(TV_1)_i-\beta(TV_1)_a=0. \tag{6.8}$$

Multiplying these equalities by V_1 and V_2, we form their difference and integrate it over S; then, on account of the Betti formula (1.10') which, as shown in Ch. III, remains valid for regular vectors in an infinite domain, we obtain

$$(1-\alpha)\int_{B_i}(V_2\Delta^*V_1-V_1\Delta^*V_2)\,d\sigma+(1+\alpha)\int_{B_a}(V_1\Delta^*V_2-V_2\Delta^*V_1)\,d\sigma+$$
$$+\beta\int_S\{[V_2(TV_2)_i+V_1(TV_1)_i]+[V_2(TV_2)_a+V_1(TV_1)_a]\}\,dS=0$$

and since $\Delta^*V_1=0$ and $\Delta^*V_2=0$

$$\beta\int_S[V_1(TV_1)+V_2(TV_2)]_i\,dS+\beta\int_S[V_1(TV_1)+V_2(TV_2)]_a\,dS=0. \tag{6.9}$$

But according to the Betti formulas (1.9'), which likewise are valid not only in a finite domain but, for regular vectors, also in an infinite one, we may write

$$\int[V_1(TV_1)+V_2(TV_2)]_i\,dS=\int_{B_i=\sum_{k=1}^{n}B_i^{(k)}}\{W(V_1,V_1)+W(V_2,V_2)\}\,d\sigma,$$

$$\int_S[V_1(TV_1)+V_2(TV_2)]_a\,dS=-\int_{B_a}\{W(V_1,V_1)+W(V_2,V_2)\}\,d\sigma,$$

where $W(u, u)$ is the positive-definite form defined by (1.12). If we write

$$J_j = \int_{B_i} W(V_j, V_j)\, d\sigma, \quad J'_j = \int_{B_a} W(V_j, V_j)\, d\sigma \qquad (j = 1, 2),$$

(6.9) takes the form

$$\beta(J_1 + J_2) - \beta(J'_1 + J'_2) = 0. \tag{6.10}$$

We now multiply (6.7) and (6.8) by V_1 and V_2, respectively, add them together and integrate over S; then in the same way we get

$$(1 - \alpha)(J_1 + J_2) + (1 + \alpha)(J'_1 + J'_2) = 0. \tag{6.11}$$

Considering (6.10) and (6.11) as a system of equations in $(J_1 + J_2)$ and $(J'_1 + J'_2)$, and keeping in mind that $\beta \neq 0$ by assumption, we obtain

$$J_1 = J_2 = J'_1 = J'_2 = 0,$$

since they cannot be negative. But now the positive-definiteness of $W(u, u)$ and the properties of a single-layer potential show that

$$V_1(x) = 0, \quad V_2(x) \equiv 0, \qquad x \in B_i + B_a.$$

Moreover, (2.5) imply $\varphi_1(x) = \varphi_2(x) = 0$.

This contradiction proves that the determinant of the system (6.10) and (6.11), which equals 2β, vanishes and hence that the eigenvalues are real.

Theorem 2. No eigenvalue of $K(x, y)$ *is less than 1 in absolute value.*

In fact, since $\beta = 0$, (6.11) is evidently of the form

$$(1 - \alpha) J_1 + (1 + \alpha) J'_1 = 0;$$

solving for α,

$$\alpha = \frac{J_1 + J'_1}{J_1 - J'_1}, \qquad |\alpha| \geqslant 1,$$

which proves the theorem.

Theorem 3. The eigenvalues of $K(x, y)$ *are simple poles of the resolvent.*

Let us assume the opposite and let, for example, $\varkappa = \varkappa_0$ be a second-order pole of the resolvent; then according to (5.58) we have the expansion

$$N(x, y; \varkappa) = \sum_{\alpha=1}^{2} B^{(\alpha)}(x, y)(\varkappa - \varkappa_0)^{-\alpha} + \sum_{\beta=0}^{\infty} A^{(\beta)}(x, y)(\varkappa - \varkappa_0)^{\beta}$$

and $B^{(2)}(x, y)$ does not vanish identically; substituting this expression for $N(x, y, \varkappa)$ in the functional equation for the resolvent (5.51), we obtain, by (5.61_1) and (5.61_2),

$$B^{(2)}(x, y) - \varkappa_0 \int_S K(x, \xi) B^{(2)}(\xi, y)\, dS_\xi = 0, \tag{6.12}$$

$$B^{(1)}(x, y) - \varkappa_0 \int_S K(x, \xi) B^{(1)}(\xi, y)\, dS_\xi = \frac{1}{\varkappa_0} B^{(2)}(x, y). \tag{6.13}$$

Treating y as a parameter, we denote

$$B_k^{(2)}(x, y) = \psi_1(x), \quad B_k^{(1)}(x, y) = \psi_2(x),$$

where k assumes one of the values 1, 2, 3, and construct single-layer potentials with the densities $\psi_1(x)$ and $\psi_2(x)$. These potentials satisfy the conditions

$$\left.\begin{aligned}&(1-\varkappa_0)(\mathbf{T}V_1)_i-(1+\varkappa_0)(\mathbf{T}V_1)_a=0,\\&(1-\varkappa_0)(\mathbf{T}V_2)_i-(1+\varkappa_0)(\mathbf{T}V_2)_a=(\mathbf{T}V_1)_i+(\mathbf{T}V_1)_a,\end{aligned}\right\} \tag{6.14}$$

which follow from representation (6.4) and (the first) equation (6.12), and from (6.4), (6.13) and (the second) (2.5).

We multiply the first of (6.14) by $-V_2$ and the second by V_1, and integrate their sum over S; this gives

$$J_1-J_1'=0; \tag{6.15}$$

but if we multiply the first of (6.14) by V_1 and integrate over S, we obtain

$$(1-\varkappa_0)J_1+(1+\varkappa_0)J_1'=0. \tag{6.16}$$

Now (6.15) and (6.16) are compatible only when $J_1=J_1'=0$; hence it follows that $V_1(x)=0$, and consequently $\psi_1(x)=0$; this contradicts the assumption that the pole is of an order higher than one, which completes the proof.

§ 2. Existence theorems for the static Problems (D_i) and (T_a)

We consider the case of a multiply-connected domain (Figure 1, Ch. II). The homogeneous equations

$$\varphi(x)-\int_S\varphi(y)K(y,x)\,dS_y=0, \tag{D_i^0}$$

$$\varphi(x)-\int_S K(x,y)\varphi(y)\,dS_y=0, \tag{T_a^0}$$

admit only trivial solutions. Let us assume the opposite and let $\psi(x)$ be some nontrivial solution of (T_a^0). The single-layer potential

$$V(x;\psi)=\frac{1}{2\pi}\int_S\Gamma(x,\xi)\psi(\xi)\,dS_\xi$$

has the following properties:

a) $\Delta^*V(x;\psi)=0$,

b) $(\mathbf{T}V(x;\psi))_a=0$ on S,

c) it satisfies at infinity the conditions (cf., (3.69))

$$V(x;\psi)=0(1),\qquad \frac{\partial V}{\partial R}=0(R^{-1}).$$

This vector must vanish according to Theorem 1 (III, 4); thus,

$$V(x,\psi)\equiv 0\qquad (x\in B_a),$$

due to the continuity of a single-layer potential

$$0=V_i(x;\psi)=V_a(x;\psi),$$

whence, by Theorem 6 (III, 4)

$$V(x;\psi)\equiv 0\qquad (x\in B_i).$$

But since

$$0=(\mathbf{T}V)_i-(\mathbf{T}V)_a=2\psi(x_0)=0\qquad (x_0\in S),$$

this leads to contradiction, which proves the assumption for equation (T_a^0). As (D_i^0) and (T_a^0) are associated systems of singular equations, the second

2109

Fredholm theorem, which was demonstrated for such systems in (V, 11), equation (D_i^0) too has none but trivial solutions.

Consequently, on account of the third Fredholm theorem (V, 13) the inhomogeneous equations (D_i) and (T_a) have unique solutions, which may be constructed by the first Fredholm theorem (V, 9), and this finally implies:

Theorem 4. Problem (D_i) with a vector $f(x)$ of class $H(\gamma)$ has a unique solution, represented by a double-layer potential.

Theorem 5. Problem (T_a) with a vector $f(x)$ of class $H(\gamma)$ has a unique solution, represented by a single-layer potential.

§ 3. The homogeneous static Problems (D_a^0) and (T_i^0)

The vector $\mathfrak{A}(x)$ with its projections on the (x_1, x_2, x_3) axes

$$\mathfrak{A}_1(x) = a + qx_3 - rx_2, \quad \mathfrak{A}_2(x) = b + rx_1 - px_3, \quad \mathfrak{A}_3(x) = c + px_2 - qx_1, \tag{6.17}$$

where a, b, c, p, q, r are arbitrary constants, represents a solution of $\Delta^* u = 0$ and satisfies on S the boundary condition (6.18).
Since the identity $\Delta^* \mathfrak{A}(x) = 0$ is obvious, it remains to verify the boundary condition (6.18).

Projecting this equality on the x_1-axis we obtain

$$(\mathbf{T}\mathfrak{A}(x))_i = 0, \qquad B_i \ni x \to x_0 \in S.$$

but

$$\mathbf{T}_1 \mathfrak{A}(x) = 2\mu \frac{\partial \mathfrak{A}_1}{\partial n} + \lambda \cos(n, x_1) \operatorname{div} \mathfrak{A}(x) + \mu (n \times \operatorname{rot} \mathfrak{A}(x))_1 =$$
$$= 2\mu (q \cos(n, x_3) - r \cos(n, x_2)) + \lambda \cos(n, x_1) \operatorname{div} \mathfrak{A} + \mu (n \times \operatorname{rot} \mathfrak{A})_1,$$

and therefore

$$\operatorname{div} \mathfrak{A}(x) = 0, \qquad (n \times \operatorname{rot} \mathfrak{A})_1 = 2r \cos(n, x_2) - 2q \cos(n, x_3),$$

One similarly obtains for the other two components $\mathbf{T}_2 \mathfrak{A}(x) = \mathbf{T}_3 \mathfrak{A}(x) = 0$, and hence

$$\mathbf{T}_1 \mathfrak{A}(x) = 0. \tag{6.19}$$

Theorem 7 (III, 4) shows that $\mathfrak{A}(x)$ is a unique solution of the static homogeneous problem (T_i^0). It is called a rigid displacement vector. The vector field $\mathfrak{A}(x)$ may be described by a double-layer potential. Since $\mathfrak{A}(x)$ is a solution of $\Delta^* u = 0$, regular in B_i, we have from (1.60)

$$\mathfrak{A}(x) = \frac{1}{4\pi} \int_S \left[\overset{0}{\Gamma}(x, y) \mathbf{T} \mathfrak{A}(y) - \mathfrak{A}(y) \mathbf{T}_y \overset{0}{\Gamma}(x, y) \right] dS_y$$

and by (6.19)

$$\mathfrak{A}(x) = -\frac{1}{4\pi} \int_S \mathfrak{A}(y) \mathbf{T}_y \overset{0}{\Gamma}(x, y) \, dS_y = -\frac{1}{2} \int_S \mathfrak{A}(y) K(y, x) \, dS_y. \tag{6.20}$$

The vector $\mathfrak{A}(x)$ satisfies the equation

$$\mathfrak{A}(x) + \int_S \mathfrak{A}(y) K(y, x) \, dS_y = 0 \qquad (x \in S). \tag{D_a^0}$$

To demonstrate this we pass to the limit in (6.20), letting x approach a boundary point on S from the inside; then from (2.1)

$$\mathfrak{A}(x) = \frac{1}{2} \mathfrak{A}(x) - \frac{1}{2} \int_S \mathfrak{A}(y) K(y, x) \, dS_y \qquad (x \in S)$$

or

$$\mathfrak{A}(x)+\int_S \mathfrak{A}(y)K(y, x)\,dS_y=0 \qquad (D_a^0). \tag{6.20'}$$

which proves the statement.

Let us set in the expression for the vector of rigid displacement

$$\mathfrak{A}(x)=i_1[a+(qx_3-rx_2)]+i_2[b+(rx_1-px_3)]+i_3[c+(px_2-qx_1)]$$

all constants save one equal to zero. Depending on the nonvanishing constant, we get in turn the vectors

$$\mathfrak{A}^{(k)}(x) \qquad (k=1, 2, 3, 4, 5, 6), \tag{6.21}$$

which are linearly independent solutions of equation (D_a^0).

We now introduce a system of $6n$ vectors

$$\varphi_j^{(k)}(x)\begin{cases} k=1, 2, 3, 4, 5, 6, \\ j=1, 2, 3, \dots, n, \end{cases}$$

defined as follows

$$\varphi_j^{(k)}(x)=\begin{cases} \mathfrak{A}^{(k)}(x) & \text{on } S_j \quad (j=1, 2, \dots, n), \\ 0 & \text{on all other surfaces}. \end{cases} \tag{6.21'}$$

Evidently, each of these $6n$ vectors solves (D_a^0) and they are linearly independent; the associated equation

$$\varphi(x)+\int_S K(x, y)\varphi(y)\,dS_y=0 \qquad (T_i^0)$$

by Fredholm's second theorem, also has $6n$ linearly independent solutions. We denote them by

$$\psi^{(k)}(x) \qquad (k=1, 2, 3, \dots, 6n) \tag{6.22}$$

and proceed to prove that the sequence (6.22) constitutes a complete system of linearly independent solutions of (T_i^0). Assuming the opposite, let $\psi(x)$ be a solution of (T_i^0) which does not depend linearly on the $\psi^{(k)}(x)$. The single-layer potentials

$$V(x;\,\psi)=\frac{1}{2\pi}\int_S \overset{0}{\Gamma}(x;\,y)\,\psi(y)\,dS_y,$$

$$V(x;\,\psi^{(k)})=\frac{1}{2\pi}\int_S \overset{0}{\Gamma}(x,\,y)\,\psi^{(k)}(y)\,dS_y \qquad (k=1, 2, \dots, 6n),$$

being solutions of

$$\Delta^* u=0, \qquad (\mathrm{T}_i u)=0$$

should represent rigid displacements, and since the last $6n$ potentials constitute a complete system of such vectors, the first should be a linear combination of them, i.e.,

$$V(x;\,\psi)=\sum_{k=1}^{6n} C_k V(x;\,\psi^{(k)}). \tag{6.23}$$

If we rewrite (6.23) as

$$\int_S \overset{0}{\Gamma}(x,\,y)\left[\psi(y)-\sum_{k=1}^{6n} C_k\psi^{(k)}(y)\right]dS_y=0,$$

we find on the right-hand side a single-layer potential with a "density" equal to

$$\psi(y) - \sum_{k=1}^{6n} C_k \psi^{(k)}(y);$$

denoting this potential by $V_*(x)$, we obtain

$$V_*(x) \equiv 0 \qquad (x \in B_i). \tag{6.24}$$

On account of the continuity of a single-layer potential

$$0 = (V_*(x))_i = (V_x(x))_a$$

and in view of Theorem 5 (III, 4)

$$V_*(x) \equiv 0 \qquad (x \in B_a). \tag{6.24'}$$

Now (6.24) and (6.24') imply, according to (2.5),

$$0 = (\dot{T}V_*)_i - (TV_*)_a = 2\left[\psi(x_0) - \sum_{s=1}^{6n} C_s \psi^{(s)}(x_0)\right] \quad \text{for} \quad x_0 \in S,$$

but this contradicts the assumption that vector $\dot{\psi}(x)$ does not depend linearly on $\psi^{(k)}(x)$, $k = 1, 2, \ldots, 6n$, and thus proves our statement that the $\psi^{(k)}(x)$, $k=1, 2, \ldots, 6n$, are a complete system of linearly independent solutions of equation (T_i^0). Hence follows the completeness of the associated system (6.21'), and the uniqueness theorem (Theorem 5 (III, 4)) shows that the double-layer potentials vanish:

$$W(x;\ \varphi_j^{(k)}) = 0 \quad (x \in B_a)\,(k = 1, 2, \ldots, 6;\ j = 1, 2, 3, \ldots, n). \tag{6.25}$$

§ 4. Solution of the Robin elastostatic problem

Let n completely rigid bodies bounded by the surface $S^{(k)}$, $k = 1, \ldots, n$, be embedded in an infinite elastic medium B_a. It is required to find the field arising in B_a as a result of displacing these inserts. This problem will be called, in analogy with the Robin problem of electrostatics, the R o b i n e l a s t o s t a t i c p r o b l e m. Any insert may only move as a whole (rigid displacement). We take these displacements to be given and denote them by

$$\mathfrak{H}_j^{(k)}(x) \qquad (k = 1, 2, \ldots, 6;\ j = 1, 2, \ldots, n).$$

In virtue of the linear independence of the vectors $V(x;\ \psi^{(k)}), k = 1, 2, 3, \ldots, 6n$, any other sequence of $6n$ linearly independent vectors expressed by homogeneous linear combinations of $V(x;\ \psi^{(k)})$ will be equivalent to the first. But according to the preceding section the $V(x;\ \psi^{(k)})$ constitute a system of rigid displacements, and thus we may construct from them a new sequence $V'_k(x)$ so that*

$$V'_k(x) = \begin{cases} \mathfrak{H}_1^{(k)}(x), & x \in S^{(1)}, \\ 0, & x \bar{\in} S^{(1)} + B_a + B_i{}^1, \end{cases} \qquad k = 1, 2, \ldots, 6;$$

$$V'_k(x) = \begin{cases} \mathfrak{H}_2^{(k-6)}(x), & x \in S^{(2)}, \\ 0, & x \bar{\in} S^{(2)} + B_a + B_i, \end{cases} \qquad k = 7, 8, 9, 10, 11, 12;$$

* The symbol $x \bar{\in} S^{(k)} + B_i + B_a$ should be understood in the following sense: x d o e s n o t b e l o n g to either $S^{(k)}$, B_i or B_a, i. e., x l i e s on one of the surfaces $S^{(1)}, S^{(2)}, \ldots, S^{(k-1)}, S^{(k+1)}, \ldots, S^{(n)}$.

$$V'_k(x) = \begin{cases} \mathfrak{H}_3^{k-12}(x), & x \in S^{(3)}, \\ 0, & x \bar{\in} S^{(3)} + B_a + B_i, \end{cases} \qquad k = 13, 14, 15, \ldots, 18;$$

. . . .

$$V'_k(x) = \begin{cases} \mathfrak{H}_n^{(k-6(n-1))}(x), & x \in S^{(n)}, \\ 0, & x \bar{\in} S^{(n)} + B_i + B_a, \end{cases} \qquad k = 6n-5, 6n-4, \ldots, 6n.$$

Then evidently

$$\sum_{s=1}^{6n} V'_s(x)$$

furnishes a solution of the Robin problem stated above.

§ 5. Existence theorems for solutions of the static Problems (D_a^0) and (T_i^0)

The necessary and sufficient conditions for the solvability of the inhomogeneous equation

$$\varphi(x) + \int_S \varphi(y) K(y, x)\, dS_y = f(x) \qquad (D_a)$$

are, according to Fredholm's third theorem (V, 13),

$$\int_S f(x)\, \psi^{(k)}(x)\, dS_x = 0 \qquad (k = 1, 2, \ldots, 6n), \qquad (6.26)$$

where the $\psi^{(k)}(x)$ form a complete system of linearly independent solutions of (T_i^0), as shown in § 3. Together with this system we consider the complete system of linearly independent solutions of (D_a^0), denoted in § 3 by $\varphi_j^{(k)}(x), j = 1, \ldots, n$, and which we shall now find more convenient to relabel $\varphi_k^*(x)$, $k = 1, \ldots, 6n$. It was shown in (V, 12) that the sets of vectors $\psi^{(k)}(x)$ and $\varphi_k^*(x)$ admit mutual biorthonormalization on account of the corresponding eigenvalues being simple poles of the resolvent*.

Suppose the biorthonormalization to have been carried out, and to avoid new notation, let the old symbols now stand for the biorthonormalized systems. We introduce the vector

$$F(x) = f(x) - \sum_{k=1}^{6n} C_k \varphi_k^*(x),$$

where the constants C_k are defined as

$$C_k = \int_S f(x)\, \psi^{(k)}(x)\, dS_x \qquad (k = 1, 2, \ldots, 6n).$$

This $F(x)$ is evidently orthogonal to every one of the vectors $\psi^{(s)}(x)$, $s = 1, 2, \ldots, 6n$, and consequently, utilizing the solutions of the integral equation

$$\varphi(x) + \int_S \varphi(y) K(y, x)\, dS_y = F(x)$$

one may construct that double-layer potential, which assumes on S an external limiting value of $F(x)$. On the other hand we know from (6.21') that the vectors

$$\varphi_j^{(k)}(x) \qquad (k = 1, 2, \ldots, 6;\ j = 1, 2, \ldots, n)$$

* It is impossible to biorthonormalize systems of solutions of associated equations when these poles are multiple, but there exist systems of principal associated vectors for which the biorthonormalization is possible (cf. /13a/, pp. 43-50 and 157-159). Weyl /4a/ did not notice this circumstance and the corresponding part of his paper is wanting in that respect.

coincide on each surface $S^{(j)}$ with some rigid displacement and may, therefore, be represented as a linear combination of the vectors $V(x;\ \psi^{(s)})$, $s=1, 2, \ldots, 6n$, which represent single-layer potentials and form themselves a complete system of rigid displacement vectors, as shown in § 3 for $x \in B_i$. Taking this combination and adding it with an appropriate sign to the aforementioned double-layer potential, we obtain a solution of $\Delta^* u=0$ which assumes on S external limiting values given by $f(x)$. We have thereby proved

Theorem 6. The static inhomogeneous problem (D_a) *is solvable for an arbitrary vector* $f(x)$ *of class* $H(\gamma)$, *and the solution is representable as a double-layer potential or as its combination with single-layer potentials.*

It is clear that one may add to the solution considered in the theorem the double-layer potentials $A_j^{(k)} W(x;\ \varphi_j^{(k)})$ with arbitrary constants $A_j^{(k)}$, since the $W(x;\ \varphi_j^{(k)})$ are solutions of the homogeneous equation (D_a^0). But in view of (6.25) these potentials vanish in B_a; this corresponds to the uniqueness theorem for the first exterior static problem (III, 4).

We now come to the inhomogeneous problem (T_i) and its integral equation

$$\varphi(x)+\int_S K(x,\ y)\, \varphi(y)\, dS_y=f(x). \tag{T_i}$$

The third Fredholm theorem again furnishes the necessary and sufficient solvability conditions

$$\int_S f(x)\, \varphi_s^*(x)\, dS_x=0 \qquad (s=1,\ 2,\ \ldots,\ 6n), \tag{6.27}$$

where $\varphi_s^*(x)$, $s=1, 2, \ldots, 6n$, is a complete system of fundamental solutions of (D_a^0). The conditions (6.27), unlike (6.26), serve here not only as conditions for the representability of the solutions in a certain form, but also express an essential mechanical property of a vector field that is regular in B_i and satisfies equation $\Delta^* u=0$ with the boundary condition $\mathbf{T}_i u=f(x)$ on S. Remember that the $\varphi_s^*(x)$ are given by (6.21'), where the six vectors $\mathfrak{A}^{(k)}(x)$ are the following

$$\left.\begin{array}{lll} \mathfrak{A}^{(1)}(a,\ 0,\ 0), & \mathfrak{A}^{(2)}(0,\ b,\ 0), & \mathfrak{A}^{(3)}(0,\ 0,\ c), \\ \mathfrak{A}^{(4)}(qx_3,\ 0,\ -qx_1), & \mathfrak{A}^{(5)}(-rx_2,\ rx_1,\ 0), & \mathfrak{A}^{(6)}(0,\ -px_3,\ px_2), \end{array}\right\} \ . \tag{6.27'}$$

and note that in virtue of the arbitrariness of a, b, c, p, q, r the conditions (6.27) are equivalent to

$$\left.\begin{array}{l} \int_{S_k} f_1(x)\, dS_x=\int_{S_k} f_2(x)\, dS_x=\int_{S_k} f_3(x)\, dS_x=0, \\ \int_{S_k} (f_1 x_3-f_3 x_1)\, dS_x=0, \quad \int_{S_k} (f_2 x_1-f_1 x_2)\, dS_x=0, \\ \int_{S_k} (f_3 x_2-f_2 x_3)\, dS_x=0 \qquad (k=1,\ 2,\ \ldots,\ n), \end{array}\right\} \tag{6.28}$$

which express the vanishing of the resultant and the resultant moment of the external loading forces applied to S.

That the conditions (6.28) are also necessary for (T_i) to be solvable follows, for example, from (1.8') upon substituting $u=\mathfrak{A}^{(k)}(x)$ and v, where v is a solution of (T_i). The sufficiency of these conditions is apparent from the foregoing; hence

Theorem 7. The inhomogeneous static problem (T_i) *is solvable for a vector function* $f(x)$ *of class* $H(\gamma)$ *only when conditions (6.28) are fulfilled. The solution may be represented as a single-layer potential and is determined up to an additive rigid displacement.*

§ 6. Existence theorems for Problems (M_i) and (M_a)

The homogeneous equation (M_i^0) admits only a trivial solution. For, assume the opposite and let $\psi(x)$ be a nontrivial solution. Then the single-layer potential

$$V(x;\ \psi)=\frac{1}{2\pi}\int_S \overset{0}{\Gamma}(x,\ y)\,\psi(y)\,dS_y$$

satisfies on S the boundary condition

$$(\mathrm{T}V+\sigma V)_i=0,\qquad \sigma>0. \tag{6.29}$$

On the other hand we get from the Betti formula (1.9')

$$\int_S V_i\cdot(\mathrm{T}V)_i dS=\int_{B_i} W(V,\ V)\,d\tau.$$

Inserting here on the left-hand side the value of $(\mathrm{T}V)_i$ from (6.29), we obtain

$$\int_S \sigma|V_i|^2 dS+\int_{B_i} W(V,\ V)\,d\tau=0;$$

since the form $W(u,\ u)$ is positive-definite, it follows that $V(x,\ \psi)=0$ in B_i, and on account of the continuity, that $V_a(x;\ \psi)=0$. But then by Theorem 5, (III, 4) $V(x;\ \psi)=0,\ x\in B_a$; this finally implies in view of (2.5) that $\psi(x)=0$. This contradiction proves our statement. Applying similar arguments to the homogeneous equation (M_a^0) and recalling the uniqueness Theorem 3 (III, 4), it may be shown that this equation admits only trivial solutions. Hence

Theorem 8. The inhomogeneous static problems (M_i) *and* (M_a) *with boundary values of class* $H(\gamma)$ *have unique solutions, representable by single-layer potentials.*

§ 7. Proof of existence of the static Green's tensors

The meaning and properties of Green's tensors were discussed in (IV, 3, 4, 5). We repeat the definition of these tensors and prove their existence.

The first static Green's tensor for a domain B is a square matrix whose elements are functions of two points, x and y, which satisfies the following conditions:

1) for $x\in B,\ x\neq y,\ \overset{0}{G}(x,\ y)$ solves the equation

$$\Delta^*\overset{0}{G}(x,\ y)=0;$$

2) for boundary points $x_0\in S$

$$\lim_{B\ni x\to x_0\in S}\overset{0}{G}(x,\ y)=0,\qquad y\in S;$$

3) the following representation is valid in B

$$\overset{0}{G}(x, y) = \overset{0}{\Gamma}(x, y) - \overset{0}{v}(x, y), \quad x, y \in B,$$

where $\overset{0}{v}(x, y)$ is a matrix solution of equation $\Delta^* u = 0$, regular in B.

To construct the matrix $\overset{0}{G}(x, y)$, it is obviously sufficient to derive the matrix $\overset{0}{v}(x, y)$, regular in B, from the conditions

$$\Delta^* \overset{0}{v}(x, y) = 0, \; x, y \in B; \qquad \lim_{B \ni x \to x_0 \in S} \overset{0}{v}(x, y) = \overset{0}{\Gamma}(x_0; y) \quad y \bar{\in} S,$$

but this is exactly the static problem (D_i) for the domain B with boundary conditions of class H. By Theorem 4 (§ 2) this problem is solvable and hence the first Green's tensor exists.

The existence of the second static Green's tensor $\overset{0}{H}(x, y)$ is a less simple matter. The latter cannot be defined for a bounded domain B as a solution of equation $\Delta^* u = 0$ from the conditions

a) $\lim_{B \ni x \to x_0 \in S} \mathrm{T}_x \overset{0}{H}(x, y) = 0, \quad y \bar{\in} S;$

b) $\overset{0}{H}(x, y) = \overset{0}{\Gamma}(x, y) - \overset{0}{W}(x, y), \quad x, y \in B;$

c) $\Delta^* \overset{0}{W}(x, y) = 0, \quad x, y \in B,$

since this would imply that for the determination of $\overset{0}{W}(x, y)$ one has to solve the problem

$$\Delta^* W(x, y) = 0, \; x, y \in B; \qquad \lim_{B \ni x \to x_0 \in S} \mathrm{T}_x W(x; y) = \mathrm{T}_{x_0} \overset{0}{\Gamma}(x_0; y), \; y \bar{\in} S,$$

which by Theorem 7 (§ 5) is solvable only when (6.28) are fulfilled; but it is clear from (6.20) that $\mathrm{T}_x \overset{0}{\Gamma}(x, y)$ does not satisfy these conditions. Weyl has found a way of overcoming this difficulty /4a/*. We shall restrict ourselves to the case $n=1$ and introduce an orthogonal rectilinear coordinate system with origin at the center of mass of the body and axes along the principal axes of inertia through it; the vectors (6.27'), which form a complete linearly independent system of solutions of the homogeneous problem, may now be written in the form

$$\left.\begin{aligned} &\mathfrak{A}^{(1)} = \left(\frac{1}{M}, 0, 0\right) \; \mathfrak{A}^{(2)} = \left(0, \frac{1}{M}, 0\right), \; \mathfrak{A}^{(3)} = \left(0, 0, \frac{1}{M}\right), \\ &\mathfrak{A}^{(4)}(x) = \left(-\frac{x_3}{S}, 0, \frac{x_1}{S}\right), \; \mathfrak{A}^{(5)}(x) = \left(\frac{x_2}{T}, \frac{-x_1}{T}, 0\right), \\ &\mathfrak{A}^{(6)}(x) = \left(0, \frac{x_3}{R}, -\frac{x_2}{R}\right), \end{aligned}\right\} \tag{6.30}$$

where M^2 is the mass of the body, and R^2, S^2, T^2 the principal moments of inertia. The orthonormality conditions

$$\int_B \mathfrak{A}^{(s)}(x) \mathfrak{A}^{(q)}(x) \, d\tau_x = \begin{cases} 0, & s \neq q, \\ 1, & s = q, \end{cases} \quad s, q = 1, 2, 3, 4, 5, 6 \tag{6.31}$$

are automatically fulfilled for this coordinate system.

* Weyl does not consider singular integral equations and his proof is therefore incomplete.

The matrix

$$\overset{0}{H}(x, y)=\left\|\begin{matrix} \overset{0}{H}{}_1^{(1)}(x, y) & \overset{0}{H}{}_1^{(2)}(x, y) & \overset{0}{H}{}_1^{(3)}(x, y) \\ \overset{0}{H}{}_2^{(1)}(x, y) & \overset{0}{H}{}_2^{(2)}(x, y) & \overset{0}{H}{}_2^{(3)}(x, y) \\ \overset{0}{H}{}_3^{(1)}(x, y) & \overset{0}{H}{}_3^{(2)}(x, y) & \overset{0}{H}{}_3^{(3)}(x, y) \end{matrix}\right\|$$

will be called a second static Green's tensor if the following conditions are satisfied:

(a) for $x \in B,\ x \neq y$,

$$\Delta^* \overset{0}{H}{}^{(k)}(x, y)=4\pi \sum_{s=1}^{6} \mathfrak{B}^{s\,(k)}(x, y) \qquad (k=1, 2, 3), \tag{6.32}$$

where $H^{(k)}(x, y)$ are column-vectors of the matrix $\overset{0}{H}(x, y)$, and the vector $\mathfrak{B}^{s\,(k)}(x, y)$ is defined in (IV, 4);

(b) for $x_0 \in S$ and $y \in B$

$$\lim_{B \ni x \to x_0 \in S} \mathrm{T}_x \overset{0}{H}(x, y) \equiv 0; \tag{6.33}$$

(c) for $x,\ y \in B$

$$\overset{0}{H}(x, y)=\overset{*}{\Gamma}(x, y)-\overset{0}{W}(x, y),$$

where $\overset{*}{\Gamma}(x, y)$ is the matrix

$$\overset{*}{\Gamma}(x, y)=\left\|\begin{matrix} \overset{*}{\Gamma}{}_1^{(1)}(x, y) & \overset{*}{\Gamma}{}_1^{(2)}(x, y) & \overset{*}{\Gamma}{}_1^{(3)}(x, y) \\ \overset{*}{\Gamma}{}_2^{(1)}(x, y) & \overset{*}{\Gamma}{}_2^{(2)}(x, y) & \overset{*}{\Gamma}{}_2^{(3)}(x, y) \\ \overset{*}{\Gamma}{}_3^{(1)}(x, y) & \overset{*}{\Gamma}{}_3^{(2)}(x, y) & \overset{*}{\Gamma}{}_3^{(3)}(x, y) \end{matrix}\right\|,$$

defined by formula (4.19), and $\overset{0}{W}(x, y)$ is a regular solution of

$$\mu \Delta u+(\lambda+\mu) \operatorname{grad} \operatorname{div} u=0.$$

Let us first prove some properties of the matrix $\overset{*}{\Gamma}(x, y)$.

Lemma A. The columns of the matrix $\overset{*}{\Gamma}(x, y)$ *satisfy, for the variable* x, *the equation*

$$\Delta^* \overset{*}{\Gamma}{}^{(k)}(x, y)=4\pi \sum_{s=1}^{6} \mathfrak{B}^{s\,(k)}(x, y) \qquad (k=1, 2, 3). \tag{6.34}$$

Lemma B. The rows of the matrix $\overset{*}{\Gamma}(x, y)$ *satisfy, for the variable* y, *the equation**

$$\Delta^* \overset{*}{\Gamma}_{(k)}(x, y)=4\pi \sum_{s=1}^{6} \mathfrak{B}^{s}_{(k)}(x, y). \tag{6.35}$$

To prove Lemma A note that the double integral on the right-hand side of the expression for $\overset{*}{\Gamma}(x, y)$ in formula (4.19), is labeled by two indices; denoting it by γ_{sq}, we have

$$\overset{*}{\Gamma}(x, y)=\overset{0}{\Gamma}(x, y)-L-M+N,$$

where the matrices $L,\ M,\ N$ are given by

$$L=\sum_{s=1}^{6} \mathfrak{A}^{(s)}(x) * \int_B \overset{0}{\Gamma}(y, \xi)\, \mathfrak{A}^{(s)}(\xi)\, d\sigma_{\xi};$$

* The vector $\mathfrak{B}^{s}_{(k)}(x, y)$ was defined in (IV, 4).

$$M=\sum_{s=1}^{6}\int_B \overset{0}{\Gamma}(x,\eta)\,\mathfrak{A}^{(s)}(\eta)\,d\sigma_\eta * \mathfrak{A}^{(s)}(y);$$

$$N=\sum_{s}^{6}\sum_{q}^{6}\mathfrak{A}^{(s)}(x)*\gamma_{sq}\mathfrak{A}^{(q)}(y).$$

The j-th component of the k-th column-vector, $L_j^{(k)}$, in the matrix L is, be definition of the product $a*b$, of the form

$$\sum_{s=1}^{6}\mathfrak{A}_j^{(s)}(x)\left(\int_B \overset{0}{\Gamma}(y,\xi)\,\mathfrak{A}^{(s)}(\xi)\,d\sigma_\xi\right)_k \qquad (j=1,2,3), \tag{6.35'}$$

where $\mathfrak{A}_j^{(s)}(x)$ and

$$\left(\int_B \overset{0}{\Gamma}(y,\xi)\,\mathfrak{A}^{(s)}(\xi)\,d\sigma_\xi\right)_k$$

denote the projections of the vectors $\mathfrak{A}^{(s)}(x)$ and

$$\int_B \overset{0}{\Gamma}(y,\xi)\,\mathfrak{A}^{(s)}(\xi)\,d\sigma_\xi.$$

on the x_j- and x_k-axes.
The elements of the rows of $M(x,y)$ are of the form

$$M_j^{(k)}(x,y)=\sum_{s=1}^{6}\left(\int_B \overset{0}{\Gamma}(x,\eta)\,\mathfrak{A}^{(s)}(\eta)\,d\sigma_\eta\right)_j \mathfrak{A}_k^{(s)}(y) \qquad (j,k=1,2,3), \tag{6.35''}$$

and, finally, the elements of the columns of $N(x,y)$ are

$$N_j^{(k)}(x,y)=\sum_{s}^{6}\sum_{q}^{6}\gamma_{sq}\mathfrak{A}_j^{(s)}(x)\,\mathfrak{A}_k^{(q)}(y) \qquad (j,k=1,2,3). \tag{6.35'''}$$

We now apply Δ^* to the matrix $\overset{*}{\Gamma}(x,y)$ with respect to the columns and the variable x; then Δ^*L and Δ^*N vanish, as $\Delta^*\mathfrak{A}^{(s)}(x)=0$. Using the Poisson formula (1.78) to evaluate Δ^*M, we find

$$4\pi\sum_{s=1}^{6}\mathfrak{A}^{(s)}(x)\,\mathfrak{A}_k^{(s)}(y)=4\pi\sum_{s=1}^{6}\mathfrak{B}^{s(k)}(x,y).$$

This proves Lemma A.

The proof of Lemma B is similar, by applying the operator Δ^* to the rows and the variable y.

Lemma C. The vector $\mathrm{T}_x\overset{*}{\Gamma}{}^{(k)}(x,y)$ *is orthogonal to all the vectors (6.30), i.e.,*

$$\int_S \mathfrak{A}^{(p)}(x)\cdot \mathrm{T}_x\overset{*}{\Gamma}{}^{(k)}(x,y)\,dS_x=0 \qquad (p=1,2,\ldots,6;\ k=1,2,3).$$

To prove this, note that since $\mathrm{T}_x\mathfrak{A}^{(s)}(x)=0$, (6.35') and (6.35'') give

$$\mathrm{T}_xL^{(k)}(x,y)=\mathrm{T}_xN^{(k)}(x,y)=0 \qquad (k=1,2,3),$$

whence

$$\int_S \mathfrak{A}^{(p)}(x)\cdot \mathrm{T}_x\overset{*}{\Gamma}{}^{(k)}(x,y)\,dS_x=\int_S \mathfrak{A}^{(p)}(x)\cdot \mathrm{T}_x\overset{0}{\Gamma}{}^{(k)}(x,y)\,dS_x-$$

$$-\int_S \mathfrak{A}^{(p)}(x)\cdot \mathrm{T}_xM^{(k)}(x,y)\,dS_x. \tag{6.36}$$

But by (6.35")

$$\int_S \mathfrak{A}^{(p)}(x)\cdot \mathrm{T}_x M^{(k)}(x, y)\,dS_x = \sum_{s=1}^{6}\int_B\left(\int_S \mathfrak{A}^{(p)}(x)\,\mathrm{T}_x\overset{0}{\Gamma}(x, \eta)\,dS_x\right)\cdot \mathfrak{A}^{(s)}(\eta)\,d\sigma_\eta \mathfrak{A}_k^{(s)}(y).$$

On the other hand (6.20') implies

$$\int_S \mathfrak{A}^{(p)}(x)\,\mathrm{T}_x\overset{0}{\Gamma}(x, \eta)\,dS_x = -2\pi\mathfrak{A}^{(p)}(\eta).$$

Substituting this in the preceding expression, we obtain in view of the orthonormality formulas (6.31)

$$\int_S \mathfrak{A}^{(p)}(x)\mathrm{T}_x M^{(k)}(x, y)\,dS_x = -2\pi\mathfrak{A}_k^{(p)}(y) \qquad (k=1, 2, 3).$$

Inserting this expression into (6.36) we finally obtain

$$\int_S \mathfrak{A}^{(p)}(x)\cdot \mathrm{T}_x\overset{*}{\Gamma}{}^{(k)}(x, y)\,dS_x = 0 \qquad (p=1, 2, \ldots, 6;\ k=1, 2, 3),$$

which completes the proof of Lemma C.

The way to the existence theorem is now clear.

To construct the matrix $\overset{0}{W}(x, y)$ it is necessary to solve the boundary-value problems

$$\Delta^* \overset{0}{W}{}^{(k)}(x, y) = 0,$$

$$\lim_{B\ni x\to x_0\in S} \mathrm{T}_x\overset{0}{W}{}^{(k)}(x, y) = \mathrm{T}_{x_0}\overset{*}{\Gamma}{}^{(k)}(x_0, y) \qquad (k=1, 2, 3), \qquad x, y\in B.$$

The necessary and sufficient conditions for solvability of these (T_i) problems are satisfied, in virtue of Lemma C and Theorem 7 of § 5. Constructing the matrix $\overset{0}{W}(x, y)$, we obtain

$$\overset{0}{H}(x, y) = \overset{*}{\Gamma}(x, y) - \overset{0}{W}(x, y).$$

By Lemmas A and B this matrix satisfies all the conditions required to make it a second Green's tensor. Lemma B also implies that $\overset{0}{H}(x, y)$ is, with respect to y and its rows, a solution of

$$\Delta^* \overset{0}{H}_{(k)}(x, y) = 4\pi\sum_{s=1}^{6}\mathfrak{B}_{(k)}^{s}(x, y), \tag{6.37}$$

where $\mathfrak{B}_{(k)}^{s}(x, y)$ is the k-th row of the matrix $\mathfrak{A}^{(s)}(x)*\mathfrak{A}^{(s)}(y)$ (IV, 4). As the matrix $\overset{0}{H}(x, y)$ is obviously determined up to an additive term of the form $\sum_{s=1}^{6}\alpha_s^k\mathfrak{A}^{(s)}(x)$, where α_s^k $(k=1, 2, 3)$ do not depend on x, we may choose the latter so that the "orthogonality conditions"

$$\int_B \overset{0}{H}(x, y)\,\mathfrak{A}^{(s)}(x)\,d\sigma_x = 0 \qquad (s=1, 2, \ldots, 6) \tag{6.38}$$

hold. To this end, replace $\overset{0}{H}(x, y)$ by a new matrix with columns

$$\overset{\tilde{0}}{H}{}^{(k)}(x, y) = \overset{0}{H}{}^{(k)}(x, y) - \sum_{s=1}^{6}\alpha_s^k\mathfrak{A}^{(s)}(x), \qquad x, y\in B,$$

$$(k=1, 2, 3)$$

and require that

$$\int_B \overset{0}{\tilde{H}}(x, y)\mathfrak{A}^{(l)}(x)\,d\sigma_x = 0 \qquad (l = 1, 2, \ldots, 6).$$

On account of (6.31) we only need choose the a_s^k in the following way

$$a_s^k = \int_B \overset{0}{H}{}^{(k)}(x, y)\mathfrak{A}^{(s)}(x)\,dS_x. \qquad (k = 1, 2, \ldots, 6).$$

Returning to the old notation, we obtain (6.38). Betti's formula (1.10'), formula (6.37) and the orthogonality conditions (6.38) imply the symmetry property of Green's tensors, namely

$$\overset{0}{H}(y, x) = \left(\overset{0}{H}(x, y)\right)^{*}, \qquad \overset{0}{G}(y, x) = \left(\overset{0}{G}(x, y)\right)^{*}.$$

We have utilized in applications to boundary-value problems (IV, 4) a representation of the solutions of (D_i) and (T_i) by means of the first and second Green's tensors. We shall now derive the corresponding formulas. Applying (1.61) to the solution $u(x)$ of (D_i), the existence of which has already been proved, and to the Green's tensor $\overset{0}{G}(x, y) = \overset{0}{\Gamma}(x, y) - \overset{0}{v}(x, y)$, we obtain*

$$u(x) = -\frac{1}{4\pi}\int_S \overset{0}{G}(x, y)\,\mathrm{T}u(y)\,dS_y + \frac{1}{4\pi}\int_S u(y)\,\mathrm{T}_y\overset{0}{G}(x, y)\,dS_y\,. \qquad x \in B.$$

But by the symmetry property and property 2) of the Green's tensor

$$\overset{0}{G}(x, y) = 0 \quad \text{for} \quad x \in B \text{ and } y \in S$$

and

$$u(x) = \frac{1}{4\pi}\int_S f(y)\,\mathrm{T}_y\overset{0}{G}(x, y)\,dS_y, \tag{6.39}$$

where $f(x)$ is the boundary value of $u(x)$. It follows that

$$\lim_{B \ni x \to x_0 \in S} \int_S f(y)\,\mathrm{T}_y\overset{0}{G}(x, y)\,dS_y = 4\pi f(x_0). \tag{6.40}$$

We turn now to derive a representation for the solution of the second problem, that is, (T_i). Let conditions (6.28) be fulfilled, which guarantees by Theorem 7 (§ 5) the existence of a solution, $u(x)$. Now apply Betti's formula in B to $u(x)$ and $\overset{0}{H}_{(k)}(x, y)$, $k = 1, 2, 3$. Since

$$\overset{0}{H}(x, y) = \overset{*}{\Gamma}(x, y) - \overset{0}{W}(x, y),$$

there is a pole at $x = y$. We exclude a sphere $\tau(x; \varepsilon)$ centered at x from the integration region; from equation (6.37), which is satisfied by $\overset{0}{H}_{(k)}(x, y)$, $k = 1, 2, 3$, we obtain

$$4\pi \int_{B-\tau(x;\,\varepsilon)} u(y)\sum_{s=1}^{6}\mathfrak{A}^{(s)}(y) * \mathfrak{A}^{(s)}(x)\,d\sigma_y = \int_{S+\bar{\tau}(x;\,\varepsilon)} \left[-\overset{0}{H}(x, y)\,\mathrm{T}u(y) + \left(\mathrm{T}_y\overset{0}{H}(x, y)\right)u(y)\right]dS_y.$$

* The positive direction is taken here, unlike in (1.61), along the inward normal.

However

$$\mathrm{T}_y \overset{0}{H}_{(k)}(x, y) = 0, \qquad y \in S; \quad x \overline{\in} S,$$
$$\mathrm{T} u(y) = f(y), \quad y \in S,$$

and thus, going to the limit as $\varepsilon \to 0$, we obtain (cf. I, 6)

$$u(x) = -\frac{1}{4\pi} \int_S \overset{0}{H}(x, y) f(y)\, dS_y - \int_B u(y) \sum_{s=1}^{6} \mathfrak{A}^{(s)}(y) * \mathfrak{A}^{(s)}(x)\, d\sigma_y. \qquad (6.41)$$

We may add to this solution an arbitrary linear combination of vector solutions $\mathfrak{A}^{(s)}(x)$ of the homogeneous problem. But if we impose the normalization conditions

$$\int_B u(y) \mathfrak{A}^{(s)}(y)\, d\sigma_y = 0 \qquad (s = 1, 2, \ldots, 6), \qquad (6.42)$$

the solution will be determined uniquely, as follows from (6.31).

Conditions (6.42) imply

$$\int_B u(y) \sum_{s=1}^{6} \mathfrak{A}^{(s)}(y) * \mathfrak{A}^{(s)}(x)\, d\sigma_y = 0.$$

In fact, by definition of the product $a * b$, we have

$$\int_B u(y) \sum_{s=1}^{6} \mathfrak{A}^{(s)}(y) * \mathfrak{A}^{(s)}(x)\, d\sigma_y = \sum_{s=1}^{6} \left(\int_B u(y) \mathfrak{A}^{(s)}(y)\, d\sigma_y \right) \mathfrak{A}^{(s)}(x) = 0.$$

Consequently (6.41) becomes

$$u(x) = -\frac{1}{4\pi} \int_S \overset{0}{H}(x, y) f(y)\, dS_y. \qquad (6.43)$$

This solution must satisfy the condition (see (6.38))

$$\int_B u(x) \mathfrak{A}^{(s)}(x)\, d\sigma_x = 0 \qquad (s = 1, 2, \ldots, 6).$$

It follows from (6.43) that

$$\lim_{B \ni x \to x_0 \in S} \mathrm{T}_x \int_S \overset{0}{H}(x, y) f(y)\, dS_y = -4\pi f(x_0). \qquad (6.44)$$

We conclude with this our investigation of static problems for homogeneous bodies and proceed to oscillation problems.

§ 8. The homogeneous dynamic Problems (D_i^0) and (T_i^0). The eigenfrequency spectrum

Solutions of the homogeneous dynamic problems (D_i^0) and (T_i^0) may be represented by means of solutions of some homogeneous Fredholm equations with symmetric kernels. For (D_i^0) these equations are of the form

$$u(x) = \frac{\omega^2}{4\pi} \int_B \overset{0}{G}(x, y)\, u(y)\, d\sigma_y, \qquad (6.41^\circ)$$

where $\overset{0}{G}(x, y)$ is the first static Green's tensor, while for (T_i^0) these equations are

$$u(x) = \frac{\omega^2}{4\pi} \int_B \overset{0}{H}(x, y)\, u(y)\, d\sigma_y, \qquad (6.42^\circ)$$

where $\overset{0}{H}(x, y)$ is the second static Green's tensor.

Applying Δ^* to both sides of (6.41⁰), one obtains in virtue of (1.78)

$$\Delta^* u(x) + \omega^2 u(x) = 0. \tag{6.43^0}$$

On the other hand, passing to the limit in (6.41°) for $x \to x_0 \in S$, and taking into account property (2) of the first static Green's tensor, we obtain

$$\lim_{B \ni x \to x_0 \in S} u(x) = 0. \tag{6.44^0}$$

Thus, the vector $u(x)$, which satisfies the homogeneous equation (6.41⁰), also satisfies equation (6.43⁰) and the boundary condition (6.44⁰), i. e., it solves the dynamic problem (D_i^0)

Similarly, applying Δ^* to both sides of (6.42⁰) and using (1.78), we get

$$\Delta^* u(x) + \omega^2 u(x) = \frac{\omega^2}{4\pi} \int_B \Delta_x^* \left[\overset{0}{H}(x, y) u(y) \right] d\sigma_y.$$

But in virtue of (6.32) the expression under the integral sign equals

$$\left(\Delta_x^* \overset{0}{H}(x, y) \right) u(y) = 4\pi \left(\sum_{s=1}^{6} \mathfrak{A}^{(s)}(x) * \mathfrak{A}^{(s)}(y) \right) u(y),$$

and the integral of this quantity over the domain B vanishes due to (6.42⁰) and (6.38); we finally get

$$\Delta^* u(x) + \omega^2 u(x) = 0.$$

On the other hand, taking the expression for $\mathbf{T}u(x)$ and passing to the limit as $x \to x_0$, we obtain from (6.42⁰) and on account of the boundary property of the second static Green's tensor

$$\lim_{B \ni x \to x_0 \in S} \mathbf{T}u(x) = 0. \tag{6.45^0}$$

This makes it clear that $u(x)$, which solves the homogeneous equation (6.42⁰), also solves equation (6.43⁰) and satisfies the boundary condition (6.45⁰), and therefore is a solution of the dynamic problem (T_i^0). The homogeneous equations

$$u(x) - \frac{\omega^2}{4\pi} \int_B \overset{0}{G}(x, y) u(y) d\sigma_y = 0, \tag{6.41^0}$$

$$u(x) - \frac{\omega^2}{4\pi} \int_B \overset{0}{H}(x, y) u(y) d\sigma_y = 0 \tag{6.42^0}$$

are, in virtue of the properties of static Green's tensors, homogeneous Fredholm systems with symmetric kernels; therefore Hilbert's theorem implies a discrete spectrum of eigenvalues of the parameter ω^2, for which equations (6.41⁰) and (6.42⁰) admit nontrivial solutions. In view of the mechanical meaning of ω^2 we will call these eigenvalues the eigenfrequencies of the homogeneous problems (D_i^0) and (T_i^0).

We shall now show that the eigenfrequencies of the homogeneous problems (D_i^0) and (T_i^0) are not negative. Let ω_1^2 and ω_2^2 be some eigenvalues of (D_i^0) and (T_i^0), respectively, and $u^{(1)}(x)$, $u^{(2)}(x)$ be the corresponding solutions of (6.41⁰) and (6.42⁰). We write down the Betti formula (1.9') for ω_1^2, $u^{(1)}(x)$ and ω_2^2, $u^{(2)}(x)$ and obtain in both cases on account of the boundary conditions

$$\int_B [W(u^{(k)}, u^{(k)}) - \omega_k^2 u^{(k)} \cdot u^{(k)}] d\sigma_x = 0 \qquad (k = 1, 2)$$

but these equalities can not be satisfied by negative values of ω_k^2, $k=1, 2$, though they may hold for $\omega_2^2=0$ provided $u^{(2)}(x)$ is a rigid displacement. Hence follows

Theorem 9. *The interior homogeneous dynamic problem* (D_i^0) *has a discrete spectrum of eigenfrequencies, which are eigenvalues of the integral equation (6.41⁰); these values are strictly positive.*

The interior homogeneous dynamic problem (T_i^0) *has a discrete spectrum of eigenfrequencies which are the eigenvalues of the integral equation (6.42⁰). These values are positive or zero;* $\omega^2=0$ *is an eigenvalue of sixth order and the solutions corresponding to it are given by the system (6.27′).*

§ 9. The generalized Lyapunov-Tauber theorem

In analogy with the known theorem in the theory of harmonic potentials on the continuity of the normal derivative of a double-layer potential, we now prove

Theorem 10. *The existence of either* $(\mathbf{T}W(x))_a$ *or* $(\mathbf{T}W(x))_i$ *of class* H *(Hölder's class), for a double-layer potential* $W(x)$ *regular in* B_a *and* B_i, *respectively, implies the existence of the other limit and the identity*

$$(\mathbf{T}W(x))_a=(\mathbf{T}W(x))_i.$$

This theorem will be called the generalized Lyapunov-Tauber theorem in view of the analogy mentioned above. We may evidently assume without loss of generality that $\omega=0$

Let an external limit $(\mathbf{T}W(x))_a$ of class H exist. We construct in the domain B_i the single-layer potential

$$V(x;\psi)=\frac{1}{2\pi}\int_S \overset{0}{\Gamma}(x,y)\psi(y)\,dS_y,$$

satisfying the boundary condition

$$(\mathbf{T}V(x))_i=(\mathbf{T}W(x))_a.$$

We obtain for the density $\psi(y)$, on account of formulas (2.5), the integral equation*

$$\psi(x_0)+\int_S K(x_0,y)\psi(y)\,dS_y=\mathbf{T}_aW(x_0) \tag{6.45}$$

As we already know from § 5, the necessary and sufficient conditions for the solvability of this equation are (cf., (6.27))

$$\int_S (\mathbf{T}_aW(y))\varphi_s^*(y)\,dS_y=0 \qquad (s=1,2,\ldots,6n), \tag{6.46}$$

where $\varphi_s^*(x)$, $s=1, 2, \ldots, 6n$, is a complete system of linearly independent solutions of the associated homogeneous equation (D_a^0)

$$\varphi_s^*(x)+\int_S \varphi_s^*(y)K(y,x)\,dS_y=0. \tag{6.47}$$

* $\mathbf{T}_aW(x_0)$ denotes here $\lim\limits_{x\to x_0}(\mathbf{T}W(x))$, with $x\in B_a$, $x_0\in S$.

We also know that the vectors $\varphi_s^*(x)$, $s=1, 2, \ldots, 6n$, are defined by (6.21') and may be expressed by means of a linear combination of single-layer potentials (cf. § 3)

$$V(x;\ \psi^{(s)}),$$

where $\psi^{(s)}(x)$, $s=1, 2, \ldots, 6n$, is a complete system of solutions of the homogeneous equation corresponding to (6.45). The solvability conditions may therefore be written

$$\int_S V(y;\ \psi^{(s)})\, \mathbf{T}_a W(y)\, dS_y = 0 \qquad (s=1, 2, 3, \ldots, 6n). \tag{6.46'}$$

We now write down the external limiting value of the given double-layer potential according to (2.1),

$$W_a(x) = \varphi(x) + \int_S \varphi(y) K(y, x)\, dS_y.$$

Considering this equality as an integral equation for $\varphi(x)$ with $W_a(x)$ given, and applying Fredholm's third theorem, we obtain

$$\int_S \psi^{(s)}(y)\, W_a(y)\, dS_y = 0 \qquad (s=1, 2, 3, \ldots, 6n). \tag{6.48}$$

Since $V(x, \psi^{(s)})$ and $W(x)$ are solutions of the equations of elasticity, regular in B_a, we may apply Betti's formula in B_a,

$$\begin{aligned} 0 &= \int_{B_a} [V(x;\ \psi^{(s)})\, \Delta^* W(x) - W(x)\, \Delta^* V(x;\ \psi^{(s)})]\, d\sigma_x = \\ &= \int_S [V_a(x;\ \psi^{(s)})\, \mathbf{T}_a W - W_a (\mathbf{T}V)_a]\, dS_x. \end{aligned} \tag{6.49}$$

By (2.5)

$$(\mathbf{T}V(x;\ \psi^{(s)}))_a = (\mathbf{T}V(x;\ \psi^{(s)}))_i - 2\psi^{(s)}(x_0) \qquad (x_0 \in S), \ldots \tag{6.50}$$

But in our case

$$(\mathbf{T}V(x;\ \psi^{(s)}))_i = 0,$$

hence by (6.50)

$$(\mathbf{T}V(x;\ \psi^{(s)}))_a = \lim_{x \to x_0} \mathbf{T}V(x;\ \psi^{(s)}) = -2\psi^{(s)}(x_0),$$

$$x \in B_a, \quad x_0 \in S \qquad (s=1, 2, \ldots, 6n),$$

and, in view of (6.48) we get from (6.49)

$$\int_S V(x;\ \psi^{(s)})\, \mathbf{T}_a W(x)\, dS_x = 0 \qquad (s=1, 2, \ldots, 6n), \tag{6.46'}$$

which is one thing that had to be proved.

Consider the vector

$$\mathbf{\Omega}(x) = \frac{1}{2}[W(x) - V(x;\ \psi)] = \frac{1}{4\pi} \int_S \overset{0}{\Gamma}_{\mathrm{I}}(x, y)\, \varphi(y)\, dS_y - \frac{1}{4\pi} \int_S \overset{0}{\Gamma}(x, y)\, \psi(y)\, dS_y, \tag{6.51}$$

where $V(x;\ \psi)$ is the single-layer potential we have just constructed.

From (2.5)

$$(\mathbf{T}V(x;\ \psi))_a - (\mathbf{T}V(x;\ \psi))_i = -2\psi(x_0)$$

and since

$$(\mathbf{T}V)_i = (\mathbf{T}W)_a,$$

we obtain from (6.51)

$$(\mathbf{T}\boldsymbol{\Omega}(x))_a = \boldsymbol{\psi}(x_0). \tag{6.52}$$

Since $\boldsymbol{\Omega}(x)$ is a solution of the equations of elasticity, and regular in B_a, it may be expressed by means of the Betti formula in the following way

$$\boldsymbol{\Omega}(x) = \frac{1}{4\pi}\int_S \left[\overset{0}{\Gamma}_{\mathrm{I}}(x, y)\,\boldsymbol{\Omega}_a(y) - \overset{0}{\Gamma}(x, y)(\mathbf{T}\boldsymbol{\Omega}(y))_a\right] dS_y. \tag{6.53}$$

Taking the difference of (6.53) and (6.51), and keeping in mind (6.52), we get

$$\frac{1}{2\pi}\int_S \overset{0}{\Gamma}_{\mathrm{I}}(x, y)\,[\boldsymbol{\Omega}_a(y) - \boldsymbol{\varphi}(y)]\, dS_y = 0, \qquad x \in B_a. \tag{6.54}$$

We pass to the limit in the last equality for x tending to x_0 on S from the outside, and obtain from (2.1)

$$[\boldsymbol{\Omega}_a(x_0) - \boldsymbol{\varphi}(x_0)] + \int_S [\boldsymbol{\Omega}_a(y) - \boldsymbol{\varphi}(y)]\, K(y, x_0)\, dS_y = 0. \tag{6.55}$$

This is the homogeneous equation (D_a^0) and its general solution is, as known from § 3, of the form

$$\sum_{s=1}^{6n} C_s \boldsymbol{\varphi}_s^*(x),$$

where C_s are arbitrary constants; therefore

$$\boldsymbol{\Omega}_a(x_0) = \boldsymbol{\varphi}(x_0) + \sum_1^{6n} C_s \boldsymbol{\varphi}_s^*(x_0). \tag{6.56}$$

Let now x lie in B_i; then

$$0 = \int_S \left[\overset{0}{\Gamma}_{\mathrm{I}}(x, y)\,\boldsymbol{\Omega}_a(y) - \overset{0}{\Gamma}(x, y)(\mathbf{T}\boldsymbol{\Omega}(y))_a\right] dS_y,$$

and we may write down, on account of (6.52) and (6.56),

$$\int_S \overset{0}{\Gamma}_{\mathrm{I}}(x, y)\,\boldsymbol{\varphi}(y)\, dS_y + \sum_{s=1}^{6n} C_s \int_S \overset{0}{\Gamma}_{\mathrm{I}}(x, y)\,\boldsymbol{\varphi}_s^*(y)\, dS_y - \int_S \overset{0}{\Gamma}(x, y)\,\boldsymbol{\psi}(y)\, dS_y = 0, \qquad x \in B_i. \tag{6.57}$$

Note now that the double-layer potentials

$$\boldsymbol{W}(x, \boldsymbol{\varphi}_s^*) \qquad (s = 1, 2, \ldots, 6n),$$

being solutions, regular in B_a, of the homogeneous problems

$$\Delta^* \boldsymbol{u}^{(s)} = 0, \qquad \boldsymbol{u}_a^{(s)} = 0,$$

must vanish in B_a. By Theorem 5 (III, 4) we have, using (2.1),

$$\boldsymbol{W}_i^*(x_0) = \sum_{s=1}^{6n} C_s (\boldsymbol{W}(x; \boldsymbol{\varphi}_s^*))_i = -2\sum_{s=1}^{6n} C_s \boldsymbol{\varphi}_s^*(x_0).$$

Choosing the disposable constants so that $\boldsymbol{\varphi}_s^*(x)$ coincide with the limiting values of the single-layer potentials $\boldsymbol{V}(x; \boldsymbol{\psi}^{(s)})$, $s = 1, 2, \ldots, 6n$, we obtain

$$\boldsymbol{W}^*(x) = \sum_{s=1}^{6n} A_s \boldsymbol{V}(x; \boldsymbol{\psi}^{(s)}),$$

where A_s are the suitably chosen constants. Substituting $\boldsymbol{W}^*(x)$ in (6.57),

$$\boldsymbol{W}(x; \boldsymbol{\varphi}) - \boldsymbol{V}(x; \boldsymbol{\psi}) + \sum_{s=1}^{6n} A_s \boldsymbol{V}(x; \boldsymbol{\psi}^{(s)}) = 0, \qquad x \in B_i,$$

but $(\mathbf{T}V(x;\ \psi^{(s)}))_i=0$, and therefore

$$(\mathbf{T}W(x;\ \varphi))_i=(\mathbf{T}V(x;\ \psi))_i.$$

Replacing the right-hand side by the expression we know to equal it, we get

$$(\mathbf{T}W(x;\ \varphi))_i=(\mathbf{T}W(x;\ \varphi))_a,$$

which completes the proof of Theorem 10.

§ 10. The relation between solutions of homogeneous problems and equations (D_a^0), (T_i^0) and (T_a^0), (D_i^0)

There exists a relation between solutions of the interior and exterior homogeneous problems, which is based on the following theorems.

Theorem 11. For a nontrivial solution of (D_a^0) *to exist it is necessary and sufficient that the parameter* ω^2 *coincide with an eigenvalue of* (T_i^0).

If ω^2 *is a* ν*-fold eigenvalue of* (T_i^0), *then* (D_a^0) *has* ν *linearly independent solutions, coinciding with the boundary values of the solutions of problem* (T_i^0).

Theorem 12. For a nontrivial solution of (T_a^0) *to exist it is necessary and sufficient that the parameter* ω^2 *coincide with an eigenvalue of* (D_i^0).

If ω^2 *is a* ν*-fold eigenvalue of* (D_i^0) *then* (T_a^0) *has* ν *linearly independent solutions, which coincide with the boundary values of the* T*-transforms of solutions of* (D_i^0).

Let us remark that in §§ 5 and 9 we have already made use of a particular case of Theorem 11 for $\omega=0$, when we expressed the fundamental solutions $\varphi_s^*(x)$, $s=1,\ 2,\ \ldots,\ 6n$, as a linear combination of the vectors $V(x;\ \psi^{(s)})$.

Proof of Theorem 11. N e c e s s i t y. If ω^2 is not an eigenfrequency of (T_i^0):

$$\left.\begin{aligned} &\Delta^* u(x)+\omega^2 u(x)=0, \quad x\in B_i,\\ &\mathbf{T}_i u(x)=0,\\ &x\to x_0\in S,\end{aligned}\right\}(T_i^0)$$

then the equation (D_a^0):

$$\varphi(x_0)+\int_S \varphi(y)K(y,\ x_0)\,dS_y=0 \qquad (D_a^0)$$

admits only a trivial solution. Let us assume the opposite. Then, by the second Fredholm theorem, also the associated equation

$$\psi(x_0)+\int_S K(x_0,\ x)\psi(x)\,dS_x=0 \qquad (T_i^0)$$

has nontrivial solutions $\psi_1,\ \psi_2,\ \ldots$, and the single-layer potentials $V(x;\ \psi_k)$, whose densities are represented by these solutions, are in turn solutions of (T_i^0). But since ω^2 is not an eigenfrequency of this problem, then by Theorem 9 the obtained solutions vanish identically in B_i, i. e.,

$$V(x;\ \psi_k)=0, \qquad x\in B_i.$$

It now follows on account of the continuity of single-layer potentials that

$$V_a(x;\ \psi_k)=0,$$

and since $V(x;\ \psi_k)$ satisfies at infinity the radiation conditions, we have by

Theorem 1 (III, 4) that $V(x; \psi_k) \equiv 0$ in B_a, and hence in virtue of the property (2.5) of single-layer potentials $\psi_k(x_0) \equiv 0$, $k = 1, 2, \ldots$

This contradiction proves the necessity of the condition.

Sufficiency. Let ω^2 be a ν-fold eigenvalue of (T_i^0) and $u^{(1)}(x), u^{(2)}(x), \ldots, \ldots, u^{(\nu)}(x)$ the corresponding linearly independent solutions. Let $-2r^{(1)}(x)$, $-2r^{(2)}(x), \ldots, -2r^{\nu}(x)$ be the boundary values of $u^{(k)}(x)$ on S. These will also be linearly independent. For, if they were not, $r^{(m)}(x) = \sum_{k=1}^{\nu}{}' C_k r^{(k)}(x)$*, and the vector $u(x) = u^{(m)}(x) - \sum_{k=1}^{\nu}{}' C_k u^{(k)}(x)$ would be a solution of the equations of elasticity that satisfies on S the boundary conditions $u_i = 0$, $(\mathbf{T}u)_i = 0$. But it is clear from (1.60) that such a solution vanishes identically and so $u^{(m)}(x) = \sum_{k=1}^{\nu}{}' C_k u^{(k)}(x)$ which contradicts the linear independence of the $u^{(k)}(x)$. The vector functions $u^{(k)}(x)$, $k = 1, 2, \ldots, \nu$, satisfy by Theorem 9 (§ 8) the equation (6.42^0), and in the closed domain $\bar{B}$, their first derivatives must belong to the Hölder class (cf., e.g., /21/, Ch. II). This is obviously sufficient for (1.63) to apply to these vectors. Since $\mathbf{T}_i u^{(k)}(x_0) = 0$, we obtain

$$\delta(x) u^{(k)}(x) = \frac{1}{2\pi} \int_S \Gamma_{\mathrm{I}}(x, y) r^{(k)}(y)\, dS_y \qquad (k = 1, 2, \ldots, \nu), \tag{6.58}$$

where

$$\delta(x) = \begin{cases} 1, & x \in B, \\ \frac{1}{2}, & x \in S, \\ 0, & x \bar{\in} B + S = \bar{B}. \end{cases}$$

We now pass to the limit as x approaches the boundary point x_0 from the outside, keeping $x \bar{\in} B + S$. This yields

$$r^{(k)}(x_0) + \frac{1}{2\pi} \int_S \Gamma_{\mathrm{I}}(x_0, y) r^{(k)}(y)\, dS_y = 0$$

but since (cf. II, 2)

$$\frac{1}{2\pi} \Gamma_{\mathrm{I}}(x_0, y) r^{(k)}(y) = K^*(y, x_0) r^{(k)}(y) = r^{(k)}(y) K(y, x_0),$$

we finally obtain

$$r^{(k)}(x_0) + \int_S r^{(k)}(y) K(y; x_0)\, dS_y = 0. \tag{D_a^0}$$

This shows that the $r^{(k)}(x_0)$, $k = 1, 2, \ldots, \nu$, are indeed solutions of equation (D_a^0), as stated in Theorem 11. It remains to show that this equation has no other linearly independent solutions. Let us assume the opposite. Then by the second Fredholm theorem, (T_i^0) has together with (D_a^0) $\mu > \nu$ linearly independent solutions

$$\sigma_1(x_0), \quad \sigma_2(x_0), \ldots, \sigma_\mu(x_0), \qquad x_0 \in S.$$

It is evident that the single-layer potentials

$$V(x; \sigma_k) \qquad (k = 1, 2, \ldots, \mu)$$

are solutions of (T_i^0), but since this problem has for the specified value of ω^2

* The prime appended to the summation symbol indicates that $k = m$ is left out.

only ν linearly independent solutions,

$$V(x;\sigma_r)=\sum_{s=1}^{\nu} C_{sr}V(x;\sigma_s) \qquad (r=\nu+1,\ \nu+2,\ \dots,\ \mu).$$

or

$$\int_S \Gamma(x,y)\left[\sum_{s=1}^{\nu} C_{sr}\sigma_s(y)-\sigma_r(y)\right]dS_y=0,$$

$$x\in B_i \qquad (r=\nu+1,\ \nu+2,\ \dots,\ \mu). \tag{6.59}$$

Consider the single-layer potential

$$V_*^{(r)}(x)=\frac{1}{2\pi}\int_S \Gamma(x,y)\left[\sum_{s=1}^{\nu} C_{sr}\sigma_s(y)-\sigma_r(y)\right]dS_y \qquad x\in B_i.$$

In view of (6.59) and of the continuity of a single-layer potential,

$$(V_*^{(r)}(x))_a=0,$$

and since the radiation conditions at infinity are fulfilled $V_*^{(r)}(x)=0,\ x\in B_a$, but then from (2.5)

$$\sigma_r(y)=\sum_{s=1}^{\nu} C_{sr}\sigma_s(y) \qquad (r=\nu+1,\ \nu+2,\ \dots,\ \mu);$$

which is a contradiction, proving that $\mu=\nu$. This completes the proof of sufficiency and thus of Theorem 11.

Proof of Theorem 12.

Necessity. Let ω^2 be an eigenfrequency of the problem

$$\left.\begin{aligned}\Delta^* u(x)+\omega^2 u(x)=0,\quad & x\in B_i,\\ u_i(x)=0,\quad &\end{aligned}\right\} \tag{D_i^0}$$

then the equation

$$\varphi(x)-\int_S K(x_0,x)\varphi(x)\,dS_x=0 \tag{T_a^0}$$

must be shown to have only a trivial solution. Let us assume the opposite; then by the second Fredholm theorem, also the associated equation

$$\psi(x_0)-\int_S \psi(x)K(x,x_0)\,dS_x=0 \tag{D_i^0}$$

will have nontrivial solutions $\psi_1(x),\ \psi_2(x),\ \dots,\ \psi_r(x)$. We construct the double-layer potentials for which these solutions serve as densities

$$W(x;\psi_k)=\frac{1}{2\pi}\int_S \Gamma_{\mathrm{I}}(x,y)\psi_k(y)\,dS_y \qquad (k=1,\ 2,\ \dots,\ r).$$

These potentials are evidently solutions of (D_i^0). But since ω^2 is not an eigenfrequency of this problem, then by Theorem 9 (D_i^0) has only a trivial solution, and consequently

$$W(x;\psi_k)=0,\quad x\in B_i \qquad (k=1,\ 2,\ \dots,\ r).$$

Now by Theorem 10

$$(\mathbf{T}W(x;\psi_k))_a=0 \qquad (k=1,\ 2,\ \dots,\ r),$$

and since furthermore $W(x;\psi_k)$ satisfies the radiation conditions, it follows from Theorem 1 (III, 4) that $W(x;\psi_k)=0,\ x\in B_a$. We conclude in view of (2.1) that $\psi_k(x_0)=0, k=1,\ 2,\ \dots,\ r$. This contradiction proves the necessity of the conditions of Theorem 12.

S u f f i c i e n c y. Let ω^2 be a ν-fold eigenfrequency of (D_i^0) and $u^{(1)}(x)\ldots$ $\ldots u^{(\nu)}(x)$ the corresponding linearly independent solutions. It follows from (6.41°) that their first derivatives belong to class H in the closed domain $\bar{B}$ (cf. /21/, Ch. II).

We denote the boundary values of $\mathbf{T}_i u^{(k)}(x),\ k=1,\ 2,\ \ldots,\ \nu$, on S by $2r_1(x)$, $2r_2(x),\ \ldots,\ 2r_\nu(x)$; the linear independence of $r_k(x)$ is proved in this case in the same manner as was done for the $r^{(k)}(x)$. Applying (1.63) again and taking the boundary conditions into account, we obtain

$$\frac{1}{2\pi}\int_S \Gamma(x,\ y)\, r_k(y)\, dS_y = \begin{cases} u^{(k)}(x) & x\in B, \\ 0 & x\bar{\in}\bar{B}. \end{cases} \tag{6.59'}$$

Let us apply the T-operator to the second of the last equalities and pass to the limit for x approaching the boundary point x_0 on S from the outside; then, using (2.5), we find

$$r_k(x_0) - \int_S K(x_0,\ y)\, r_k(y)\, dS_y = 0. \tag{T_a^0}$$

This demonstrates that the vectors $r_k(x_0),\ k=1,\ 2,\ \ldots,\ \nu$, are indeed solutions of (T_a^0), as stated in Theorem 12. It remains to show that (T_a^0) has no other linearly independent solutions. Let us assume the opposite, and let equation (T_a^0) have $\mu>\nu$ linearly independent solutions; then by the second Fredholm theorem also the associated equation (D_i^0) will have $\mu>\nu$ solutions $\sigma_1(x),\ \ldots,\ \sigma_\mu(x)$; we construct the double-layer potentials $W(x;\ \sigma_k)$, which are obviously solutions of (D_i^0). But since this problem has for the given value of ω^2 only ν linearly independent solutions, we must have for $x\in B_i$

$$W(x;\ \sigma_r) = \sum_{k=1}^{\nu} C_{kr} W(x;\ \sigma_k) \qquad (r=\nu+1,\ \nu+2,\ \ldots,\ \mu). \tag{6.60}$$

Consider the double-layer potentials

$$W_*^{(r)}(x) = \frac{1}{2\pi}\int_S \Gamma_{\mathrm{I}}(x,\ y)\left[\sigma_r(y) - \sum_{k=1}^{\nu} c_{kr}\sigma_k(y)\right] dS_y$$
$$(r=\nu+1,\ \nu+2,\ \ldots,\ \mu).$$

It follows from (6.60) that these potentials vanish in B_i, whence by Theorem 10

$$(\mathbf{T}W_*^{(r)}(x))_a = 0 \qquad (r=\nu+1,\ \nu+2,\ \ldots,\ \mu),$$

and since the $W_*^{(r)}(x)$ satisfy the radiation conditions at infinity and solve the equations of elasticity, Theorem 1 (III, 4) implies $W_*^{(r)}(x)=0,\ x\in B_a$, and from (2.1)

$$\sigma_r - \sum_{k=1}^{\nu} C_{kr}\sigma_k = 0 \qquad (r=\nu+1,\ \nu+2,\ \ldots,\ \mu),$$

which contradicts the linear independence of the vectors $\sigma_k(x),\ k=1,\ 2,\ \ldots,\ \mu$. This completes the proof of sufficiency and thus of Theorem 12.

§ 11. Investigation of the poles of the resolvent

It follows directly from Theorems 11 and 12 of the preceding section that for some values of ω^2, $\varkappa=-1$ is an eigenvalue of the equation

$$\varphi(x) - \varkappa\int_S K(x,\ y)\,\varphi(y)\, dS_y = 0 \tag{6.61}$$

while $\varkappa=+1$ is an eigenvalue of the equation

$$\varphi(x)-\varkappa\int_S \varphi(y) K(y, x) dS_y=0 \tag{6.62}$$

We shall show that these eigenvalues are simple poles of the resolvent. Let us assume the opposite, and let $\varkappa=-1$ be a pole of order $p>1$. Then, by (5.61_1) and (5.61_2),

$$\begin{gathered}
B^{(p)}(x, y)+\int_S K(x, \xi) B^{(p)}(\xi, y) dS_\xi=0, \\
B^{(p-1)}(x, y)+\int_S K(x, \xi) B^{(p-1)}(\xi, y) dS_\xi=-B^{(p)}(x, y),
\end{gathered} \tag{6.63}$$

where $B^{(p)}(x, y)$ and $B^{(p-1)}(x, y)$ cannot vanish identically. Hence, by the third Fredholm theorem,

$$\int_S B^{(p)}(x, y) \varphi_k^*(x) dS_x=0 \quad (k=1, 2, \ldots, \nu), \tag{6.64}$$

where $\varphi_k^*(x)$, $k=1, 2, \ldots, \nu$ is a complete system of linearly independent solutions of the associated homogeneous equation

$$\varphi(x)+\int_S \varphi(y) K(y, x) dS_y=0. \tag{D_a^0}$$

These solutions are by Theorem 11 equal to the boundary values of the single-layer potentials, for which the linearly independent solutions of

$$\psi(x)+\int_S K(x, y) \psi(y) dS_y=0, \tag{T_i^0}$$

serve as the densities, and which are of the form

$$V(x; \psi_k)=\frac{1}{2\pi}\int_S \Gamma(x, y) \psi_k(y) dS_y \quad (k=1, 2, \ldots, \nu). \tag{6.65}$$

We shall show that together with these potentials also the complex conjugate potentials (indicated by tilde)

$$\tilde{V}(x, \tilde{\psi}_k)=\frac{1}{2\pi}\int_S \tilde{\Gamma}(x, y) \tilde{\psi}_k(y) dS_y \tag{6.66}$$

provide by their boundary values a complete system of fundamental solutions of (D_a^0). In fact the potentials $\tilde{V}(x; \tilde{\psi}_k)$ may, by means of the Betti formula (1.63), be represented on S in the following way

$$\tilde{V}(x_0; \tilde{\psi}_k)=\frac{1}{2\pi}\int_S [\Gamma(x_0, y)(\mathbf{T}\tilde{V})_i-\Gamma_{\mathrm{I}}(x_0, y) \tilde{V}(y; \tilde{\psi}_k)] dS_y.$$

But $(\mathbf{T}\tilde{V})_i=0$, since $(\mathbf{T}V)_i=0$, and consequently

$$\tilde{V}(x_0; \tilde{\psi}_k)+\int_S \tilde{V}(y; \tilde{\psi}_k) K(y, x_0) dS_\xi=0. \tag{D_a^0}$$

This proves precisely what we stated. Therefore the solvability conditions of (6.64) may be written

$$\int_S B^{(p)}(x, y) \cdot \tilde{V}(x; \tilde{\psi}_k) dS_x=0.. \tag{6.67}$$

Let the vector $B^{(p)}(x, y)$ be chosen as some solution of (T_i^0), say, $\psi_q(x)$, $q \leqslant \nu$; it should be orthogonal to all the $\tilde{V}(x; \tilde{\psi}_k)$ and in particular to $\tilde{V}(x; \tilde{\psi}_q)$. It is not difficult to see that

$$\tilde{V}(x;\ \tilde{\psi}_q)\cdot\psi_q-\tilde{\psi}_q\cdot V(x;\ \psi_q)=2i\,\mathrm{Im}\,[\tilde{V}(x;\ \tilde{\psi}_q)\cdot\psi_q]. \tag{6.68}$$

We apply the Betti formula to the vectors $V(x;\ \psi_q)$ and $\tilde{V}(x,\ \tilde{\psi}_q)$ in the domain B_a' bounded by S and by a sphere Σ_R of a sufficiently large radius R with its center lying in B.

Since in this domain both vectors are regular solutions of

$$\Delta^* u+\omega^2 u=0,$$

we get

$$\int_{S+\Sigma_R}[V(x;\ \psi_q)\cdot(\mathrm{T}\tilde{V}(x;\ \tilde{\psi}_q))_a-\tilde{V}(x;\ \tilde{\psi}_q)\cdot(\mathrm{T}V(x;\ \psi_q))_a]\,dS_x=0. \tag{6.69}$$

But as $(\mathrm{T}V)_i=0$ by condition, we have from (2.5) that on S

$$(\mathrm{T}V(x_0;\ \psi_q))_a=-2\psi_q(x_0),\qquad (\mathrm{T}\tilde{V}(x_0;\ \tilde{\psi}_q))_a=-2\tilde{\psi}_q(x_0);$$

therefore, from (6.69),

$$\int_S[V(x;\ \psi_q)\tilde{\psi}_q(x)-\tilde{V}(x;\ \tilde{\psi}_q)\psi_q(x)]\,dS_x-\int_{\Sigma_R}[V(x;\ \psi_q)(\mathrm{T}\tilde{V})-\tilde{V}(x;\ \tilde{\psi}_q)(\mathrm{T}V)]\,dS_x=0$$

or, in virtue of (6.68) and (6.67),

$$\int_{\Sigma_R}[V(x;\ \psi_q)(\mathrm{T}\tilde{V})-\tilde{V}(x;\ \tilde{\psi}_q)(\mathrm{T}V)]\,dS_x=-4i\,\mathrm{Im}\int_S\psi_q(x)\tilde{V}(x;\ \psi_q)\,dS_x=0. \tag{6.69'}$$

On the other hand, the following equality is valid*

$$\begin{aligned}
\int_{\Sigma_R}[\tilde{V}_q(\mathrm{T}V_q)-V_q(\mathrm{T}\tilde{V}_q)]\,dS_x=&\int_{\Sigma_R}[\tilde{V}_{q,p}(\mathrm{T}V_{q,p}-i\omega\sqrt{\lambda+2\mu}\,V_{q,p})+\\
&+\tilde{V}_{q,p}(\mathrm{T}V_{q,s}-i\omega\sqrt{\mu}V_{q,s})+\tilde{V}_{q,s}(\mathrm{T}V_{q,p}-i\omega\sqrt{\lambda+2\mu}\,V_{q,p})+\\
&+\tilde{V}_{q,s}(\mathrm{T}V_{q,s}-i\omega\sqrt{\mu}V_{q,s})-V_{q,p}(\mathrm{T}\tilde{V}_{q,p}+i\omega\sqrt{\lambda+2\mu}\,\tilde{V}_{q,p})-\\
&-V_{q,p}(\mathrm{T}\tilde{V}_{q,s}+i\omega\sqrt{\mu}\tilde{V}_{q,s})-V_{q,s}(\mathrm{T}\tilde{V}_{q,p}+i\omega\sqrt{\lambda+2\mu}\,\tilde{V}_{q,p})-\\
&-V_{q,s}(\mathrm{T}\tilde{V}_{q,s}+i\omega\sqrt{\mu}\tilde{V}_{q,s})]\,d\Sigma_x+2i\omega\sqrt{\lambda+2\mu}\int_{\Sigma_R}|V_{q,p}|^2\,d\Sigma_x+\\
&+2i\omega\sqrt{\mu}\int_{\Sigma_R}|V_{q,s}|^2\,d\Sigma_x+i\omega\sqrt{\lambda+2\mu}\int_{\Sigma_R}[V_{q,s}\tilde{V}_{q,p}+\tilde{V}_{q,s}V_{q,p}]\,d\Sigma_x+\\
&+i\omega\sqrt{\mu}\int_{\Sigma_R}[\tilde{V}_{q,p}V_{q,s}+V_{q,p}V_{q,s}]\,d\Sigma_x.
\end{aligned}$$

The right-hand side may be simplified by applying the radiation conditions (3.15), (3.16), (3.52)–(3.55), and we obtain in virtue of (6.69')

$$2i\omega\sqrt{\lambda+2\mu}\int_{\Sigma_R}|V_{q,p}|^2\,d\Sigma_x+2i\omega\sqrt{\mu}\int_{\Sigma_R}|V_{q,s}|^2\,d\Sigma_x+0(1)=0.$$

Hence it follows that

$$\int_{\Sigma_R}|V_{q,p}|^2\,d\Sigma_x=\int_{\Sigma_?}|V_{q,s}|^2\,d\Sigma_x=0(1)$$

and by Theorem 2 (III, 4)

$$V_q\equiv V(x;\ \psi_q)=0,\qquad x\in B_a\qquad (q=1,\ 2,\ \ldots,\ \nu).$$

* Here $V_q=V(x;\ \psi_q)$, $\tilde{V}_q=\tilde{V}(x;\ \tilde{\psi}_q)$, $V_{q,p}$ and $\tilde{V}_{q,p}$ are the potential components; V_q and $\tilde{V}_q$, $V_{q,s}$ and $\tilde{V}_{q,s}$ are the solenoidal components.

This implies, in view of $TV(x;\ \psi_q)_i = 0$, and of the properties of a single-layer potential, that $\psi_q(x_0) = 0$; this contradiction shows that since p cannot exceed one, necessarily

$$p = 1.$$

This result plays a decisive part in the theory of elastic potentials (see next section). It is utilized considerably by Weyl in /4a/, though without the required proofs; the above proof does not apply at least to some of the cases considered by Weyl.

§ 12. Existence theorems for the dynamic Problems (D_a) and (T_a)

The results established in §§ 11 and 10 enable us to prove the following existence theorems for the exterior problems (D_a) and (T_a).

Theorem 13. *The exterior inhomogeneous dynamic problem* (D_a) *has a unique solution for any boundary condition of class* H *and any value of* ω^2. *The solution is represented by a double-layer potential (of the first kind), if* ω^2 *is not an eigenfrequency of the interior problem* (T_i^0), *and by a linear combination of a double-layer potential and some single-layer potentials, if it is.*

Theorem 14. *The exterior inhomogeneous dynamic problem* (T_a) *has a unique solution for any boundary values of class* H *and any value of* ω^2. *The solution is represented by a single-layer potential (of the first kind), if* ω^2 *is not an eigenfrequency of the interior homogeneous problem* (D_i^0), *and by a linear combination of a single-layer potential and some double-layer potentials (of the first kind), if it is.*

Proof of Theorem 13. Consider the following cases: (a) ω^2 is not an eigenfrequency of (T_i^0) and (b) ω^2 is an eigenfrequency of (T_i^0). In case (a) the homogeneous equation (D_a^0) admits, by Theorem 11, only a trivial solution, and consequently, by the first Fredholm theorem the inhomogeneous equation (D_a) has a unique solution, which is also a solution of (D_a). The homogeneous problem (D_a^0) has, by the uniqueness theorem, only a trivial solution, and therefore the solution of the inhomogeneous problem (D_a) is uniquely represented by a double-layer potential (of the first kind). In case (b) equation (D_a) is, again by Theorem 11, solvable only when the following conditions are satisfied

$$\int_S f(x)\,\psi_k(x)\,dS_k = 0 \qquad (k = 1,\ 2,\ \ldots,\ \nu), \tag{6.70}$$

where $f(x)$, of class H, prescribes the external boundary values, and $\{\psi_k(x)\}$, $k = 1, 2, \ldots, \nu$, is a complete system of fundamental solutions of the associated homogeneous equation (T_i^0). The conditions (6.70) are not generally fulfilled for arbitrary $f(x)$, and therefore we introduce instead of $f(x)$ the vector

$$F(x) = f(x) + \sum_{k=1}^{\nu} A_k \varphi_k(x),$$

which is defined on S and satisfies there the Hölder condition, since the vectors $\varphi_1(x), \varphi_2(x), \ldots, \varphi_\nu(x)$, being solutions of the homogeneous equation (D_a^0), belong to class H. Since the pole of the resolvent is simple (cf., § 11) we may apply to the associated systems of fundamental vectors

$$\varphi_1,\ \varphi_2,\ \ldots,\ \varphi_\nu(x),$$
$$\psi_1,\ \psi_2,\ \ldots,\ \psi_\nu(x)$$

the biorthonormalization formulas (5.78), and then, choosing the constants A_k so that

$$A_k = \int_S f(x)\psi_k(x)\,dS_x \qquad (k=1,\ 2,\ \ldots,\ \nu),$$

we get

$$\int_S F(x)\psi_k(x)\,dS_x = 0 \qquad (k=1,\ 2,\ \ldots,\ \nu).$$

Solving the integral equation

$$\varphi(x) + \int_S \varphi(y) K(y,\ x)\,dS_y = F(x),$$

we construct by Fredholm's third theorem the double-layer potential $W(x;\ \varphi)$ whose external boundary values are $F(x)$.

Consider the vector

$$U(x) = W(x;\ \varphi) - \sum_{k=1}^{\nu} A_k V(x;\ \psi_k),$$

where $V(x;\ \psi_k)$ are single-layer-potential solutions of (T_i^0). On the boundary surface S they coincide, by Theorem 11, with some solutions, $\varphi_1(x) \ldots \varphi_\nu(x)$, of (D_a^0). Therefore the external limiting value of $U(x)$ on S is $f(x)$. On the other hand this vector satisfies the equations $\Delta^* u + \omega^2 u = 0$ in B_a, and the radiation conditions at infinity. We have obtained a regular solution of (D_a); it is uniquely represented as a linear combination of double- and single-layer potentials. This completes the proof of Theorem 13.

Proof of Theorem 14. We again distinguish between two cases. If ω^2 is not an eigenfrequency of (D_i^0), then (T_a^0) has by Theorem 12 (§ 10) only a trivial solution, and by Fredholm's first theorem the inhomogeneous equation is solvable. Since (T_a) has, by the uniqueness theorem, only a trivial solution, (T_a^0) has in this case a unique solution, which may be represented by means of a single-layer potential. Consider next the case of ω^2 coinciding with an eigenfrequency of (D_i^0). The necessary and sufficient conditions for the solvability of (T_a) are then, by Theorem 12,

$$\int_S f(x)\cdot\varphi_k(x)\,dS_x = 0 \qquad (k=1,\ 2,\ \ldots,\ \nu),$$

where $f(x)$ is a given vector (of class H) of external boundary values, and $\varphi_1(x),\ \ldots,\varphi_\nu(x)$ a complete system of fundamental solutions of the associated homogeneous equation

$$\varphi(x) - \int_S \varphi(y) K(y,\ x)\,dS_y = 0. \qquad (D_i^0)$$

We introduce, as above, a vector $F(x)$ of class H, defined on S

$$F(x) = f(x) + \sum_{k=1}^{\nu} A_k \psi_k(x).$$

Here $\psi_1(x),\ \ldots,\ \psi_\nu(x)$ is a complete system of linearly independent solutions of (T_a^0). By the third Fredholm theorem, the integral equation

$$\varphi(x) - \int_S K(x,\ y)\varphi(y)\,dS_y = F(x) \qquad (6.71)$$

is solvable if the constants A_k are chosen as

$$A_k = \int_S f(x) \cdot \varphi_k(x)\, dS_x \qquad (k = 1, 2, \ldots, \nu).$$

This follows from the biorthonormalization formulas (5.78), which obviously remain valid in the present case. Solution of (6.71) enables us to construct a single-layer potential $V(x; \varphi)$, and a T-operation applied to this potential gives in the external limit on S the vector $F(x)$.

Consider the vector

$$U(x) = V(x; \varphi) - \sum_{k=1}^{\nu} A_k W(x; \varphi_k),$$

where $W(x; \varphi_k)$, $k = 1, 2, \ldots, \nu$ are double-layer-potential solutions of (D_i^0), which, by Theorem 12, assume under the T-operation external limit values on S that equal $\psi_k(x)$, i. e., equal the solutions of (T_a^0)

The same values are, by Theorem 10 (§ 9), assumed externally on S under a T-operation on $W(x; \varphi_k)$. It is clear that the external limiting values of $TU(x)$ on S are $f(x)$. On the other hand, $U(x)$ is evidently a solution of the dynamic equations of elasticity, regular in B_a, and by the uniqueness theorem, is a unique solution of (T_a).

This completes the proof of Theorem 14.

§ 13. Existence theorem for the exterior mixed dynamic Problem (M_a)

The following proposition may be proved on the basis of the uniqueness Theorem 3 (III, 4):

Theorem 15. *The mixed dynamic exterior problem (M_a) has a unique solution for any boundary conditions of class H. This solution may be expressed by a single-layer potential, if ω^2 does not coincide with an eigenfrequency of (D_i^0), and as a linear combination of potentials of the single-layer type, if it does.*

We are looking for a solution of problem (M_a) of the form

$$V(x) = \frac{1}{2\pi} \int_S \Gamma(x, y)\, \varphi(y)\, dS_y + \sum_{s=1}^{r} A_s \Gamma^{(k)}(x; y_{(s)}), \qquad (6.72)$$

where the A_s are unknown constants, r is an as yet undetermined integer, $y_{(s)}$ are fixed points in B_i, and $\Gamma^{(k)}(x, y)$, $k = 1, 2, 3$, the k-th column vector of the matrix $\Gamma(x, y)$. We obtain then from (2.5) the following integral equation for the unknown vector $\varphi(y)$:

$$-\varphi(x) + \frac{1}{2\pi} \int_S [T_x \Gamma(x, y) + \sigma(x) \Gamma(x, y)]\, \varphi(y)\, dS_y =$$

$$= -\sum_{s=1}^{r} A_s [T_x \Gamma^{(k)}(x, y_{(s)}) + \sigma(x) \Gamma^{(k)}(x, y_{(s)})] + f(x). \qquad (6.73)$$

We shall now show that the homogeneous equation corresponding to (6.73) has only a trivial solution if ω^2 is distinct from the frequencies of normal modes of oscillation of (D_i^0). To do that, let us assume the opposite and let $\psi(x)$ be a nontrivial solution of

$$-\psi(x) + \int_S [K(x, y) + \sigma(x) \Gamma(x, y)]\, \psi(y)\, dS_y = 0.$$

We use this solution as a density for the single-layer potential $V(x;\ \psi)$ and obtain the boundary-value equation

$$(TV(x;\ \psi)+\sigma(x)V(x;\ \psi))_a=0. \tag{6.74}$$

On the other hand, since $V(x;\ \psi)$ is a solution of the equations of elasticity, and regular in B_a, the uniqueness theorem (Theorem 3 (III, 4)) and condition (6.74) imply $V(x;\ \psi)\equiv 0$ in B_a. Hence, in virtue of the continuity of a single-layer potential, we get on the inside of S

$$V_i(x;\ \psi)=0;$$

but $V(x;\ \psi)$ solves the equations of elasticity in B_i and since ω^2 is not an eigenvalue, $V(x;\ \psi)\equiv 0$ in B_i; this implies in view of (2.5) that $\psi(x)\equiv 0$. This contradiction proves our assertion, and the inhomogeneous equation (6.73) is in this case solvable provided that $A_s=0,\ s=1,2,\ \ldots,\ r$. The solution may be expressed by a single-layer potential, which proves the first part of the theorem. Let now ω^2 coincide with an eigenvalue, and let $\psi_1(x),\ \psi_2(x),\ \ldots,\ \psi_r(x)$ be a complete system of linearly independent solutions of the associated equation

$$-\psi(x)+\int\limits_S \psi(y)\,[K(y,\ x)+\sigma(y)\,\Gamma(y,\ x)]\,dS_y=0. \tag{6.75}$$

The necessary and sufficient conditions for the solvability of (6.73) may now be written

$$\sum_{s=1}^{r} A_s D_m^{(k)}(y_{(s)})=f_m \qquad (m=1,\ 2,\ \ldots,\ r; \quad k=1,\ 2,\ 3), \tag{6.76}$$

where

$$D_m^{(k)}(y_{(s)})=\int\limits_S [T_x\Gamma^{(k)}(x,\ y_{(s)})+\sigma(x)\Gamma^{(k)}(x,\ y_{(s)})]\,\psi_m(x)\,dS_x,$$

$$f_m=\int\limits_S f(x)\,\psi_m(x)\,dS_x.$$

It is clear that if the constants A_s, $s=1,\ 2,\ \ldots,\ r$, could be derived from equations (6.76), then (6.72) would provide a solution and Theorem 15 would be proved. To show that it is possible to determine the A_s from (6.76) it is sufficient to demonstrate the linear independence of $D_m^{(k)}(y)$ with $y\in B_i$, at least for one of the values $k=1,\ 2,\ 3$. In fact, it is possible to choose in this case r points $y_{(s)}$ in B_i, such that for at least one of the values $k=1,\ 2,\ 3$, the following condition is satisfied:

$$D^{(k)}=\begin{vmatrix} D_1^{(k)}(y_1) & D_1^{(k)}(y_2) & \ldots & D_1^{(k)}(y_r)\\ D_2^{(k)}(y_1) & D_2^{(k)}(y_2) & \ldots & D_2^{(k)}(y_r)\\ \cdot & \cdot & \cdot & \cdot\\ D_r^{(k)}(y_1) & D_r^{(k)}(y_2) & \ldots & D_r^{(k)}(y_r)\end{vmatrix}\neq 0. \tag{6.77}$$

Suppose the $D_m^{(k)}(y)$ with $y\in B_i$ are not independent:

$$\int\limits_S [T_x\Gamma^{(k)}(x,\ y)+\sigma(x)\Gamma^{(k)}(x;\ y)]\,\psi(x)\,dS_x=0, \qquad y\in B_i, \tag{6.78}$$

where

$$\psi(x)=\sum_{s=1}^{r} C_s\psi_s(x) \tag{6.79}$$

and at least one of the constants C_s does not vanish. Then, following T. Burchuladze /2a/, we consider the mixed potential, defined in the entire space $y \in \overline{B}_i + B_a$:

$$\Omega(y) = W(y;\ \psi) + V(y;\ \sigma\psi), \tag{6.80}$$

where

$$W(y,\ \psi) = \frac{1}{2\pi}\int_S \mathrm{T}_x \Gamma^{(k)}(x,\ y)\,\psi(x)\,dS_x,$$

$$V(y;\ \sigma\psi) = \frac{1}{2\pi}\int_S \Gamma^{(k)}(x,\ y)\,\sigma(x)\,\psi(x)\,dS_x.$$

It is readily verified that (6.78) gives for $y \in B_i$,

$$\Omega(y) = 0. \tag{6.81}$$

Using the properties of single- and double-layer potentials (2.1) and (2.5), we may write on account of (6.80) and (6.81)

$$0 = \Omega_i(y_0) = -\psi(y_0) + W(y_0;\ \psi) + V_i(y_0;\ \sigma\psi) \qquad y_0 \in S,$$

$$\Omega_a(y_0) = \psi(y_0) + W(y_0,\ \psi) + V_a(y_0;\ \sigma\psi) = \Omega_i(y_0) + 2\psi(y_0) = 2\psi(y_0)$$

and

$$0 = \mathrm{T}_i\Omega(y_0) = \mathrm{T}_i W(y_0;\ \psi) + \sigma(y_0)\,\psi(y_0) + \mathrm{T}V(y_0;\ \sigma\psi), \tag{6.82}$$

$$\mathrm{T}_a\Omega(y_0) = \mathrm{T}_a W(y_0;\ \psi) - \sigma(y_0)\,\psi(y_0) + \mathrm{T}V(y_0;\ \sigma\psi),\ \ y_0 \in S. \tag{6.83}$$

Applying the generalized Lyapunov-Tauber theorem and seeing that (6.82) implies the existence of $\mathrm{T}_i W(y_0;\ \psi)$, we obtain upon subtracting (6.82) from (6.83),

$$\mathrm{T}_a\Omega(y_0) = -2\sigma(y_0)\,\psi(y_0).$$

Finally $\Omega(y)$ turns out to be a solution of the following problem:

$$\Delta^*\Omega(y) + \omega^2\Omega(y) = 0, \qquad y \in B_a,$$

$$\mathrm{T}_a\Omega(y_0) + \sigma(y_0)\,\Omega_a(y_0) = 0.$$

Since $\Omega(y)$ satisfies the radiation condition at infinity, it follows from Theorem 3 (III, 9) that

$$\Omega(y) = 0, \qquad y \in B_a. \tag{6.84}$$

Now (6.78) and (6.84) imply $\psi(x) = \sum C_s\psi_s(x) = 0$, i.e., the vectors $\psi_s(x)$ are dependent. This contradicts the assumed condition, and therefore assures the linear independence of $D_m^{(k)}(y)$, $y \in B_i$, and consequently the solvability of the system of equations (6.76) for the constants A_s, $s = 1,\ 2,\ \ldots,\ r$.

Substituting the coefficients A_s thus derived into (6.72), we obtain a solution of (M_a), which completes the proof of Theorem 15.

§ 14. Remarks on higher-order poles

The existence theorems which we have proved above on the strength of the resolvent having simple poles may also be proved without recourse to that assumption. This was shown by the author for Fredholm equations and problems of membrane- and elastic oscillations in /13a, e/. The same result was obtained later (in 1952) by Weyl /4b/ in the particular case of the Dirichlet problem and only for the membrane equation. In order to extend that method to systems of singular integral equations, it is necessary to adapt the theory of Ch. V to Goursat's theory of principal functions and canonical kernels /7/, which clearly is not difficult. This however does not concern us here, since as we have seen nonsimple poles do not appear in the theory of elasticity.

Chapter VII

EXISTENCE THEOREMS. INHOMOGENEOUS MEDIA

§ 1. Case of equal Poisson's ratios. Proof of existence theorem for Problem (*A*)

The basic existence theorems for homogeneous bodies were proved in the preceding chapter. In this chapter we shall prove existence theorems for the boundary value problems of inhomogeneous media, considered in Ch. IV. We begin with Problem (*A*) in the case of equal Poisson's ratios of the media occupying B_i and B_a. The functional equations associated with Problem (*A*) in this case are (IV, 6)

$$\varkappa(x)\, u(x) = \frac{1}{4\pi}\,\omega^2(\mu_a - \mu_i)\int_{B_i} u(y)\,\Gamma_{(a)}(x,\, y)\,d\sigma_y + \\ + \frac{1}{4\pi}(\mu_a - \mu_i)\int_S u_i(y)\,T_y^{(a)}\Gamma_{(a)}(x,\, y)\,dS_y + \mu_a E(x;\, x_*). \tag{7.1}$$

Let us first prove the converse theorem: *If (7.1) has a regular solution then this is a solution of Problem* (*A*).
Let the point x belong to the domain B_i. Applying $\Delta_a^{(*)} + \omega^2$ to both sides of (7.1), utilizing the properties of volume and double-layer potentials and remembering that $\Delta_a^{(*)}E + \omega^2 E = 0$, we obtain

$$\mu_i\left(\overset{*}{\Delta}_{(a)} + \omega^2\right) u(x) = -\,\omega^2(\mu_a - \mu_i)\, u(x). \tag{7.2}$$

But since the Poisson's ratios are equal

$$\lambda_i\mu_a - \lambda_a\mu_i = 0, \tag{7.3}$$

and (7.2) takes the form

$$\overset{*}{\Delta}_{(i)} u(x) + \omega^2 u(x) = 0, \qquad x \in B_i. \tag{7.4}$$

Let x now lie in B_a. Applying again $(\overset{*}{\Delta}_{(a)} + \omega^2)$ to both sides of (7.1), which may now be inserted under the integral sign, we obtain

$$\overset{*}{\Delta}_{(a)} u(x) + \omega^2 u(x) = 0, \qquad x \in B_a. \tag{7.5}$$

Consider the difference

$$\mu_i u_i(x_0) - \mu_a u_a(x_0), \qquad x_0 \in S.$$

The theorems on the continuity of a volume potential and the discontinuities of a double-layer potential imply

$$\mu_i u_i(x_0) - \mu_a u_a(x_0) = -(\mu_a - \mu_i)\, u_i(x_0),$$

that is,

$$u_i(x_0)=u_a(x_0), \quad x_0\in S. \tag{7.6}$$

Consider the difference

$$\mu_i(T^{(a)}u)_i-\mu_a(T^{(a)}u)_a,$$

where $u(x)$ is a regular solution of (7.1). By the continuity of first derivatives of a volume potential, and by the generalized Lyapunov-Tauber theorem (Theorem 10 (VI, 9)) this difference must vanish:

$$\mu_i(T^{(a)}u)_i-\mu_a(T^{(a)}u)_a=0. \tag{7.7}$$

We may write, in view of (7.3),

$$\mu_i(T^{(a)}u)_i=\mu_i\mu_a\left[2\left(\frac{\partial u}{\partial n}\right)_i+\frac{\lambda_i}{\mu_i}n(\operatorname{div}u)_i+(n\times\operatorname{rot}u)_i\right]=\mu_a(T^{(i)}u)_i. \tag{7.7'}$$

Replacing $\mu_i(T^{(a)}u)_i$ by $\mu_a(T^{(i)}u)_i$ in (7.7),

$$(T^{(i)}u)_i=(T^{(a)}u)_a. \tag{7.8}$$

Finally, taking the difference $\mu_a[u(x)-E(x;\,x_*)]$ and keeping in mind that in B_a the integrals on the right-hand side of (7.1) are regular solutions of $\overset{*}{\Delta}_{(a)}u+\omega^2u=0$, we conclude that $u(x)-E(x;\,x_*)$ is likewise a regular solution of this equation.

Thus we have shown that if (7.1) has a regular solution then this solution satisfies (7.4), (7.5), (7.6), (7.8), and the difference $u(x)-E(x;\,x_*)$ is regular in B_a; but then $u(x)$ is a solution of Problem (A), which proves our statement.

It is clear from this discussion that a solution of the homogeneous equation

$$\varkappa(x)u_0(x)-\frac{1}{4\pi}\omega^2(\mu_a-\mu_i)\int_{B_i}u_0(y)\Gamma_{(a)}(x,\,y)\,d\sigma_y-$$
$$-\frac{1}{4\pi}(\mu_a-\mu_i)\int_S u_0(y)\,T_y^{(a)}\Gamma_{(a)}(x;\,y)\,dS_y=0 \tag{7.1^0}$$

is a solution of the homogeneous problem (A^0), and since this problem has, by Theorem 4, (III, 4) only a trivial solution, we have

Theorem 1. The homogeneous equation (7.1^0) associated with (7.1), admits only a trivial solution.

We shall now pass to the proof of the existence theorem and first assume that (7.1) in fact has a regular solution. We introduce the notation

$$\Phi(x)=\frac{\mu_a}{\mu_i}E(x;\,x_*)+\frac{1}{4\pi}\left(\frac{\mu_a}{\mu_i}-1\right)\int_S u_i(y)\,T^{(a)}\Gamma_{(a)}(x,\,y)\,dS_y, \tag{7.8'}$$

so that (7.1) may be rewritten for $x\in B_i$ as

$$u(x)+\lambda_1\int_{B_i}u(y)\Gamma_{(a)}(x,\,y)\,d\sigma_y=\Phi(x), \tag{7.9}$$

where

$$\lambda_1=\frac{\omega^2}{4\pi}\left(1-\frac{\mu_a}{\mu_i}\right).$$

Since we have assumed the existence of a solution, there obviously exists a vector $u(x)$ which solves (7.9) as a second kind Fredholm equation. It is possible to derive the solution for given $\Phi(x)$ by means of Fredholm's first theorem, provided that a resolvent exists for the kernel $\Gamma_{(a)}(x,\,y)$.

To ensure the existence of the resolvent it is sufficient to show that the homogeneous equation

$$v(x)+\lambda_1 \int_{B_i} v(y)\Gamma_{(a)}(x, y)\,d\sigma_y=0, \qquad x\in B_i, \tag{7.10}$$

has only a trivial solution. Assuming the opposite, let $v(x)$ be a nontrivial solution of (7.10) in B_i; consider the vector

$$v(x)=-\lambda_1 \int_{B_i} v(y)\Gamma_{(a)}(x, y)\,d\sigma_y, \qquad x\in B_a+\bar{B}_i, \tag{7.10'}$$

defined in the entire space. We will show that it vanishes. Applying $(\Delta^*_{(a)}+\omega^2)$ to the two sides of (7.10'), we get for $x\in B_i$

$$\Delta^*_{(a)}v+\omega^2 v=\omega^2\left(1-\frac{\mu_a}{\mu_i}\right)v$$

or, in virtue of (7.3),

$$(\Delta^*_{(i)}+\omega^2)\,v=0$$

and for $x\in B_a$

$$(\Delta^*_{(a)}+\omega^2)\,v=0.$$

The continuity of a volume potential and of its first derivatives implies

$$v_i(x_0)=v_a(x_0), \qquad (\mathrm{T}^{(a)}v)_i=(\mathrm{T}^{(a)}v)_a. \tag{7.11}$$

But by (7.7')

$$(\mathrm{T}^{(a)}v)_i=\frac{\mu_a}{\mu_i}(\mathrm{T}^{(i)}v)_i,$$

and the second equality of (7.11) becomes

$$\mu_a(\mathrm{T}^{(i)}v)_i=\mu_i(\mathrm{T}^{(a)}v)_a. \tag{7.12}$$

Thus the vector $v(x)$ satisfies the conditions

$$\begin{gathered}
\Delta^*_{(i)}v(x)+\omega^2 v(x)=0, \qquad x\in B_i,\\
\Delta^*_{(a)}v(x)+\omega^2 v(x)=0, \qquad x\in B_a,\\
v_i(x_0)=v_a(x_0), \qquad \mu_a(\mathrm{T}^{(i)}v)_i=\mu_i(\mathrm{T}^{(a)}v)_a
\end{gathered}$$

and the radiation condition at infinity. By Theorem 4 (III, 4) such a vector vanishes identically, which proves our assumption.

Substituting the expression for $\Phi(x)$ from (7.8') in (7.13), we get after simple manipulations

$$u(x)+\frac{\lambda_1}{\omega^2}\int_S u_i(y)\,\mathrm{T}^{(a)}\Gamma_{(a)}(x, y)\,dS_y+\lambda_2\int_S u_i(y)L(x, y)\,dS_y=F(x), \tag{7.14}$$

where $x\in B_i$ and

$$\lambda_2=-\frac{\omega^2}{16\pi^2}\left(1-\frac{\mu_a}{\mu_i}\right)^2,$$

$$L(x, y)=\int_{B_i}\mathrm{T}^{(a)}\Gamma_{(a)}(\xi, y)R(\xi, x)\,d\sigma_\xi,$$

$$F(x)=\frac{\mu_a}{\mu_i}E(x; x_*)+\frac{\omega^2}{4\pi}\frac{\mu_a}{\mu_i}\left(\frac{\mu_a}{\mu_i}-1\right)\int_{B_i}E(y; x_*)R(y, x)\,d\sigma_y.$$

The kernel $L(x, y)$ may only have a logarithmic singularity. By Theorem 1 (V, 2) the kernel $\mathrm{T}^{(a)}\Gamma_{(a)}(x, y)$ is actually of class $\in N^{(1,1)}$; but the Fredholm resolvent is known to be of the same class as the corresponding kernel, so that $R(x, y)\in N^{(2)}$.

The statement concerning $L(x, y)$ follows from the following theorem, due to Giraud:

If $K_1(x, y) \in N^{(\alpha, \lambda)}$ and $K_2(x, y) \in N^{(\beta)}$ for some α, β and if $\alpha+\beta \geqslant m$ where m is the dimension of the space, then the composition

$$K(x, y) = \int_{B_i} K_1(x, \xi) K_2(\xi, y) d\sigma_\xi$$

is of class $N^{(\alpha+\beta; \mu)}$, where $\lambda \geqslant \mu$, $\alpha > \mu$.

This theorem is analogous to Theorem 2 (V, 3); its proof may be found in /10a/.

We pass to the limit in (7.14) as x approaches the point y_0 on S from the inside. Formulas (2.1) show that

$$\frac{1}{2}\left(1+\frac{\mu_a}{\mu_i}\right) u_i(y_0) + \frac{\lambda_1}{\omega^2} \int_S u_i(y) \mathrm{T}_y^{(a)} \Gamma_{(a)}(y_0, y) dS_y + \\ + \lambda_2 \int_S u_i(y) L(y_0, y) dS_y = F(y_0). \tag{7.15}$$

Noting that

$$\left| \frac{2\mu_i \lambda_1}{\omega^2(\mu_i+\mu_a)} \right| = \frac{1}{2\pi} \left| \frac{\mu_i-\mu_a}{\mu_i+\mu_a} \right| < 1,$$

we infer that (7.15) is a singular integral equation of the type considered in Chs. V and VI and for which the Fredholm theorems and alternative hold.

So far we have assumed that Problem (A) admits a solution under the conditions implied by (7.3). This assumption has lead us to equation (7.15). We shall now drop the assumption of the existence of solution, and consider (7.15) as the initial integral equation. We will show that (7.15) is solvable and that its solutions permit the construction of a solution of (7.14), and further of (7.1). Let $u_0(y_0)$ be a nontrivial solution of the homogeneous equation corresponding to (7.15). Consider the vector, given in B_i,

$$v(x) = -\frac{\lambda_1}{\omega^2} \int_S u_0(y) \mathrm{T}_y^{(a)} \Gamma_{(a)}(x, y) dS_y - \lambda_2 \int_S u_0(y) L(x, y) dS_y.$$

Approaching the boundary from B_l, we get in the limit, on account of (7.15),

$$v_i(y_0) = \frac{1}{2}\left(1-\frac{\mu_a}{\mu_i}\right) u_0(y_0) - \frac{\lambda_1}{\omega^2} \int_S u_0(y) \mathrm{T}_y^{(a)} \Gamma_{(a)}(y_0, y) dS_y - \\ - \lambda_2 \int_S u_0(y) L(y_0, y) dS_y = u_0(y_0).$$

Let $u_0(x)$ be defined in B_l by the relation

$$u_0(x) = v(x) \qquad x \in B_l,$$

then

$$u_0(x) + \frac{\lambda_1}{\omega^2} \int_S u_0(y) \mathrm{T}_y^{(a)} \Gamma_{(a)}(x, y) dS_y + \lambda_2 \int_S u_0(y) L(x, y) dS_y = 0 \\ x \in B_l.$$

This is the homogeneous equation corresponding to (7.14) with $E=0$, or, equivalently, to (7.1) with $E=0$. Theorem 1 now implies that $u_0(x)=0$, $x \in B_l$, and the solvability of equation (7.15) follows from Fredholm's alternative. Consider the vector

$$v_*(x) = -\frac{\lambda_1}{\omega^2} \int_S u_*(y) \mathrm{T}_y^{(a)} \Gamma_{(a)}(x, y) dS_y - \lambda_2 \int_S u_*(y) L(x, y) dS_y + F(x). \tag{7.16}$$

where $u_*(y)$ is a solution of the inhomogeneous equation (7.15). We pass here to the limit as x approaches from B_i the point y_0 on S, and obtain

$$(v_*(x))_i = u_*(y_0) \qquad y_0 \in S, \quad x \in B_i.$$

Let $u_*(x)$ be defined in B_i by

$$u_*(x) = v_*(x), \qquad x \in B_i, \tag{7.17}$$

then

$$u_*(x) + \frac{\lambda_1}{\omega^2}\int_S u_*(y)\, T_y^{(a)}\Gamma_{(a)}(x,\ y)\, dS_y + \lambda_2 \int_S u_*(y)\, L(x,\ y)\, dS_y = F(x).$$

This equation coincides with (7.14), and its solution $u_*(x)$ is a vector defined by (7.17) and (7.16), where in the latter $u_*(y)$, $y \in S$ is obtained from (7.15). It is clear from the derivation of (7.14) that its solution also satisfies (7.1), proving that a solution to the latter exists. If this solution is a regular vector function (i. e., the Betti relations apply) then it also solves Problem (A), provided that the hypothesis (7.3) is fulfilled; but should the obtained solution be irregular, Problem (A) would lack a solution in the usual sense; in that case $u_*(x)$ may be regarded as its generalized solution.

The conditions under which the first or the second case obtains were investigated by Z. M. Gogniashvili /6b/ (cf. also § 4).

§ 2. Theorems on the eigenvalues of the integral equations of Problems (A) and (B_1)

Several theorems on the eigenvalues of the integral equations corresponding to the problems (A) and (B_1), which are important for applications (IX, 12), maybe proved under the assumption (7.3) in the static case $\omega = 0$. Then (7.1) reduces to

$$\varkappa(x)\, u(x) = \frac{1}{4\pi}(\mu_a - \mu_i)\int_S u_i(y)\, T_y^{(a)}\overset{0}{\Gamma}_{(a)}(x,\ y)\, dS_y + \mu_a E(x;\ x_*). \tag{A}$$

Similarly, (4.34) and (4.35), which correspond to the static problems (B_1) and (B_2) (IV, 4), become

$$\varkappa(x)\, u(x) = \frac{1}{4\pi}(\mu_a - \mu_i)\int_S u_i(y)\, T_y^{(a)}\overset{0}{G}(x,\ y)\, dS_y + \frac{1}{4\pi}\mu_a \int_{S_a} f(y)\, T_y^{(a)}\overset{0}{G}(x,\ y)\, dS_y, \tag{B_1}$$

$$\varkappa(x)\, u(x) = \frac{1}{4\pi}(\mu_a - \mu_i)\int_S u_i(y)\, T_y^{(a)}\overset{0}{H}(x,\ y)\, dS_y - \frac{1}{4\pi}\mu_a \int_{S_a} f(y)\, \overset{0}{H}(x,\ y)\, dS_y, \tag{B_2}$$

where $\overset{0}{G}(x,\ y)$ and $\overset{0}{H}(x,\ y)$ are the first and second Green's tensors for the domain $B = \bar{B}_i + B_a$.

We pass to the limit in these functional equations as x approaches from B_i the boundary point y_0 on S, and write down the corresponding integral equations

$$u_i(y_0) - \frac{1}{2\pi}\frac{\mu_a - \mu_i}{\mu_a + \mu_i}\int_S u_i(y)\, T_y^{(a)}\overset{0}{\Gamma}_{(a)}(y_0,\ y)\, dS_y = \frac{2\mu_a}{\mu_a + \mu_i} E(y_0;\ x_*), \tag{A'}$$

$$u_i(y_0) - \frac{1}{2\pi}\frac{\mu_a - \mu_i}{\mu_a + \mu_i}\int_S u_i(y)\, T_y^{(a)}\overset{0}{G}(y_0,\ y)\, dS_y = \frac{\mu_a}{2\pi(\mu_a + \mu_i)}\int_{S_a} f(y)\, T_y^{(a)}\overset{0}{G}(y_0,\ y)\, dS_y, \tag{B_1'}$$

2109

$$u_i(y_0)-\frac{1}{2\pi}\frac{\mu_a-\mu_i}{\mu_a+\mu_i}\int_S u_i(y)\,T_y^{(a)}\overset{0}{H}(y_0,\ y)\,dS_y=$$

$$=-\frac{\mu_a}{2\pi(\mu_a+\mu_i)}\int_{S_a} f(y)\,\overset{0}{H}(y_0,\ y)\,dS_y. \qquad (B_2')$$

The kernels of these equations depend only on the parameters μ_a and λ_a, not on μ_i and λ_i; therefore, assuming λ_a and μ_a constant and defining

$$\varkappa=\frac{\mu_a-\mu_i}{\mu_a+\mu_i},$$

we may consider the kernels of equations (A'), (B_1'), (B_2') to be independent of $\varkappa$. We further introduce the designations

$$\overset{0}{K}(y,\ x)=\frac{1}{2\pi}\,T_y^{(a)}\overset{0}{\Gamma}_{(a)}(x,\ y),\quad \overset{0}{L}(y,\ x)=\frac{1}{2\pi}\,T_y^{(a)}\overset{0}{G}(x,\ y),$$

$$\overset{0}{M}(y,\ x)=\frac{1}{2\pi}\,T_y^{(a)}\overset{0}{H}(x,\ y);$$

equations (A'), (B_1'), (B_2') may now be written

$$u_i(y_0)-\varkappa\int_S u_i(y)\,\overset{0}{K}(y,\ y_0)\,dS_y=\frac{2\mu_a}{\mu_i+\mu_a}\,E(y_0;\ x_*), \qquad (A')$$

$$u_i(y_0)-\varkappa\int_S u_i(y)\,\overset{0}{L}(y,\ y_0)\,dS_y=\frac{\mu_a}{2\pi(\mu_i+\mu_a)}\int_{S_a} f(y)\,\overset{0}{L}(y,\ y_0), \qquad (B_1')$$

$$u_i(y_0)-\varkappa\int_S u_i(y)\,\overset{0}{M}(y,\ y_0)\,dS_y=-\frac{\mu_a}{2\pi(\mu_i+\mu_a)}\int_{S_a} f(y)\,H(y_0,\ y). \qquad (B_2')$$

Equation (A') coincides with (6.1) for which Theorems 1, 2, 3 (VI, 1) are valid. We will now show that these theorems also apply to equation (B_1').

Theorem 1'. The eigenvalues of the kernel $\overset{0}{L}(y_0,\ y)$ *are real.*

Consider along with the homogeneous equation (B_1^0) also the adjoint operator

$$\varphi(y_0)-\varkappa\int_S \overset{0}{L}(y_0,\ y)\,\varphi(y)\,dS_y.$$

For the single-layer potential

$$V(x;\ \varphi)=\frac{1}{2\pi}\int_S \overset{0}{G}(x,\ y)\,\varphi(y)\,dS_y,$$

one may easily verify that

$$\frac{1}{2}(1-\varkappa)(TV)_i-\frac{1}{2}(1+\varkappa)(TV)_a=\varphi(y_0)-\frac{1}{2\pi}\varkappa\int_S\left(T_{y_0}\overset{0}{G}(y_0,\ y)\right)\varphi(y)\,dS_y. \qquad (7.18)$$

Let some eigenvalue be complex: $\varkappa=\alpha+\beta i$, $\beta\neq 0$; let $\varphi_1+i\varphi_2$ be a solution corresponding to this eigenvalue. Taking this solution as density, we construct the single-layer potential $V=V_1+iV_2$. Inserting V into (7.18) and separating real and imaginary parts, we obtain

$$(1-\alpha)(TV_1)_i-(1+\alpha)(TV_1)_a+\beta(TV_2)_i+\beta(TV_2)_a=0, \qquad (7.19_1)$$

$$(1-\alpha)(TV_2)_i-(1+\alpha)(TV_2)_a-\beta(TV_1)_i-\beta(TV_1)_a=0. \qquad (7.19_2)$$

We multiply these relations respectively by V_2 and V_1, form their difference, integrate over the surface S, and add the expression

$$(1+\alpha)\int_{S_a}[V_1TV_2-V_2TV_1]\,dS+\beta\int_{S_a}[V_1TV_1+V_2TV_2]\,dS,$$

which vanishes in virtue of the properties of Green's first tensor; then we have

$$(1-\alpha)\int_S (V_2 TV_1 - V_1 TV_2)_i\, dS + (1+\alpha)\int_{S+S_a} (V_1 TV_2 - V_2 TV_1)_a\, dS +$$
$$+\beta\int_S (V_1 TV_1 + V_2 TV_2)_i\, dS + \beta\int_{S+S_a} (V_1 TV_1 + V_2 TV_2)_a\, dS = 0.$$

Making use of the Betti relation (1.10'), we may write

$$(1-\alpha)\int_{B_i} (V_2 \overset{*}{\Delta}_{(a)} V_1 - V_1 \overset{*}{\Delta}_{(a)} V_2)\, dv +$$
$$+(1+\alpha)\int_{B_a} (V_1 \overset{*}{\Delta}_{(a)} V_2 - V_2 \overset{*}{\Delta}_{(a)} V_1)\, dv + \beta\int_S (V_1 TV_1 + V_2 TV_2)_i\, dS +$$
$$+\beta\int_{S+S_a} (V_1 TV_1 + V_2 TV_2)_a\, dS = 0$$

and, since $\overset{*}{\Delta}_{(a)} V_1 = \overset{*}{\Delta}_{(a)} V_2 = 0$,

$$\beta\int_S (V_1 TV_1 + V_2 TV_2)_i\, dS + \beta\int_{S+S_a} (V_1 TV_1 + V_2 TV_2)_a\, dS = 0. \qquad (*)$$

Applying now the Betti relation (1.9'), and taking the normal as pointing from B_i into B_a, we get

$$\int_S (V_1 TV_1 + V_2 TV_2)_i\, dS = \int_{B_i} [W(V_1, V_1) + W(V_2, V_2)]\, dv,$$

$$\int_{S+S_a} (V_1 TV_1 + V_2 TV_2)_a\, dS = -\int_{B_a} [W(V_1, V_1) + W(V_2, V_2)]\, dv,$$

where $W(u, u)$ is a positive-definite form given by (1.12). We now write

$$J_j = \int_{B_i} W(V_j, V_j)\, dv, \quad J'_j = \int_{B_a} W(V_j, V_j)\, dv \qquad (j = 1, 2),$$

so that equation (*) becomes

$$\beta(J_1 + J_2) - \beta(J'_1 + J'_2) = 0.$$

We multiply (7.19_1) and (7.19_2) respectively, by V_1 and V_2, add them together, integrate over S, and again add a vanishing term, obtaining in the same way

$$(1-\alpha)(J_1 + J_2) + (1+\alpha)(J'_1 + J'_2) = 0. \qquad (**)$$

From these relations, since $\beta \neq 0$, it follows that

$$J_1 = J_2 = J'_1 = J'_2 = 0.$$

This implies the absence of strain, so that the potentials $V_1(x)$ and $V_2(x)$ must represent rigid displacements and

$$TV_k(x) = 0 \qquad (k = 1, 2);$$

it now follows from (2.5) that $\varphi_1(x) = \varphi_2(x) = 0$. This contradiction shows that $2\beta = 0$, which proves Theorem 1'.

Theorem 2'. The eigenvalues of the kernel $\overset{0}{L}(y_0, y)$ *are not smaller than unity in absolute value.*

Since $\beta = 0$, (**) takes the form

$$(1-\alpha) J_1 + (1+\alpha) J'_1 = 0.$$

Solving for α, we get

$$\alpha=\frac{J_1+J_1'}{J_1-J_1'},$$

whence

$$|\alpha|\geqslant 1,$$

which proves Theorem 2'.

Theorem 3'. *The eigenvalues of the kernel* $\overset{0}{L}(y_0, y)$ *are simple poles of the resolvent.*

The proof is similar to that of Theorem 3.

It is of interest to prove these theorems for the kernel $\overset{0}{M}(y_0, y)$

Theorem 4'. *Solutions of the integral equations* (A') *and* (B_1') *are simultaneously unique solutions of the functional equations* (A) *and* (B_1), *respectively.*

The equations (A') and (B_1') are singular. They are solvable for $|\varkappa|<1$, by Theorem 2'. Since in that case

$$|\varkappa|=\left|\frac{\mu_a-\mu_i}{\mu_a+\mu_i}\right|<1,$$

equations (A') and (B_1') possess unique solutions, by the first Fredholm theorem (V, 9). Substituting these solutions in (A) and (B_1), we get

$$\varkappa(x)\,v^{(1)}(x)=\frac{1}{4\pi}(\mu_a-\mu_i)\int_S u_i(y)\,\mathrm{T}_y^{(a)}\overset{0}{\Gamma}_{(a)}(x, y)\,dS_y+\mu_a E(x; x_*),$$

$$\varkappa(x)\,v^{(2)}(x)=\frac{1}{4\pi}(\mu_a-\mu_i)\int_S u_i(y)\,\mathrm{T}_y^{(a)}\overset{0}{G}(x, y)\,dS_y+$$
$$+\frac{1}{4\pi}\mu_a\int_{S_a} f(y)\,\mathrm{T}_y^{(a)}\overset{0}{G}(x, y)\,dS_y.$$

It may be verified easily, using (7.4), (A') and (B_1'), that

$$\overset{*}{\Delta}_{(i)}v^{(1)}=0,\quad \lim_{x\to y_0} v^{(1)}(x)=u_i(y_0);\quad \overset{*}{\Delta}_{(i)}v^{(2)}=0,\quad \lim_{x\to y_0} v^{(2)}(x)=u_i(y_0),$$

from which the existence theorem follows directly. If the functional equations (A) and (B_1) were to possess two solutions, then the corresponding homogeneous equations would possess nontrivial ones; but then also the homogeneous equations $(A')^0$ and $(B_1')^0$ would have nontrivial solutions, which contradicts Theorem 2'. This proves Theorem 4'.

§ 3. Existence theorems for Problems (B_1) and (B_2). Case of equal Poisson constants

The equations corresponding to the dynamic problems (B_1) and (B_2) are (IV, 3) of the form (4.11) and (4.13). Setting in these equations $\lambda_i\mu_a-\lambda_a\mu_i=0$, we obtain

$$\varkappa(x)\,u(x)=\frac{1}{4\pi}\omega^2(\mu_a-\mu_i)\int_{B_i} u(y)\,G(x, y)\,dv_y+$$
$$+\frac{1}{4\pi}(\mu_a-\mu_i)\int_S u_i(y)\,\mathrm{T}_y^{(a)}G(x, y)\,dS_y+$$
$$+\frac{1}{4\pi}\mu_a\int_{S_a} f(y)\,\mathrm{T}_y^{(a)}G(x, y)\,dS. \qquad (7.20)$$

$$\varkappa(x)\,u(x)=\frac{1}{4\pi}\,\omega^2(\mu_a-\mu_i)\int\limits_{B_i}u(y)\,H(x,\ y)\,dv_y+$$

$$+\frac{1}{4\pi}(\mu_a-\mu_i)\int\limits_{S}u_i(y)\,\mathrm{T}_y^{(a)}H(x,\ y)\,dS_y-$$

$$-\frac{1}{4\pi}\mu_a\int\limits_{S_a}f(y)\,H(x,\ y)\,dS_y. \qquad (7.21)$$

Comparing these equations with (7.1) we notice that their solutions in the present case satisfy (7.4) and (7.5) and the boundary conditions (7.6) and (7.8). This follows from the fact that the volume and double-layer potentials formed with the kernels $G(x,\ y)$, $H(x,\ y)$, $\mathrm{T}^{(a)}G(x,\ y)$, $\mathrm{T}^{(a)}H(x,\ y)$ have in a domain and on its boundary the same properties as the corresponding potentials formed with the kernels $\Gamma_{(a)}(x,\ y)$, $\mathrm{T}^{(a)}\Gamma_{(a)}(x,\ y)$. The conditions at infinity are replaced here by the behavior of Green's tensors on the external surface S_a; one should further keep in mind that

$$\overset{0}{\Delta^*}H(x,\ y)=4\pi\sum_{k=1}^{6}\mathfrak{A}^{(k)}(x)*\mathfrak{A}^{(k)}(y).$$

We will now show that the boundary conditions on S_a are indeed fulfilled.

Applying $\mathrm{T}^{(a)}$ to the two sides of (7.21) and passing to the limit in (7.20) and (7.21) as x approaches y_0 on S_a, we get, by definition of the Green's tensors,

$$G(y_0;\ y)=0,\quad \mathrm{T}_{y_0}H(y_0;\ y)=0,\quad y_0\in S_a,\quad y\,\overline{\in}\,S_a.$$

Then (7.20) and (7.21) become

$$\lim_{x\to y_0\in S_0}u(x)=\frac{1}{4\pi}\lim_{x\to y_0}\int\limits_{S_a}f(y)\,\mathrm{T}_y^{(a)}G(x,\ y)\,dS_y,$$

$$\lim_{x\to y_0\in S_a}\mathrm{T}^{(a)}u(x)=-\frac{1}{4\pi}\lim_{x\to y_0}\mathrm{T}^{(a)}\int\limits_{S_a}f(y)\,H(x,\ y)\,dS_y.$$

On the other hand we have, in view of (6.40) and (6.44),

$$\lim_{x\to y_0}\int\limits_{S_a}f(y)\,\mathrm{T}_y^{(a)}G(x,\ y)\,dS_y=4\pi f(y_0),$$

$$\lim_{x\to y_0}\mathrm{T}^{(a)}\int\limits_{S_a}f(y)\,H(x,\ y)\,dS_y=-4\pi f(y_0),\quad y_0\in S_a,$$

which shows clearly that the conditions on S_a are fulfilled. We may now formulate the following inverse theorem for the problems (B_1) and (B_2):

Regular solutions of the integral equations (7.20) and (7.21) are solutions of problems (B_1) *and* (B_2), *respectively.*

We can prove by this theorem and the uniqueness theorem (III, 4), as we did in § 1 of the present chapter, the following assertion:

Theorem 2. The homogeneous equations corresponding to (7.20) and (7.21) have only trivial solutions.

Applying this theorem and repeating the arguments of § 1, we obtain the existence theorem for the dynamic problems (B_1) and (B_2) when ω^2 is not an eigenfrequency for the domain B and the Poisson constants of B_i and B_a are equal. The obtained solution should be understood in the generalized sense whenever it is not a solution of the usual kind (cf. end of § 1).

Assuming $\omega=0$, we derive from (7.20) and (7.21) the equations for the static problems

$$4\pi\varkappa(x)\,u(x)=(\mu_a-\mu_i)\int_S u_i(y)\,\mathrm{T}_y^{(a)}\overset{0}{G}(x,\ y)\,dS_y+$$
$$+\mu_a\int_{S_a} f(y)\,\mathrm{T}_y^{(a)}\overset{0}{G}(x,\ y)\,dS_y \qquad (7.22)$$

and

$$4\pi\varkappa(x)\,u(x)=(\mu_a-\mu_i)\int_S u_i(y)\,\mathrm{T}_y^{(a)}\overset{0}{H}(x,\ y)\,dS_y-$$
$$-\mu_a\int_{S_a} f(y)\,\overset{0}{H}(x,\ y)\,dS_y, \qquad (7.23)$$

where $\overset{0}{G}(x,\ y)$ and $\overset{0}{H}(x,\ y)$ are the first and second static Green's tensors for $B=\bar{B}_i+B_a$ (IV, 4). The solvability of (7.23) now follows on account of the identity

$$\Delta^{*}_{(a)}\left(\mathrm{T}\overset{0}{H}(x,\ y)\right)=0,$$

which will be proved in § 9.

It will be shown (IX, 12) that equation (7.22) may be solved by successive approximations.

§ 4. Existence theorem for Problem (*A*) in the general case

Equation (4.10_i) can be transformed as follows. We have for $x\in B_i$

$$\varkappa(x)=\mu_a l=\frac{1}{3}\left(2\mu_i+\mu_a\frac{\lambda_i+2\mu_i}{\lambda_a+2\mu_a}\right)=\mu_i+\frac{m}{3(\lambda_a+2\mu_a)},$$

$$\mu_a\mathrm{T}_y^{*}\Gamma_{(a)}^{(k)}(x,\ y)=(\mu_a-\mu_i)\,\mathrm{T}_y^{(a)}\Gamma_{(a)}(x,\ y)-mn_y\operatorname{div}_y\Gamma_{(a)}^{(k)}(x,\ y)$$
$$(k=1,\ 2,\ 3),$$

hence (4.10_i) is equivalent to

$$4\pi\left(\mu_i+\frac{m}{3(\lambda_a+2\mu_a)}\right)u_k(x)=\omega^2(\mu_a-\mu_i)\int_{B_i} u(y)\,\Gamma_{(a)}^{(k)}(x,\ y)\,d\sigma_y+$$
$$+m\int_{B_i} u(y)\operatorname{grad}\operatorname{div}\Gamma_{(a)}^{(k)}(x,\ y)\,d\sigma_y+$$
$$+(\mu_a-\mu_i)\int_S u_i(y)\,\mathrm{T}_y^{(a)}\Gamma_{(a)}^{(k)}(x,\ y)\,dS_y-$$
$$-m\int_S u_i(y)\,n_y\operatorname{div}_y\Gamma_{(a)}^{(k)}(x,\ y)\,dS_y+\mu_a E_k(x;\ x_*). \qquad (7.24)$$

We are looking for a solution of this equation expressed as a power series in the small parameter $m=\lambda_i\mu_a-\lambda_a\mu_i$:

$$u(x)=\sum_{s=0}^{\infty} m^s u^{(s)}(x), \qquad (7.25)$$

where $u^{(s)}(x)$, $s=1,\ 2,\ 3,\ \ldots$ are new unknown vectors. We assume that the series (7.25) converges uniformly and that its sum, as well as all the $u^{(s)}(x)$, belong to a Hölder class with some exponent α. Inserting the series (7.25) in equation (7.24) and equating coefficients of equal powers of m, we obtain

$$4\pi\mu_i u_k^{(0)}(x)-\omega^2(\mu_a-\mu_i)\int_{B_i} u^{(0)}(y)\,\Gamma_{(a)}^{(k)}(x,\ y)\,d\sigma_y-$$
$$-(\mu_a-\mu_i)\int_S u_i^{(0)}(y)\,\mathrm{T}_y^{(a)}\Gamma_{(a)}^{(k)}(x,\ y)\,dS_y=\mu_a E_k(x;\ x_*). \qquad (7.26_0)$$

$$4\pi\mu_i u_k^{(1)}(x) - \omega^2(\mu_a - \mu_i)\int_{B_i} u^{(1)}(y)\cdot\Gamma_{(a)}^{(k)}(x, y)\,d\sigma_y -$$

$$-(\mu_a - \mu_i)\int_S u_i^{(1)}(y)\,\mathrm{T}_y^{(a)}\Gamma_{(a)}^{(k)}(x, y)\,dS_y = F_k^{(1)}(x; x_*), \qquad (7.26_1)$$

$$4\pi\mu_i u_k^{(s)}(x) - \omega^2(\mu_a - \mu_i)\int_{B_i} u^{(s)}(y)\,\Gamma_{(a)}^{(k)}(x, y)\,d\sigma_y -$$

$$-(\mu_a - \mu_i)\int_S u_i^{(s)}(y)\,\mathrm{T}_y^{(a)}\Gamma_{(a)}^{(k)}(x, y)\,dS_y = F_k^{(s)}(x; x_*), \qquad (7.26_s)$$

where

$$F_k^{(s)}(x; x_*) = \int_{B_i} u^{(s-1)}(y)\operatorname{grad}\operatorname{div}\Gamma_{(a)}^{(k)}(x, y)\,d\sigma_y -$$

$$-\int_S u_i^{(s-1)}(y)\left[n_y \operatorname{div}_y \Gamma_{(a)}^{(k)}(x, y)\right]dS_y - \frac{4\pi}{3(\lambda_a + 2\mu_a)}u_k^{(s-1)}(x),$$

$$(s = 1, 2, 3, \ldots, \; k = 1, 2, 3).$$

On the right-hand side of (7.26_0) appears the function $\mu_a E_k(x; x_*)$, which is analytic in $\bar{B}_i$; this equation coincides with (7.1), and its solution $u_k^{(0)}(x)$, $k = 1, 2, 3$, given by (7.16) and (7.17) belongs in $\bar{B}_i$ to class H. Equation (7.26_1) also coincides with (7.1), but on its right-hand side appears the function

$$F_k^{(1)}(x; x_*) = \int_{B_i} u^{(0)}(y)\operatorname{grad}\operatorname{div}\Gamma_{(a)}^{(k)}\,d\sigma_y -$$

$$-\int_S u_i^{(0)}(y)\left[n_y \operatorname{div}_y \Gamma_{(a)}^{(k)}\right]dS_y - \frac{4\pi}{3(\lambda_a + 2\mu_a)}u_k^{(0)}(x),$$

where $u^{(0)}(x)$ is, as we have seen, a solution of (7.26_0) of class H. Let the Hölder exponent of $u^{(0)}(x)$ be α; it will be shown later on that in $\bar{B}_i$ $F_k^{(1)}(x; x_*)$ belongs to class H as well. Consequently, the solution $u^{(1)}(x)$ of (7.26_1) belongs, in $\bar{B}_i$, to class H. Since (7.26_s) coincides with (7.1) and has on the right-hand side H-class functions, we may continue this process and construct the sequence

$$\{u^{(s)}(x)\} \qquad (s = 0, 1, 2, \ldots),$$

all of class H in $\bar{B}_i$. It remains to demonstrate that the series (7.25) converges uniformly and that its sum is of class H.

We first show that

$$F_k^{(s+1)}(x; x_*) = \int_{B_i}\left[u^{(s)}(y) - u^{(s)}(x)\right]\operatorname{grad}\operatorname{div}\Gamma_{(a)}^{(k)}\,d\sigma_i -$$

$$-\int_S \left[u_i^{(s)}(y) - u^{(s}(x)\right] n_y \operatorname{div}\Gamma_{(a)}^{(k)}\,dS_y. \qquad (7.27)$$

Denoting the right-hand side by J, we have for $x \in B_i$

$$F_k^{(s+1)}(x; x_*) = J + u^{(s)}(x)\left[\int_{B_i}\operatorname{grad}\operatorname{div}\Gamma_{(a)}^{(k)}\,d\sigma_i - \int_S n_y \operatorname{div}\Gamma_{(a)}^{(k)}\,dS_y\right] - \frac{4\pi}{3(\lambda_a + 2\mu_a)}u_k^{(s)}(x). \qquad (*)$$

We write J_k' for the expression in square brackets, and note that by (1.34)

$$\operatorname{div}\Gamma_{(a)}^{(k)}(x, y) = \frac{1}{\lambda_a + 2\mu_a}\frac{\partial}{\partial y_k}\frac{e^{ik_1 r}}{r},$$

whence

$$J_k'=\frac{1}{\lambda_a+2\mu_a}\left[\int\limits_{B_i}\operatorname{grad}\left(\frac{\partial}{\partial y_k}\frac{e^{ik_1r}}{r}\right)d\sigma_y-\int\limits_{S}n_y\frac{\partial}{\partial y_k}\frac{e^{ik_1r}}{r}dS_y\right].$$

By definition of the principal value of an integral we have

$$\int\limits_{B_i}\frac{\partial}{\partial y_j}\left(\frac{\partial}{\partial y_k}\frac{e^{ik_1r}}{r}\right)d\sigma_y=\lim_{\varepsilon\to 0}\int\limits_{B_i-\tau(x;\,\varepsilon)}\frac{\partial}{\partial y_j}\left(\frac{\partial}{\partial y_k}\frac{e^{ik_1r}}{r}\right)d\sigma_y$$
$$(j,\ k=1,\ 2,\ 3). \tag{7.27'}$$

However,

$$\int\limits_{B_i-\tau(x;\,\varepsilon)}\frac{\partial}{\partial y_j}\left(\frac{\partial}{\partial y_k}\frac{e^{ik_1r}}{r}\right)d\sigma_y=\int\limits_{S}\frac{\partial}{\partial y_k}\frac{e^{ik_1r}}{r}\cos(n_y,\ x_j)dS_y+$$
$$+\int\limits_{\sigma(x;\,\varepsilon)}\frac{\partial}{\partial y_k}\frac{e^{ik_1r}}{r}\cos(n_y,\ x_j)\,dS_y=\int\limits_{S}\cos(n_y,\ x_j)\frac{\partial}{\partial y_k}\frac{e^{ik_1r}}{r}dS_y+$$
$$+\int\limits_{\sigma(x;\,\varepsilon)}\cos(n_y,\ x_j)\frac{\partial}{\partial y_k}\left(\frac{e^{ik_1r}}{r}-\frac{1}{r}\right)dS_y+$$
$$+\int\limits_{\sigma(x;\,\varepsilon)}\cos(n_y,\ x_j)\frac{\partial}{\partial y_k}\frac{1}{r}dS_y. \tag{7.27''}$$

The last integral on the right-hand side may be calculated:

$$\int\limits_{\sigma(x;\,\varepsilon)}\frac{\partial}{\partial y_k}\frac{1}{r}\cos(n_y,\ x_j)\,dS_y=-\int\limits_{\sigma(x;\,\varepsilon)}\frac{\partial}{\partial y_k}\frac{1}{r}\cos(r,\ x_j)\,dS_y=$$
$$=\int\limits_{\sigma(x;\,\varepsilon)}\frac{\cos(r,\ x_k)\cos(r,\ x_j)}{r^2(x,\ y)}dS_y=\begin{cases}\frac{4}{3}\pi, & k=j,\\ 0, & k\neq j.\end{cases}$$

Further,

$$\lim_{\varepsilon\to 0}\int\limits_{\sigma(x;\,\varepsilon)}\cos(n_y,\ x_j)\frac{\partial}{\partial y_k}\left(\frac{e^{ik_1r}}{r}-\frac{1}{r}\right)dS_y=0.$$

Inserting the obtained expression for the integral (7.27'') in (7.27') and passing to the limit, we find

$$\int\limits_{B_i}\operatorname{grad}\left(\frac{\partial}{\partial y_k}\frac{e^{ik_1r}}{r}\right)d\sigma_y=\int\limits_{S}n_y\frac{\partial}{\partial y_k}\frac{e^{ik_1r}}{r}dS_y+\frac{4}{3}\pi\delta^{(k)},$$

where $\delta^{(k)}$ stands for the vector $(\delta_{k1},\ \delta_{k2},\ \delta_{k3})$, and δ_{kj} is the Kronecker symbol. Substituting this value of the volume integral in the expression for J_k', we obtain

$$J_k'=\frac{4\pi}{3(\lambda_a+2\mu_a)}\delta^{(k)}\qquad(k=1,\ 2,\ 3)$$

and finally, inserting the last expression into (*), we obtain (7.27). Let us define some new notations: the functions $f_k(x)$, $k=1,\ 2,\ 3$ satisfy the Hölder condition

$$|f_k(x')-f_k(x'')|\leqslant H_k|x'-x''|^{\alpha_k}\qquad(0<\alpha_k\leqslant 1),$$

in the closed domain $\overline{B}_i$, of which x' and x'' are arbitrary points; H_k and α_k are positive constants, independent of x' and x''. The lower bound of the set of numbers H_k that satisfy the above inequality will sometimes be denoted by $H(f_k,\ \alpha_k;\ \overline{B}_i)$. Let further $C(f_k,\ \overline{B}_i)$ be defined as*

$$C(f_k;\ \overline{B}_i)=\max_{x\in\overline{B}_i}|f_k(x)|+H(f_k,\ \alpha_k;\ \overline{B}_i)$$

The largest of these numbers, when k takes on the values 1, 2, 3, will be

* The symbols $C(f_k,\ B_i)$ and $C(f_k,\ S)$ are defined analogously.

denoted by the same symbols but without indices, for example

$$H(f, \alpha, \bar{B}_l) = \max\{H(f_k, \alpha_k; \bar{B}_l)\}, \quad C(f; \bar{B}_l) = \max\{C(f_k; \bar{B}_l)\}$$
$$(k = 1, 2, 3).$$

It has been asserted above that

If $u^{(s)}(x)$ is of class H with exponent α in the closed domain B_l, then also $F^{(s+1)}(x; x_*)$ belongs in $\bar{B}_l$ to a Hölder class with exponent not exceeding α.

The proof is identical for both integral terms appearing in the expression of $F^{(s+1)}(x; x_*)$; we will sketch it for the term

$$\int_{B_l} u^{(s)}(y) \operatorname{grad} \operatorname{div} \Gamma^{(k)}_{(a)}(x, y)\, d\sigma_y.$$

It is sufficient to show the validity of the assertion for integrals of the form

$$\int_{B_l} u_j^{(s)}(y) \frac{\partial^2}{\partial y_j \partial y_k} \frac{1}{r(x, y)} d\sigma_y \qquad (7.27_1')$$

in the three-dimensional case and for integrals of the form

$$\int_{B_l} u_j^{(s)}(y) \frac{\partial^2}{\partial y_j \partial y_k} \ln r(x, y)\, d\sigma_y \qquad (7.27_1'')$$

in the plane case. The calculations are simplified in the latter case if one uses the complex representation

$$x_1 + ix_2 = z, \quad y_1 + iy_2 = \zeta, \quad \zeta - z = \sigma; \quad |\sigma| = r(x, y),$$
$$\ln r(x, y) = \ln|\sigma| = \operatorname{Re} \ln \sigma;$$

then

$$\int_{B_l} u_j^{(s)}(y) \frac{\partial^2}{\partial y_j \partial y_k} \ln r\, d\sigma_y = \gamma_{jk} \operatorname{Re} \int_{B_l} \frac{u_j^{(s)}(y_1, y_2)}{(\zeta - z)^2} dy_1 dy_2$$
$$(j, k = 1, 2),$$

where Re denotes the real part, and γ_{jk} $(j, k = 1, 2)$ are certain constants which need not be known explicitly.

Integrals of the type

$$g(z) = \int_{B_l} \frac{\varphi(\zeta)}{(\zeta - z)^2} d\zeta,$$

where $\varphi(\zeta)$ is in the closed domain $\bar{B}_l$ of the Hölder class with exponent γ, $0 < \gamma \leqslant 1$, satisfy the inequality

$$|g(z') - g(z'')| \leqslant AC(\varphi; \bar{B}_l)|z' - z''|^{\gamma},$$

where A is a constant depending on γ and B_l*. This implies the indicated property for integrals of the form $(7.27_1'')$, and consequently for (7.27_1).

The inequality

$$|F_k^{(s+1)}(x'; x_*) - F_k^{(s+1)}(x''; x_*)| \leqslant A_1 C(u^{(s)}, \bar{B}_l) r^{\alpha}(x', x'') \qquad (7.28)$$

consequently holds for any x' and x'' in $\bar{B}_l$. We get from (7.27)

$$|F_k^{(s+1)}(x; x_*)| \leqslant M(\alpha, B_l) H(u^{(s)}, \alpha, \bar{B}_l) \leqslant M(\alpha, B_l) C(u^{(s)}; \bar{B}_l), \qquad (7.29)$$

* The proof may be found, e.g., in /3b/, pp. 73–75; it is mentioned there that this result is originally due to Giraud /10a/.

where

$$M(\alpha, B_i) > \left\{ \int_{B_i} | r^{\alpha}(x, y) \operatorname{grad} \operatorname{div} \Gamma^{(k)}(x, y) | d\sigma_y + \right.$$

$$\left. + \int_S | r^{\alpha}(x, y) n_y \operatorname{div} \Gamma^{(k)}_{(a)} | dS_y \right\} \quad (k = 1, 2, 3)$$

and depends only on α and B_i; $H(u^{(s)}, \alpha, \bar{B}_i)$ is the largest Hölder constant of $u_k^{(s)}(x)$ $(k = 1, 2)$. It follows from (7.28) and (7.29) that

$$C(F_k^{(s+1)}; \bar{B}_i) \leqslant M_1(\alpha, B_i) C(u^{(s)}, \bar{B}_i). \tag{7.30}$$

where

$$M_1(\alpha, B_i) > \{A_1 + M(\alpha, B_i)\}.$$

The functional equation (7.26_s) reduces, as shown in § 1, to the integral equation

$$u_k^{(s)}(x_0) + \lambda_1 \int_S u_i^{(s)}(y) \mathrm{T}^{(a)} \Gamma^{(k)}_{(a)}(x_0, y) dS_y +$$

$$+ \lambda_2 \int_S u_i^{(s)}(y) L(x_0, y) dS_y = P_k^{(s)}(x_0, x_*), \tag{7.31}$$

here $x_0 \in S$

$$\lambda_1 = \frac{1}{2\pi} \frac{\mu_i - \mu_a}{\mu_i + \mu_a}, \qquad \lambda_2 = -\frac{\omega^2}{8\pi^2} \frac{(\mu_i - \mu_a)^2}{\mu_i(\mu_i + \mu_a)},$$

$$L(x_0, y) = \int_{B_i} \mathrm{T}^{(a)} \Gamma_{(a)}(\xi, y) R(\xi, x_0) d\sigma_\xi,$$

$$P^{(s)}(x_0; x_*) = \frac{2}{\mu_i + \mu_a} \left\{ F^{(s)}(x_0; x_*) + \frac{1}{4\pi} \left(\frac{\mu_a}{\mu_i} - 1 \right) \int_S F^{(s)}(y, x_*) R(y, x_0) dS_y \right\}.$$

Here $R(x, y)$ is a Fredholm resolvent of class $N^{(2)}$, and the kernel $L(x, y)$ admits a logarithmic singularity. The existence of solution of equation (7.31) was already proved in § 1. This solution, in view of (5.52), may be represented in the form*

$$u^{(s)}(x_0) = [I + \varkappa^2 \Phi(x_0; \varkappa)]^{-1} P^{(s)}(x_0; x_*) + \varkappa \int_S N(x_0, \xi; \varkappa) P^{(s)}(\xi; x_*) dS_\xi, \qquad x_0 \in S,$$

where $\Phi(x_0; \varkappa)$ is regular and given by (5.37), and the meromorphic matrix function $N(x_0, \xi; \varkappa)$, given by (5.41), has a simple pole at $x_0 = \xi$. We now introduce the notation

$$[I + \varkappa^2 \Phi(x_0; \varkappa)]^{-1} P^{(s)}(x_0; x_*) = Y^{(s)}(x_0; x_*)$$

and show that $Y^{(s)}(x_0; x_*)$ belongs, on S, to class H with the exponent α, and that it satisfies an inequality of the type (7.30). It is sufficient for this to prove that the same properties are possessed by $P^{(s)}(x_0; x_*)$. The first property follows for $P^{(s)}(x_0; x_*)$ from (7.28) and from the fact that since $R(x, y) \in N^{(2)}$, the integral

$$f^{(s)}(x_0) = \int_S F^{(s)}(y; x_*) R(y, x_0) dS_y, \qquad x_0 \in S,$$

itself belongs to Hölder's class with exponent α. In order to prove the second property it is necessary to show that

$$C(f_k^{(s)}; S) \leqslant A_2 C(u^{(s-1)}; \bar{B}_i) (A_2 \text{ constant}) \quad (k = 1, 2). \tag{7.32}$$

* We write here $\varkappa$ for λ_1.

But we have from (7.29),

$$|f_k^{(s)}(x_0)| \leqslant \sum_{j=1}^{2}\left|\int_S F_j^{(s)}(y;\, x_*) R_{jk}(y,\, x_0)\, dS_y\right| \leqslant$$

$$\leqslant \sum_{j=1}^{2} \max_{x_0 \in S} |F_j^{(s)}(x_0;\, x_*)| \int_S |R_{jk}(y,\, x_0)|\, dS_y \leqslant M_2(\alpha, \bar{B}_i)\, C(u^{(s-1)};\, \bar{B}_i),$$

where $M_2(\alpha,\, \bar{B}_i)$ depends only on α and B_i. On the other hand, by (7.29) we may write for $(x_0',\, x_0'') \in S$,

$$|f_k^{(s)}(x_0') - f_k^{(s)}(x_0'')| = \left|\sum_{j=1}^{2} \int_S [F_j^{(s)}(y;\, x_*)\, R_{jk}(y,\, x_0') - F_j^{(s)}(y;\, x_*)\, R_{jk}(y,\, x_0'')]\, dS_y \leqslant\right.$$

$$\leqslant \sum_{j=1}^{2} \max_{x_0 \in S} |F_j^{(s)}(x_0;\, x_*)| \int_S |R_{jk}(y,\, x_0') - R_{jk}(y,\, x_0'')|\, dS_y \leqslant$$

$$\leqslant M_2'(\alpha,\, B_i)\, C(u^{(s-1)};\, \bar{B}_i)\, |x_0' - x_0''|^{\beta};$$

this implies (7.32), and thus proves our statement about $Y^{(s)}(x_0;\, x_*)$.

We shall now show that the integral

$$\varphi^{(s)}(x_0) = \int_S N(x_0,\, \xi;\, \varkappa)\, P^{(s)}(\xi;\, x_*)\, dS_\xi$$

also satisfies inequalities of the type (7.28) and (7.29). We note that in view of (5.41),

$$N(x_0,\, \xi;\, \varkappa) = [I + \varkappa^2 \Phi(x_0;\, \varkappa)]^{-1} H(x_0,\, \xi;\, \varkappa) + O(r^{h-1}(x,\, \xi)), \quad h > 0.$$

Considering the elements of the matrices (5.32') and (5.33), where $\rho^{-2}(x,\, y)$ should be replaced by $\rho^{-1}(x,\, y)$, because we are dealing now with the plane case, observe that they may be represented as a linear combination of terms of the type

$$\chi(\theta) \frac{\partial}{\partial y_k} \ln \rho(x_0,\, y) \qquad (k = 1,\, 2),$$

where θ is the angle between the direction of $\rho(x_0,\, y)$ and one of the coordinate axes, and $\chi(\theta)$ is a sufficiently smooth function; hence the above proof applies also in this case for $\varphi_k^{(s)}(x_0)$ $(k = 1,\, 2)$, and the inequalities (7.28) and (7.30) obtain to within constant factors.

Writing the solution of equation (7.31) in component form,

$$u_k^{(s)}(x_0) = Y_k^{(s)}(x_0;\, x_*) + \varkappa \sum_{j=1}^{2} \int_S N_{jk}(x_0,\, \xi;\, \varkappa)\, P_j^{(s)}(\xi;\, x_*)\, dS_\xi \quad (k = 1,\, 2),$$

whence

$$|u_k^{(s)}(x_0)| \leqslant M_3(\alpha,\, B_i)\, C(u^{(s-1)};\, \bar{B}_i). \tag{7.33}$$

On the other hand, for arbitrary $(x_0',\, x_0'') \in S$,

$$|u_k^{(s)}(x_0') - u_k^{(s)}(x_0'')| \leqslant M_4(\alpha,\, S)\, C(u^{(s-1)},\, \bar{B}_i)\, |x_0' - x_0''|^{\alpha}. \tag{7.33$_1$}$$

Now (7.33) and (7.33$_1$) imply

$$C(u_k^{(s)},\, S) \leqslant M_5(\alpha,\, B_i)\, C(u^{(s-1)};\, \bar{B}_i). \tag{7.34}$$

Until now the point x_0 was assumed to lie on S. If it should be located in B_i, then the solution of (7.31) would be represented by (7.16), and hence, taking into account (7.33), (7.33$_1$), (7.34) and repeating the previous arguments,

$$C(u_k^{(s)},\ B_i) \leqslant M_6(\alpha,\ B_i)\, C(u^{(s-1)};\ \bar{B}_i).$$

Finally, the last result gives together with (7.34)

$$C(u_k^{(s)},\ \bar{B}_i) \leqslant M_7(\alpha,\ B_i)\, C(u^{(s-1)};\ \bar{B}_i) \leqslant DC(u^{(s-1)};\ \bar{B}_i),$$

where $M_7(\alpha,\ B_i)$ is a positive constant depending on α and B_i, and D is a constant not less than $M_7(\alpha,\ B_i)$. A series of the type

$$C(u^{(0)};\ \bar{B}_i) \sum_{s=0}^{\infty} (mD)^s,$$

majorizes (7.25), and hence the latter converges uniformly when

$$|m| < D^{-1} \qquad (D \neq 0).$$

The sum of the series (7.25) obviously belongs to class H. It is possible to derive an accurate estimate of the upper bound of the constant D. This proof of convergence was given by Zh. Rukhadze /27/, and has been somewhat abbreviated and modified here.

If the sum of the series (7.25) is a regular vector $u(x)$ in B_i, then substituting it in (4.10_a), we obtain a continuation of $u(x)$ in B_a and the regular solution of the system of functional equations (4.10_i) and (4.10_a), obtained in this way, furnishes a unique solution of Problem A, as shown in § 7. But if the sum of (7.25) is not regular in B_i, i.e., the Betti relations are inapplicable, then that vector when continued into B_a still furnishes a solution of (4.10_i), (4.10_a), but it is not a solution of the problem in the ordinary sense. It may be considered as a weak, or generalized solution of Problem (A). It is clear that in this case Problem (A) has generally no solution in the ordinary sense.

The conditions under which a generalized solution reduces to an ordinary one are stated by Z. Gogniashvili in /6b/. It is sufficient to require that the function which appears in the equation of the "neighborhood" $S(x;\ \varepsilon_0)$ in local coordinates (V, 1), viz.

$$\xi_3 = \xi_0(\xi_1,\ \xi_2),$$

possess second derivatives of class H.

A proof of the convergence of the series (7.25) in the three-dimensional case may be found in /6a, c/.

§ 5. Existence theorems for the dynamic Problems (B_1) and (B_2)

The equations for these problems are in the general case (IV, 3) the functional equations (4.11) and (4.13). Assuming series-solutions akin to (7.25) and equating coefficients of equal powers of m, as in the preceding section, we obtain equations and formulas analogous to (7.26_0), (7.26_1)... (7.26_s), (7.27), with the one difference that now the matrix $\Gamma_{(a)}(x,\ y)$ is replaced by the tensor $G(x,\ y)$ in the equations of Problem (B_1), and by the tensor $H(x,\ y)$ in the equations of Problem (B_2). The equations corresponding to (7.26_0) are of the form

$$4\pi\varkappa(x)\, u^{(0)}(x) = (\mu_a - \mu_i)\,\omega^2 \int_{B_i} u^{(0)}(y)\, G(x,\ y)\, d\sigma_y +$$

$$+ (\mu_a - \mu_i) \int_S u_i^0(y)\, \mathrm{T}_y^{(a)} G(x,\ y)\, dS_y + \mu_a \int_{S_a} u_i^0(y)\, \mathrm{T}_y^{(a)} G(x,\ y)\, dS_y, \qquad (7.35)$$

$$4\pi\varkappa(x)\,u^{(0)}(x)=(\mu_a-\mu_l)\,\omega^2\int\limits_{B_l} u_l^{(0)}(y)\,H(x,\ y)\,d\sigma_y+$$

$$+(\mu_a-\mu_l)\int\limits_{S} u_l^{(0)}(y)\,\mathrm{T}_y^{(a)}H(x,\ y)\,dS_y-\mu_a\int\limits_{S_a}(\mathrm{T}^{(a)}u^0(y))\,H(x,\ y)\,dS_y. \qquad (7.36)$$

The solvability of these equations may be proved in the same way as in § 3. The solutions of (7.35), (7.36) determine the right-hand (given) side of the integral equations, and the treatment is analogous to that of the preceding section. Those values of ω for which the homogeneous Problems (B_1) and (B_2) have nontrivial solutions must be excluded; this remark obviously also refers to Theorem 2. Problems (C) and also the static Problems (A), (B) need not be considered separately.

§ 6. Equivalence theorems. Some lemmas

The existence theorems for the integral equations of Problems (A), (B), (C) were considered in the preceding sections. It will be shown in the remaining part of this chapter that the regular solutions of these equations respectively solve Problems (A), (B), (C). These inverse theorems, called the equivalence theorems, together with the existence theorems mentioned above, prove the existence of solutions for Problems (A), (B), (C). Let us first prove a few simple lemmas. Let $A(x,\ y)$ be the matrix

$$A(x,\ y)=\left\|\begin{matrix} A_1^{(1)}(x,\ y) & A_1^{(2)}(x,\ y) & A_1^{(3)}(x,\ y)\\ A_2^{(1)}(x,\ y) & A_2^{(2)}(x,\ y) & A_2^{(3)}(x,\ y)\\ A_3^{(1)}(x,\ y) & A_3^{(2)}(x,\ y) & A_3^{(3)}(x,\ y)\end{matrix}\right\|$$

and $\varphi(y)$ a vector independent of x. We then have the two vectors

$$A(x,\ y)\,\varphi(y)=\sum_s\sum_k i_s A_s^{(k)}(x,\ y)\,\varphi_k(y)$$

and

$$\varphi(y)\,A(x,\ y)=\sum_s\sum_k i_s A_k^{(s)}(x,\ y)\,\varphi_k(y).$$

Lemma A. The vector $A(x,\ y)\,\varphi(y)$ *is a solution of* $\Delta^* u+\omega^2 u=0$, *if the column-vectors of* $A(x,\ y)$ *satisfies this equation with respect to* x.

The proof is obtained by direct verification.

Corollary. The vector $\varphi(y)\,A(x,\ y)$ *is a solution of* $\Delta^* u+\omega^2 u=0$ *if the row-vectors of* $A(x,\ y)$ *satisfy this equation with respect to* x.

This follows from Lemma A since

$$\varphi(y)\,A(x,\ y)=A^*(x,\ y)\,\varphi(y).$$

Lemma B. The double-layer potential

$$W(x)=\frac{1}{2\pi}\int\limits_S \varphi(y)\,\mathrm{T}_y^{(l)}\Gamma_{(a)}(x,\ y)\,dS_y$$

is a solution of $\overset{*}{\Delta}_{(a)}u+\omega^2 u=0$, *for* x *not on* S.

It is clearly sufficient to prove that

$$(\overset{*}{\Delta}_{(a)}+\omega^2)_x\,(\varphi(y)\,\mathrm{T}_y^{(l)}\Gamma_{(a)}(x,\ y))=0,$$

but this would follow if we could show that the rows of the matrix

$$\Pi(x, y)=\begin{Vmatrix} T^{(i)}_{1,y}\Gamma^{(1)}_{(a)} & T^{(i)}_{2,y}\Gamma^{(1)}_{(a)} & T^{(i)}_{3,y}\Gamma^{(1)}_{(a)} \\ T^{(i)}_{1,y}\Gamma^{(2)}_{(a)} & T^{(i)}_{2,y}\Gamma^{(2)}_{(a)} & T^{(i)}_{3,y}\Gamma^{(2)}_{(a)} \\ T^{(i)}_{1,y}\Gamma^{(3)}_{(a)} & T^{(i)}_{2,y}\Gamma^{(3)}_{(a)} & T^{(i)}_{3,y}\Gamma^{(3)}_{(a)} \end{Vmatrix}$$

which is the transpose of $T^{(i)}_y\Gamma_{(a)}(x, y)$, satisfy $\overset{*}{\Delta}_{(a)}\boldsymbol{u}(x)+\omega^2\boldsymbol{u}(x)=0$. To prove this, let the k-th column-vector of $\Pi(x, y)$ be $\Pi^{(k)}(x, y)$; then its projection on the x_s-axis is

$$\Pi^{(k)}_s(x, y)=T^{(i)}_{k,y}\Gamma^{(s)}_{(a)}=2\mu_i\frac{\partial\Gamma^{(s)}_k}{\partial n_y}+\lambda_i\cos(\boldsymbol{n}_y, \boldsymbol{x}_k)\operatorname{div}_y\Gamma^{(s)}(x, y)+\mu_i(\boldsymbol{n}_y\times\operatorname{rot}_y\Gamma^{(s)})_{x_k}. \quad (7.37)$$

In view of (1.30) and (1.34)*,

$$\left.\begin{aligned}&\Gamma^{(k)}_s(x, y)=\Gamma^{(s)}_k(y, x), \quad \operatorname{div}_x\Gamma^{(k)}(x, y)=\frac{\partial}{\partial x_k}\Phi(x, y),\\ &\frac{\partial}{\partial x_k}\Phi(x, y)=-\frac{\partial}{\partial y_k}\Phi(x, y).\end{aligned}\right\} \quad (7.38)$$

Taking the divergence and the curl of both sides of

$$\mu_a\Delta\Gamma^{(k)}_{(a)}(x, y)+(\lambda_a+\mu_a)\operatorname{grad}\operatorname{div}\Gamma^{(k)}_{(a)}(x, y)+\omega^2\Gamma^{(k)}_{(a)}(x, y)=0, \quad (7.39)$$

we obtain

$$(\lambda_a+2\mu_a)\Delta\left(\operatorname{div}\Gamma^{(k)}_{(a)}\right)+\omega^2\operatorname{div}\Gamma^{(k)}_{(a)}=0, \quad (7.40_a)$$

$$\mu_a\Delta\left(\operatorname{rot}\Gamma^{(k)}_{(a)}\right)+\omega^2\operatorname{rot}\Gamma^{(k)}_{(a)}=0. \quad (7.40_b)$$

We infer that $\Phi(x, y)$ is also a solution of

$$\Delta\Phi+\frac{\omega^2}{\lambda_a+2\mu_a}\Phi=\sigma(y).$$

Let us calculate $\operatorname{div}_x\Pi^{(k)}(x, y)$ from (7.37). We have

$$\operatorname{div}_x\Pi^{(k)}(x, y)=\sum_s\frac{\partial}{\partial x_s}\Pi^{(k)}_s(x, y)=$$

$$=2\mu_i\frac{\partial}{\partial n_y}\sum_s\frac{\partial\Gamma^{(s)}_k(x, y)}{\partial x_s}+\lambda_i\cos(\boldsymbol{n}_y, \boldsymbol{x}_k)\operatorname{div}_y\sum\frac{\partial\Gamma^{(s)}(x, y)}{\partial x_s}+$$

$$+\mu_i\left(\boldsymbol{n}_y\times\operatorname{rot}_y\sum_s\frac{\partial\Gamma^{(s)}}{\partial x_s}\right)_{x_k}.$$

But

$$\sum_s\frac{\partial\Gamma^{(s)}}{\partial x_s}=\sum_s\sum_k\boldsymbol{i}_k\frac{\partial\Gamma^{(s)}_k(x, y)}{\partial x_s}=\sum_s\sum_k\boldsymbol{i}_k\frac{\partial\Gamma^{(k)}_s(y, x)}{\partial x_s}=$$

$$=\sum_k\boldsymbol{i}_k\operatorname{div}_x\Gamma^{(k)}(y, x)=\operatorname{grad}_x\Phi(x, y)=-\operatorname{grad}_y\Phi(x, y).$$

Therefore

$$\operatorname{div}_x\Pi^{(k)}(x, y)=2\mu_i\frac{\partial}{\partial n_y}\operatorname{div}\Gamma^{(k)}(y, x)-\lambda_i\cos(\boldsymbol{n}_y, \boldsymbol{x}_k)\Delta\Phi(x, y)-$$

$$-\mu_i(\boldsymbol{n}_y\times\operatorname{rot}_y\operatorname{grad}_y\Phi)_{x_k}=2\mu_i\frac{\partial}{\partial n_y}\operatorname{div}\Gamma^{(k)}(y, x)+$$

$$+\left[\frac{\lambda_i}{\lambda_a+2\mu_a}\omega^2\Phi(x, y)-\sigma(y)\right]\cos(\boldsymbol{n}_y, \boldsymbol{x}_k).$$

Substituting the value of $\operatorname{div}_x\Pi^{(k)}(x, y)$ and of $\Pi^{(k)}_s(x, y)$ in the left-hand side of the equality to be proved,

$$\mu_a\Delta\Pi^{(k)}_s(x, y)+(\lambda_a+\mu_a)\frac{\partial}{\partial x_s}\operatorname{div}\Pi^{(k)}(x, y)+\omega^2\Pi^{(k)}_s(x, y)=0,$$

* Here we also know the function $\Phi(x, y)$ explicitly, but this is not necessary for the proof of the lemma.

we obtain

$$[(\overset{*}{\Delta}_{(a)}+\omega^2)_x(\Pi^{(k)}(x, y))]_{x_s} =$$
$$=2\mu_i\frac{\partial}{\partial n_y}\Big[\mu_a\Delta_x\Gamma_k^{(s)}(x, y)+(\lambda_a+\mu_a)\frac{\partial}{\partial x_s}\operatorname{div}_x\Gamma^{(k)}(y, x)+\omega^2\Gamma_k^{(s)}(x, y)\Big]+$$
$$+\lambda_i\cos(n_y, x_k)\Big[\mu_a\Delta_x\operatorname{div}_y\Gamma^{(s)}(x, y)+\frac{\lambda_a+\mu_a}{\lambda_a+2\mu_a}\omega^2\frac{\partial}{\partial x_s}\Phi(x, y)+$$
$$+\omega^2\operatorname{div}_y\Gamma^{(s)}(x, y)\Big]+\mu_i[(n_y\times\mu_a\Delta_x(\operatorname{rot}_y\Gamma^{(s)}(x, y))_{x_k}+$$
$$+\omega^2(n_y\times\operatorname{rot}_y\Gamma^{(s)}(x, y))_{x_k}].$$

Since

$$\Gamma_k^{(s)}(x, y)=\Gamma_s^{(k)}(y, x),$$

the expression in the first square brackets on the right may be rewritten

$$\mu_a\Delta_x\Gamma_s^{(k)}(y, k)+(\lambda_a+\mu_a)\frac{\partial}{\partial x_s}\operatorname{div}_x\Gamma^{(k)}(y, x)+\omega^2\Gamma_s^{(k)}(y, x)$$

and it vanishes in virtue of (7.39).

Since on account of (7.38) and (7.40_a)

$$\omega^2\frac{\partial}{\partial x_s}\Phi(x, y)=\omega^2\operatorname{div}_x\Gamma^{(s)}(x, y)=-\omega^2\operatorname{div}_y\Gamma^{(s)}(x, y)=(\lambda_a+2\mu_a)\Delta_x\big(\operatorname{div}\Gamma_{(a)}^{(s)}(x, y)\big),$$

the expression in the second square brackets may be written in the form

$$(\lambda_a+\mu_a)\Delta\big(\operatorname{div}_y\Gamma_{(a)}^{(s)}(x, y)\big)+\omega^2\Gamma_{(a)}^{(s)}(x, y)$$

and it vanishes because of (7.40_a).

The expression in the last square brackets has the form

$$\{n_y\times[\mu_a\Delta_x(\operatorname{rot}_y\Gamma_{(a)}^{(s)}(x, y))+\omega^2\operatorname{rot}_y\Gamma_{(a)}^{(s)}(x, y)]\}_{x_k}$$

and vanishes in view of (7.40_b). This completes the proof of Lemma B.

Corollary. For $\lambda_i=\lambda_a$, $\mu_i=\mu_a$ *we obtain from Lemma B the relation*

$$(\overset{*}{\Delta}_{(a)}+\omega^2)_x\int_S\varphi(y)\,T_y^{(a)}\Gamma_{(a)}(x, y)\,dS_y=0. \tag{7.41}$$

(This relation was used before.)

Lemma C. For $x\neq y$

$$(\overset{*}{\Delta}_{(a)}+\omega^2)_x(\varphi(y)\operatorname{grad}\operatorname{div}\Gamma_{(a)}(x, y))=0. \tag{7.42}$$

We have, by definition,

$$\operatorname{grad}_y\operatorname{div}_y\Gamma[(x, y)]=\left\|\begin{matrix}\frac{\partial}{\partial y_1}\operatorname{div}_y\Gamma^{(1)} & \frac{\partial}{\partial y_1}\operatorname{div}_y\Gamma^{(2)} & \frac{\partial}{\partial y_1}\operatorname{div}_y\Gamma^{(3)}\\ \frac{\partial}{\partial y_2}\operatorname{div}_y\Gamma^{(1)} & \frac{\partial}{\partial y_2}\operatorname{div}_y\Gamma^{(2)} & \frac{\partial}{\partial y_2}\operatorname{div}_y\Gamma^{(3)}\\ \frac{\partial}{\partial y_3}\operatorname{div}_y\Gamma^{(1)} & \frac{\partial}{\partial y_3}\operatorname{div}_y\Gamma^{(2)} & \frac{\partial}{\partial y_3}\operatorname{div}_y\Gamma^{(3)}\end{matrix}\right\|,$$

therefore

$$\varphi(y)\operatorname{grad}_y\operatorname{div}_y\Gamma_{(a)}(x, y)=\sum_m\sum_n i_m\varphi_n(y)\frac{\partial}{\partial y_n}\operatorname{div}_y\Gamma_{(a)}^{(m)}(x, y).$$

Projecting the vector

$$(\overset{*}{\Delta}_{(a)}+\omega^2)_x[\varphi(y)\operatorname{grad}\operatorname{div}_y\Gamma_{(a)}(x, y)]$$

on the x_s-axis, we get

$$\mu_a \Delta_x \sum_n \varphi_n(y) \frac{\partial}{\partial y_n} \operatorname{div}_y \Gamma^{(s)}_{(a)}(x, y) +$$

$$+ (\lambda_a + \mu_a) \frac{\partial}{\partial x_s} \operatorname{div}_x \sum_m \sum_n i_m \varphi_n(y) \frac{\partial}{\partial y_n} \operatorname{div}_y \Gamma^{(m)}_{(a)}(x, y) +$$

$$+ \omega^2 \sum_n \varphi_n(y) \frac{\partial}{\partial y_n} \operatorname{div}_y \Gamma^{(s)}_{(a)}(x, y) =$$

$$= \sum_n \varphi_n(y) \frac{\partial}{\partial y_n} \left[\mu_a \Delta_x \left(\operatorname{div}_y \Gamma^{(s)}_{(a)}(x, y) \right) + \right.$$

$$\left. + (\lambda_a + \mu_a) \frac{\partial}{\partial x_s} \operatorname{div}_x \sum_m i_m \operatorname{div}_y \Gamma^{(m)}_{(a)} + \omega^2 \operatorname{div}_y \Gamma^{(s)}_{(a)} \right] \qquad (*)$$

Further

$$(\lambda_a + \mu_a) \frac{\partial}{\partial x_s} \operatorname{div}_x \sum_m i_m \operatorname{div}_y \Gamma^{(m)}_{(a)}(x, y) =$$

$$= (\lambda_a + \mu_a) \frac{\partial}{\partial x_s} \operatorname{div}_y \sum_m \frac{\partial \Gamma^{(m)}(x, y)}{\partial x_m} =$$

$$= (\lambda_a + \mu_a) \frac{\partial}{\partial x_s} \operatorname{div}_y \sum_m \sum_n i_n \frac{\partial \Gamma^{(m)}_n(x, y)}{\partial x_m} =$$

$$= (\lambda_a + \mu_a) \frac{\partial}{\partial x_s} \operatorname{div}_y \sum_n i_n \operatorname{div}_x \Gamma^{(n)}(y, x) =$$

$$= (\lambda_a + \mu_a) \frac{\partial}{\partial x_s} \operatorname{div}_y \operatorname{grad}_x \Phi(x, y) = -(\lambda_a + \mu_a) \frac{\partial}{\partial x_s} \Delta_x \Phi(x, y).$$

Now since $\Phi(x, y)$ satisfies

$$\Delta_x \Phi(x, y) = -\frac{\omega^2}{\lambda_a + 2\mu_a} \Phi(x, y) + \sigma(y),$$

the preceding expression becomes

$$-(\lambda_a + \mu_a) \frac{\partial}{\partial x_s} \Delta_x \Phi(x, y) = \omega^2 \frac{\lambda_a + \mu_a}{\lambda_a + 2\mu_a} \frac{\partial}{\partial x_s} \Phi(x, y) = -\omega^2 \frac{\lambda_a + \mu_a}{\lambda_a + 2\mu_a} \operatorname{div}_y \Gamma^{(s)}(x, y).$$

Substituting this expression in (*), we get

$$\mu_a \sum_n \varphi_n(y) \frac{\partial}{\partial y_n} \left[\Delta_x \left(\operatorname{div}_y \Gamma^{(s)}(x, y) + \frac{\omega^2}{\lambda_a + 2\mu_a} \operatorname{div}_y \Gamma^{(s)}(x, y) \right) \right],$$

which vanishes on account of (7.40_a), proving Lemma C.

The following observation will be important later on. The proofs of Lemmas A, B, C and their corollaries could be simplified if we had made use of the fact that here $\Phi(x, y)$ is known explicitly:

$$\Phi(x, y) = \frac{1}{a^2} \frac{e^{ik_1 r}}{r(x, y)}, \quad a^2 = \lambda_a + 2\mu_a, \quad k_1^2 = \frac{\omega^2}{a^2}.$$

However, we have not utilized this fact, and so our proof holds also for those cases when the function $\Phi(x, y)$ is not given explicitly, and all we know is that it possesses the properties (7.38) on which the proof is based. This is the case when the matrix $\Gamma_{(a)}(x, y)$ is replaced by the first and second Green's tensors in Problems (B_1) and (B_2) (functions $\Phi(x, y)$ with the required properties exist for these tensors). Thus we have the following lemma:

Lemma D. *Lemmas A, B, C and their corollaries remain valid if the matrix $\Gamma_{(a)}(x, y)$ is replaced by $G(x, y)$ or $H(x, y)$.*

§ 7. Equivalence theorem for Problem (A)

Theorem 3. A regular solution of the functional equations (4.10ᵢ), (4.10ₐ) solves Problem **(A)**.

Equations (4.10_i), (4.10_a) are of the form

$$4\pi\varkappa(x)\,u(x) = (\mu_a - \mu_i)\,\omega^2 \int_{B_i} u(y)\,\Gamma_{(a)}(x, y)\,d\sigma_y + m \int_{B_i} u(y)\,\mathrm{grad}\,\mathrm{div}\,\Gamma_{(a)}\,d\sigma_y +$$
$$+ \mu_a \int_S u_i(y)\,\overset{*}{\mathrm{T}}_y \Gamma_{(a)}(x, y)\,dS_y + 4\pi\mu_a E(x; x_*). \tag{7.43}$$

Let the point x lie in B_a. Applying $(\overset{*}{\Delta}_{(a)} + \omega^2)$ to (7.43) with respect to x (the operator may be inserted under the integral sign), using Lemmas B and C, and remembering that

$$(\overset{*}{\Delta}_{(a)} + \omega^2)\,\Gamma_{(a)}(x, y) = (\overset{*}{\Delta}_{(a)} + \omega^2)\,E(x; x_*) = 0 \qquad x \in B_a,$$

we obtain

$$\overset{*}{\Delta}_{(a)} u(x) + \omega^2 u(x) = 0 \qquad x \in B_a. \tag{7.44}$$

Thus, a solution of equation (7.43) which is regular in B_a satisfies equation (7.44).

Next let x lie in B_i. Applying the Betti relation to the vecotrs $u(y)$ and $\Gamma^{(k)}_{(a)}(x, y)$ $(k = 1, 2, 3)$ in B_i, having first excluded a sphere $\tau(x; \varepsilon)$ from B_i, we obtain

$$\int_{B_i - \tau(x;\varepsilon)} \left[u(y)\, \overset{*}{\Delta}_{(i)} \Gamma^{(k)}_{(a)}(x, y) - \Gamma^{(k)}_{(a)}(x, y) \overset{*}{\Delta}_{(i)} u(y) \right] d\sigma_y =$$
$$= \int_{S + \sigma(x;\varepsilon)} \left[u_i(y)\,\mathrm{T}^{(i)}_y \Gamma^{(k)}_{(a)}(x, y) - \Gamma^{(k)}_{(a)}(x, y)\,(\mathrm{T}^{(i)} u(y))_i \right] dS_y.$$
$$(k = 1, 2, 3)$$

In (IV, 2) we have also made use of the last formula, and then of the relation

$$\overset{*}{\Delta}_{(i)} u(x) = -\omega^2 u(x),$$

which we cannot do now; upon passing to the limit for $\varepsilon \to 0$ we get

$$4\pi l \mu_a u_k(x) = -\omega^2 \mu_i \int_{B_i} u(y)\,\Gamma^{(k)}_{(a)}(x, y)\,d\sigma_y -$$
$$- \mu_a \int_{B_i} \Gamma^{(k)}_{(a)}(x, y)\,\overset{*}{\Delta}_{(i)} u(y)\,d\sigma_y + m \int_{B_i} u(y)\,\mathrm{grad}\,\mathrm{div}\,\Gamma^{(k)}_{(a)}\,d\sigma_y +$$
$$+ \mu_a \int_S \left[\Gamma^{(k)}_{(a)}(x, y)\,(\mathrm{T}^{(i)} u(y))_i - u_i(y)\,(\mathrm{T}^{(i)}_y \Gamma^{(k)}_{(a)}) \right] dS_y. \tag{7.45}$$

Applying again the Betti relation to the vectors $D(y) = u(y) - E(y; x_*)$ and $\Gamma^{(k)}_{(a)}(x, y)$ in B_a, and letting again x lie in B_i, we obtain

$$\int_{B_a} \left[D(y)\,\overset{*}{\Delta}_{(a)} \Gamma^{(k)}_{(a)}(x, y) - \Gamma^{(k)}_{(a)}(x, y)\,\overset{*}{\Delta}_{(a)} D \right] d\sigma_y =$$
$$= \int_S \left[D_a \mathrm{T}^{(a)}_y \Gamma^{(k)}_{(a)} - \Gamma^{(k)}_{(a)}(x, y)\,(\mathrm{T}^{(a)} D(y))_a \right] dS_y.$$

But since it was shown before that a solution of (7.43) in B_a as well as the given vector $E(x, x_*)$ satisfy the equation $\overset{*}{\Delta}_{(a)} u + \omega^2 u = 0$, we may write

$$\int_S \left[\Gamma^{(k)}_{(a)}(x, y)\,(\mathrm{T}^{(a)} D)_a - D_a(y)\,(\mathrm{T}^{(a)}_y \Gamma^{(k)}_{(a)}(x, y)) \right] dS_y = 0. \tag{7.45'}$$

Here we assume the positive normal to point from B_l into B_a. Multiplying the last equality by $\frac{1}{4\pi}\mu_a$, we add it to (7.43) for $x \in B_l$, which is permitted, since x in both inequalities belongs to B_l; in view of

$$E_k(x;\ x_*) = \frac{1}{4\pi}\int_S [\Gamma^{(k)}_{(a)}(x,\ y)(\mathrm{T}^{(a)}E) - E(y;\ x_*)(\mathrm{T}^{(a)}\Gamma^{(k)}_{(a)})]\, dS_y,$$

we then get

$$4\pi\mu_a l u_k(x) = (\mu_a - \mu_l)\,\omega^2 \int_{B_l} u(y)\,\Gamma^{(k)}_{(a)}(x,\ y)\, d\sigma_y +$$

$$+ m \int_{B_l} u(y) \operatorname{grad}\operatorname{div}\Gamma^{(k)}_{(a)}(x,\ y)\, d\sigma_y + \mu_a \int_S (u_l - u_a)\,\mathrm{T}^{(a)}_y \Gamma^{(k)}_{(a)}(x,\ y)\, dS_y -$$

$$- \mu_a \int_S u_l(y)\,\mathrm{T}^{(l)}_y \Gamma^{(k)}_{(a)}(x,\ y)\, dS_y + \mu_a \int_S \Gamma^{(k)}_{(a)}(x,\ y)(\mathrm{T}^{(a)}u)_a\, dS_y.$$

Subtracting (7.45),

$$\int_{B_l} \Gamma^{(k)}_{(a)}(x,\ y)\,(\overset{*}{\Delta}_{(l)}u + \omega^2 u(y))\, d\sigma_y + \int_S (u_l - u_a)\,\mathrm{T}^{(a)}_y \Gamma^{(k)}_{(a)}(x,\ y)\, dS_y +$$

$$+ \int_S \Gamma^{(k)}_{(a)}(x,\ y)\,((\mathrm{T}^{(a)}u)_a - (\mathrm{T}^{(l)}u)_l)\, dS_y = 0$$

or in matrix notation

$$\int_{B_l} (\overset{*}{\Delta}_{(l)}u + \omega^2 u(y))\,\Gamma_{(a)}(x,\ y)\, d\tau_y + \int_S (u_l - u_a)\,\mathrm{T}^{(a)}_y \Gamma_{(a)}(x,\ y)\, dS_y +$$

$$+ \int_S [(\mathrm{T}^{(a)}u)_a - (\mathrm{T}^{(l)}u)_l]\,\Gamma_{(a)}(x,\ y)\, dS_y = 0.$$

Denoting for brevity the expression on the left by $Qu(x)$, we have

$$Qu(x) = 0, \qquad x \in B_l. \tag{7.46}$$

It is now necessary to evaluate $Qu(x)$ in B_a. For this purpose take x fixed in B_a and apply Betti's relation to the vectors $u(y)$ and $\Gamma^{(k)}_{(a)}(x,\ y)$ in B_l. Since

$$\overset{*}{\Delta}_{(l)}\Gamma^{(k)}_{(a)}(x,\ y) = -\frac{\mu_l}{\mu_a}\,\omega^2\Gamma^{(k)}_{(a)}(x,\ y) + \frac{m}{\mu_a}\operatorname{grad}_y \operatorname{div}_y \Gamma^{(k)}_{(a)}(x,\ y),$$

we obtain

$$\mu_l\omega^2 \int_{B_l} u(y)\,\Gamma^{(k)}_{(a)}(x,\ y)\, d\sigma_y -$$

$$- m \int_{B_l} u(y) \operatorname{grad}\operatorname{div}\Gamma^{(k)}_{(a)}(x,\ y)\, d\sigma_y + \mu_a \int_S \Gamma^{(k)}_{(a)} \overset{*}{\Delta}_{(l)} u\, d\tau_y +$$

$$+ \mu \int_S [u_l(y)\,\mathrm{T}^{(l)}_y \Gamma^{(k)}_{(a)}(x,\ y) - \Gamma^{(k)}_{(a)}(x,\ y)(\mathrm{T}^{(l)}u)_l]\, dS_y = 0. \tag{7.47}$$

Applying again the Betti relation to $D(y) = u(y) - E(y;\ x_*)$ and $\Gamma^{(k)}_{(a)}(x,\ y)$ in B_a for $x \in B_a$, and since we have shown that there $\overset{*}{\Delta}_{(a)}u + \omega^2 u = 0$, we have

$$u(x) = \frac{1}{4\pi}\int_S [u_a(y)\,\mathrm{T}^{(a)}_y \Gamma_{(a)}(x,\ y) - \Gamma_{(a)}(x,\ y)(\mathrm{T}^{(a)}u(y))_a]\, dS_y + E(x;\ x_*), \tag{7.47'}$$

where the normal points from B_l into B_a. We subtract (7.47') from (7.43), first dividing the latter by μ_a, and obtain after some simplifications

$$\left(1 - \frac{\mu_l}{\mu_a}\right)\omega^2 \int_{B_l} u(y)\,\Gamma_{(a)}(x,\ y)\, d\sigma_y + \frac{m}{\mu_a}\int_{B_l} u(y) \operatorname{grad}\operatorname{div}\Gamma_{(a)}(x,\ y)\, d\sigma_y +$$

$$+ \int_S (u_l - u_a)\,\mathrm{T}^{(a)}_y \Gamma_{(a)}(x,\ y)\, dS_y - \int_S u_l(y)\,\mathrm{T}^{(l)}_y \Gamma_{(a)}(x,\ y)\, dS_y + \int_S \Gamma_{(a)}(x,\ y)(\mathrm{T}^{(a)}u(y))_a\, dS_y = 0.$$

We finally add this equality to (7.47), first dividing the latter by μ_a, and obtain

$$Qu(x)=0, \qquad x\in B_a. \tag{7.48}$$

Let us calculate the difference in the limiting values according to (7.46) and (7.48)

$$(Qu(x))_i-(Qu(x))_a \text{ and } (\mathbf{T}^{(a)}Qu(x))_i-(\mathbf{T}^{(a)}Qu(x))_a.$$

To do this we invoke the continuity theorems for a volume potential, its first derivatives, and a single-layer potential, and the theorems on the boundary discontinuities of a double-layer potential and of the T-transform of a single-layer potential, and finally the generalized Lyapunov-Tauber theorem concerning the continuity of the T-transform of a double-layer potential, which obviously holds here; the result is

$$u_i-u_a=0, \tag{7.49}$$

$$(\mathbf{T}^{(a)}u)_a-(\mathbf{T}^{(i)}u)_i=0. \tag{7.50}$$

Applying $(\overset{*}{\Delta}_{(a)}+\omega^2)$ to (7.46) for $x\in B_i$, we obtain from Poisson's formula

$$\overset{*}{\Delta}_{(i)}u(x)+\omega^2u(x)=0, \qquad x\in B_i. \tag{7.51}$$

The relations (7.44) and (7.49)-(7.51) prove the equivalence theorem for Problem (A). This obviously implies as a particular case the equivalence theorem for the static Problem (A^0).

With some additional assumptions one may prove the equivalence theorems also directly, by checking the relevant properties of solutions of the functional equations $(4.10_{i,a})$. Let us demonstrate this briefly for equation (7.51). The Poisson formula (1.77) gives

$$m\int_{B_i} u(y)\,\mathrm{grad\,div}\,\Gamma_{(a)}(x, y)\,d\sigma_y=$$

$$=4\pi\mu_a lu(x)-\omega^2(\mu_a-\mu_i)\int_{B_i} u(y)\Gamma_{(a)}(x, y)\,d\sigma_y+$$

$$+\mu_a(\overset{*}{\Delta}_{(i)}+\omega^2)\int_{B_i} u(y)\Gamma_{(a)}(x, y)\,d\sigma_y.$$

Substituting this in (4.10_i), we obtain

$$(\overset{*}{\Delta}_{(i)}+\omega^2)\int_{B_i} u(y)\Gamma_{(a)}(x, y)\,d\sigma_y+\int_S u_i(y)\,\overset{*}{\mathbf{T}}_y\Gamma_{(a)}(x, y)\,dS_y+4\pi E(x;\,x_*)=0.$$

Applying $(\overset{*}{\Delta}_{(a)}+\omega^2)$, and keeping in mind that

$$(\overset{*}{\Delta}_{(a)}+\omega^2)_x(\overset{*}{\mathbf{T}}_y\Gamma_{(a)}(x, y))=0, \qquad \overset{*}{\Delta}_{(a)}E+\omega^2E=0,$$

we get

$$(\overset{*}{\Delta}_{(a)}+\omega^2)(\overset{*}{\Delta}_{(i)}+\omega^2)\int_{B_i} u(y)\Gamma_{(a)}(x, y)\,d\sigma_y=0.$$

We interchange the operators $(\overset{*}{\Delta}_{(a)}+\omega^2)$ and $(\overset{*}{\Delta}_{(i)}+\omega^2)$, assuming that this is permitted, and apply the Poisson formula (1.78); we then obtain

$$\overset{*}{\Delta}_{(i)}u(x)+\omega^2u(x)=0, \qquad x\in B_i;$$

which coincides with (7.51).

§ 8. Equivalence theorems for the dynamic Problems (B_1) and (B_2)

We shall consider in detail Problem (B_1) and the corresponding equations (4.11), which we write out for clarity

$$4\pi l \mu_a u(x) = \omega^2 (\mu_a - \mu_i) \int_{B_i} u(y)\, G(x, y)\, d\sigma_y + m \int_{B_i} u(y) \operatorname{grad} \operatorname{div} G\, d\sigma_y + \\ + \mu_a \int_S u_i(y)\, \overset{*}{T}_y G\, dS_y + \mu_a \int_{S_a} f(y)\, T_y^{(a)} G\, dS_y, \qquad (7.52_a)$$

$$4\pi \mu_a u(x) = \omega^2 (\mu_a - \mu_i) \int_{B_i} u(y)\, G(x, y)\, d\sigma_y + m \int_{B_i} u(y) \operatorname{grad} \operatorname{div} G\, d\sigma_y + \\ + \mu_a \int_S u_i(y)\, \overset{*}{T}_y G\, dS_y + \mu_a \int_{S_a} f(y)\, T_y^{(a)} G\, dS_y. \qquad (7.52_i)$$

Repeating the arguments which led in § 7 to the proof of (7.44), and applying Lemma D of § 6, we conclude that a regular solution of (7.52_a) in B_a satisfies the equation

$$\overset{*}{\Delta}_{(a)} u(x) + \omega^2 u(x) = 0. \qquad (7.53)$$

Let $x \in B_i$. Applying Betti's relation to the vectors $u(y)$ and $G^{(k)}(x, y)$ $(k = 1, 2, 3)$ in B_i and proceeding as in § 7, we get

$$4\pi l \mu_a u_k(x) = -\omega^2 \mu_i \int_{B_i} u(y)\, G^{(k)}(x, y)\, d\sigma_y - \\ - \mu_a \int_{B_i} G^{(k)}(x, y)\, \overset{*}{\Delta}_{(i)} u(y)\, d\sigma_y + m \int_{B_i} u(y) \operatorname{grad} \operatorname{div} G^{(k)}\, d\sigma_y + \\ + \mu \int_S \left[G^{(k)} \left(T^{(i)} u\right)_i - u_i \left(T_y^{(i)} G^{(k)}\right)\right] dS_y. \qquad (7.54)$$

Applying the Betti relation to the same vectors in B_a, we obtain

$$\int_{B_a} \left[u(y)\, \overset{*}{\Delta}_{(a)} G^{(k)}(x, y) - G^{(k)}(x, y)\, \overset{*}{\Delta}_{(a)} u(y)\right] d\sigma_y = \\ = \int_S \left[u_a \left(T^{(a)} G^{(k)}\right) - G^{(k)} \left(T^{(a)} u\right)_a\right] dS_y + \int_{S_a} f(y)\, T^{(a)} G^{(k)}\, dS_y,$$

where $f(x)$ gives the boundary value of $u(x)$ on S.

Since (7.53) holds in B_a, we now have

$$\int_S \left[G^{(k)}(x, y) \left(T^{(a)} u\right)_a - u_a(y) \left(T_y^{(a)} G^{(k)}(x, y)\right)\right] dS_y - \\ - \int_{S_a} f(y)\, T_y^{(a)} G^{(k)}(x, y)\, dS_y = 0 \qquad (k = 1, 2, 3), \qquad (7.55)$$

where the positive normal is directed from B_i to B_a, i. e., inwards to B_a.

Multiplying (7.55) by μ_a and adding it to (7.52_i),

$$4\pi l \mu_a u_k(x) = m \int_{B_i} u(y) \operatorname{grad} \operatorname{div} G^{(k)}\, d\sigma_y + \\ + \mu_a \int_S (u_i - u_a)\, T_y^{(a)} G^{(k)}(x, y)\, dS_y - \mu_a \int_S \left[u_i(y)\, T_y^{(i)} G^{(k)}(x, y) - \right. \\ \left. - G^{(k)}(x, y) \left(T^{(a)} u(y)\right)_a\right] dS_y. \qquad (7.56)$$

We finally take the difference of (7.56) and (7.54), and obtain

$$0 = \int_{B_i} G^{(k)}(x, y) \left(\overset{*}{\Delta}_{(i)} u + \omega^2 u(y)\right) d\sigma_y + \int_S G^{(k)}(x, y) \left[\left(T^{(a)} u\right)_a - \left(T^{(i)} u\right)_i\right] dS_y + \\ + \int_S (u_i - u_a)\, T_y^{(a)} G^{(k)}(x, y)\, dS_y. \qquad (7.57)$$

Using the matrix form and the same notation as in § 7,

$$Qu(x)=\int_{B_l}(\overset{*}{\Delta}_{(l)}u+\omega^2u)\,G(x,\ y)\,d\sigma_y+$$

$$+\int_S[(T^{(a)}u)_a-(T^{(l)}u)_l]\,G(x,\ y)\,dS_y+\int_S(u_l-u_a)\,T_y^{(a)}G(x,\ y)\,dS_y,$$

we express (7.57) in the form

$$Qu(x)=0,\qquad x\in B_l. \tag{7.58}$$

Let us now calculate $Qu(x)$ for $x\in B_a$. We apply the Betti relation to $u(y)$ and $G^{(k)}(x,\ y)$ $(k=1,\ 2,\ 3)$ in B_l, keeping in mind that $x\in B_a$.

Since

$$\overset{*}{\Delta}_{(l)}G^{(k)}(x,\ y)=-\omega^2\frac{\mu_l}{\mu_a}G^{(k)}(x,\ y)+\frac{m}{\mu_a}\operatorname{grad}\operatorname{div}G^{(k)}(x,\ y),$$

we have

$$\omega^2\mu_l\int_{B_l}u(y)\,G^{(k)}(x,\ y)\,d\sigma_y-$$

$$-m\int_{B_l}u(y)\operatorname{grad}\operatorname{div}G^{(k)}(x,\ y)\,d\sigma_y+\mu_a\int_{B_l}G^{(k)}(x,\ y)\,\overset{*}{\Delta}_{(l)}u(y)\,d\sigma_y+$$

$$+\mu_a\int_S[u_l(y)\,(T^{(l)}G^{(k)})-G^{(k)}\,(T^{(l)}u)_l]\,dS_y=0. \tag{7.59}$$

Finally, applying the Betti relation to the same vectors in B_a, we obtain

$$u_k(x)=\frac{1}{4\pi}\int_S\left[u_a(y)\,T_y^{(a)}G^{(k)}(x,\ y)-G^{(k)}(x,\ y)\,(T^{(a)}u)_a\right]dS_y+$$

$$+\frac{1}{4\pi}\int_{S_a}f(y)\,(T^{(a)}G^{(k)}(x,\ y))\,dS_y, \tag{7.60}$$

the positive normal now pointing from B_l into B_a.

We divide (7.52_a) by μ_a and subtract from it (7.60), and after a few elementary manipulations obtain

$$0=\left(1-\frac{\mu_l}{\mu_a}\right)\omega^2\int_{B_l}u(y)\,G^{(k)}(x,\ y)\,d\sigma_y+$$

$$+\frac{m}{\mu_a}\int_{B_l}u(y)\operatorname{grad}\operatorname{div}G^{(k)}(x,y)\,d\sigma_y+\int_S(u_l-u_a)\,T_y^{(a)}G^{(k)}(x,y)\,dS_y-$$

$$-\int_S[u_l\,(T^{(l)}G^{(k)})-G^{(k)}\,(T^{(a)}u)_a]\,dS_y \tag{7.61}$$

to which we add (7.59) and (7.61); finally we have for $x\in B_a$

$$Qu(x)=\int_{B_l}(\overset{*}{\Delta}_l u(y)+\omega^2u(y))\,G(x,\ y)\,d\sigma_y+$$

$$+\int_S(u_l-u_a)\,T_y^{(a)}G(x,\ y)\,dS_y+$$

$$+\int_S[(T^{(a)}u)_a-(T^{(l)}u)_l]\,G(x,\ y)\,dS_y=0. \tag{7.62}$$

We have thus shown that the equations (7.58) and (7.62),

$$Qu(x)=0, \tag{7.63}$$

are valid in B_l as well as in B_a.

Let us now evaluate the differences

$$(Qu(x))_i - (Qu(x))_a \quad \text{and} \quad (\mathrm{T}^{(a)}Qu(x))_i - (\mathrm{T}^{(a)}Qu(x))_a.$$

To do this we again use the theorems concerning the properties of potentials — the continuity of a volume potential together with its first derivatives, the continuity of a single-layer potential, the discontinuities of a double-layer potential and of the T-transform of a single-layer potential, and the generalized Lyapunov-Tauber theorem on the continuity of the T-transform of a double-layer potential; the result is again

$$u_i - u_a = 0, \tag{7.64}$$

$$(\mathrm{T}^{(a)}u)_a - (\mathrm{T}^{(i)}u)_i = 0. \tag{7.65}$$

Finally, applying $\overset{*}{\Delta}_{(a)} + \omega^2$ to (7.63) in B_i, we obtain as in § 7

$$\overset{*}{\Delta}_{(i)}u(x) + \omega^2 u(x) = 0, \quad x \in B_i. \tag{7.66}$$

It remains to verify the fulfilment of the boundary conditions on S_a. We need to know the limiting values of $u(x)$ as x approaches from B_a the point x_0 on S_a. Now with regard to equation (7.52_a), which is satisfied by $u(x)$ in B_a, we observe that since Green's first tensor vanishes if one of the points lies on S_a and the other does not, all the terms but the last vanish on the right-hand side of (7.52_a). The latter reduces by (6.40) to $\mu_a f(x_0)$, and so finally

$$\lim_{x \to x_0 \in S_a} u(x) = f(x_0). \tag{7.67}$$

The relations (7.53) and (7.64)–(7.67) prove the equivalence theorem for Problem (B_1).

The proof of the equivalence theorem for Problem (B_2) essentially repeats the preceding; the unimportant difference is that now the boundary condition on S_a is fulfilled since the T-transform of Green's second tensor vanishes on S_a and the limit

$$\lim_{x \to x_0 \in S_a} \mathrm{T}_x \int_{S_a} f(y) H(x, y) dS_y$$

is by (6.44) equal to $-4\pi f(x_0)$; therefore all terms on the right-hand side of (4.13) for $x \in B_a$ (after applying T and passing to the limit $B_a \ni x \to x_0 \in S_a$) vanish but for the last one, which reduces to $4\pi\mu_a f(x_0)$. This proves the equivalence theorem for Problem (B_2).

§ 9. Equivalence theorems for the static Problems (B_1) and (B_2)

Since $\omega = 0$ is an eigenvalue of Problem (T_i^0), the proof of the equivalence theorem for Problem (B_2), which essentially contains the elements of problem (T_i^0), is slightly different from the proof in § 8 for the dynamic case, where ω was assumed to be distinct from an eigenvalue. This difference does not occur in Problem (B_1) and the equivalence theorem for the latter follows directly from the results of § 8. Hence we shall turn our attention to Problem (B_2).

Let us remind the reader of some notations and definitions.

The matrix which constitutes the second Green's tensor is denoted by $\overset{0}{H}(x, y)$:

$$\overset{0}{H}(x, y) = \begin{Vmatrix} \overset{0}{H}{}_1^{(1)} & \overset{0}{H}{}_1^{(2)} & \overset{0}{H}{}_1^{(3)} \\ \overset{0}{H}{}_2^{(1)} & \overset{0}{H}{}_2^{(2)} & \overset{0}{H}{}_2^{(3)} \\ \overset{0}{H}{}_3^{(1)} & \overset{0}{H}{}_3^{(2)} & \overset{0}{H}{}_3^{(3)} \end{Vmatrix}.$$

The column-vectors of this matrix are denoted by $\overset{0}{H}{}^{(k)}(x, y)\ (k=1, 2, 3)$, so that

$$\overset{0}{H}(x, y) = \left(\overset{0}{H}{}^{(1)}, \overset{0}{H}{}^{(2)}, \overset{0}{H}{}^{(3)}\right).$$

The row-vectors of $\overset{0}{H}(x, y)$ are denoted by $\overset{0}{H}_{(k)}(x, y)\ (k=1, 2, 3)$, so that one has for the transposed matrix

$$\overset{0}{H}{}^*(x, y) = \left(\overset{0}{H}_{(1)}, \overset{0}{H}_{(2)}, \overset{0}{H}_{(3)}\right).$$

The components of the vectors $\overset{0}{H}{}^{(k)}(x, y)\ (k=1, 2, 3)$ along the axes are $\overset{0}{H}{}_1^{(k)}$, $\overset{0}{H}{}_2^{(k)}$, $\overset{0}{H}{}_3^{(k)}$, and the components of the vectors $\overset{0}{H}_{(k)}(x, y)\ (k=1, 2, 3)$ are $\overset{0}{H}{}_{(k)}^1$, $\overset{0}{H}{}_{(k)}^2$, $\overset{0}{H}{}_{(k)}^3$. Obviously

$$\overset{0}{H}{}_s^{(k)}(x, y) = \overset{0}{H}{}_{(s)}^k(x, y) \qquad (s, k=1, 2, 3).$$

Further, T^* is the operator

$$\mathrm{T}^* = 2(\mu_a - \mu_i)\frac{\partial}{\partial n} + (\lambda_a - \lambda_i)\, \boldsymbol{n}\operatorname{div} + (\mu_a - \mu_i)(\boldsymbol{n} \times \operatorname{rot})$$

and

$$\mathrm{T}^*\overset{0}{H}{}^*(x, y) = \begin{Vmatrix} \overset{*}{\mathrm{T}}_1\overset{0}{H}_{(1)} & \overset{*}{\mathrm{T}}_1\overset{0}{H}_{(2)} & \overset{*}{\mathrm{T}}_1\overset{0}{H}_{(3)} \\ \overset{*}{\mathrm{T}}_2\overset{0}{H}_{(1)} & \overset{*}{\mathrm{T}}_2\overset{0}{H}_{(2)} & \overset{*}{\mathrm{T}}_2\overset{0}{H}_{(3)} \\ \overset{*}{\mathrm{T}}_3\overset{0}{H}_{(1)} & \overset{*}{\mathrm{T}}_3\overset{0}{H}_{(2)} & \overset{*}{\mathrm{T}}_3\overset{0}{H}_{(3)} \end{Vmatrix},$$

where

$$\overset{*}{\mathrm{T}}_k\overset{0}{H}_{(s)} = 2(\mu_a - \mu_i)\frac{\partial}{\partial n_y}\overset{0}{H}{}_{(s)}^k(x, y) + (\lambda_a - \lambda_i)\cos(\boldsymbol{n}_y, \boldsymbol{x}_k)\operatorname{div}_y \overset{0}{H}_{(s)}(x, y) +$$
$$+ (\mu_a - \mu_i)\left(\boldsymbol{n}_y \times \operatorname{rot}_y \overset{0}{H}_{(s)}(x, y)\right)_{x_k}.$$

Finally, we will denote the row-vectors of the matrix $\mathrm{T}^*\overset{0}{H}{}^*(x, y)$ by $\Pi_{(1)}$, $\Pi_{(2)}$, $\Pi_{(3)}$. The symbol $\operatorname{grad}\operatorname{div}\overset{0}{H}{}^*(x, y)$ we remember, stands for the matrix

$$\operatorname{grad}_x \operatorname{div}_x \overset{0}{H}{}^*(x, y) = \begin{Vmatrix} \frac{\partial}{\partial x_1}\operatorname{div}\overset{0}{H}_{(1)} & \frac{\partial}{\partial x_1}\operatorname{div}\overset{0}{H}_{(2)} & \frac{\partial}{\partial x_1}\operatorname{div}\overset{0}{H}_{(3)} \\ \frac{\partial}{\partial x_2}\operatorname{div}\overset{0}{H}_{(1)} & \frac{\partial}{\partial x_2}\operatorname{div}\overset{0}{H}_{(2)} & \frac{\partial}{\partial x_2}\operatorname{div}\overset{0}{H}_{(3)} \\ \frac{\partial}{\partial x_3}\operatorname{div}\overset{0}{H}_{(1)} & \frac{\partial}{\partial x_3}\operatorname{div}\overset{0}{H}_{(2)} & \frac{\partial}{\partial x_3}\operatorname{div}\overset{0}{H}_{(3)} \end{Vmatrix}.$$

Equation (4.35), which expresses the solution of Problem (B_2), may be written in the form

$$4\pi\varkappa(x)\,\boldsymbol{u}(x) = m\int_{B_i}\boldsymbol{u}(y)\operatorname{grad}\operatorname{div}\overset{0}{H}{}^*(x, y)\,d\sigma_y +$$
$$+ \mu_a\int_S \boldsymbol{u}(y)\,\mathrm{T}_y^*\overset{0}{H}{}^*(x, y)\,dS_y - \mu_a\int_S \overset{0}{H}(x, y)\,\boldsymbol{f}(y)\,dS_y. \qquad (7.68)$$

It is required to prove that a regular solution of this equation solves Problem (B_2) when $\omega=0$.

It was shown (VI, 7; IV, 4) that

$$\overset{\bullet}{\Delta}_{(a)}\overset{0}{H}{}^{(k)}(x, y)=4\pi\sum_{s=1}^{6}\mathfrak{B}^{s(k)}(x, y), \tag{7.69}$$

$$(k=1, 2, 3),$$

$$\overset{\bullet}{\Delta}_{(a)}\overset{0}{H}_{(k)}(x, y)=4\pi\sum_{s=1}^{6}\mathfrak{B}^{s}_{(k)}(x, y) \tag{7.70}$$

where in the first equation $\overset{\bullet}{\Delta}_{(a)}$ operates on the point x and the columns of $\overset{0}{H}(x, y)$, while in the second it operates on y and the rows of $\overset{0}{H}(x, y)$.

The vectors $\mathfrak{B}^{s(k)}(x, y)$ and $\mathfrak{B}^{s}_{(k)}(x, y)$ are defined respectively as the k-th column and the k-th row of the matrix

$$\mathfrak{A}^{(s)}(x)\ast\mathfrak{A}^{(s)}(y)=\left\|\begin{matrix}\mathfrak{A}_1^{(s)}(x)\mathfrak{A}_1^{(s)}(y) & \mathfrak{A}_1^{(s)}(x)\mathfrak{A}_2^{(s)}(y) & \mathfrak{A}_1^{(s)}(x)\mathfrak{A}_3^{(s)}(y)\\ \mathfrak{A}_2^{(s)}(x)\mathfrak{A}_1^{(s)}(y) & \mathfrak{A}_2^{(s)}(x)\mathfrak{A}_2^{(s)}(y) & \mathfrak{A}_2^{(s)}(x)\mathfrak{A}_3^{(s)}(y)\\ \mathfrak{A}_3^{(s)}(x)\mathfrak{A}_1^{(s)}(y) & \mathfrak{A}_3^{(s)}(x)\mathfrak{A}_2^{(s)}(y) & \mathfrak{A}_3^{(s)}(x)\mathfrak{A}_3^{(s)}(y)\end{matrix}\right\|.$$

We now form the divergence and curl of the two members of (7.70) with respect to y,

$$(\lambda_a+2\mu_a)\Delta\left(\operatorname{div}_y\overset{0}{H}_{(k)}(x, y)\right)=4\pi\sum_{s=1}^{6}\operatorname{div}_y\mathfrak{B}^{s}_{(k)}(x, y),$$

$$\mu_a\Delta\left(\operatorname{rot}_y\overset{0}{H}_k(x, y)\right)=4\pi\sum_{s=1}^{6}\operatorname{rot}_y\mathfrak{B}^{s}_{(k)}(x, y), \tag{7.71}$$

and evaluate the right-hand members. By (6.30) and the definition of the vectors $\mathfrak{B}^{s(k)}(x, y)$ and $\mathfrak{B}^{s}_{(k)}(x, y)$,

$$\operatorname{div}_y\mathfrak{B}^{s}_{(k)}(x, y)=0\quad\text{for}\quad k=1, 2, 3\quad\text{and for all } s;$$

for $k=1, 2, 3,\ \ s=1, 2, 3$

$$\operatorname{rot}_y\mathfrak{B}^{s}_{(k)}(x, y)=\mathfrak{A}_k^{(s)}(x)\operatorname{rot}_y\mathfrak{A}^{(s)}(y)=0,$$

and for $s=4, 5, 6,\ \ k=1, 2, 3$

$$\operatorname{rot}_y\mathfrak{B}^{4}_{(k)}(x, y)=\mathfrak{A}_k^{(4)}(x)\left(0, -\frac{2}{S}, 0\right),$$

$$\operatorname{rot}_y\mathfrak{B}^{5}_{(k)}(x, y)=\mathfrak{A}_k^{(5)}(x)\left(0, 0, -\frac{2}{T}\right), \tag{7.71'}$$

$$\operatorname{rot}_y\mathfrak{B}^{6}_{(k)}(x, y)=\mathfrak{A}_k^{(6)}(x)\left(-\frac{2}{R}, 0, 0\right).$$

Substituting these values of $\operatorname{div}\mathfrak{B}^{s}_{(k)}(x, y)$ and $\operatorname{rot}\mathfrak{B}^{s}_{(k)}(x, y)$ in (7.71), we obtain

$$\Delta(\operatorname{div}_y\overset{0}{H}_{(k)}(x, y)=0, \tag{7.72}$$

$$\mu_a\Delta(\operatorname{rot}_y\overset{0}{H}_{(k)}(x, y)=-8\pi\left(\frac{\mathfrak{A}_k^{(6)}(x)}{R}i_1+\frac{\mathfrak{A}_k^{(4)}(x)}{S}i_2+\frac{\mathfrak{A}_k^{(5)}(x)}{T}i_3\right)$$

$$(k=1, 2, 3). \tag{7.73}$$

We shall now prove

***Lemma A*⁰.** *For* $x\in B$ *and distinct from* y,

$$\overset{\bullet}{\Delta}_{(a)}\left[u(y)\,\mathrm{T}^{\bullet}\overset{0}{H}{}^{\bullet}(x, y)\right]=0.$$

***Lemma B*⁰.** *For* $x\in B$ *and distinct from* y,

$$\overset{\bullet}{\Delta}_{(a)}\left[u(y)\operatorname{grad}\operatorname{div}\overset{0}{H}{}^{\bullet}(x, y)\right]=0.$$

Lemma C . For x not on S,

$$\Delta^*_{(a)}\left(\int_S u(y)\,\mathrm{T}^*\overset{0}{H}{}^*(x, y)\,dS_y\right)=0.$$

In order to prove Lemma A^0 it is sufficient to show (in view of the Corollary to Lemma A, § 6) that for $k=1, 2, 3$

$$(\Delta^*_{(a)}\Pi_{(k)}(x, y))_{x_s}=\mu_a\Delta\Pi^s_{(k)}(x, y)+(\lambda_a+\mu_a)\frac{\partial}{\partial x_s}\operatorname{div}\Pi_{(k)}(x, y)=0$$
$$(s=1, 2, 3). \tag{7.74}$$

Let us evaluate

$$\operatorname{div}_x\Pi_{(k)}(x, y).$$

Since $\mathrm{T}^*_k\overset{0}{H}_{(m)}(x, y)=\Pi^m_{(k)}(x, y)$, we get

$$\operatorname{div}_x\Pi_{(k)}(x, y)=\sum_m^3\frac{\partial}{\partial x_m}\Pi^m_{(k)}(x, y)=$$
$$=\sum_m^3\frac{\partial}{\partial x_m}\Big[2(\mu_a-\mu_i)\frac{\partial}{\partial n_y}\overset{0}{H}{}^k_{(m)}(x, y)+(\lambda_a-\lambda_i)\cos(n_y, x_k)\times$$
$$\times\operatorname{div}_y\overset{0}{H}_{(m)}(x, y)+(\mu_a-\mu_i)\left(n_y\times\operatorname{rot}_y\overset{0}{H}_{(m)}(x, y)_{x_k}\right.\Big].$$

But

$$\sum_{m=1}^3\frac{\partial\overset{0}{H}_{(m)}(x, y)}{\partial x_m}=\sum_{m=1}^3\sum_{n=1}^3 i_n\frac{\partial\overset{0}{H}{}^n_{(m)}}{\partial x_m}=\sum_n i_n\operatorname{div}_x\overset{0}{H}{}^{(n)}(x, y)=$$
$$=\operatorname{grad}_x\Phi(x, y)=-\operatorname{grad}_y\Phi(x, y).$$

Hence

$$\operatorname{div}\Pi_{(k)}(x,y)=2(\mu_a-\mu_i)\frac{\partial}{\partial n_y}\operatorname{div}_x\overset{0}{H}{}^{(k)}(x, y)-(\lambda_a-\lambda_i)\cos(n_y, x_k)\,\sigma(y),$$

where $\sigma(y)$ does not depend on x. Besides,

$$\mu_a\Delta\Pi^s_{(k)}(x, y)=2(\mu_a-\mu_i)\frac{\partial}{\partial n_y}\left(\mu_a\Delta_x\overset{0}{H}{}^k_{(s)}\right)+$$
$$+\mu_a(\lambda_a-\lambda_i)\cos(n_y, x_k)\Delta_x\left(\operatorname{div}_y\overset{0}{H}_{(s)}\right)+\mu_a(\mu_a-\mu_i)(n_y\times\Delta_x\operatorname{rot}_y H_{(s)})_{x_k}.$$

We substitute these expressions for $\operatorname{div}_x\Pi_{(k)}$ and $\mu_a\Delta\Pi^s_{(k)}$ in (7.74), apply (7.72), and obtain

$$(\Delta^*_a\Pi_{(k)}(x, y))_{x_s}=2(\mu_a-\mu_i)\frac{\partial}{\partial n_y}\Big[\mu_a\Delta_x\overset{0}{H}{}^k_{(s)}(x, y)+$$
$$+(\lambda_a+\mu_a)\frac{\partial}{\partial x_s}\operatorname{div}_x\overset{0}{H}{}^{(k)}(x, y)\Big]+$$
$$+\mu_a(\mu_a-\mu_i)\left[\left(n_y\times\Delta_x\operatorname{rot}_y\overset{0}{H}_{(s)}(x, y)\right)_{x_k}\right]$$

or, by virtue of the symmetry relations,

$$\overset{0}{H}{}^{(k)}_s(x, y)=\overset{0}{H}{}^s_{(k)}(y; x),$$

$$(\Delta^*_{(a)}\Pi_{(k)}(x, y))_{x_s}=2(\mu_a-\mu_i)\frac{\partial}{\partial n_y}\Big[\mu_a\Delta_x\overset{0}{H}{}^s_{(k)}(y, x)+$$
$$+(\lambda_a+\mu_a)\frac{\partial}{\partial x_s}\operatorname{div}_x\overset{0}{H}_{(k)}(y, x)\Big]+$$
$$+\mu_a(\mu_a-\mu_i)\left[n_y\times\Delta_x\operatorname{rot}_y\overset{0}{H}_{(s)}(x, y)\right)_{x_k}\Big]. \tag{7.74'}$$

The expression in the first square brackets on the right-hand side is precisely the x_s-projection of the $\overset{*}{\Delta}_{(a)}$-transform (with respect to x) of the k-th row of $\overset{0}{H}(y, x)$ (not $\overset{0}{H}(x, y)$); it follows from (7.70) that

$$\overset{*}{\Delta}_{(a)}\overset{0}{H}_{(k)}(y, x) = 4\pi \sum_{m=1}^{6} \mathfrak{B}_{(k)}^{m}(y, x). \tag{7.75}$$

Projecting $\mathfrak{B}_{(k)}^{m}(y, x)$ on the x_s-axis and differentiating along the normal at y, we get

$$4\pi 2(\mu_a - \mu_i)\frac{\partial}{\partial n_y}\sum_{m=1}^{6}\left(\mathfrak{B}_{(k)}^{m}(y, x)\right)_{x_s} = 8\pi(\mu_a - \mu_i)\sum_{m=4}^{6}\mathfrak{A}_s^{(m)}(x)\frac{\partial}{\partial n_y}\mathfrak{A}_k^{(m)}(y).$$

Inserting this expression into the first square bracket on the right of (7.74'), and replacing the expression in the second square bracket by its equivalent according to (7.73), we obtain

$$\left(\overset{*}{\Delta}_{(a)}\Pi_{(k)}(x, y)\right)_{x_s} = 0.$$

Let for example $k=1,\ s=2$; (6.30) implies in this case

$$\frac{\partial}{\partial n_y}\mathfrak{A}_1^{(4)}(y) = -\frac{1}{S}\cos(\boldsymbol{n}_y, \boldsymbol{x}_3), \quad \frac{\partial}{\partial n_y}\mathfrak{A}_1^{(5)}(y) = \frac{1}{T}\cos(\boldsymbol{n}_y, \boldsymbol{x}_2), \quad \frac{\partial}{\partial n_y}\mathfrak{A}_1^{(6)}(y) = 0$$

and

$$\sum_{m=4}^{6}\mathfrak{A}_2^{(m)}\frac{\partial}{\partial n_y}\mathfrak{A}_1^{(m)}(y) = \frac{\mathfrak{A}_2^{(5)}(x)}{T}\cos(\boldsymbol{n}_y, \boldsymbol{x}_2) - \frac{\mathfrak{A}_2^{(4)}(x)}{S}\cos(\boldsymbol{n}_y, \boldsymbol{x}_3).$$

On the other hand, (7.73) gives

$$-8\pi(\mu_a - \mu_i)\left[\boldsymbol{n}_y \times \Delta\left(\mathrm{rot}_y \overset{0}{H}_{(2)}(x, y)\right)\right]_{x_1} =$$
$$= -8\pi(\mu_a - \mu_i)\left(\frac{\mathfrak{A}_2^{(5)}(x)}{T}\cos(\boldsymbol{n}_y, \boldsymbol{x}_2) - \frac{\mathfrak{A}_2^{(4)}(x)}{S}\cos(\boldsymbol{n}_y, \boldsymbol{x}_3)\right)$$

and substituting in (7.74') we obtain

$$\left(\overset{*}{\Delta}_{(a)}\Pi_{(1)}(x, y)\right)_{x_2} = 0.$$

This proves Lemma A^0.

It is not necessary to consider the proofs of Lemmas B^0 and C^0 since they essentially repeat the proofs of the counterpart lemmas in § 6 (cf. the above proof of Lemma A^0).

We may now turn to the main object of this section— the proof of the equivalence theorems.

Let us assume that the vector $\boldsymbol{f}(y)$, given by

$$\lim_{x \to y \in S_a} \mathsf{T}\boldsymbol{u}(x) = \boldsymbol{f}(y),$$

satisfies the orthogonality conditions

$$\int_{S_a} \boldsymbol{f}(y)\,\mathfrak{A}^{(m)}(y)\,dS_y = 0 \qquad (m = 1, 2, \ldots, 6), \tag{7.76}$$

which are, by Theorem 7 of Ch. VI, necessary and sufficient for the solvability of Problem (T_i).

We shall show that a regular solution of equation (7.68) in B_a satisfies the equation

$$\overset{*}{\Delta}_{(a)}\boldsymbol{u}(x) = 0.$$

Let $x \in B_a$; applying $\overset{*}{\Delta}_{(a)}$ to the two sides of (7.68), and inserting the differential operators under the integral signs (this is obviously allowed in our case), we conclude from Lemmas A^0, B^0, C^0 that

$$\mu_a \overset{*}{\Delta}_{(a)} u(x) = -\mu_a \int_{S_a} \left[\overset{*}{\Delta}_{(a)} \overset{0}{H}(x, y) \right] f(y)\, dS_y.$$

But according to (7.69) the application of $\overset{*}{\Delta}_{(a)}$ to the columns with respect to x yields

$$\overset{*}{\Delta}_{(a)} \overset{0}{H}(x, y) = 4\pi \sum_{m=1}^{6} \mathfrak{A}^{(m)}(x) * \mathfrak{A}^{(m)}(y)$$

and

$$\mu_a \overset{*}{\Delta}_{(a)} u(x) = -4\pi\mu_c \sum_{m=1}^{6} \left[i_1 \mathfrak{A}_1^{(m)}(x) + i_2 \mathfrak{A}_2^{(m)}(x) + i_3 \mathfrak{A}_3^{(m)}(x) \right] \int_{S_a} f(y)\, \mathfrak{A}^{(m)}(y)\, dS_y;$$

hence, taking into account the solvability conditions (7.76), we obtain

$$\overset{*}{\Delta}_{(a)} u(x) = 0 \qquad x \in B_a, \tag{7.77}$$

which completes the proof.

We know from the foregoing sections that starting from (7.77), the proof of the equivalence theorems proceeds in the same way in all cases; it is therefore unnecessary to repeat that part of the proof. Thus, the equivalence theorem for the static Problem (B_2) is proved.

The equivalence theorem for the static Problem (B_1) follows from § 8, as explained in the beginning of this section.

The necessary and sufficient conditions (7.76) for the solvability of the second interior static problem (T_i) for homogeneous bodies (cf. VI, 5) play, as we have seen, the same part in the case of inhomogeneous media. This is due to the fact that if the inclusion B_i which constitutes the inhomogeneity of the medium is removed, say, by contracting the domain B_i to a point, equation (7.68) will take the form

$$u(x) = -\frac{1}{4\pi} \int_{S_a} \overset{0}{H}(x, y)\, f(y)\, dS_y,$$

which represents solutions of problem (T_i) for a homogeneous medium by means of Green's tensor, provided the existence theorem is valid.

Chapter VIII

ANISOTROPIC BODIES. THEORY OF THE PLANE PROBLEM

The potential-theoretic methods, which in the preceding chapters were applied to boundary-value problems for homogeneous and piecewise homogeneous isotropic bodies, may be extended to anisotropic elastic bodies. This requires, on the one hand, a further elaboration of the theory of the various kinds of fundamental solutions for systems of elliptic equations with discontinuous coefficients and, on the other hand, an extension of the theory of many-dimensional singular integral equations to systems of equations having these fundamental solutions as their kernels. These problems, which present new difficulties, are of considerable interest and should be made the subject of future investigations.

It is known that the methods of the preceding chapters may be almost completely carried over to one particular, but quite important anisotropic case, that of the plane problem. Some typical cases of this problem will be discussed in this and the following chapters. These problems have also been treated before (using other methods) by many authors.

Intensive studies of the plane problem of anisotropic bodies began in the 1930's. At first, the main trend of those studies was to apply methods of the theory of functions of a complex variable to anisotropic bodies, a technique that at the hands of G. V. Kolosov and especially N. I. Muskhelishvili had already led to important results in the isotropic plane problem. In the 1940's the theory of the anisotropic plane problem was already well advanced along these lines thanks to the work of S.G. Lekhnitskii /17/, G. N. Savin /28/, S. G. Mikhlin /22d/, D. I. Sherman /29/ and others. These investigations are based on a representation of the displacements and stresses by means of analytic functions of complex variables and are concerned with static problems, mainly for homogeneous bodies; the case of a piecewise-homogeneous body is treated in /29/.

M. O. Basheleishvili /14/ has proposed in 1954 a different method of investigating the anisotropic plane problem, based on the application of potential-theoretic methods and integral equations; there he has shown for the first time how the results obtained by these methods for isotropic bodies are extended to anisotropic bodies. His basic idea was further developed and made use of in different ways by T. V. Burchuladze /2a, b, c, d/, K. M. Meskhi /20/, Zh. A. Rukhadze /27/ and others*. Finally, a theory of boundary-value problems, based on these ideas, was presented in succinct terms by M. O. Basheleishvili in his new papers /1a, b, c, d/. It should be mentioned that it is shown in /1a, b, c/ that the new methods can be used to construct explicit solutions of the boundary-value problems in some of

* These ideas had already appeared earlier in the work of N. S. Kakhniashvili /11/ on isotropic plane problems.

the cases not amenable to function-theoretic methods. These results are presented with some abbreviations and modifications in §§ 1–6 of this and the next chapter.

§ 1. Basic equations and fundamental solutions

In the absence of body forces the equations of plane strain of a homogeneous anisotropic body may be written in the form

$$\frac{\partial \tau_{11}}{\partial x_1}+\frac{\partial \tau_{12}}{\partial x_2}=0, \quad \frac{\partial \tau_{12}}{\partial x_1}+\frac{\partial \tau_{22}}{\partial x_2}=0; \tag{8.1}$$

$$\begin{aligned} \tau_{11} &= A_{11}u_{11}+A_{12}u_{22}+A_{13}u_{12}, \\ \tau_{22} &= A_{12}u_{11}+A_{22}u_{22}+A_{23}u_{12}, \\ \tau_{12} &= A_{13}u_{11}+A_{23}u_{22}+A_{33}u_{12}, \end{aligned} \tag{8.2}$$

where $A_{11}, A_{12}, A_{13}, A_{22}, A_{23}, A_{33}$ are the elastic constants of the medium, relative to the coordinate system $x_1x_2x_3$; it is assumed that they satisfy the conditions

$$A_{11}>0, \quad \begin{vmatrix} A_{11} & A_{12} \\ A_{12} & A_{22} \end{vmatrix}>0, \quad \begin{vmatrix} A_{11} & A_{12} & A_{13} \\ A_{12} & A_{22} & A_{23} \\ A_{13} & A_{23} & A_{33} \end{vmatrix}>0. \tag{8.3}$$

Assuming the strain components u_{11}, u_{22}, u_{12} to be related to the components of the displacement vector $\boldsymbol{u}(u_1, u_2)$ through

$$u_{11}=\frac{\partial u_1}{\partial x_1}, \quad u_{22}=\frac{\partial u_2}{\partial x_2}, \quad u_{12}=\frac{\partial u_1}{\partial x_2}+\frac{\partial u_2}{\partial x_1}$$

and inserting these relations in (8.2), we obtain from equations (8.1)

$$\begin{aligned} \Delta_1^{*}\boldsymbol{u} \equiv A_{11}\frac{\partial^2 u_1}{\partial x_1^2}+2A_{13}\frac{\partial^2 u_1}{\partial x_1 \partial x_2}+A_{33}\frac{\partial^2 u_1}{\partial x_2^2}+ \\ +A_{13}\frac{\partial^2 u_2}{\partial x_1^2}+(A_{12}+A_{33})\frac{\partial^2 u_2}{\partial x_1 \partial x_2}+A_{23}\frac{\partial^2 u_2}{\partial x_2^2}=0, \\ \Delta_2^{*}\boldsymbol{u} \equiv A_{13}\frac{\partial^2 u_1}{\partial x_1^2}+(A_{12}+A_{33})\frac{\partial^2 u_1}{\partial x_1 \partial x_2}+A_{23}\frac{\partial^2 u_1}{\partial x_2^2}+ \\ +A_{33}\frac{\partial^2 u_2}{\partial x_1^2}+2A_{23}\frac{\partial^2 u_2}{\partial x_1 \partial x_2}+A_{22}\frac{\partial^2 u_2}{\partial x_2^2}=0 \end{aligned} \tag{8.4}$$

or concisely

$$\Delta^{*}\boldsymbol{u}=0,$$

where Δ^{*} is the differential vector operator with the components

$$\Delta_1^{*} \text{ and } \Delta_2^{*}.$$

We have thus obtained the basic system of differential equations in the displacements for the plane static problem in absence of body forces. By making use of the inequalities (8.3) equations (8.4) can be shown to constitute a system of elliptic differential equations, whose characteristic equation

$$\begin{aligned} (A_{22}A_{33}-A_{23}^2)\alpha^4+2(A_{13}A_{22}-A_{12}A_{23})\alpha^3+ \\ +(A_{11}A_{22}+2A_{13}A_{23}-A_{12}^2-2A_{12}A_{33})\alpha^2+2(A_{11}A_{23}-A_{12}A_{13})\alpha+ \\ +(A_{11}A_{33}-A_{13}^2)=0 \end{aligned} \tag{8.5}$$

possesses only complex roots

$$\alpha_k = a_k + ib_k, \quad \tilde{\alpha}_k = a_k - ib_k, \quad b_k > 0 \quad (k = 1, 2). \tag{8.6}$$

Let

$$u_1^{(1)} = A_{33}\frac{\partial^2\psi}{\partial x_1^2} + 2A_{23}\frac{\partial^2\psi}{\partial x_1 \partial x_2} + A_{22}\frac{\partial^2\psi}{\partial x_2^2},$$

$$u_2^{(1)} = -\left[A_{13}\frac{\partial^2\psi}{\partial x_1^2} + (A_{12} + A_{33})\frac{\partial^2\psi}{\partial x_1 \partial x_2} + A_{23}\frac{\partial^2\psi}{\partial x_2^2}\right], \tag{8.7$_1$}$$

$$u_1^{(2)} = -\left[A_{13}\frac{\partial^2\psi}{\partial x_1^2} + (A_{12} + A_{33})\frac{\partial^2\psi}{\partial x_1 \partial x_2} + A_{23}\frac{\partial^2\psi}{\partial x_2^2}\right],$$

$$u_2^{(2)} = A_{11}\frac{\partial^2\psi}{\partial x_1^2} + 2A_{13}\frac{\partial^2\psi}{\partial x_1 \partial x_2} + A_{33}\frac{\partial^2\psi}{\partial x_2^2}. \tag{8.7$_2$}$$

When we use (8.7_1) or (8.7_2) for u_1 and u_2 in (8.5), we obtain in both cases the same fourth-order differential equation in ψ:

$$(A_{11}A_{33} - A_{13}^2)\frac{\partial^4\psi}{\partial x_1^4} + 2(A_{11}A_{23} - A_{12}A_{13})\frac{\partial^4\psi}{\partial x_1^3 \partial x_2} +$$
$$+ (A_{11}A_{22} + 2A_{13}A_{23} - A_{12}^2 - 2A_{12}A_{33})\frac{\partial^4\psi}{\partial x_1^2 \partial x_2^2} +$$
$$+ 2(A_{13}A_{22} - A_{12}A_{23})\frac{\partial^4\psi}{\partial x_1 \partial x_2^3} + (A_{22}A_{33} - A_{23}^2)\frac{\partial^4\psi}{\partial x_2^4} = 0. \tag{8.8}$$

Seeking to establish the fundamental solutions of (8.8) by the known method /18/, we readily find that this equation is satisfied by

$$\psi(x; y) = a\,\mathrm{Im}\sum_{k=1}^{2} d_k \sigma_k^2 \ln \sigma_k, \tag{8.9}$$

where

$$\sigma_k = (x_1 - y_1) + \alpha_k(x_2 - y_2), \quad a = -\frac{1}{A_{22}A_{33} - A_{23}^2}, \tag{8.10}$$

d_k being the cofactor of the element α_k^3, divided by d, and

$$d = \begin{vmatrix} 1 & \alpha_1 & \alpha_1^2 & \alpha_1^3 \\ 1 & \tilde{\alpha}_1 & \tilde{\alpha}_1^2 & \tilde{\alpha}_1^3 \\ 1 & \alpha_2 & \alpha_2^2 & \alpha_2^3 \\ 1 & \tilde{\alpha}_2 & \tilde{\alpha}_2^2 & \tilde{\alpha}_2^3 \end{vmatrix} = -4b_1b_2[(a_1 - a_2)^2 + (b_1 - b_2)^2][(a_1 - a_2)^2 + (b_1 + b_2)^2];$$

evidently $x(x_1, x_2)$ and $y(y_1, y_2)$ are points in the plane.

It may be shown that

$$\sum_{k=1}^{2} d_k = -\frac{i(b_1 + b_2)}{2b_1b_2[(a_1 - a_2)^2 + (b_1 + b_2)^2]}; \tag{8.11}$$

$$\sum_{k=1}^{2} \alpha_k d_k = -\frac{i(a_2b_1 + a_1b_2)}{2b_1b_2[(a_1 - a_2)^2 + (b_1 + b_2)^2]};$$

$$\sum_{k=1}^{2} \alpha_k^2 d_k = -\frac{i[b_1(a_2^2 + b_2^2) + b_2(a_1^2 + b_1^2)]}{2b_1b_2[(a_1 - a_2)^2 + (b_1 + b_2)^2]};$$

$$\sum_{k=1}^{2} \alpha_k^3 d_k = \frac{1}{2} - \frac{i[a_1b_2(a_1^2 + b_1^2 + 2b_1b_2) + a_2b_1(a_2^2 + b_2^2 + 2b_1b_2)]}{2b_1b_2[(a_1 - a_2)^2 + (b_1 + b_2)^2]};$$

these relations lead to considerable simplifications in the following calculations.

We now insert ψ from (8.9) into (8.7_1) and (8.7_2), considering them as column-vectors, and define the matrix

$$\Gamma(x, y) = \operatorname{Im} \sum_{k=1}^{2} \left\| \begin{matrix} A_k & B_k \\ B_k & C_k \end{matrix} \right\| \ln \sigma_k, \tag{8.12}$$

where

$$\begin{aligned} A_k &= 2a\left(A_{22}\alpha_k^2 + 2A_{23}\alpha_k + A_{33}\right) d_k, \\ B_k &= -2a\left[A_{23}\alpha_k^2 + (A_{12} + A_{33})\alpha_k + A_{13}\right] d_k, \\ C_k &= 2a\left(A_{33}\alpha_k^2 + 2A_{13}\alpha_k + A_{11}\right) d_k \qquad (k = 1, 2). \end{aligned} \tag{8.13}$$

This $\Gamma(x, y)$ will be called the matrix of fundamental solutions of the system (8.4). One may verify directly that (8.4) is also satisfied by each column of the matrix

$$M(x, y) = \operatorname{Im} \sum_{k=1}^{2} \left\| \begin{matrix} A'_k & B'_k \\ C'_k & D'_k \end{matrix} \right\| \ln \sigma_k, \tag{8.14}$$

where

$$\begin{aligned} A'_k &= \left(A_{22}\alpha_k^2 + 2A_{23}\alpha_k + A_{33}\right) \frac{(-1)^k}{p_k(\alpha_1 - \alpha_2)}, \\ B'_k &= -\left[A_{23}\alpha_k^2 + (A_{12} + A_{33})\alpha_k + A_{13}\right] \frac{(-1)^k \alpha_1\alpha_2}{q_k(\alpha_1 - \alpha_2)}, \\ C'_k &= -\left[A_{23}\alpha_k^2 + (A_{12} + A_{33})\alpha_k + A_{13}\right] \frac{(-1)^k}{p_k(\alpha_1 - \alpha_2)}, \\ D'_k &= \left(A_{33}\alpha_k^2 + 2A_{13}\alpha_k + A_{11}\right) \frac{(-1)^k \alpha_1\alpha_2}{q_k(\alpha_1 - \alpha_2)} \end{aligned}$$

and

$$\begin{aligned} p_k &= \left(A_{22}A_{33} - A_{23}^2\right)\alpha_k^2 + \left(A_{13}A_{22} - A_{12}A_{23}\right)\alpha_k + \left(A_{13}A_{23} - A_{12}A_{33}\right), \\ q_k &= \left(A_{13}A_{23} - A_{12}A_{33}\right)\alpha_k^2 + \left(A_{11}A_{23} - A_{12}A_{13}\right)\alpha_k + \left(A_{11}A_{33} - A_{13}^2\right), \end{aligned}$$

are regarded as vectors. The matrix $M(x, y)$ will be called the second fundamental solution of the system (8.4).

§ 2. Generalized stress operator. Stress and pseudostress operators

The vector operator Πu with the components

$$\begin{aligned} \Pi_1 u &= \left(A_{11}\frac{\partial u_1}{\partial x_1} + \beta_1\frac{\partial u_1}{\partial x_2} + A_{13}\frac{\partial u_2}{\partial x_1} + \gamma_1\frac{\partial u_2}{\partial x_2}\right)\cos(n, x_1) + \\ &+ \left(\beta_2\frac{\partial u_1}{\partial x_1} + A_{33}\frac{\partial u_1}{\partial x_2} + \gamma_2\frac{\partial u_2}{\partial x_1} + A_{23}\frac{\partial u_2}{\partial x_2}\right)\cos(n, x_2), \\ \Pi_2 u &= \left(A_{13}\frac{\partial u_1}{\partial x_1} + \delta_1\frac{\partial u_1}{\partial x_2} + A_{33}\frac{\partial u_2}{\partial x_1} + \eta_1\frac{\partial u_2}{\partial x_2}\right)\cos(n, x_1) + \\ &+ \left(\delta_2\frac{\partial u_1}{\partial x_1} + A_{23}\frac{\partial u_1}{\partial x_2} + \eta_2\frac{\partial u_2}{\partial x_1} + A_{22}\frac{\partial u_2}{\partial x_2}\right)\cos(n, x_2), \end{aligned} \tag{8.15}$$

where $\beta_1, \beta_2, \gamma_1, \gamma_2, \delta_1, \delta_2, \eta_1, \eta_2$ are arbitrary real numbers, satisfying the relations

$$\begin{aligned} \beta_1 + \beta_2 &= 2A_{13}, & \gamma_1 + \gamma_2 &= A_{12} + A_{33}, \\ \delta_1 + \delta_2 &= A_{12} + A_{33}, & \eta_1 + \eta_2 &= 2A_{23}, \end{aligned} \tag{8.16}$$

will be called the generalized stress operator. The operator obtained from Π by interchanging the elements of the pairs (β_1, β_2), (η_1, η_2), (γ_1, δ_2), (γ_2, δ_1), will be called the generalized operator conjugate to Π and denoted by Π^*.

If we set in (8.16)

$$\begin{aligned} \beta_1 &= A_{13}, & \beta_2 &= A_{13}, & \gamma_1 &= A_{12}, & \gamma_2 &= A_{33}, \\ \delta_1 &= A_{33}, & \delta_2 &= A_{12}, & \eta_1 &= A_{23}, & \eta_2 &= A_{23}, \end{aligned}$$

then Π reduces to the stress operator T and

$$T^* \equiv T.$$

Let us establish the effect of applying Π to the matrix $\Gamma(x, y)$ with respect to the point y. We note that

$$\frac{\partial}{\partial s_y} \ln \sigma_k = \frac{\partial}{\partial y_2} \ln \sigma_k \cos(n_y, x_1) - \frac{\partial}{\partial y_1} \ln \sigma_k \cos(n_y, x_2) =$$
$$= \frac{1}{\sigma_k} (\cos(n_y, x_2) - \alpha_k \cos(n_y, x_1)), \tag{8.17}$$

and that α_k satisfies the equation

$$A_k C_k - B_k^2 = 0 \qquad (k = 1, 2),$$

as may be verified by means of (8.5) and (8.13). It is also easy to verify the relations

$$(A_{11} + \beta_1 \alpha_k) A_k + (A_{13} + \gamma_1 \alpha_k) B_k = -\alpha_k [(\beta_2 + A_{33}\alpha_k) A_k + (\gamma_2 + A_{23}\alpha_k) B_k],$$
$$(A_{11} + \beta_1 \alpha_k) B_k + (A_{13} + \gamma_1 \alpha_k) C_k = -\alpha_k [(\beta_2 + A_{33}\alpha_k) B_k + (\gamma_2 + A_{23}\alpha_k) C_k],$$
$$(A_{13} + \delta_1 \alpha_k) A_k + (A_{33} + \eta_1 \alpha_k) B_k = -\alpha_k [(\delta_2 + A_{23}\alpha_k) A_k + (\eta_2 + A_{22}\alpha_k) B_k],$$
$$(A_{13} + \delta_1 \alpha_k) B_k + (A_{33} + \eta_1 \alpha_k) C_k = -\alpha_k [(\delta_2 + A_{23}\alpha_k) B_k + (\eta_2 + A_{22}\alpha_k) C_k].$$

Letting Π operate on the columns of $\Gamma(x, y)$ with respect to y, we then obtain

$$\Pi_y \Gamma(x, y) = \operatorname{Im} \sum_{k=1}^{2} \begin{Vmatrix} P_k & R_k \\ Q_k & S_k \end{Vmatrix} \frac{\partial}{\partial s_y} \ln \sigma_k,$$

where

$$\begin{aligned} P_k &= -[(\beta_2 + A_{33}\alpha_k) A_k + (\gamma_2 + A_{23}\alpha_k) B_k], \\ Q_k &= -[(\delta_2 + A_{23}\alpha_k) A_k + (\eta_2 + A_{22}\alpha_k) B_k], \\ R_k &= -[(\beta_2 + A_{33}\alpha_k) B_k + (\gamma_2 + A_{23}\alpha_k) C_k], \\ S_k &= -[(\delta_2 + A_{23}\alpha_k) B_k + (\eta_2 + A_{22}\alpha_k) C_k]. \end{aligned} \tag{8.18}$$

Consider the matrix

$$\overline{\Pi_y \Gamma(x, y)} = \operatorname{Im} \sum_{k=1}^{2} \begin{Vmatrix} P_k & Q_k \\ R_k & S_k \end{Vmatrix} \frac{\partial}{\partial s_y} \ln \sigma_k, \tag{8.19}$$

that is, the transpose of $\Pi_y \Gamma(x, y)$; it may be shown, exactly as in (I,3), that *each column-vector of the matrix (8.19) satisfies equations (8.4) with respect to x.*

We introduce the notation

$$\sigma = (x_1 - y_1) + i(x_2 - y_2)$$

and write the matrix $\overline{\Pi_y \Gamma(x, y)}$ in the form

$$\overline{\Pi_y \Gamma(x, y)} = \operatorname{Im} \sum_{k=1}^{2} \begin{Vmatrix} P_k & Q_k \\ R_k & S_k \end{Vmatrix} \frac{\partial}{\partial s_y} \ln \frac{\sigma_k}{\sigma} + \operatorname{Im} \sum_{k=1}^{2} \begin{Vmatrix} P_k & Q_k \\ R_k & S_k \end{Vmatrix} \frac{\partial}{\partial s_y} \ln \sigma. \tag{8.20}$$

Now the expression

$$\frac{\partial}{\partial s_y} \ln \frac{\sigma_k}{\sigma} = (i - \alpha_k) \frac{(x_1 - y_1) \cos(n_y, x_1) + (x_2 - y_2) \cos(n_y, x_2)}{\sigma_k \sigma} =$$
$$= \frac{i - \alpha_k}{\sigma_k \sigma} r(x, y) \cos(r, n_y), \qquad r = \sqrt{(x_1 - y_1)^2 + (x_2 - y_2)^2}, \tag{8.21}$$

obviously has* at $y = x$ a singularity which is integrable in the ordinary sense; in order that the matrix $\overline{\Pi_y \Gamma(x, y)}$ should have only this kind of

* On a Liapunov curve.

singularity it is necessary and sufficient that

$$\operatorname{Im}\sum_{k=1}^{2}P_k=0,\quad \operatorname{Im}\sum_{k=1}^{2}Q_k=0,\quad \operatorname{Im}\sum_{k=1}^{2}R_k=0,\quad \operatorname{Im}\sum_{k=1}^{2}S_k=0. \tag{8.22}$$

These conditions are fulfilled if the constants β_2, γ_2, δ_2, η_2 are chosen as follows

$$\left.\begin{aligned}
&\beta_2=A_{13},\quad \gamma_2=A_{33}+\frac{1}{\Delta}\Big[-\operatorname{Im}\sum_{k=1}^{2}N_k\operatorname{Im}\sum_{k=1}^{2}B_k+\\
&\qquad\qquad +\operatorname{Im}\sum_{k=1}^{2}L_k\operatorname{Im}\sum_{k=1}^{2}A_k\Big]=A_{33}-\frac{C}{A^*},\\
&\delta_2=A_{12}+\frac{1}{\Delta}\Big[\operatorname{Im}\sum_{k=1}^{2}M_k\operatorname{Im}\sum_{k=1}^{2}C_k-\\
&\qquad -\operatorname{Im}\sum_{k=1}^{2}H_k\operatorname{Im}\sum_{k=1}^{2}B_k\Big]=A_{12}+\frac{C}{A^*},\quad \eta_2=A_{23},
\end{aligned}\right\} \tag{8.23}$$

where

$$\left.\begin{aligned}
&N_k=-\frac{(-1)^k\alpha_k}{\alpha_1-\alpha_2}+2\omega\alpha_k d_k,\quad M_k=-\frac{N_k}{\alpha_k},\\
&L_k=-\frac{(-1)^k\alpha_1\alpha_2}{\alpha_1-\alpha_2}+2\omega\alpha_k^2 d_k,\quad H_k=-\frac{L_k}{\alpha_k},\\
&\omega=b_1b_2-a_1a_2-a(A_{13}A_{23}-A_{12}A_{13}),\\
&A^*=\operatorname{Im}\sum_k A_k=\frac{\omega a_{11}C}{BC-A^2}[1-(BC-A)^2],\\
&a_{11}=\frac{1}{\Delta}(A_{22}A_{33}-A_{23}^2),\quad C=\frac{(b_1+b_2)\,\omega}{b_1b_2[(a_1-a_2)^2+(b_1+b_2)^2]},
\end{aligned}\right\} \tag{8.24}$$

$$\Delta=\begin{vmatrix}A_{11}&A_{12}&A_{13}\\A_{12}&A_{22}&A_{23}\\A_{13}&A_{23}&A_{33}\end{vmatrix}.$$

Using the relations (8.11), we obtain

$$\sum_k N_k=1-iA,\quad \sum_k L_k=-iB,\quad \sum_k M_k=iC,\quad \sum_k H_k=1+iA, \tag{8.25}$$

where

$$A=\frac{(a_2b_1+a_1b_2)\,\omega}{b_1b_2[(a_1-a_2)^2+(b_1+b_2)^2]},\quad B=\frac{[b_1(a_2^2+b_2^2)+b_2(a_1^2+b_1^2)]\,\omega}{b_1b_2[(a_1-a_2)^2+(b_1+b_2)^2]}, \tag{8.26}$$

A, B, C do not vanish, and

$$BC-A^2=\frac{\omega^2}{b_1b_2[(a_1-a_2)^2+(b_1+b_2)^2]}. \tag{8.27}$$

Let us insert the values (8.23) of β_2, γ_2, δ_2, η_2 into the expressions (8.18) for P_k, R_k and Q_k, S_k, and then substitute the latter in the matrix (8.19); we then obtain the new matrix

$$\overline{\mathsf{N}_y\Gamma(x,y)}=\Gamma_{II}(x,y)=\operatorname{Im}\sum_{k=1}^{2}\begin{Vmatrix}E_k&F_k\\G_k&I_k\end{Vmatrix}\frac{\partial}{\partial s_y}\ln\sigma_k, \tag{8.28}$$

where

$$\left.\begin{aligned}
&E_1=\frac{B_1C_2}{B_1C_2-B_2C_1},\quad E_2=-\frac{B_2C_1}{B_1C_2-B_2C_1},\\
&F_1=-\frac{B_1B_2}{B_1C_2-B_2C_1},\quad F_2=\frac{B_1B_2}{B_1C_2-B_2C_1},
\end{aligned}\right\} \tag{8.29}$$

2109

$$\left.\begin{aligned} G_1 &= \frac{C_1C_2}{B_1C_2 - B_2C_1}, \qquad G_2 = -\frac{C_1C_2}{B_1C_2 - B_2C_1}, \\ I_1 &= -\frac{B_2C_1}{B_1C_2 - B_2C_1}, \quad I_2 = \frac{B_1C_2}{B_1C_2 - B_2C_1}, \quad E_1 = I_2, \quad E_2 = I_1. \end{aligned}\right\} \tag{8.29}$$

The only singularities of this matrix are integrable in the ordinary sense. The operator N will be called a pseudostress operator, and the matrix (8.28) — each of whose columns obviously satisfies (8.4) with respect to x — a fundamental solution of the second kind.

The matrix of solutions (8.19) with the following choice of constants

$$\beta_1 = A_{13}, \quad \gamma_1 = A_{12}, \quad \delta_1 = A_{12}, \quad \eta_1 = A_{23}.$$

will be called a fundamental solution of the first kind.

In this case the operator Π reduces, as shown above, to T and the matrix $\overline{\Pi_y\Gamma(x, y)}$ becomes

$$\Gamma_{\mathrm{I}}(x, y) = \overline{\mathsf{T}_y\Gamma(x, y)} = \operatorname{Im} \sum_{k=1}^{2} \begin{Vmatrix} N_k & M_k \\ L_k & H_k \end{Vmatrix} \frac{\partial}{\partial s_y} \ln \sigma_k, \tag{8.30}$$

where the constants N_k, M_k, L_k, H_k are defined by (8.24). The matrix of fundamental solutions of the first kind $\Gamma_{\mathrm{I}}(x, y)$ has in view of (8.25), a simple pole at the point $x = y$ on a Lyapunov curve.

It is also clear that

$$\mathsf{T}^* \equiv \mathsf{T}, \quad \mathsf{N}^* \equiv \mathsf{N}. \tag{8.31}$$

Let us mention one more important property of the second fundamental solution $M(x, y)$.

Applying T to the matrix $M(x, y)$ with respect to x,

$$\mathsf{T}_x M(x, y) = \operatorname{Im} \sum_{k=1}^{2} \begin{Vmatrix} e_k & g_k \\ h_k & f_k \end{Vmatrix} \frac{\partial}{\partial s_x} \ln \sigma_k, \tag{8.32}$$

where

$$\begin{aligned} e_k &= \frac{(-1)^{k-1}\alpha_k}{\alpha_1 - \alpha_2}, \qquad h_k = \frac{(-1)^k}{\alpha_1 - \alpha_2}, \\ g_k &= \frac{(-1)^{k-1}\alpha_1\alpha_2}{\alpha_1 - \alpha_2}, \qquad f_k = \frac{(-1)^k \alpha_1\alpha_2}{\alpha_k(\alpha_1 - \alpha_2)}. \end{aligned} \tag{8.33}$$

Hence we readily obtain

$$\operatorname{Im} \sum_{k=1}^{2} e_k = \operatorname{Im} \sum_{k=1}^{2} g_k = \operatorname{Im} \sum_{k=1}^{2} h_k = \operatorname{Im} \sum_{k=1}^{2} f_k = 0. \tag{8.34}$$

The singularity of $\mathsf{T}_x M(x, y)$ at $x = y$, on a Lyapunov curve, is therefore, in view of (8.21), integrable in the ordinary sense, exactly as for an N-operation on the matrix $\Gamma(x, y)$. This property of the second fundamental solution will prove very useful later on.

§ 3. Elastic potentials of an anisotropic medium

Let l be a closed Lyapunov curve. The integrals

$$V_{\mathrm{I}}(x) = \frac{1}{\pi} \int_l \Gamma(x, y)\varphi(y)\,dl_y, \quad V_{\mathrm{II}}(x) = \frac{1}{\pi} \int_l M(x, y)\varphi(y)\,dl_y,$$

where $\varphi(y)$ is a vector-function of class $H(\gamma)$, will be called the single-layer potentials of the first and second kind, respectively, and the integrals

$$W_{\mathrm{I}}(x)=\frac{1}{\pi}\int_l \Gamma_{\mathrm{I}}(x,\ y)\varphi(y)\,dl_y,\quad W_{\mathrm{II}}(x)=\frac{1}{\pi}\int_l \Gamma_{\mathrm{II}}(x,\ y)\varphi(y)\,dl_y$$

the double-layer potentials of the first and second kind; the single-layer potential of the second kind, $V_{\mathrm{II}}(x)$, is the counterpart of the antenna layer potential of (I,6) and will also be called the antenna potential.

Finally, we shall need also potentials of the type

$$U(x)=\frac{1}{2\pi}\int_{S_l} \Gamma(x,\ y)\varphi(y)\,dS_y,$$

where S_l is a plane region bounded by a smooth closed Liapunov curve l. We will call these mass potentials.

The properties of these plane potentials are analogous to those of the three-dimensional potentials studied in Ch. I and II, and can be proved in essentially the same way as in Ch. I. The following theorems are valid.

Theorem 1. *The single-layer potential of the first kind is continuous everywhere.*

Theorem 2. *The double-layer potentials of the first and second kind tend to the following finite limits as x approaches the point x_0 on l from the inside or the outside:*

$$\begin{aligned}
(W_{\mathrm{I}})_i&=+\varphi(x_0)+\frac{1}{\pi}\int_l \Gamma_{\mathrm{I}}(x_0,\ y)\varphi(y)\,dl_y,\\
(W_{\mathrm{I}})_a&=-\varphi(x_0)+\frac{1}{\pi}\int_l \Gamma_{\mathrm{I}}(x_0,\ y)\varphi(y)\,dl_y,\\
(W_{\mathrm{II}})_i&=+\varphi(x_0)+\frac{1}{\pi}\int_l \Gamma_{\mathrm{II}}(x_0,\ y)\varphi(y)\,dl_y,\\
(W_{\mathrm{II}})_a&=-\varphi(x_0)+\frac{1}{\pi}\int_l \Gamma_{\mathrm{II}}(x_0,\ y)\varphi(y)\,dl_y.
\end{aligned}\tag{8.35}$$

The integrals on the right-hand side of the first two relations are defined in the sense of the Cauchy principal value.

Theorem 3. *The T-transforms of the single-layer potentials of the first and second kind tend to the following finite limits as x approaches the boundary point $x_0\in l$ from the inside or the outside:*

$$\begin{aligned}
(\mathrm{T}V_{\mathrm{I}})_i&=-\varphi(x_0)+\frac{1}{\pi}\int_l (\mathrm{T}_{x_0}\Gamma(x_0,\ y))\,\varphi(y)\,dl_y,\\
(\mathrm{T}V_{\mathrm{I}})_a&=+\varphi(x_0)+\frac{1}{\pi}\int_l (\mathrm{T}_{x_0}\Gamma(x_0,\ y))\,\varphi(y)\,dl_y,
\end{aligned}\tag{8.36}$$

for a single layer of the first kind, and

$$\begin{aligned}
(\mathrm{T}V_{\mathrm{II}})_i&=-\varphi(x_0)+\frac{1}{\pi}\int_l (\mathrm{T}_{x_0}M(x_0,\ y))\,\varphi(y)\,dl_y,\\
(\mathrm{T}V_{\mathrm{II}})_a&=+\varphi(x_0)+\frac{1}{\pi}\int_l (\mathrm{T}_{x_0}M(x_0,\ y))\,\varphi(y)\,dl_y,
\end{aligned}$$

for a single layer of the second kind.

The proof of this theorem is based on the relations

$$\mathsf{T}V_{\mathrm{I}}(x)=\operatorname{Im}\sum_{k=1}^{2}\begin{Vmatrix}N_k & L_k\\ M_k & H_k\end{Vmatrix}\int_l \frac{\partial}{\partial s_x}\ln\sigma_k\varphi(y)\,dl_y,$$

$$\mathsf{T}V_{\mathrm{II}}(x)=\operatorname{Im}\sum_{k=1}^{2}\begin{Vmatrix}e_k & h_k\\ g_k & f_k\end{Vmatrix}\int_l \frac{\partial}{\partial s_x}\ln\sigma_k\varphi(y)\,dl_y,$$

and the continuity of the function

$$\frac{\partial}{\partial s_x}\ln\sigma_k+\frac{\partial}{\partial s_y}\ln\sigma_k=\frac{1}{\sigma_k}\left[\alpha_k(\cos(\boldsymbol{n}_x,\,x_1)-\cos(\boldsymbol{n}_y,\,x_1))-(\cos(\boldsymbol{n}_x,\,x_2)-\cos(\boldsymbol{n}_y,\,x_2))\right]$$

as x moves along the curve l.

Theorem 4. *If one of the limits* $(\mathsf{T}W_{\mathrm{I}}(x))_a$ *or* $(\mathsf{T}W_{\mathrm{I}}(x))_i$ *exists and belongs to class* $H(\gamma)$ $(0<\gamma\leqslant 1)$ *for a double layer potential of the first kind* $W_{\mathrm{I}}(x)$ *which is respectively regular in* S_a *or* S_i, *then the other limit exists and* $(\mathsf{T}W_{\mathrm{I}}(x))_i=(\mathsf{T}W_{\mathrm{I}}(x))_a$.

Here S_i is the interior of the closed curve l and S_a is the external infinite domain; the definition of regularity is the same as in the three-dimensional case, with the only difference that the regular solution is bounded at infinity. Theorem 4 is the generalized Lyapunov-Tauber theorem for the plane, and its proof is analogous to that given in (VI,9).

Theorem 5. *The volume potential*

$$U(x)=\frac{1}{2\pi}\int_{S_i}\Gamma(x,\,y)\,\varphi(y)\,dS_y$$

satisfies in S_i *the Poisson equation*

$$\Delta^{*}U(x)=-\varphi(x). \tag{8.37}$$

§ 4. Formulas analogous to the Betti relations

Let u and v be two vector functions defined in S_i, and let Green's formulas hold for them. Consider the expressions

$$u\Pi^{*}v=A_1\cos(\boldsymbol{n}_y,\,x_1)+A_2\cos(\boldsymbol{n}_y,\,x_2), \tag{8.38}$$

$$v\Pi u=B_1\cos(\boldsymbol{n}_y,\,x_1)+B_2\cos(\boldsymbol{n}_y,\,x_2), \tag{8.39}$$

where $y\in S_i+l$, Π^{*} is the conjugate of the operator Π as defined in § 2, and A_1, A_2, B_1, B_2 are given by

$$\begin{aligned}A_1={}&u_1\left(A_{11}\frac{\partial v_1}{\partial y_1}+\beta_2\frac{\partial v_1}{\partial y_2}+A_{13}\frac{\partial v_2}{\partial y_1}+\delta_2\frac{\partial v_2}{\partial y_2}\right)+\\&+u_2\left(A_{13}\frac{\partial v_1}{\partial y_1}+\gamma_2\frac{\partial v_1}{\partial y_2}+A_{33}\frac{\partial v_2}{\partial y_1}+\eta_2\frac{\partial v_2}{\partial y_2}\right),\\A_2={}&u_1\left(\beta_1\frac{\partial v_1}{\partial y_1}+A_{33}\frac{\partial v_1}{\partial y_2}+\delta_1\frac{\partial v_2}{\partial y_1}+A_{23}\frac{\partial v_2}{\partial y_2}\right)+\\&+u_2\left(\gamma_1\frac{\partial v_1}{\partial y_1}+A_{23}\frac{\partial v_1}{\partial y_2}+\eta_1\frac{\partial v_2}{\partial y_1}+A_{22}\frac{\partial v_2}{\partial y_2}\right),\end{aligned} \tag{8.40$_1$}$$

$$\begin{aligned}B_1={}&v_1\left(A_{11}\frac{\partial u_1}{\partial y_1}+\beta_1\frac{\partial u_1}{\partial y_2}+A_{13}\frac{\partial u_2}{\partial y_1}+\gamma_1\frac{\partial u_2}{\partial y_2}\right)+\\&+v_2\left(A_{13}\frac{\partial u_1}{\partial y_1}+\delta_1\frac{\partial u_1}{\partial y_2}+A_{33}\frac{\partial u_2}{\partial y_1}+\eta_1\frac{\partial u_2}{\partial y_2}\right),\end{aligned} \tag{8.40$_2$}$$

$$B_2 = v_1\left(\beta_2 \frac{\partial u_1}{\partial y_1} + A_{33}\frac{\partial u_1}{\partial y_2} + \gamma_2 \frac{\partial u_2}{\partial y_1} + A_{23}\frac{\partial u_2}{\partial y_2}\right) + \\ + v_2\left(\delta_2 \frac{\partial u_1}{\partial y_1} + A_{23}\frac{\partial u_1}{\partial y_2} + \eta_2 \frac{\partial u_2}{\partial y_1} + A_{22}\frac{\partial u_2}{\partial y_2}\right). \qquad (8.40_2)$$

Applying the Green's formula

$$\int_{S_i} \left(\frac{\partial P}{\partial y_1} + \frac{\partial Q}{\partial y_2}\right) dy_1\, dy_2 = \int_l (P\cos(\boldsymbol{n}_y, \boldsymbol{x}_1) + Q\cos(\boldsymbol{n}_y, \boldsymbol{x}_2))\, dl$$

we obtain from (8.38), (8.39), (8.40_1), (8.40_2)

$$\int_{S_i} \boldsymbol{u}\Delta^* \boldsymbol{v}\, dS = \int_l \boldsymbol{u}\Pi^* \boldsymbol{v}\, dl_y - \int_S E(\boldsymbol{u}, \boldsymbol{v})\, dS, \qquad (8.41)$$

$$\int_{S_i} \boldsymbol{v}\Delta^* \boldsymbol{u}\, dS = \int_l \boldsymbol{v}\Pi \boldsymbol{u}\, dl_y - \int_S E(\boldsymbol{v}, \boldsymbol{u})\, dS, \qquad (8.42)$$

where

$$E(\boldsymbol{u}, \boldsymbol{v}) = E(\boldsymbol{v}, \boldsymbol{u}) = A_{11}\frac{\partial u_1}{\partial y_1}\frac{\partial v_1}{\partial y_1} + \beta_2 \frac{\partial u_1}{\partial y_1}\frac{\partial v_1}{\partial y_2} + A_{13}\frac{\partial u_1}{\partial y_1}\frac{\partial v_2}{\partial y_1} + \\ + \delta_2 \frac{\partial u_1}{\partial y_1}\frac{\partial v_2}{\partial y_2} + A_{13}\frac{\partial u_2}{\partial y_1}\frac{\partial v_1}{\partial y_1} + \gamma_2 \frac{\partial u_2}{\partial y_1}\frac{\partial v_1}{\partial y_2} + A_{33}\frac{\partial u_2}{\partial y_1}\frac{\partial v_2}{\partial y_1} + \\ + \eta_2 \frac{\partial u_2}{\partial y_1}\frac{\partial v_2}{\partial y_2} + \beta_1 \frac{\partial u_1}{\partial y_2}\frac{\partial v_1}{\partial y_1} + A_{33}\frac{\partial u_1}{\partial y_2}\frac{\partial v_1}{\partial y_2} + \delta_1 \frac{\partial u_1}{\partial y_2}\frac{\partial v_2}{\partial y_1} + \\ + A_{23}\frac{\partial u_1}{\partial y_2}\frac{\partial v_2}{\partial y_2} + \gamma_1 \frac{\partial u_2}{\partial y_2}\frac{\partial v_1}{\partial y_1} + A_{23}\frac{\partial u_2}{\partial y_2}\frac{\partial v_1}{\partial y_2} + \\ + \eta_1 \frac{\partial u_2}{\partial y_2}\frac{\partial v_2}{\partial y_1} + A_{22}\frac{\partial u_2}{\partial y_2}\frac{\partial v_2}{\partial y_2}, \qquad (8.43)$$

and $\Delta^*(\Delta_1^*, \Delta_2^*)$ is the operator whose components along the $\boldsymbol{x}_1$- and $\boldsymbol{x}_2$-axes are

$$\Delta_1^* \boldsymbol{u} = A_{11}\frac{\partial^2 u_1}{\partial y_1^2} + 2A_{13}\frac{\partial^2 u_1}{\partial y_1 \partial y_2} + A_{33}\frac{\partial^2 u_1}{\partial y_2^2} + A_{13}\frac{\partial^2 u_2}{\partial y_1^2} + \\ + (A_{12} + A_{33})\frac{\partial^2 u_2}{\partial y_1 \partial y_2} + A_{23}\frac{\partial^2 u_2}{\partial y_2^2},$$

$$\Delta_2^* \boldsymbol{u} = A_{13}\frac{\partial^2 u_1}{\partial y_1^2} + (A_{12} + A_{33})\frac{\partial^2 u_1}{\partial y_1 \partial y_2} + A_{23}\frac{\partial^2 u_1}{\partial y_2^2} + \\ + A_{33}\frac{\partial^2 u_2}{\partial y_1^2} + 2A_{23}\frac{\partial^2 u_2}{\partial y_1 \partial y_2} + A_{22}\frac{\partial^2 u_2}{\partial y_2^2}. \qquad (8.44)$$

The relations (8.41), (8.42), (8.43) imply

$$\int_{S_i} (\boldsymbol{v}\Delta^* \boldsymbol{u} - \boldsymbol{u}\Delta^* \boldsymbol{v})\, dS = \int_l (\boldsymbol{v}\Pi \boldsymbol{u} - \boldsymbol{u}\Pi^* \boldsymbol{v})\, dl, \qquad (8.45)$$

whence we obtain for the case $\Pi \equiv \mathrm{T}$ (then $\mathrm{T}^* = \mathrm{T}$) the Betti relation

$$\int_{S_i} (\boldsymbol{v}\Delta^* \boldsymbol{u} - \boldsymbol{u}\Delta^* \boldsymbol{v})\, dS = \int_l (\boldsymbol{v}\mathrm{T} \boldsymbol{u} - \boldsymbol{u}\mathrm{T} \boldsymbol{v})\, dl. \qquad (8.46)$$

Setting in (8.42) $\boldsymbol{u} = \boldsymbol{v}$, $\Pi \equiv \mathrm{T}$ and $\Delta^* \boldsymbol{u} = 0$, we obtain

$$\int_{S_i} E(\boldsymbol{u}, \boldsymbol{u})\, dS = \int_l \boldsymbol{u}\mathrm{T}\boldsymbol{u}\, dl, \qquad (8.47)$$

where

$$E(\boldsymbol{u}, \boldsymbol{u}) = \tau_{11}u_{11} + \tau_{22}u_{22} + \tau_{12}u_{12} = A_{11}u_{11}^2 + 2A_{12}u_{11}u_{22} + \\ + 2A_{13}u_{11}u_{12} + A_{22}u_{22}^2 + 2A_{23}u_{22}u_{12} + A_{33}u_{12}^2. \qquad (8.48)$$

It may be shown by applying (8.3) that (8.48) is a positive-definite form.

If $\boldsymbol{u}$ and $\boldsymbol{v}$ are defined in S_a and satisfy at infinity the conditions

$$\boldsymbol{u}(x) = O(1), \qquad \boldsymbol{v}(x) = O(1), \\ r^2 \frac{\partial \boldsymbol{u}}{\partial R} = O(1), \qquad r^2 \frac{\partial \boldsymbol{v}}{\partial R} = O(1), \qquad (8.49)$$

where R is an arbitrary direction, and r the distance from x to some fixed point in S_i, then (8.41), (8.42), (8.45), (8.46), (8.47) remain valid in the external (infinite) domain S_a, but with the sign of their right-hand members reversed.

Let $\Gamma^{(k)}(x, y)$ denote the k-th column of the matrix $\Gamma(x, y)$; taking in (8.46) $v=\Gamma^{(k)}(x, y)$, as was done in (I,6), we now obtain

$$\delta(x)\, u_k(x)=\frac{1}{\pi}\int_l [u \mathrm{T}_y \Gamma^{(k)}(x, y)-\Gamma^{(k)}(x, y)\, \mathrm{T}u(y)]\, dl_y+ \\ +\frac{1}{\pi}\int_{S_l} \Gamma^{(k)}(x, y)\, \Delta^* u(y)\, dS_y \qquad (k=1, 2), \tag{8.50}$$

where

$$\delta(x)=\begin{cases} 2 & x\in S_i, \\ 1 & x\in l, \\ 0 & x\in S_a. \end{cases}$$

The relation (8.50) remains valid in S_a if conditions (8.49) are fulfilled. In particular, we get for $\Delta^* u=0$

$$\delta(x)\, u_k(x)=\frac{1}{\pi}\int_l u(y)\, \mathrm{T}_y \Gamma^{(k)}(x, y)\, dl_y-\frac{1}{\pi}\int_l \Gamma^{(k)}(x, y)\, \mathrm{T}u(y)\, dl_y \qquad (k=1, 2), \tag{8.51}$$

or

$$\delta(x)\, u(x)=\frac{1}{\pi}\int_l \Gamma_1(x, y)\, u(y)\, dl_y-\frac{1}{\pi}\int_l \Gamma(x, y)(\mathrm{T}u)\, dl_y. \tag{8.51'}$$

§ 5. Integral equations for boundary-value problems. Existence and uniqueness theorems

We shall consider the first and second boundary-value problems (see II, 2). We seek to construct solutions of the system (8.4). Looking for the solution of the first problem in the form of a double-layer potential of the first kind, and of the second — in the form of a single-layer potential of the first kind, we obtain by Theorems 2 and 3 of § 3 the integral equations

$$\left.\begin{aligned} &\varphi(x_0)+\frac{1}{\pi}\int_l \Gamma_1(x_0, y)\, \varphi(y)\, dl=f(x_0), && (D_i)\\ -&\varphi(x_0)+\frac{1}{\pi}\int_l \Gamma_1(x_0, y)\, \varphi(y)\, dl=f(x_0), && (D_a)\\ -&\varphi(x_0)+\frac{1}{\pi}\int_l (\mathrm{T}_{x_0}\Gamma(x_0, y))\, \varphi(y)\, dl=f(x_0). && (T_i)\\ &\varphi(x_0)+\frac{1}{\pi}\int_l (\mathrm{T}_{x_0}\Gamma(x_0, y))\, \varphi(y)\, dl=f(x_0). && (T_a) \end{aligned}\right\} \tag{8.52}$$

Where (D_i) and (T_i) correspond to the interior problems, and (D_a) and (T_a) to the exterior problems; the vector function $f(x_0)$, given on l, belongs to class H. The equations of the mixed problem will be derived and investigated in X, 36–37.

The above integral equations are singular; unlike the corresponding equations of Ch. II, they are contour or one-dimensional integral equations. Equations (8.52) represent a particular case of the systems of singular equations considered in Ch. V, and an analogous theory of solvability may be developed for these equations in exactly the same way, which would demonstrate the validity of the three Fredholm theorems and alternative.

This however is not necessary. The theory of systems of one-dimensional singular integral equations with general Cauchy-type kernels was worked out sufficiently in the 1940's and is presented in /24b/ and /13a/. It was shown that the theorem stating that the number of linearly independent solutions of the original and the adjoint systems, which is valid for systems of Fredholm equations, does not hold generally for systems of singular equations. It may be proved that the difference between the numbers of linearly independent solutions of the two systems is equal to the so-called index of the system, introduced in the simple case of a single equation by Noether and extended to systems of equations by Muskhelishvili /24b/. The Fredholm case thus obtains only when the index of the system of singular equations is zero, and only then do we have a theory of solvability analogous to that of Fredholm. It will be shown below that equations (D_i), (D_a), (T_i), (T_a) belong to that particular type, so that the Fredholm theorems and alternative apply to them; moreover, the equations (D_i), (T_a), and also (D_a), (T_i) are mutually associated. In the next section we shall make use of these properties of our equations to prove the existence theorems for the first and second problem.

In the case of the plane problem, however, singular equations may be avoided altogether. Actually, if the solution of the first problem is sought in the form of a double-layer potential of the second kind, and the solution of the second — in the form of a single-layer potential of the second kind, then by Theorems 2 and 3 of § 3 we obtain the following integral equations

$$\left.\begin{aligned} \varphi(x_0)+\frac{1}{\pi}\int_l \Gamma_{II}(x_0, y)\varphi(y)\,dl &= f(x_0), && (D_i)\\ -\varphi(x_0)+\frac{1}{\pi}\int_l \Gamma_{II}(x_0, y)\varphi(y)\,dl &= f(x_0), && (D_a)\\ -\varphi(x_0)+\frac{1}{\pi}\int_l (\mathrm{T}_{x_0}M(x_0, y))\varphi(y)\,dl &= f(x_0), && (T_i)\\ \varphi(x_0)+\frac{1}{\pi}\int_l (\mathrm{T}_{x_0}M(x_0, y))\varphi(y)\,dl &= f(x_0). && (T_a) \end{aligned}\right\} \qquad (8.53)$$

Relations (8.28) and (8.32) imply that equations (8.53) are ordinary Fredholm equations if the integration contour l is a Lyapunov curve; consequently these equations may in some cases have a certain advantage over the singular equations (8.52); for example, it is not necessary to assume in (8.53) that $f(x_0)$ if of class H, and it is sufficient to suppose, for instance, that it is continuous in the usual sense. But on the other hand, the four equations (8.53) do not consist of mutually associated pairs. This property is possessed only by equations (8.52) and will be utilized when we return to them in the next section.

We shall now give some uniqueness theorems, which follow almost immediately from the formulas derived in the preceding section.

Suppose the considered boundary-value problems have two different regular solutions. Taking their difference, which obviously vanishes on l, and applying to this difference the formula (8.47) first in the internal and then in the external domain, we obtain the following theorems.

Theorem 6. If a solution of equations (8.4), which is regular in S_i or S_a, vanishes on the boundary, then it vanishes identically.

Theorem 7. If the application of T *nullifies on l a solution of equations*

(8.4) which is regular in S_i or S_a, then this solution is a rigid displacement in S_i and a constant vector in S_a.

§ 6. Proof of the existence theorems

We first show that the one-dimensional equations (8.52) are in fact singular in the sense of Cauchy. Consider the equation (D_i) of (8.52). By (8.30), the kernel of this equation is

$$\Gamma_1(x_0, y) = \operatorname{Im} \sum_{k=1}^{2} \begin{Vmatrix} N_k & M_k \\ L_k & H_k \end{Vmatrix} \frac{\partial}{\partial s_y} \ln \sigma_k.$$

From (8.21) we have*

$$\begin{aligned} \frac{\partial}{\partial s_y} \ln \sigma_k &= \frac{\partial}{\partial s_y} \ln \frac{\sigma_k}{r} + \frac{\partial}{\partial s_y} \ln r = \frac{\partial}{\partial s_y} \ln r + \frac{\partial}{\partial s_y} \ln \frac{\sigma_k}{\sqrt{\sigma \tilde{\sigma}}} = \\ &= \frac{\partial}{\partial s_y} \ln r + \frac{\partial}{\partial s_y} \ln \frac{\sigma_k}{\sigma} - \frac{1}{2} \frac{\partial}{\partial s_y} \ln \frac{\tilde{\sigma}}{\sigma} = \\ &= \frac{\partial}{\partial s_y} \ln r + \frac{i - \alpha_k}{\sigma_k \sigma} r \cos(r, n_y) - \frac{i \cos(r, n_y)}{r}. \end{aligned} \tag{8.54}$$

On the other hand

$$\frac{\partial}{\partial s_y} \ln r \, dl_y = \frac{dr}{r} = \frac{dt}{t - t_0} - i\, d\theta,$$

where t and t_0 are the arc-coordinates of the points y and x_0 on l. On account of (8.25), equation (D_i) now assumes the form

$$\varphi(t_0) + \frac{1}{\pi} \begin{Vmatrix} -A & C \\ -B & A \end{Vmatrix} \int_l \frac{\varphi(t)}{t - t_0} dt + \mathrm{K}\varphi = f(t_0), \tag{8.55}$$

where

$$\mathrm{K}\varphi = \frac{1}{\pi} \operatorname{Im} \sum_{k=1}^{2} \int_l \varphi(t)\, d \left\{ \begin{Vmatrix} N_k & M_k \\ L_k & H_k \end{Vmatrix} \left(\ln \frac{\sigma_k}{r} - i\theta \right) \right\},$$

and N_k, M_k, L_k, H_k are given by (8.24).

$\mathrm{K}\varphi$ is a completely continuous operator, and (8.55) is a one-dimensional singular equation. Fredholm's theorems and alternative apply to this equation if its index is zero. The index of a system of equations of the type (8.55) is the number

$$\varkappa = \frac{1}{2\pi} \left[\arg \frac{\det S}{\det D} \right]_l,$$

where

$$S = \begin{Vmatrix} 1 + iA & -Ci \\ Bi & 1 - Ai \end{Vmatrix}, \quad D = \begin{Vmatrix} 1 - Ai & Ci \\ -Bi & 1 + A_i \end{Vmatrix}$$

and $[\ldots]_l$ stands for the increment of the bracketed expression as the variable point completes a circuit along the closed contour l. Since this expression is in our case constant, it suffices to show that it is neither zero nor infinity. We have

$$\det S = \det D = 1 + A^2 - BC,$$

and hence it is necessary to show that

$$1 + A^2 - BC \neq 0 \quad (\text{or } \infty).$$

* The tilde denotes complex conjugation.

That this is actually the case is shown as follows:

$$A^* = \operatorname{Im} \sum_{k=1}^{2} A_k = \frac{\omega a_{11} C}{BC - A^2} [1 - (BC - A^2)] =$$
$$= \frac{1}{a_{11}\omega\Delta} (A_{22}B + 2A_{23}A + A_{33}C) > \frac{C}{\omega A_{22}} > 0, \tag{8.55'}$$

whence, by (8.27)

$$1 + A^2 - BC \neq \begin{cases} 0, \\ \infty. \end{cases}$$

Equation (T_i) is also reducible to the form (8.55), and since the expression

$$\frac{\partial}{\partial s_x} \ln \sigma_k + \frac{\partial}{\partial s_y} \ln \sigma_k$$

is continuous as the point x moves along the contour l, we deduce easily that the index of the system is in that case given by

$$\varkappa = \frac{1}{2\pi} \left[\arg \frac{\det S'}{\det D'} \right]_l,$$

where

$$S' = \begin{Vmatrix} -1 + Ai & -Ci \\ Bi & -1 - Ai \end{Vmatrix}, \quad D' = \begin{Vmatrix} -1 - Ai & Ci \\ -Bi & -1 + Ai \end{Vmatrix};$$

hence

$$\det S' = \det D' = 1 + A^2 - BC \quad \text{and} \quad \varkappa = 0.$$

We have thus shown that the indices of the systems of equations (D_i) and (T_i) are zero; but the difference between the numbers of linearly independent solutions of associated systems (cf. /24b/) equals the index of the system; the systems (T_a) and (D_a), respectively associated with (D_i) and (T_i) therefore have the same number of linearly independent solutions as the latter. This proves the second Fredholm theorem; the first and third Fredholm theorems may also be proved easily (cf., e.g., /13a/).

Now that we have proved the Fredholm theorems and the uniqueness Theorems 6 and 7 of the preceding section for equations (8.52), we can go on to prove the existence theorems as in the case of isotropic bodies /1a/.

We have seen in VI, 2 and 5, that the existence proof is entirely based on the above two facts. In /1a/ the existence theorems are also proved by means of regular Fredholm equations. The existence of the first and second Green's tensors follows, by repeating the reasoning of Ch. VI.

§ 7. Equilibrium of a piecewise-homogeneous anisotropic body

The method of investigation of boundary-value problems of piecewise-homogeneous isotropic bodies, developed in Ch. IV and VII, may obviously be applied also to anisotropic bodies; here we shall deal with the case of orthotropic bodies, considered by Zh. A. Rukhadze /27/.

The Hooke constants A_{13} and A_{23} vanish for orthotropic bodies and equations (8.4) become simpler. Let a plane orthotropic body with the Hooke constants A^a_{11}, A^a_{22}, A^a_{33}, A^a_{12} and boundary l_a contain an inclusion completely embedded in it of another orthotropic substance, characterized by the constants A^i_{11}, A^i_{22}, A^i_{33}, A^i_{12} and bounded by the curve l. We denote the domain occupied by the inclusion by S_i, the remaining domain by S_a, and introduce the notations

$$\overset{*}{\Delta}_{(a)}\boldsymbol{u}=(\overset{*}{\Delta}_{1\,(a)}\boldsymbol{u},\ \overset{*}{\Delta}_{2\,(a)}\boldsymbol{u}),$$

where

$$\overset{*}{\Delta}_{1\,(a)}\boldsymbol{u}=A_{11}^{a}\frac{\partial^2 u_1}{\partial x_1^2}+A_{33}^{a}\frac{\partial^2 u_1}{\partial x_2^2}+(A_{12}^{a}+A_{33}^{a})\frac{\partial^2 u_2}{\partial x_1\,\partial x_2},$$

$$\overset{*}{\Delta}_{2\,(a)}\boldsymbol{u}=A_{33}^{a}\frac{\partial^2 u_2}{\partial x_1^2}+A_{22}^{a}\frac{\partial^2 u_2}{\partial x_2^2}+(A_{12}^{a}+A_{33}^{a})\frac{\partial^2 u_1}{\partial x_1\,\partial x_2},$$

and

$$\overset{*}{\Delta}_{(i)}\boldsymbol{u}=(\overset{*}{\Delta}_{1\,(i)}\boldsymbol{u},\ \overset{*}{\Delta}_{2\,(i)}\boldsymbol{u}),$$

where

$$\overset{*}{\Delta}_{1\,(i)}\boldsymbol{u}=A_{11}^{i}\frac{\partial^2 u_1}{\partial x_1^2}+A_{33}^{i}\frac{\partial^2 u_1}{\partial x_2^2}+(A_{12}^{i}+A_{33}^{i})\frac{\partial^2 u_2}{\partial x_1\,\partial x_2},$$

$$\overset{*}{\Delta}_{2\,(i)}\boldsymbol{u}=A_{33}^{i}\frac{\partial^2 u_2}{\partial x_1^2}+A_{22}^{i}\frac{\partial^2 u_2}{\partial x_2^2}+(A_{12}^{i}+A_{33}^{i})\frac{\partial^2 u_1}{\partial x_1\,\partial x_2},$$

and further

$$\mathrm{T}^{(a)}\boldsymbol{u}=(\mathrm{T}_1^{(a)}\boldsymbol{u},\ \mathrm{T}_2^{(a)}\boldsymbol{u}),$$

where

$$\mathrm{T}_1^{(a)}\boldsymbol{u}=\left(A_{11}^{a}\frac{\partial u_1}{\partial x_1}+A_{12}^{a}\frac{\partial u_2}{\partial x_2}\right)\cos(\boldsymbol{n},\ \boldsymbol{x}_1)+A_{33}^{a}\left(\frac{\partial u_1}{\partial x_2}+\frac{\partial u_2}{\partial x_1}\right)\cos(\boldsymbol{n},\ \boldsymbol{x}_2),$$

$$\mathrm{T}_2^{(a)}\boldsymbol{u}=A_{33}^{a}\left(\frac{\partial u_1}{\partial x_2}+\frac{\partial u_2}{\partial x_1}\right)\cos(\boldsymbol{n},\ \boldsymbol{x}_1)+\left(A_{12}^{a}\frac{\partial u_1}{\partial x_1}+A_{22}^{a}\frac{\partial u_2}{\partial x_2}\right)\cos(\boldsymbol{n},\ \boldsymbol{x}_2)$$

and

$$\mathrm{T}^{(i)}\boldsymbol{u}=(\mathrm{T}_1^{(i)}\boldsymbol{u},\ \mathrm{T}_2^{(i)}\boldsymbol{u}),$$

where

$$\mathrm{T}_1^{(i)}\boldsymbol{u}=\left(A_{11}^{i}\frac{\partial u_1}{\partial x_1}+A_{12}^{i}\frac{\partial u_2}{\partial x_2}\right)\cos(\boldsymbol{n},\ \boldsymbol{x}_1)+A_{33}^{i}\left(\frac{\partial u_1}{\partial x_2}+\frac{\partial u_2}{\partial x_1}\right)\cos(\boldsymbol{n},\ \boldsymbol{x}_2),$$

$$\mathrm{T}_2^{(i)}\boldsymbol{u}=A_{33}^{i}\left(\frac{\partial u_1}{\partial x_2}+\frac{\partial u_2}{\partial x_1}\right)\cos(\boldsymbol{n},\ \boldsymbol{x}_1)+\left(A_{12}^{i}\frac{\partial u_1}{\partial x_1}+A_{22}^{i}\frac{\partial u_2}{\partial x_2}\right)\cos(\boldsymbol{n},\ \boldsymbol{x}_2).$$

Consider the following boundary-value problems.

It is required to find a regular vector function $\boldsymbol{u}(x)$ which satisfies the conditions:

1) for $x\in S_i$ $\overset{*}{\Delta}_{(i)}\boldsymbol{u}(x)=0$;

2) for $x\in S_a$ $\overset{*}{\Delta}_{(a)}\boldsymbol{u}(x)=0$;

3) for $x\in l$ $\boldsymbol{u}_i=\boldsymbol{u}_a$, $(\mathrm{T}^{(i)}\boldsymbol{u})_i=(\mathrm{T}^{(a)}\boldsymbol{u})_a$;

4) for $x_0\in l_a$ $\lim\limits_{x\to x_0}\boldsymbol{u}(x)=\boldsymbol{f}(x_0)$ $(\boldsymbol{f}(x_0)\in H(\gamma))$.

This is Problem (*A*) for a plane piecewise-homogeneous orthotropic body. Problem (*B*) consists in finding a regular vector function $\boldsymbol{u}(x)$ which satisfies the same first three conditions while the fourth is replaced by

$$\lim_{x\to x_0}\mathrm{T}^{(a)}\boldsymbol{u}(x)=\boldsymbol{f}(x_0),\qquad x_0\in l_a.$$

Let us first consider Problem (*A*) and reduce it to the equivalent integral equations. The domain bounded by the curve l_a will be denoted by S: $S=\overline{S}_i+S_a$. Let $G(x,\ y)$ be the static first Green's tensor for S and the equation $\Delta_a^* u = 0$

$$G(x, y) = \Gamma_{(a)}(x, y) - v(x, y),$$

where

$$\Gamma_{(a)}(x, y) = \operatorname{Im} \sum_{s=1}^{2} \begin{Vmatrix} A_s^a & B_s^a \\ B_s^a & C_s^a \end{Vmatrix} \ln \sigma_s,$$

and

$$\Delta_{(a)}^* v(x, y) = 0,$$

where $G^{(k)}$ denotes the k-th column of the matrix $G(x, y)$ $(k = 1, 2)$. We assume that Problem (A) has a solution $u(x)$. Applying formula (8.46) to $u(y)$ and $G^{(k)}(x, y)$, we obtain for $x \in S_l$

$$\int_{S_l - \tau(x;\,\varepsilon)} u(y)\, \Delta_{(l)}^* G^{(k)}(x, y)\, d\sigma_y =$$

$$= \int_{l + \bar{\tau}(x;\,\varepsilon)} [u(y)\, \mathrm{T}^{(l)} G^{(k)}(x, y) - G^{(k)}(x, y)(\mathrm{T}^{(l)} u(y))]\, dl, \tag{8.56}$$

where $\tau(x;\, \varepsilon)$ is a disk of radius ε, centered at x, and $\bar{\tau}(x;\, \varepsilon)$ is its circular boundary.

We have by definition

$$\begin{aligned} \Delta_{1\,(l)}^* G^{(k)} &= (A_{12}^l + A_{33}^l)\left(\frac{A_{11}^l}{A_{12}^l + A_{33}^l}\frac{\partial^2 G_1^{(k)}}{\partial y_1^2} + \frac{A_{33}^l}{A_{12}^l + A_{33}^l}\frac{\partial^2 G_1^{(k)}}{\partial y_2^2} + \frac{\partial^2 G_2^{(k)}}{\partial y_1\, \partial y_2}\right), \\ \Delta_{2\,(l)}^* G^{(k)} &= (A_{12}^l + A_{33}^l)\left(\frac{A_{33}^l}{A_{12}^l + A_{33}^l}\frac{\partial^2 G_2^{(k)}}{\partial y_1^2} + \frac{A_{22}^l}{A_{12}^l + A_{33}^l}\frac{\partial^2 G_2^{(k)}}{\partial y_2^2} + \frac{\partial^2 G_1^{(k)}}{\partial y_1\, \partial y_2}\right). \end{aligned} \tag{*}$$

On the other hand, since

$$\Delta_{(a)}^* G^{(k)} = 0,$$

we may write

$$\begin{aligned} \Delta_{1\,(a)}^* G^{(k)} &= (A_{12}^l + A_{33}^l)\left(\frac{A_{11}^a}{A_{12}^a + A_{33}^a}\frac{\partial^2 G_1^{(k)}}{\partial y_1^2} + \frac{A_{33}^a}{A_{12}^a + A_{33}^a}\frac{\partial^2 G_1^{(k)}}{\partial y_2^2} + \frac{\partial^2 G_2^{(k)}}{\partial y_1\, \partial y_2}\right) = 0, \\ \Delta_{2\,(a)}^* G^{(k)} &= (A_{12}^l + A_{33}^l)\left(\frac{A_{33}^a}{A_{12}^a + A_{33}^a}\frac{\partial^2 G_2^{(k)}}{\partial y_1^2} + \frac{A_{22}^a}{A_{12}^a + A_{33}^a}\frac{\partial^2 G_2^{(k)}}{\partial y_2^2} + \frac{\partial^2 G_1^{(k)}}{\partial y_1\, \partial y_2}\right) = 0. \end{aligned} \tag{**}$$

Subtracting (**) from (*), we get

$$\begin{aligned} \Delta_{1\,(l)}^* G^{(k)} &= (A_{12}^l + A_{33}^l)\left(\tau_1 \frac{\partial^2 G_1^{(k)}}{\partial y_1^2} + \tau_2 \frac{\partial^2 G_1^{(k)}}{\partial y_2^2}\right), \\ \Delta_{2\,(l)}^* G^{(k)} &= (A_{12}^l + A_{33}^l)\left(\tau_2 \frac{\partial^2 G_2^{(k)}}{\partial y_1^2} + \tau_3 \frac{\partial^2 G_2^{(k)}}{\partial y_2^2}\right), \end{aligned} \tag{8.57}$$

where

$$\tau_1 = \frac{A_{11}^l}{A_{12}^l + A_{33}^l} - \frac{A_{11}^a}{A_{12}^a + A_{33}^a}, \quad \tau_2 = \frac{A_{33}^l}{A_{12}^l + A_{33}^l} - \frac{A_{33}^a}{A_{12}^a + A_{33}^a},$$

$$\tau_3 = \frac{A_{22}^l}{A_{12}^l + A_{33}^l} - \frac{A_{22}^a}{A_{12}^a + A_{33}^a}.$$

We further have

$$\int_{\bar{\tau}(x;\,\varepsilon)} u(y)\, \mathrm{T}^{(l)} G^{(k)}(x, y)\, dl_y = \int_{\bar{\tau}(x;\,\varepsilon)} [u(y) - u(x)]\, \mathrm{T}^{(l)} G^{(k)}\, dl + u(x) \int_{\bar{\tau}(x;\,\varepsilon)} \mathrm{T}^{(l)} G^{(k)}(x, y)\, dl_y \tag{8.58}$$

and passing to the limit for $\varepsilon \to 0$,

$$\lim \int_{\tau(x;\,\varepsilon)} u(y)\, \mathrm{T}^{(i)} G^{(k)}(x,\, y)\, dl_y = \alpha_{kk}^{i,\,a} u_k(x), \tag{8.59}$$

where the $\alpha_{kk}^{i,\,a}$ $(k=1,\,2)$ are certain constants which may be easily calculated.
Passing to the limit in (8.56) for $\varepsilon \to 0$, we obtain in virtue of (8.59)*

$$\alpha_{kk}^{i,\,a} u_k(x) = \int_{S_i} u(y)\, \overset{*}{\Delta}_{(i)} G^{(k)}(x,\, y)\, d\sigma_y + \\ + \int_{l} [G^{(k)}(x,\, y)\, \mathrm{T}^{(i)} u(y) - u(y)\, \mathrm{T}^{(i)} G^{(k)}(x,\, y)]\, dl_y. \tag{8.60}$$

For $x \in S_i$, moreover,

$$\int_{S_a} \left(u(y)\, \overset{*}{\Delta}_{(a)} G^{(k)}(x,\, y) - G^{(k)}(x,\, y)\, \overset{*}{\Delta}_{(a)} u(y)\right) d\sigma_y = \\ = \int_{l+l_a} [u(y)\, \mathrm{T}^{(a)} G^{(k)}(x,\, y) - G^{(k)}_{x,\,y}\, \mathrm{T}^{(a)} u(y)]\, dl_y,$$

and since in S_a we have $\overset{*}{\Delta}_{(a)} G^{(k)} = 0$, $\overset{*}{\Delta}_{(a)} u = 0$ and $G^{(k)}(x,\, y) = 0$ for $y \in l_a$,

$$\int_{l} [u(y)\, \mathrm{T}^{(a)} G^{(k)}(x,\, y) - G^{(k)}(x,\, y)\, \mathrm{T}^{(a)} u(y)]\, dl + \\ + \int_{l_a} f(y)\, \mathrm{T}^{(a)} G^{(k)}(x,\, y)\, dl_y = 0.$$

Adding this relation to (8.60), and taking into account the boundary conditions on l,

$$u_i = u_a, \quad (\mathrm{T}^{(i)} u)_i = (\mathrm{T}^{(a)} u)_a,$$

we obtain

$$\alpha_{kk}^{ia} u_k(x) = \int_{S_i} u(y)\, \overset{*}{\Delta}_{(i)} G^{(k)}(x,\, y)\, d\sigma_y + \int_{l} u_i(y)\, \mathrm{T}^{*} G^{(k)}(x,\, y)\, dl_y + \\ + \int_{l_a} f(y)\, \mathrm{T}^{(a)} G^{(k)}(x,\, y)\, dl_y \quad (k=1,\, 2), \tag{8.61$_i$}$$

where $x \in S_i$, $\mathrm{T}^{*} = \mathrm{T}^{(a)} - \mathrm{T}^{(i)}$, and $f(x)$ is the value of $u(x)$ on l_a.
Let now $x \in S_a$; then, proceeding as before, we get instead of (8.56)

$$\int_{S_i} u(y)\, \overset{*}{\Delta}_{(i)} G^{(k)}(x,\, y)\, d\sigma_y = \int_{l} [u_i(y)\, \mathrm{T}^{(i)} G^{(k)}(x,\, y) - G^{(k)}(x,\, y)\, (\mathrm{T}^{(i)} u)]\, dl_y. \tag{8.62}$$

Finally, applying again formula (8.46) in S_a,

$$\alpha_{kk}^{a} u_k(x) = \int_{l+l_a} \left[u_a(y)\, \mathrm{T}^{(a)} G^{(k)}(x,\, y) - G^{(k)}(x,\, y) \left(\mathrm{T}^{(a)} u(y)\right)_a\right] \ (k=1,\, 2),$$

where the α_{kk}^{a} are certain easily calculable constants. The normal here points from S_i into S_a. Adding this equality to (8.62) and taking into account the conditions on l, we obtain

$$\alpha_{kk}^{a} u_k(x) = \int_{S_i} u(y)\, \overset{*}{\Delta}_{(i)} G^{(k)}(x,\, y)\, d\sigma_y + \int_{l} u_i(y)\, \mathrm{T}^{*} G^{(k)}(x,\, y)\, dl_y + \\ + \int_{l_a} f(y)\, \mathrm{T}^{(a)} G^{(k)}(x,\, y)\, dl_y \tag{8.61$_a$}$$

$$(k=1,\, 2) \quad (x \in S_a).$$

* The first integral in (8.60) is defined in the sense of the principal value; its existence follows from (I, 7).

We have thereby proved

Theorem 8. A regular solution of Problem (A) *for a piecewise-homogeneous orthotropic body solves the functional equations* (8.61_l), (8.61_a).

Substituting the expressions for $\Delta^*_{1(l)}G^{(k)}$ and $\Delta^*_{2(l)}G^{(k)}$ from (*), we obtain (8.61_l), (8.61_a) in the form

$$\alpha^{la}_{kk}u_k(x)=(A^l_{12}+A^l_{33})\int_{S_l}\Big[u_1(y)\Big(\tau_1\frac{\partial^2 G^{(k)}_1}{\partial y_1^2}+\tau_2\frac{\partial^2 G^{(k)}_1}{\partial y_2^2}\Big)+$$

$$+u_2(y)\Big(\tau_2\frac{\partial^2 G^{(k)}_2}{\partial y_1^2}+\tau_3\frac{\partial^2 G^{(k)}_2}{\partial y_2^2}\Big)\Big]d\sigma_y+\int_l \boldsymbol{u}_l(y)\,\mathrm{T}^*G^{(k)}(x,y)\,dl_y+$$

$$+\int_{l_a} \boldsymbol{f}(y)\,\mathrm{T}^{(a)}G^{(k)}(x,y)\,dl_y \qquad (x\in S_l), \tag{8.61$'_l$}$$

$$\alpha^{a}_{kk}u_k(x)=(A^l_{12}+A^l_{33})\int_{S_l}\Big[u_1(y)\Big(\tau_1\frac{\partial^2 G^{(k)}_1}{\partial y_1^2}+\tau_2\frac{\partial^2 G^{(k)}_1}{\partial y_2^2}\Big)+$$

$$+u_2(y)\Big(\tau_2\frac{\partial^2 G^{(k)}_2}{\partial y_1^2}+\tau_3\frac{\partial^2 G^{(k)}_2}{\partial y_2^2}\Big)\Big]d\sigma_y+\int_l \boldsymbol{u}_l(y)\,\mathrm{T}^*G^{(k)}(x,y)\,dl_y+$$

$$+\int_{l_a} \boldsymbol{f}(y)\,\mathrm{T}^{(a)}G^{(k)}(x,y)\,dl_y \qquad (x\in S_l). \tag{8.61$'_a$}$$

These equations are analogous to the corresponding equations, derived for Problem (B_1) of an isotropic body in the static case (Ch. IV); equations analogous to those obtained for isotropic bodies, may also be easily derived for the other problems considered in Ch. IV. We now give a short proof of the existence theorems for Problems (A) and (B).

Adding formulas (8.47) for the domains S_l and S_a, we obtain in virtue of the boundary conditions on l

$$\int_{S_l} E(\boldsymbol{u},\boldsymbol{u})\,d\sigma+\int_{S_a} E(\boldsymbol{u},\boldsymbol{u})\,d\sigma=\int_{l_a}\boldsymbol{u}\mathrm{T}\boldsymbol{u}\,dl. \tag{8.63}$$

Assuming that Problem (A) or (B) has two different solutions, and writing the identity (8.63) for their difference, $\boldsymbol{v}$, we obtain

$$\int_{S_l} E(\boldsymbol{v},\boldsymbol{v})\,d\sigma+\int_{S_a} E(\boldsymbol{v},\boldsymbol{v})\,d\sigma=0.$$

It follows that $\boldsymbol{v}$ is a rigid displacement in S_l as well as in S_a; for Problem (A) $\boldsymbol{v}=0$ on l_a and hence $\boldsymbol{v}=0$ everywhere in S_a*; but in that case $\boldsymbol{v}_l=\boldsymbol{v}_a=0$ on l so that $\boldsymbol{v}$ vanishes everywhere in S_l. We have thus proved

Theorem 9. For a piecewise-homogeneous orthotropic body the homogeneous Problem (A) *possesses a trivial solution, and the homogeneous Problem* (B) *— a solution expressed by a vector of rigid displacement.*

§ 8. The case of equal Poisson's ratios

If in equations $(8.61'_l)$ and $(8.61'_a)$

$$\tau_1=\tau_2=\tau_3=0, \tag{8.64}$$

* It is assumed that l_a contains three points which do not lie on a straight line.

then

$$\alpha_{kk}^{ia} u_k(x) = \int_l u_i(y)\, \mathsf{T}^* G^{(k)}(x, y)\, dl_y +$$

$$+ \int_{l_a} f(y)\, \mathsf{T}^{(a)} G^{(k)}(x, y)\, dl_y \qquad (x \in S_i), \qquad (8.64_i)$$

$$\alpha_{kk}^{a} u_k(x) = \int_l u_i(y)\, \mathsf{T}^* G^{(k)}(x, y)\, dl_y +$$

$$+ \int_{l_a} f(y)\, \mathsf{T}^{(a)} G^{(k)}(x, y)\, dl_y \quad (x \in S_a) \qquad (k = 1, 2). \qquad (8.64_a)$$

This may be called the case of equal Poisson's ratios. For isotropic bodies

$$A_{11} = A_{22} = \lambda + 2\mu, \qquad A_{12} = \lambda, \qquad A_{33} = \mu$$

and the conditions (8.64) are equivalent to

$$m = \lambda_i \mu_a - \lambda_a \mu_i = 0,$$

which in the isotropic case follows from the equality of Poisson's ratios; it thus stands to reason that the constants τ_1, τ_2, τ_3 play in this theory the same role as the constant m (a quantity proportional to the difference between the Poisson's ratios of adjoining media) plays in the theory of piecewise-homogeneous isotropic bodies.

Conditions (8.64) imply

$$\mathsf{T}^* G^{(k)} = \frac{A_{12}^a + A_{33}^a - A_{12}^l - A_{33}^l}{A_{12}^a + A_{33}^a} \mathsf{T}^{(a)} G^{(k)},$$

and also

$$\alpha_{11}^{al} = \alpha_{22}^{al}, \quad \alpha_{11}^{a} = \alpha_{22}^{a}.$$

Whence it follows that

$$\text{for } x \in S_i \ \ \Delta_{(i)}^* u(x) = 0; \quad \text{for } x \in S_a \ \ \Delta_{(a)}^* u(x) = 0. \qquad (8.65)$$

Let us write $(8.64_{i,a})$ in the form

$$\alpha_{kk}^{ia} u_k(x) - \frac{A_{12}^a + A_{33}^a - A_{12}^l - A_{33}^l}{A_{12}^a + A_{33}^a} \int_l u_i(y)\, \mathsf{T}^{(a)} G^{(k)}(x, y)\, d\sigma_y =$$

$$= \int_{l_a} f(y)\, \mathsf{T}^{(a)} G^{(k)}(x, y)\, d\sigma_y, \qquad x \in S_i, \qquad (8.64_i')$$

$$\alpha_{kk}^{a} u_k(x) - \frac{A_{12}^a + A_{33}^a - A_{12}^l - A_{33}^l}{A_{12}^a + A_{33}^a} \int_l u_i(y)\, \mathsf{T}^{(a)} G^{(k)}(x, y)\, d\sigma_y =$$

$$= \int_{l_a} f(y)\, \mathsf{T}^{(a)} G^{(k)}(x, y)\, d\sigma_y, \qquad x \in S_a, \qquad (8.64_a')$$

and pass to the limit for $x \to x_0 \in l$; we then obtain

$$\alpha_{kk}^{ia} (u_k(x_0))_i + \frac{\alpha_{kk}^a}{2} \frac{A_{12}^a + A_{33}^a - A_{12}^l - A_{33}^l}{A_{12}^a + A_{33}^a} (u_k(x_0))_i -$$

$$- \frac{A_{12}^a + A_{33}^a - A_{12}^l - A_{33}^l}{A_{12}^a + A_{33}^a} \int_l u_i(y)\, \mathsf{T}^{(a)} G^{(k)}(x_0, y)\, d\sigma_y =$$

$$= \int_{l_a} f(y)\, \mathsf{T}^{(a)} G^{(k)}(x_0, y)\, d\sigma_y,$$

$$\alpha_{kk}^{a}(u_k(x_0))_a-\frac{\alpha_{kk}^{a}}{2}\,\frac{A_{12}^{a}+A_{33}^{a}-A_{12}^{l}-A_{33}^{l}}{A_{12}^{a}+A_{33}^{a}}(u_k(x_0))_l-$$
$$-\frac{A_{12}^{a}+A_{33}^{a}-A_{12}^{l}-A_{33}^{l}}{A_{12}^{a}+A_{33}^{a}}\int_{l}u_i(y)\,\mathrm{T}^{(a)}G^{(k)}\,d\sigma_y=\int_{l_a}f(y)\,\mathrm{T}^{(a)}G^{(k)}(x_0,y)\,d\sigma_y.$$

Taking the difference of these expressions, we get

$$\left(\alpha_{kk}^{la}+\alpha_{kk}^{a}\frac{A_{12}^{a}+A_{33}^{a}-A_{12}^{l}-A_{33}^{l}}{A_{12}^{a}+A_{33}^{a}}\right)(u_k(x_0))_l-\alpha_{kk}^{a}(u_k(x_0))_a=0.$$

But conditions (8.64) imply

$$\alpha_{kk}^{la}=\frac{A_{12}^{l}+A_{33}^{l}}{A_{12}^{a}+A_{33}^{a}}\alpha_{kk}^{a},$$

and hence

$$\alpha_{kk}^{la}+\alpha_{kk}^{a}\frac{A_{12}^{a}+A_{33}^{a}-A_{12}^{l}-A_{33}^{l}}{A_{12}^{a}+A_{33}^{a}}=\alpha_{kk}^{a}$$

and

$$\alpha_{kk}^{a}\{(u_k(x_0))_l-(u_k(x_0))_a\}=0;$$

finally, since $\alpha_{kk}^{a}\neq 0$,

$$(u_k(x_0))_l=(u_k(x_0))_a\qquad(k=1,\ 2),$$

i. e.,

$$u_l=u_a \text{ on } l. \tag{8.66}$$

Applying $\mathrm{T}^{(a)}$ to the equalities ($8.64'_l$) and ($8.64'_a$), subtracting the results, and passing to the limit for $x\to x_0\in l$ (in the first equality from the inside of the domain, and in the second from the outside), we find again in view of the Lyapunov-Tauber theorem

$$\alpha^{la}(\mathrm{T}^{(a)}u(x))_l-\alpha^{a}(\mathrm{T}^{(a)}u(x))_a=0, \tag{8.67}$$

where α^{la} is the matrix

$$\alpha^{la}=\begin{Vmatrix}\alpha_{11}^{la} & 0\\ 0 & \alpha_{22}^{la}\end{Vmatrix},$$

and α^{a} is the matrix

$$\alpha^{a}=\begin{Vmatrix}\alpha_{11}^{a} & 0\\ 0 & \alpha_{22}^{a}\end{Vmatrix}.$$

But (8.64) implies

$$\mathrm{T}^{(a)}u(x)=\frac{A_{12}^{a}+A_{33}^{a}}{A_{12}^{l}+A_{33}^{l}}\mathrm{T}^{(l)}u(x),$$

and since

$$\alpha_{kk}^{a}=\frac{A_{12}^{a}+A_{33}^{a}}{A_{12}^{l}+A_{33}^{l}}\alpha_{kk}^{la}\qquad(k=1,\ 2),$$

we now obtain from (8.67)

$$\alpha^{a}\left[(\mathrm{T}^{(l)}u(x))_l-(\mathrm{T}^{(a)}u(x))_a\right]=0;$$

which gives, seeing that $\alpha_{kk}^{a}\neq 0$,

$$(\mathrm{T}^{(l)}u(x))_l=(\mathrm{T}^{(a)}u(x))_a. \tag{8.68}$$

Finally, when x approaches the point x_0 on l_a, we obtain in view of the properties of the Green's tensor,

$$\lim_{x \to x_0 \in l_a} u(x) = f(x_0). \tag{8.69}$$

The relations (8.65), (8.66), (8.67), (8.69) show that a solution of equations ($8.64'_{i,a}$) actually is a solution of the equilibrium Problem (A) for a piece-wise-homogeneous orthotropic body.

We shall now prove the existence theorem for equations ($8.64'_{i,a}$). We first note that the foregoing and the uniqueness theorem for Problem (A) (Theorem 9) imply that the homogeneous equations corresponding to ($8.64'_{i,a}$) may only have trivial solutions. As for the solution of the system ($8.64'_{i,a}$), we remark that for $x_0 \in l$ one obtains from ($8.64'_i$), upon passing to the limit from the inside,

$$\frac{\alpha^a_{kk}}{2}\frac{A^a_{12}+A^a_{33}+A^l_{12}+A^l_{33}}{A^a_{12}+A^a_{33}}u_k -$$
$$-\frac{A^a_{12}+A^a_{33}-A^l_{12}-A^l_{33}}{A^a_{12}+A^a_{33}}\int_l u_i(y)\,\mathrm{T}^{(a)}G^{(k)}(x_0,\ y)\,d\sigma_y =$$
$$= \int_{l_a} f(y)\,\mathrm{T}^{(a)}G^{(k)}(x_0,\ y)\,d\sigma_y \ \ldots \tag{8.70}$$

This is a singular system of integral equations of the same type as was met in § 6; and its index may be shown to vanish in exactly the same way. Consequently the Fredholm alternative is valid. It remains to show that the homogeneous equation corresponding to (8.70) has only a trivial solution. To see this, we assume the opposite and let $u^*_i(x_0)$ be a nontrivial solution. Consider the vectors

$$\alpha^{la}_{kk}v_k(x) = \frac{A^a_{12}+A^a_{33}-A^l_{12}-A^l_{33}}{A^a_{12}+A^a_{33}}\int_l u^*_i(y)\,\mathrm{T}^{(a)}G^{(k)}(x,\ y)\,d\sigma_y, \quad x \in S_l,$$

$$\alpha^{a}_{kk}v_k(x) = \frac{A^a_{12}+A^a_{33}-A^l_{12}-A^l_{33}}{A^a_{12}+A^a_{33}}\int_l u^*_i(y)\,\mathrm{T}^{(a)}G^{(k)}(x,\ y)\,d\sigma_y, \quad x \in S_a.$$

Passing to the inner limit, we obtain

$$\alpha^{la}(v(x_0))_i = -\frac{\alpha^a}{2}\frac{A^a_{12}+A^a_{33}-A^l_{12}-A^l_{33}}{A^a_{12}+A^a_{33}}u^*_i(x_0) +$$
$$+\frac{A^a_{12}+A^a_{33}-A^l_{12}-A^l_{33}}{A^a_{12}+A^a_{33}}\int_l u^*_i(y)\,\mathrm{T}^{(a)}G^{(k)}(x_0,\ y)\,d\sigma_y = \alpha^{la}u^*_i(x_0).$$

Introducing now the vector

$$u^*(x) = v(x), \quad x \in S_l \text{ and } x \in S_a,$$

we get

$$\alpha^{la}_{kk}u^*_k(x) - \frac{A^a_{12}+A^a_{33}-A^l_{12}-A^l_{33}}{A^a_{12}+A^a_{33}}\int_l u^*_i(y)\,\mathrm{T}^{(a)}G^{(k)}(x,\ y)\,d\sigma_y = 0, \ x \in S_l,$$

$$\alpha^{a}_{kk}u^*_k(x) - \frac{A^a_{12}+A^a_{33}-A^l_{12}-A^l_{33}}{A^a_{12}+A^a_{33}}\int_l u^*_i(y)\,\mathrm{T}^{(a)}G^{(k)}(x,\ y)\,d\sigma_y = 0, \ x \in S_a.$$

But this is the homogeneous system corresponding to ($8.64'_{l,a}$), which by the uniqueness theorem can only have a trivial solution; consequently

$$u^*(x_0) \equiv 0 \text{ on } l,$$

and the solvability of the inhomogeneous system (8.70) follows on account of the Fredholm alternative; this completes the proof of the existence theorem for Problem (*A*) in the case of a piecewise-homogeneous orthotropic body with equal Poisson ratios. Zh. A. Rukhadze has investigated Problem (*A*) in the general case and proved the existence theorem for small values of the parameters τ_1, τ_2, τ_3 /27/.

T. V. Burchuladze /2a, b, c, d/ has studied the most general case of equations with constant coefficients for two independent variables and the associated boundary-value problems by methods of potential theory and integral equations. He also obtained /2e, f/ asymptotic estimates for the eigenfunctions of some boundary-value problems.

Chapter IX

SOLUTIONS OF SOME PARTICULAR PROBLEMS

The method of potentials is applied in this chapter to several particular cases which may be solved explicitly. Some of these problems (§§ 8–11) have as yet not been solved explicitly by other methods.

§ 1. Circular isotropic plate

Consider the second boundary-value problem. Let the origin be placed at the center of the disk. Let R be the disk radius, $r(x, y)=\sqrt{(x_1-y_1)^2+(x_2-y_2)^2}$, and let the outward normal be taken positive. We denote the circular contour by s, and its element by ds. We are looking for a solution of this problem in the form of a single-layer potential (of the first kind):

$$u(x)=\frac{1}{\pi}\int_s \Gamma(x, y)\varphi(y)\,ds_y, \tag{9.1}$$

$$\Gamma(x, y)=\left\|\begin{matrix} n\ln r-m\left(\frac{\partial r}{\partial x_1}\right)^2 & -m\frac{\partial r}{\partial x_1}\frac{\partial r}{\partial x_2} \\ -m\frac{\partial r}{\partial x_1}\frac{\partial r}{\partial x_2} & n\ln r-m\left(\frac{\partial r}{\partial x_2}\right)^2 \end{matrix}\right\|, \tag{9.2}$$

$$n=\frac{\lambda+3\mu}{2\mu(\lambda+2\mu)}, \qquad m=\frac{\lambda+\mu}{2\mu(\lambda+2\mu)}. \tag{9.3}$$

Applying T_x to (9.2), we obtain

$$\mathrm{T}_x\Gamma(x, y)=\left\|\begin{matrix} a\frac{\partial}{\partial n_x}\ln r+2b\left(\frac{\partial r}{\partial x_1}\right)^2\frac{\partial}{\partial n_x}\ln r & -a\frac{\partial}{\partial s_x}\ln r+2b\frac{\partial r}{\partial x_1}\frac{\partial r}{\partial x_2}\frac{\partial}{\partial n_x}\ln r \\ a\frac{\partial}{\partial s_x}\ln r+2b\frac{\partial r}{\partial x_1}\frac{\partial r}{\partial x_2}\frac{\partial}{\partial n_x}\ln r & a\frac{\partial}{\partial n_x}\ln r+2b\left(\frac{\partial r}{\partial x_2}\right)^2\frac{\partial}{\partial n_x}\ln r \end{matrix}\right\|, \tag{9.4}$$

where

$$a=\frac{\mu}{\lambda+2\mu}, \qquad b=\frac{\lambda+\mu}{\lambda+2\mu},$$

$$\begin{aligned} \frac{\partial}{\partial n_x}&=\frac{\partial}{\partial x_1}\cos(n_x, x_1)+\frac{\partial}{\partial x_2}\cos(n_x, x_2), \\ \frac{\partial}{\partial s_x}&=\frac{\partial}{\partial x_2}\cos(n_x, x_1)-\frac{\partial}{\partial x_1}\cos(n_x, x_2). \end{aligned} \tag{9.5}$$

Passing to the limit for $x\to x_0$, where x_0 lies on the circumference, we obtain from (8.36) the following singular integral equation for $\varphi(y)$:

$$-\varphi(x_0)+\frac{1}{\pi}\int_s \mathrm{T}_{x_0}\Gamma(x_0, y)\varphi(y)\,ds_y=f(x_0), \tag{9.6}$$

where $f(x_0)$ is the prescribed traction on the circumference; we assume that $f(x)$ belongs to class H. Let us derive an expression for $\mathrm{T}_{x_0}\Gamma(x_0, y)$. Transforming to polar coordinates, we get

$$\frac{\partial}{\partial x_0}\ln r(x_0, y)\,ds_y = \frac{1}{2}\,d\theta, \quad \frac{\partial}{\partial s_{x_0}}\ln(x_0, y)\,ds_y = -\frac{1}{2}\operatorname{ctg}\frac{\theta-\theta_0}{2}\,d\theta,$$

$$\left(\frac{\partial r}{\partial x_1}\right)^2 = \frac{1}{2}[1-\cos(\theta+\theta_0)], \quad \frac{\partial r}{\partial x_1}\frac{\partial r}{\partial x_2} = -\frac{1}{2}\sin(\theta+\theta_0),$$

$$\left(\frac{\partial r}{\partial x_2}\right)^2 = \frac{1}{2}[1+\cos(\theta+\theta_0)].$$

Remembering that $a+b=1$, we hence obtain

$$\mathrm{T}_{x_0}\Gamma(x_0, y)\,ds_y = \frac{1}{2}\left\|\begin{matrix} 1-b\cos(\theta+\theta_0) & a\operatorname{ctg}\frac{\theta-\theta_0}{2}-b\sin(\theta+\theta_0) \\ -a\operatorname{ctg}\frac{\theta-\theta_0}{2}-b\sin(\theta+\theta_0) & 1+b\cos(\theta+\theta_0)\end{matrix}\right\| d\theta. \quad (9.7)$$

Let us introduce the notations

$$\left.\begin{aligned} &\alpha = \frac{1}{2\pi}\int_0^{2\pi}\varphi(\theta)\,d\theta, \quad \beta = \frac{1}{2\pi}\int_0^{2\pi}\varphi(\theta)\cos\theta\,d\theta, \quad \gamma = \frac{1}{2\pi}\int_0^{2\pi}\varphi(\theta)\sin\theta\,d\theta, \\ &I_1 = \left\|\begin{matrix}0 & 1\\ -1 & 0\end{matrix}\right\|, \quad A(\theta_0) = \left\|\begin{matrix}\cos\theta_0 & \sin\theta_0\\ \sin\theta_0 & -\cos\theta_0\end{matrix}\right\|, \quad B(\theta_0) = \left\|\begin{matrix}-\sin\theta_0 & \cos\theta_0\\ \cos\theta_0 & \sin\theta_0\end{matrix}\right\|. \end{aligned}\right\} \quad (9.8)$$

In virtue of (9.7) and (9.8), the system of integral equations (9.6) takes the form

$$\mathrm{K}\varphi \equiv -\varphi(\theta_0) + \frac{a}{2\pi}I_1\int_0^{2\pi}\operatorname{ctg}\frac{\theta-\theta_0}{2}\varphi(\theta)\,d\theta + \alpha - bA(\theta_0)\beta - bB(\theta_0)\gamma = f(\theta_0), \quad (9.9)$$

where evidently

$$\varphi(y) \equiv \varphi(R, \theta) \equiv \varphi(\theta), \quad f(x_0) \equiv f(\theta_0).$$

Consider the regularizing operator

$$\mathrm{M}\psi \equiv -\psi(\theta_0) - \frac{a}{2\pi}I_1\int_0^{2\pi}\operatorname{ctg}\frac{\theta-\theta_0}{2}\psi(\theta)\,d\theta. \quad (9.10)$$

Applying the known formulas

$$\left.\begin{aligned} &\int_0^{2\pi}\operatorname{ctg}\frac{\theta-\theta_0}{2}\,d\theta = 0, \\ &-\frac{1}{(2\pi)^2}\int_0^{2\pi}\operatorname{ctg}\frac{\theta-\theta_0}{2}\,d\theta\int_0^{2\pi}\operatorname{ctg}\frac{\theta'-\theta}{2}\varphi(\theta')\,d\theta' = \varphi(\theta_0) - \alpha, \\ &I_1^2 = -\left\|\begin{matrix}1 & 0\\ 0 & 1\end{matrix}\right\| = -I, \\ &\frac{1}{2\pi}\int_0^{2\pi}A(\theta)\operatorname{ctg}\frac{\theta-\theta_0}{2}\,d\theta = B(\theta_0), \quad \frac{1}{2\pi}\int_0^{2\pi}B(\theta)\operatorname{ctg}\frac{\theta-\theta_0}{2}\,d\theta = -A(\theta_0), \end{aligned}\right. \quad (9.11)$$

we obtain, after applying M to $\mathrm{K}\varphi$ and simplifying the result,

$$\mathrm{MK}\varphi \equiv (1-a^2)\varphi(\theta_0) - (1-a^2)\alpha + b(1+a)A(\theta_0)\beta + b(1+a)B(\theta_0)\gamma = \mathrm{M}f(\theta_0),$$

which, since $b = 1-a$, becomes

$$\varphi(\theta_0) - \alpha + A(\theta_0)\beta + B(\theta_0)\gamma = \frac{1}{1-a^2}\mathrm{M}f(\theta_0). \quad (9.12)$$

Multiplying successively (9.12) by the factors $\frac{1}{2\pi}d\theta_0$, $\frac{1}{2\pi}\cos\theta_0\,d\theta_0$, $\frac{1}{2\pi}\sin\theta_0\,d\theta_0$ and integrating over the interval $(0, 2\pi)$, we obtain in the notation of (9.8)

$$\alpha - \alpha = \frac{1}{2\pi(1-a^2)} \int_0^{2\pi} \mathbf{M}f(\theta)\, d\theta, \tag{9.13}$$

$$\beta + \frac{1}{2}\begin{Vmatrix}1 & 0\\ 0 & -1\end{Vmatrix}\beta + \frac{1}{2}\begin{Vmatrix}0 & 1\\ 1 & 0\end{Vmatrix}\gamma = \frac{1}{2\pi(1-a^2)} \int_0^{2\pi} \mathbf{M}f(\theta)\cos\theta\, d\theta,$$

$$\gamma + \frac{1}{2}\begin{Vmatrix}0 & 1\\ 1 & 0\end{Vmatrix}\beta + \frac{1}{2}\begin{Vmatrix}-1 & 0\\ 0 & 1\end{Vmatrix}\gamma = \frac{1}{2\pi(1-a^2)} \int_0^{2\pi} \mathbf{M}f(\theta)\sin\theta\, d\theta. \tag{9.14}$$

But, as may be easily verified $\left(\text{using the fact that } \int_0^{2\pi} \operatorname{ctg}\frac{\theta-\theta'}{2}\, d\theta' = 0\right)$

$$\int_0^{2\pi} \mathbf{M}f(\theta)\, d\theta = -\int_0^{2\pi} f(\theta)\, d\theta.$$

Now (9.13) shows that

$$\int_0^{2\pi} f(\theta)\, d\theta = 0, \tag{9.15}$$

which simply means that the net external force vanishes; thus, if this condition is satisfied, the vector α is determined by (9.13) (it turns out to be an arbitrary constant).

We write out (9.14) in terms of its components as

$$3\beta_1 + \gamma_2 = \frac{1}{\pi(1-a^2)} \int_0^{2\pi} (\mathbf{M}f(\theta))_1 \cos\theta\, d\theta,$$

$$\beta_1 + 3\gamma_2 = \frac{1}{\pi(1-a^2)} \int_0^{2\pi} (\mathbf{M}f(\theta))_2 \sin\theta\, d\theta, \tag{9.16}$$

$$\beta_2 + \gamma_1 = \frac{1}{\pi(1-a^2)} \int_0^{2\pi} (\mathbf{M}f(\theta))_2 \cos\theta\, d\theta,$$

$$\beta_2 + \gamma_1 = \frac{1}{\pi(1-a^2)} \int_0^{2\pi} (\mathbf{M}f(\theta))_1 \sin\theta\, d\theta, \tag{9.17}$$

The determinant of the system (9.16) is not zero, and β_1 and γ_2 are uniquely determined. We shall need below the value of $\beta_1+\gamma_2$, for which (9.16) gives

$$\beta_1 + \gamma_2 = \frac{1}{4\pi(1-a^2)} \int_0^{2\pi} [(\mathbf{M}f)_1 \cos\theta + (\mathbf{M}f)_2 \cos\theta]\, d\theta. \tag{9.18}$$

The condition

$$\int_0^{2\pi} (\mathbf{M}f)_2 \cos\theta\, d\theta - \int_0^{2\pi} (\mathbf{M}f)_1 \sin\theta\, d\theta = 0$$

must be satisfied in order that $\beta_2+\gamma_1$ can be determined from (9.17). It may be verified easily that

$$\int_0^{2\pi} [(\mathbf{M}f)_2 \cos\theta - (\mathbf{M}f)_1 \sin\theta]\, d\theta = (1+a) \int_0^{2\pi} (f_2(\theta)\cos\theta - f_1(\theta)\sin\theta)\, d\theta.$$

Since $1+a \neq 0$, we arrive at the condition

$$\int_0^{2\pi} [f_2(\theta)\cos\theta - f_1(\theta)\sin\theta]\, d\theta = 0. \tag{9.19}$$

This is simply the condition that the resultant moment of the external forces must vanish. Therefore, the sum $\beta_2+\gamma_1$ is determined by (9.17) whenever this condition is fulfilled.

We can now write (9.12) in the form

$$\varphi(\theta_0)=\frac{1}{-a^2+1}\mathbf{M}f(\theta_0)+\alpha-\begin{pmatrix}\cos\theta_0\\ \sin\theta_0\end{pmatrix}(\beta_1+\gamma_2)-\begin{pmatrix}\sin\theta_0\\ -\cos\theta_0\end{pmatrix}(\beta_2-\gamma_1), \tag{9.20}$$

where $\beta_1+\gamma_2$ is given by (9.18), α is an arbitrary constant vector, and $(\beta_2-\gamma_1)$ is chosen consistently with (9.17). The relation (9.20) represents the general solution of the system (9.6), and in order to solve the problem it only remains to insert the obtained expression for $\varphi(y)$ into the formula of the single-layer potential (9.1); the solution is of the form

$$u(x)=\frac{R}{\pi}\int_0^{2\pi}\Gamma(\rho,\ \theta;\ R,\ \theta')\Big[\frac{1}{-a^2+1}\mathbf{M}f(\theta')-$$
$$-\begin{pmatrix}\cos\theta'\\ \sin\theta'\end{pmatrix}(\beta_1+\gamma_2)-\begin{pmatrix}\sin\theta'\\ -\cos\theta'\end{pmatrix}(\beta_2-\gamma_1)+\alpha\Big]d\theta'. \tag{9.21}$$

Here ρ, θ are the polar coordinates of the point x. The last expression may be simplified.

Simple calculations show that

$$\frac{1}{\pi}\int_0^{2\pi}\Gamma(\rho,\ \theta;\ R,\ \theta')\,d\theta'=2\begin{Vmatrix}n\ln R-\frac{m}{2} & 0\\ 0 & n\ln R-\frac{m}{2}\end{Vmatrix},$$
$$\frac{1}{\pi}\int_0^{2\pi}\Gamma(\rho,\ \theta;\ R,\ \theta')\begin{pmatrix}\sin\theta'\\ -\cos\theta'\end{pmatrix}d\theta'=-\frac{1}{\mu R}\begin{pmatrix}+x_2\\ -x_1\end{pmatrix}, \tag{9.22}$$
$$\frac{1}{\pi}\int_0^{2\pi}\Gamma(\rho,\ \theta;\ R,\ \theta')\begin{pmatrix}\cos\theta'\\ \sin\theta'\end{pmatrix}d\theta'=-\frac{1}{(\lambda+2\mu)R}\begin{pmatrix}x_1\\ x_2\end{pmatrix}.$$

Using these formulas, we transform (9.21) to

$$u(x)=\frac{R}{\pi(-a^2+1)}\int_0^{2\pi}\Gamma(\rho,\ \theta;\ R,\ \theta')\,\mathbf{M}f(\theta')\,d\theta'+$$
$$+\frac{1}{\lambda+2\mu}\begin{pmatrix}x_1\\ x_2\end{pmatrix}(\beta_1+\gamma_2)+\frac{1}{\mu}\begin{pmatrix}x_2\\ -x_1\end{pmatrix}(\beta_2-\gamma_1)-$$
$$-\begin{Vmatrix}2n\ln R-m & 0\\ 0 & 2n\ln R-m\end{Vmatrix}R\alpha.$$

The last two terms in this expression represent rigid displacements, and since by Theorem 7 of (VIII,5) our problem is uniquely solvable up to an additive displacement, we may now drop them, remaining with

$$u(x)=\frac{R}{\pi(a^2-1)}\int_0^{2\pi}\Gamma(\rho,\ \theta;\ R,\ \theta')\,\mathbf{M}f(\theta')\,d\theta+\frac{1}{\lambda+2\mu}\begin{pmatrix}x_1\\ x_2\end{pmatrix}(\beta_1+\gamma_2). \tag{9.23}$$

For a further simplification of this expression, it is necessary to calculate the integral

$$\frac{1}{2\pi}\int_0^{2\pi}\Gamma(\rho,\ \theta;\ R,\ \theta')\operatorname{ctg}\frac{\theta'-\psi}{2}\,d\theta'.$$

This may be done by means of the known relations

$$\frac{1}{\pi}\int_0^{2\pi}\ln r(x,\ y)\operatorname{ctg}\frac{\theta'-\psi'}{2}\,d\theta'=\operatorname{arctg}\frac{x_2-y_2}{x_1-y_1}-\psi'=\psi-\psi',$$

where

$$\psi=\operatorname{arctg}\frac{x_2-y_2}{x_1-y_1},$$

R and ψ' being the polar coordinates of the point $y \in s$, and

$$\frac{1}{2\pi}\int_0^{2\pi}\left(\frac{\partial r(x, y)}{\partial x_1}\right)^2 \operatorname{ctg}\frac{\theta'-\psi'}{2}\,d\theta' = -\frac{\partial r(x, y)}{\partial x_1}\frac{\partial r(x, y)}{\partial x_2},$$

$$\frac{1}{2\pi}\int_0^{2\pi}\frac{\partial r(x, y)}{\partial x_1}\frac{\partial r(x, y)}{\partial x_2}\operatorname{ctg}\frac{\theta'-\psi'}{2}\,d\theta' = \left(\frac{\partial r(x, y)}{\partial x_1}\right)^2 - \frac{1}{2}.$$

$$\frac{1}{2\pi}\int_0^{2\pi}\left(\frac{\partial r(x, y)}{\partial x_2}\right)^2 \operatorname{ctg}\frac{\theta'-\psi'}{2}\,d\theta' = \frac{\partial r(x, y)}{\partial x_1}\frac{\partial r(x, y)}{\partial x_2}.$$

From these equalities it follows that

$$\frac{1}{2\pi}\int_0^{2\pi}\Gamma(\rho, \theta; R, \theta')\operatorname{ctg}\frac{\theta'-\psi'}{2}\,d\theta' =$$

$$= \left\| \begin{matrix} n(\psi-\psi') + m\dfrac{\partial r}{\partial x_1}\dfrac{\partial r}{\partial x_2} & -m\left[\left(\dfrac{\partial r}{\partial x_1}\right)^2 - \dfrac{1}{2}\right] \\ -m\left[\left(\dfrac{\partial r}{\partial x_1}\right)^2 - \dfrac{1}{2}\right] & n(\psi-\psi') - m\dfrac{\partial r}{\partial x_1}\dfrac{\partial r}{\partial x_2} \end{matrix} \right\|, \tag{9.24}$$

whence

$$\frac{1}{2\pi}\int_0^{2\pi}\Gamma(\rho, \theta; R, \theta')\operatorname{ctg}\frac{\theta'-\psi'}{2}\,d\theta' \cdot \left\|\begin{matrix} 0 & 1 \\ -1 & 0 \end{matrix}\right\| =$$

$$= \left\| \begin{matrix} m\left[\left(\dfrac{\partial r}{\partial x_1}\right)^2 - \dfrac{1}{2}\right] & n(\psi-\psi') + m\dfrac{\partial r}{\partial x_1}\dfrac{\partial r}{\partial x_2} \\ -n(\psi-\psi') + m\dfrac{\partial r}{\partial x_1}\dfrac{\partial r}{\partial x_2} & m\left[\left(\dfrac{\partial r}{\partial x_2}\right)^2 - \dfrac{1}{2}\right] \end{matrix} \right\|$$

Using the last results, we obtain

$$\int_0^{2\pi}\frac{1}{2\pi}\int_0^{2\pi}\Gamma(\rho, \theta; R, \theta')\operatorname{ctg}\frac{\theta'-\psi'}{2}\left\|\begin{matrix} 0 & 1 \\ -1 & 0 \end{matrix}\right\| f(\psi')\,d\theta'\,d\psi' =$$

$$= -\int_0^{2\pi}\left\| \begin{matrix} -m\left[\left(\dfrac{\partial r}{\partial x_1}\right)^2 - \dfrac{1}{2}\right] & -n(\psi-\theta') - m\dfrac{\partial r}{\partial x_1}\dfrac{\partial r}{\partial x_2} \\ n(\psi-\theta') - m\dfrac{\partial r}{\partial x_1}\dfrac{\partial r}{\partial x_2} & -m\left[\left(\dfrac{\partial r}{\partial x_2}\right)^2 - \dfrac{1}{2}\right] \end{matrix} \right\| f(\theta')\,d\theta, \tag{9.25}$$

where $r = \sqrt{(x_1-y_1)^2 + (x_2-y_2)^2}$. Let us now write (9.23) in the form

$$u(x) = \frac{R}{\pi(a^2-1)}\int_0^{2\pi}\Gamma(\rho, \theta; R, \theta')f(\theta')\,d\theta -$$

$$-\frac{R}{\pi(a^2-1)}\frac{a}{2\pi}\int_0^{2\pi}\int_0^{2\pi}\Gamma(\rho, \theta; R, \theta')\operatorname{ctg}\frac{\theta'-\psi'}{2}\left\|\begin{matrix} 0 & 1 \\ -1 & 0 \end{matrix}\right\| f(\psi')\,d\theta'\,d\psi' +$$

$$+\frac{1}{\lambda+2\mu}\begin{pmatrix} x_1 \\ x_2 \end{pmatrix}(\beta_1+\gamma_2).$$

Applying (9.25) and performing some simple manipulations, we obtain

$$u(x) = -\frac{R}{\pi(1-a^2)}\times$$

$$\times\int_0^{\pi}\left\| \begin{matrix} n\ln r - (1+a)m\left(\dfrac{\partial r}{\partial x_1}\right)^2 + \dfrac{am}{2} & na(\theta'-\psi) - (1+a)m\dfrac{\partial r}{\partial x_1}\dfrac{\partial r}{\partial x_2} \\ na(\psi-\theta') - (1+a)m\dfrac{\partial r}{\partial x_1}\dfrac{\partial r}{\partial x_2} & n\ln r - (1+a)m\left(\dfrac{\partial r}{\partial x_2}\right)^2 + \dfrac{am}{2} \end{matrix} \right\|\times$$

$$\times f(\theta')\,d\theta' + \frac{1}{\lambda+2\mu}\begin{pmatrix} x_1 \\ x_2 \end{pmatrix}(\beta_1+\gamma_2). \tag{9.25'}$$

Noting that

$$\frac{n}{1-a^2}=\frac{\lambda+2\mu}{2\mu(\lambda+\mu)}, \qquad \frac{(1+a)m}{1-a^2}=\frac{1}{2\mu}, \qquad \frac{na}{1-a^2}=\frac{1}{2(\lambda+\mu)},$$

$$\frac{1}{\lambda+2\mu}(\beta_1+\gamma_2)=-\frac{1}{4\pi(\lambda+\mu)}\int_0^{2\pi}(f_1\cos\theta'+f_2\sin\theta')\,d\theta',$$

and dropping again a rigid displacement vector, we obtain from (9.25')

$$\boldsymbol{u}(x)=-\frac{1}{\pi}\int_S [M(x, y)+A(x, y)]\boldsymbol{f}(y)\,ds_y; \tag{9.26}$$

here

$$M(x, y)=\left\|\begin{matrix} \frac{\lambda+2\mu}{2\mu(\lambda+\mu)}\ln r-\frac{1}{2\mu}\left(\frac{\partial r}{\partial x_1}\right)^2 & -\frac{1}{2(\lambda+\mu)}\psi-\frac{1}{2\mu}\frac{\partial r}{\partial x_1}\frac{\partial r}{\partial x_2} \\ \frac{1}{2(\lambda+\mu)}\psi-\frac{1}{2\mu}\frac{\partial r}{\partial x_1}\frac{\partial r}{\partial x_2} & \frac{\lambda+2\mu}{2\mu(\lambda+\mu)}\ln r-\frac{1}{2\mu}\left(\frac{\partial r}{\partial x_2}\right)^2 \end{matrix}\right\| \tag{9.27}$$

and

$$A(x, y)=\frac{1}{4R^2(\lambda+\mu)}\left\|\begin{matrix} x_1y_1 & x_1y_2 \\ x_2y_1 & x_2y_2 \end{matrix}\right\|.$$

The above treatment is due to M. O. Basheleishvili.

The same method was also used earlier by N. S. Kakhniashvili to solve a somewhat simpler first problem for the circle. Cf. also /1c, d/.

§ 2. Infinite isotropic plane with a circular aperture

Consider the second problem. We are looking for a solution in the form of a single-layer potential (of the first kind)

$$\boldsymbol{u}(x)=\frac{1}{\pi}\int_S \Gamma(x, y)\,\boldsymbol{\varphi}(y)\,ds_y. \tag{9.28}$$

Using (8.36), we obtain

$$\boldsymbol{\varphi}(x_0)+\frac{1}{\pi}\int_S (\mathrm{T}_{x_0}\Gamma(x_0, y))\,\boldsymbol{\varphi}(y)\,ds_y=\boldsymbol{f}(x_0). \tag{9.29}$$

Repeating the arguments of the preceding section, we bring (9.29) to the form

$$\mathbf{K}\boldsymbol{\varphi}=\boldsymbol{\varphi}(x_0)+\frac{a}{2\pi}I_1\int_0^{2\pi}\operatorname{ctg}\frac{\theta-\theta_0}{2}\boldsymbol{\varphi}(\theta)\,d\theta+\alpha-bA(\theta_0)\beta-bB(\theta_0)\gamma=\boldsymbol{f}(x_0). \tag{9.30}$$

Applying the regularizing operator

$$\mathbf{M}\boldsymbol{\psi}=\boldsymbol{\psi}(x_0)-\frac{a}{2\pi}I_1\int_0^{2\pi}\operatorname{ctg}\frac{\theta-\theta_0}{2}\boldsymbol{\psi}(\theta)\,d\theta \tag{9.31}$$

to (9.30) and using (9.11), we obtain

$$\mathbf{MK}\boldsymbol{\varphi}\equiv(1-a^2)\boldsymbol{\varphi}(\theta_0)+(1+a^2)\boldsymbol{\alpha}-b(1-a)A(\theta_0)\boldsymbol{\beta}-b(1-a)B(\theta_0)\boldsymbol{\gamma}=M\boldsymbol{f}(\theta_0). \tag{9.32}$$

Multiplying this system in turn by $\frac{1}{2\pi}d\theta_0$, $\frac{1}{2\pi}\cos\theta_0\,d\theta_0$, $\frac{1}{2\pi}\sin\theta_0\,d\theta_0$ and integrating over the interval $(0, 2\pi)$, we obtain in the notation of (9.8)

$$(1-a^2)\boldsymbol{\alpha}+(1+a^2)\boldsymbol{\alpha}=\frac{1}{2\pi}\int_0^{2\pi}\mathbf{M}\boldsymbol{f}(\theta_0)\,d\theta_0, \tag{9.33}$$

$$(1-a)^2\beta-\frac{b(1-a)}{2}\begin{Vmatrix}1&0\\0&-1\end{Vmatrix}\beta-\frac{b(1-a)}{2}\begin{Vmatrix}0&1\\1&0\end{Vmatrix}\gamma=$$
$$=\frac{1}{2\pi}\int_0^{2\pi}\mathbf{M}f(\theta_0)\cos\theta_0\,d\theta_0,$$
$$(1-a^2)\gamma-\frac{b(1-a)}{2}\begin{Vmatrix}0&1\\1&0\end{Vmatrix}\beta-\frac{b(1-a)}{2}\begin{Vmatrix}-1&0\\0&1\end{Vmatrix}\gamma=$$
$$=\frac{1}{2\pi}\int_0^{2\pi}\mathbf{M}f(\theta_0)\sin\theta_0\,d\theta_0. \tag{9.34}$$

From (9.33) it follows that

$$\alpha=\frac{1}{4\pi}\int_0^{2\pi}\mathbf{M}f(\theta_0)\,d\theta_0=\frac{1}{4\pi}\int_0^{2\pi}f(\theta_0)\,d\theta_0. \tag{9.35}$$

It is known that the condition

$$\int_0^{2\pi}\varphi(\theta_0)\,d\theta_0=0$$

is necessary for the boundedness of a plane single-layer potential at infinity. This condition gives together with (9.35)

$$\int_0^{2\pi}f(\theta_0)\,d\theta_0=0, \tag{9.36}$$

which is equivalent to the vanishing of the net external force. Thus it is necessary to demand the fulfilment of condition (9.36) in order to get a solution bounded at infinity, and in that case

$$\alpha=0. \tag{9.37}$$

We now write out (9.34) in terms of its components

$$(1+a)\beta_1-\frac{b}{2}\beta_1-\frac{b}{2}\gamma_2=\frac{1}{2\pi(1-a)}\int(\mathbf{M}f)_1\cos\theta_0\,d\theta_0, \tag{9.38$_1$}$$

$$(1+a)\gamma_2-\frac{b}{2}\beta_1-\frac{b}{2}\gamma_2=\frac{1}{2\pi(1-a)}\int_0^{2\pi}(\mathbf{M}f)_2\sin\theta_0\,d\theta_0, \tag{9.38$_2$}$$

$$(1+a)\beta_2+\frac{b}{2}\beta_2-\frac{b}{2}\gamma_1=\frac{1}{2\pi(1-a)}\int_0^{2\pi}(\mathbf{M}f)_2\cos\theta_0\,d\theta_0, \tag{9.39$_1$}$$

$$(1+a)\gamma_1-\frac{b}{2}\beta_2+\frac{b}{2}\gamma_1=\frac{1}{2\pi(1-a)}\int_0^{2\pi}(\mathbf{M}f)_1\sin\theta_0\,d\theta_0. \tag{9.39$_2$}$$

The determinants of these systems are equal to $2a(1+a)$ and $2(1+a)$, respectively, and since neither a nor $1+a$ vanish, the unknowns β_1, γ_2, β_2, γ_1 are uniquely determined by (9.38) and (9.39).

We shall need below the values of $\beta_2-\gamma_1$ and $\beta_1+\gamma_2$. Adding together (9.38$_1$) and (9.38$_2$), we obtain

$$\beta_1+\gamma_2=\frac{1}{4\pi a(1-a)}\int_0^{2\pi}[(\mathbf{M}f)_1\cos\theta_0+(\mathbf{M}f)_2\sin\theta_0]\,d\theta_0=\frac{1}{4\pi a}\int_0^{2\pi}(f_1\cos\theta_0+f_2\sin\theta_0)\,d\theta_0 \tag{9.40}$$

and subtracting them,

$$\beta_2-\gamma_1=\frac{1}{4\pi(1-a)}\int_0^{2\pi}[(\mathbf{M}f)_2\cos\theta_0-(\mathbf{M}f)_1\sin\theta_0]\,d\theta_0=\frac{1}{4\pi}\int_0^{2\pi}(f_2\cos\theta_0-f_1\sin\theta_0)\,d\theta_0. \tag{9.41}$$

Using (9.37), (9.40) and (9.41), we obtain (9.32) in the form

$$\varphi(\theta_0)=\frac{1}{1-a^2}\mathbf{M}f(\theta_0)+\frac{1-a}{1+a}\begin{pmatrix}\cos\theta_0\\ \sin\theta_0\end{pmatrix}(\beta_1+\gamma_2)-\frac{1-a}{1+a}\begin{pmatrix}-\sin\theta_0\\ \cos\theta_0\end{pmatrix}(\beta_2-\gamma_1). \qquad (9.42)$$

where $(\beta_1+\gamma_2)$ and $(\beta_2-\gamma_1)$ are given by (9.40) and (9.41). The expression (9.42) represents a solution of the system (9.29). Substituting (9.42) in (9.28),

$$u(x)=\frac{R}{\pi(1-a^2)}\int_0^{2\pi}\Gamma(\rho,\theta;R,\theta')\mathbf{M}f(\theta')\,d\theta'+$$

$$+\frac{R}{\pi}\frac{1-a}{1+a}(\beta_1+\gamma_2)\int_0^{2\pi}\Gamma(\rho,\theta;R,\theta')\begin{pmatrix}\cos\theta'\\ \sin\theta'\end{pmatrix}d\theta'+$$

$$+\frac{R}{\pi}\frac{1-a}{1+a}(\beta_2-\gamma_1)\int_0^{2\pi}\Gamma(\rho,\theta;R,\theta')\begin{pmatrix}\sin\theta'\\ -\cos\theta'\end{pmatrix}d\theta'.$$

This expression may be further simplified. To do this, note that the following formulas hold when the point x lies outside the disk

$$\ln r(x,y)=\ln\rho-\sum_{k=1}^{\infty}\left(\frac{R}{\rho}\right)^k\frac{\cos k(\theta'-\theta)}{k},$$

$$\psi=\operatorname{arctg}\frac{x_2-y_2}{x_1-y_1}=\theta-\sum_{k=1}^{\infty}\left(\frac{R}{\rho}\right)^k\frac{\sin k(\theta'-\theta)}{k},$$

$$\left(\frac{\partial r(x,y)}{\partial x_1}\right)^2=\frac{1}{2}+\frac{1}{2}\frac{\rho^2-R^2}{\rho^2}\cos 2\theta-\frac{1}{2}\frac{R}{\rho}\cos(\theta'+\theta)+$$

$$+\frac{\rho^2-R^2}{2\rho^2}\sum_{k=1}^{\infty}\left(\frac{R}{\rho}\right)^k\cos[k\theta'-(k+2)\theta],$$

$$\frac{\partial r(x,y)}{\partial x_1}\frac{\partial r(x,y)}{\partial x_2}=\frac{1}{2}\frac{\rho^2-R^2}{\rho^2}\sin 2\theta-\frac{1}{2}\frac{R}{\rho}\sin(\theta'+\theta)-$$

$$-\frac{\rho^2-R^2}{2\rho^2}\sum_{k=1}^{\infty}\left(\frac{R}{\rho}\right)^k\sin[k\theta'-(k+2)\theta],$$

$$\left(\frac{\partial r(x,y)}{\partial x_2}\right)^2=\frac{1}{2}-\frac{1}{2}\frac{\rho^2-R^2}{\rho^2}\cos 2\theta+\frac{1}{2}\frac{R}{\rho}\cos(\theta'+\theta)-$$

$$-\frac{\rho^2-R^2}{2\rho^2}\sum_{k=1}^{\infty}\left(\frac{R}{\rho}\right)^k\cos[k\theta'-(k+2)\theta].$$

Using these relations, we obtain

$$\begin{aligned}&\frac{1}{\pi}\int_0^{2\pi}\Gamma(\rho,\theta;R,\theta')\begin{pmatrix}\cos\theta'\\ \sin\theta'\end{pmatrix}d\theta'=-\frac{R}{(\lambda+2\mu)\rho}\begin{pmatrix}\cos\theta\\ \sin\theta\end{pmatrix},\\ &\frac{1}{\pi}\int_0^{2\pi}\Gamma(\rho,\theta;R,\theta')\begin{pmatrix}\sin\theta'\\ -\cos\theta'\end{pmatrix}d\theta'=-\frac{R}{\mu\rho}\begin{pmatrix}\sin\theta\\ -\cos\theta\end{pmatrix},\end{aligned} \qquad (9.43)$$

$$\frac{R}{\pi(1-a^2)}\int_0^{2\pi}\Gamma(\rho,\theta;R,\theta')\mathbf{M}f\,d\theta'=\frac{R}{\pi}\int_0^{2\pi}\Big\{M(\rho,\theta;R,\theta')-$$

$$-\frac{1}{2(\lambda+3\mu)}\frac{R}{\rho}\begin{Vmatrix}-\cos(\theta+\theta') & \sin(\theta+\theta')\\ \sin(\theta+\theta') & \cos(\theta+\theta')\end{Vmatrix}\Big\}f(\theta')\,d\theta',$$

where the matrix $M(\rho,\theta;R,\theta')$ is defined by (9.27). From (9.40), (9.41),

(9.43) we now obtain

$$\frac{R}{\pi}\frac{1-a}{1+a}\left[(\beta_1+\gamma_2)\int_0^{2\pi}\Gamma(\rho,\theta;R,\theta')\begin{pmatrix}\cos\theta'\\ \sin\theta'\end{pmatrix}d\theta'+\right.$$

$$\left.+(\beta_2-\gamma_1)\int_0^{2\pi}\Gamma(\rho,\theta;R,\theta')\begin{pmatrix}\sin\theta'\\ -\cos\theta'\end{pmatrix}d\theta'\right]=$$

$$=-\frac{R(\lambda+\mu)}{4\pi\mu(\lambda+3\mu)}\int_0^{2\pi}\frac{R}{\rho}\begin{Vmatrix}\cos(\theta+\theta') & \sin(\theta+\theta')\\ \sin(\theta+\theta') & -\cos(\theta+\theta')\end{Vmatrix}f(\theta')\,d\theta'.$$

Applying the last result, we obtain from (9.29) after some manipulations

$$u(x)=\frac{1}{\pi}\int_l\left\{M(x,y)-\frac{1}{4\mu}\begin{Vmatrix}\frac{x_1y_1-x_2y_2}{\rho^2} & \frac{x_2y_1+x_1y_2}{\rho^2}\\ \frac{x_2y_1+x_1y_2}{\rho^2} & \frac{x_2y_1-x_1y_2}{\rho^2}\end{Vmatrix}\right\}f(y)\,ds_y.$$

This solution of the problem of the circular aperture was also derived by M. O. Basheleishvili. A similar solution of the first problem for an isotropic plane with a circular aperture was first obtained using the same method by N. S. Kakhniashvili /11/. Cf. also /1c, d/.

§ 3. Anisotropic circular and elliptic plates. Solution of the first boundary-value problem

We shall consider in detail the case of the ellipse, which includes the problem of the circular disk as a particular case. This problem may be solved by means of regular as well as by singular integral equations; this was done in the preceding section for the second problem in case of an isotropic disk.

We first solve the problem by means of regular equations. Let us look for a solution in the form of a double-layer potential of the second kind

$$u(x)=\frac{1}{\pi}\int_l\Gamma_{II}(x,y)\,\varphi(y)\,dS_y.$$

Here $\varphi(y)$ is an unknown vector, and by (9.38)

$$\Gamma_{II}(x,y)=\mathrm{Im}\sum_{k=1}^{2}\begin{Vmatrix}E_k & F_k\\ G_k & I_k\end{Vmatrix}\frac{\partial}{\partial s_y}\ln\sigma_k,$$

where the constants E_k, G_k, F_k, I_k are defined by (8.29). The formulas (8.35) give, on account of the boundary condition, the following integral equation for the vector $\varphi(x_0)$:

$$\varphi(x_0)+\frac{1}{\pi}\int_l\Gamma_{II}(x_0,y)\,\varphi(y)\,dS_y=f(x_0),$$

where $f(x_0)$ is a given continuous vector function which depends on the contour l. The equation of the ellipse

$$y_1=a\cos\omega,\quad y_2=b\sin\omega,\quad a\geqslant b,\quad 0\leqslant\omega\leqslant 2\pi,$$

gives, in view of (8.17),

$$\frac{\partial}{\partial s_y}\ln\sigma_k\,ds_y=i\left(1+\frac{t_{k1}}{e^{i\omega}-t_{k1}}+\frac{t_{k2}}{e^{i\omega}-t_{k2}}\right)d\omega,$$

where

$$t_{k1}=\frac{z_k+\sqrt{z_k^2-(a^2+b^2\alpha_k^2)}}{a-ib\alpha_k},\quad t_{k2}=\frac{z_k-\sqrt{z_k^2-(a^2+b^2\alpha_k^2)}}{a-ib\alpha_k},$$

$$z_k=x_1+\alpha_k x_2\qquad (k=1,\ 2).$$

When x lies in the interior of the ellipse, S_l,

$$|t_{k1}|<1,\quad |t_{k2}|<1\qquad (k=1,\ 2).$$

But when x_0 lies on the elliptic contour l,

$$t_{k1}=e^{i\omega_0},\quad t_{k2}=\lambda_k e^{-i\omega_0},$$

where ω_0 is the value of the parameter of x_0 on the contour, and

$$\lambda_k=\frac{a+ib\alpha_k}{a-ib\alpha_k},\quad |\lambda_k|<1.$$

Since on l

$$\operatorname{Re}\left(1+\frac{e^{i\omega_0}}{e^{i\omega}-e^{i\omega_0}}\right)=\frac{1}{2}$$

and

$$\frac{t_{k2}}{e^{i\omega}-t_{k2}}=\sum_{n=1}^{\infty}\lambda_k^n e^{-in(\omega+\omega_0)},\tag{9.44}$$

we may, using (8.29), represent the integral equation of our problem in the form

$$\varphi(\omega_0)+X_0+2\operatorname{Re}\sum_{k=1}^{2}\sum_{n=1}^{\infty}\begin{Vmatrix}E_k & F_k\\ G_k & I_k\end{Vmatrix}\lambda_k^n e^{-in\omega_0}X_{-n}=f(\omega_0),\tag{9.45}$$

where

$$X_0=\frac{1}{2\pi}\int_0^{2\pi}\varphi(\omega)\,d\omega,$$

$$X_n=\frac{1}{2\pi}\int_0^{2\pi}\varphi(\omega)\,e^{in\omega}\,d\omega,\quad X_{-n}=\frac{1}{2\pi}\int_0^{2\pi}\varphi(\omega)\,e^{-in\omega}\,d\omega,\quad n\geqslant 1.\tag{9.46}$$

We now define

$$f_n=\frac{1}{2\pi}\int_0^{2\pi}f(\omega)\,e^{in\omega}d\omega,\ n=0,\ \pm 1,\ \pm 2,\ \ldots\tag{9.47}$$

Multiplying (9.45) in turn by $\frac{1}{2\pi}e^{in\omega_0}\,d\omega_0$ and $\frac{1}{2\pi}e^{-in\omega_0}\,d\omega_0$ and integrating over the interval $(0,\ 2\pi)$, we obtain in the notation of (9.46) and (9.47),

$$X_0+X_0=f_0,\tag{9.48}$$

$$\left.\begin{aligned}X_n+\sum_{k=1}^{2}\begin{Vmatrix}E_k & F_k\\ G_k & I_k\end{Vmatrix}\lambda_k^n X_{-n}&=f_n,\\ X_{-n}+\sum_{k=1}^{2}\begin{Vmatrix}\tilde{E}_k & \tilde{F}_k\\ \tilde{G}_k & \tilde{I}_k\end{Vmatrix}\tilde{\lambda}_k^n X_n&=f_{-n}\end{aligned}\right\}\quad (n=1,\ 2,\ 3,\ \ldots).\tag{9.49}$$

(a tilde, we recall, denotes the complex conjugate). By (9.48)

$$X_0=\frac{1}{2}f_0.\tag{9.50}$$

We now eliminate X_{-n} between the two relations (9.49), obtaining

$$\left(E-\sum_{k=1}^{2}\begin{Vmatrix}E_k & F_k\\ G_k & I_k\end{Vmatrix}\lambda_k^n\sum_{k=1}^{2}\begin{Vmatrix}\tilde{E}_k & \tilde{F}_k\\ \tilde{G}_k & \tilde{I}_k\end{Vmatrix}\tilde{\lambda}_k^n\right)X_n=f_n-\sum_{k=1}^{2}\begin{Vmatrix}E_k & F_k\\ G_k & I_k\end{Vmatrix}\lambda_k^n f_{-n},\tag{9.51}$$

where E is the unit matrix. Simple calculations show that

$$\Delta_n = \mathrm{Det}\left(E - \sum_{k=1}^{2}\begin{Vmatrix} E_k & F_k \\ G_k & I_k \end{Vmatrix}\lambda_k^n \sum_{k=1}^{2}\begin{Vmatrix} \tilde{E}_k & \tilde{F}_k \\ \tilde{G}_k & \tilde{I}_k \end{Vmatrix}\tilde{\lambda}_k^n\right) =$$

$$= (1 - \lambda_1^n\tilde{\lambda}_1^n)(1 - \lambda_2^n\tilde{\lambda}_2^n) -$$

$$- \frac{(1-\lambda_1\tilde{\lambda}_1)(1-\lambda_2\tilde{\lambda}_2)P(\alpha_1, \tilde{\alpha}_1)P(\alpha_2, \tilde{\alpha}_2)}{(\lambda_1-\lambda_2)(\tilde{\lambda}_1-\tilde{\lambda}_2)P(\alpha_1, \alpha_2)P(\tilde{\alpha}_1, \tilde{\alpha}_2)}(\lambda_1^n - \lambda_2^n)(\tilde{\lambda}_1^n - \tilde{\lambda}_2^n), \tag{9.52}$$

where

$$P(\alpha, \beta) = [A_{33}(A_{12} + A_{33}) - 2A_{13}A_{23}]\alpha\beta +$$
$$+ (A_{13}A_{33} - A_{11}A_{23})(\alpha + \beta) + [2A_{13}^2 - A_{11}(A_{12} + A_{33})]. \tag{9.53}$$

Noting that

$$\frac{P(\alpha_1, \tilde{\alpha}_1)P(\alpha_2, \tilde{\alpha}_2)}{P(\alpha_1, \alpha_2)P(\tilde{\alpha}_1, \tilde{\alpha}_2)} \neq 1$$

and that $\Delta_n \to 1$ for $n \to \infty$, it is possible to show that

$$\Delta_n \neq 0$$

for $n = 1, 2, 3, \ldots$ We then find from (9.51)

$$X_n = \frac{D_n}{\Delta_n}\left(f_n - \sum_{k=1}^{2}\begin{Vmatrix} E_k & F_k \\ G_k & I_k \end{Vmatrix}\lambda_k^n f_{-n}\right), \tag{9.54}$$

where

$$D_n = \begin{Vmatrix} 1 - \sum\limits_{k,s}^{2}(G_k\tilde{F}_s + I_k\tilde{I}_s)\lambda_k^n\tilde{\lambda}_s^n & \sum\limits_{k,s}^{2}(E_k\tilde{F}_s + F_k\tilde{I}_s)\lambda_k^n\tilde{\lambda}_s^n \\ \sum\limits_{k,s}^{2}(G_k\tilde{F}_s + I_k\tilde{G}_s)\lambda_k^n\tilde{\lambda}_s^n & 1 - \sum\limits_{k,s}^{2}(E_k\tilde{E}_s + F_k\tilde{G}_s)\lambda_k^n\tilde{\lambda}_s^n \end{Vmatrix} \tag{9.55}$$

Relation (9.54) implies

$$X_{-n} = \frac{\tilde{D}_n}{\Delta_n}\left(f_{-n} - \sum_{k=1}^{2}\begin{Vmatrix} \tilde{E}_k & \tilde{F}_k \\ \tilde{G}_k & \tilde{I}_k \end{Vmatrix}\tilde{\lambda}_k^n f_n\right). \tag{9.56}$$

Substituting the expressions (9.50) and (9.56) in (9.45) and then inserting the value of $\varphi(\omega_0)$ in the original potential, we obtain the following representation for the solution of our problem

$$u(x) = f_0 + 2\,\mathrm{Re}\sum_{k=1}^{2}\sum_{n=1}^{\infty}\begin{Vmatrix} E_k & F_k \\ G_k & I_k \end{Vmatrix}(t_{k1}^n + t_{k2}^n)X_{-n}, \tag{9.57}$$

where X_{-n} is determined by (9.56); the convergence of this series follows from the inequalities which precede (9.44). The series (9.57) thus provides a solution for the first problem of an anisotropic ellipse.

Solution by means of singular equations. We look for a solution in the form of a double-layer potential of the first kind

$$u(x) = \frac{1}{\pi}\int_l \Gamma_{\mathrm{I}}(x, y)\varphi(y)\,dS_y, \tag{9.58}$$

where the matrix $\Gamma_{\mathrm{I}}(x, y)$ is defined by (8.30),

$$\Gamma_{\mathrm{I}}(x, y) = \mathrm{Im}\sum_{k=1}^{2}\begin{Vmatrix} N_k & M_k \\ L_k & H_k \end{Vmatrix}\frac{\partial}{\partial s_y}\ln\sigma_k. \tag{9.59}$$

Formulas (8.52) give, for our boundary condition, the following system of singular integral equations for $\varphi(y)$

$$\varphi(x_0) + \frac{1}{\pi}\int_l \Gamma_{\mathrm{I}}(x_0, y)\varphi(y)\,ds_y = f(x_0). \tag{9.60}$$

where $f(x_0)$ is a vector function of class $H(\gamma)$, given on l. Since

$$\operatorname{Re}\sum_{k=1}^{2}\begin{Vmatrix} N_k & M_k \\ L_k & H_k \end{Vmatrix}\left(1+\frac{e^{i\omega_0}}{e^{i\omega}-e^{i\omega_0}}\right)=\frac{1}{2}E-\frac{1}{2}\begin{Vmatrix} A & -C \\ B & -A \end{Vmatrix}\operatorname{ctg}\frac{\omega-\omega_0}{2},$$

where A, B, C are determined by (8.26), and using (9.39), (9.41), (9.42), we obtain (9.60) in the form

$$\mathbf{K}\varphi \equiv \varphi(\omega_0)-\frac{1}{2\pi}\begin{Vmatrix} A & -C \\ B & -C \end{Vmatrix}\int_0^{2\pi}\operatorname{ctg}\frac{\omega-\omega_0}{2}\varphi(\omega)\,d\omega+\boldsymbol{X}_0+$$

$$+2\operatorname{Re}\sum_{k=1}^{2}\sum_{n=1}^{\infty}\begin{Vmatrix} N_k & M_k \\ L_k & H_k \end{Vmatrix}\lambda_k^n e^{in\omega_0}\boldsymbol{X}_{-n}=\boldsymbol{f}(\omega_0), \tag{9.61}$$

where $\boldsymbol{X}_0$ and $\boldsymbol{X}_{-n}$ are given by (9.46). We choose a regularizing operator for equation (9.61) of the form

$$\mathbf{M}\psi=\psi(\omega_0)+\frac{1}{2\pi}\begin{Vmatrix} A & -C \\ B & -C \end{Vmatrix}\int_0^{2\pi}\operatorname{ctg}\frac{\omega-\omega_0}{2}\psi(\omega)\,d\omega \tag{9.62}$$

and apply the formulas

$$-\frac{1}{(2\pi)^2}\int_0^{2\pi}\operatorname{ctg}\frac{\omega-\omega_0}{2}\,d\omega\int_0^{2\pi}\operatorname{ctg}\frac{\theta-\omega}{2}\varphi(\theta)\,d\theta=\varphi(\omega_0)-\boldsymbol{X}_0,$$

$$\int_0^{2\pi}\operatorname{ctg}\frac{\omega-\omega_0}{2}\,d\omega=0,$$

$$\frac{1}{2\pi}\int_0^{2\pi}e^{in\omega}\operatorname{ctg}\frac{\omega-\omega_0}{2}\,d\omega=ie^{in\omega_0}\qquad (n=\pm 1,\ \pm 2,\ \ldots),$$

$$\begin{Vmatrix} A & -C \\ B & -A \end{Vmatrix}\begin{Vmatrix} A & -C \\ B & -A \end{Vmatrix}=(A^2-BC)E.$$

Then, after elementary manipulations,

$$\mathbf{MK}\varphi\equiv(1+A^2-BC)\varphi(\omega_0)+(1-A^2+BC)\boldsymbol{X}_0+$$

$$+\begin{Vmatrix} 1-iA & iC \\ -iB & 1+iA \end{Vmatrix}\sum_{k=1}^{2}\sum_{n=1}^{\infty}\begin{Vmatrix} N_k & M_k \\ L_k & H_k \end{Vmatrix}\lambda_k^n e^{-in\omega_0}\boldsymbol{X}_{-n}+$$

$$+\begin{Vmatrix} 1+iA & -iC \\ iB & 1-iA \end{Vmatrix}\sum_{k=1}^{2}\sum_{n=1}^{\infty}\begin{Vmatrix} \tilde{N}_k & \tilde{M}_k \\ \tilde{L}_k & \tilde{H}_k \end{Vmatrix}\tilde{\lambda}_k^n e^{in\omega_0}\boldsymbol{X}_n=\mathbf{M}\boldsymbol{f}(\omega_0). \tag{9.63}$$

Repeating the arguments of the derivation of $\boldsymbol{X}_0$, $\boldsymbol{X}_n$ and $\boldsymbol{X}_{-n}$, we obtain

$$(1+A^2-BC)\boldsymbol{X}_0+(1-A^2+BC)\boldsymbol{X}_0=\boldsymbol{f}_0 \tag{9.64}$$

$$(1+A^2-BC)\boldsymbol{X}_n+\begin{Vmatrix} 1-iA & iC \\ -iB & 1+iA \end{Vmatrix}\sum_{k=1}^{2}\begin{Vmatrix} N_k & M_k \\ L_k & H_k \end{Vmatrix}\lambda_k^n\boldsymbol{X}_{-n}=$$

$$=\begin{Vmatrix} 1-iA & iC \\ -iB & 1+iA \end{Vmatrix}\boldsymbol{f}_n, \tag{9.65}$$

$$(1+A^2-BC)\boldsymbol{X}_{-n}+\begin{Vmatrix} 1+iA & -iC \\ iB & 1-iA \end{Vmatrix}\sum_{k=1}^{2}\begin{Vmatrix} \tilde{N}_k & \tilde{M}_k \\ \tilde{L}_k & \tilde{H}_k \end{Vmatrix}\tilde{\lambda}_k^n\boldsymbol{X}_n=$$

$$=\begin{Vmatrix} 1+iA & -iC \\ iB & 1-iA \end{Vmatrix}\boldsymbol{f}_n.$$

Now (9.64) implies

$$\boldsymbol{X}_0=\frac{1}{2}f_0. \tag{9.63'}$$

Relations (9.65) may be written in the form

$$\begin{Vmatrix} 1+iA & -iC \\ iB & 1-iA \end{Vmatrix} X_n + \sum_{k=1}^{2} \begin{Vmatrix} N_k & M_k \\ L_k & H_k \end{Vmatrix} \lambda_k^n X_{-n} = f_n,$$

$$\begin{Vmatrix} 1-iA & iC \\ -iB & 1+iA \end{Vmatrix} X_{-n} + \sum_{k=1}^{2} \begin{Vmatrix} \tilde{N}_k & \tilde{M}_k \\ \tilde{L}_k & \tilde{H}_k \end{Vmatrix} \tilde{\lambda}_k^n X_n = f_{-n}. \qquad (9.65')$$

We eliminate X_{-n} between these two equations; then, using the formulas

$$\begin{aligned} N_k &= E_k(1-iA) - iBF_k, & M_k &= iCE_k + (1+iA)F_k, \\ L_k &= G_k(1-iA) - iBI_k, & H_k &= iCG_k + (1+iA)I_k, \end{aligned} \qquad (9.66)$$

which may be easily verified, we obtain

$$\left(\begin{Vmatrix} 1+iA & -iC \\ iB & 1-iA \end{Vmatrix} - \sum_{k=1}^{2} \begin{Vmatrix} E_k & F_k \\ G_k & I_k \end{Vmatrix} \lambda_k^n \sum_{k=1}^{2} \begin{Vmatrix} \tilde{N}_k & \tilde{M}_k \\ \tilde{L}_k & \tilde{H}_k \end{Vmatrix} \tilde{\lambda}_k^n \right) X_n =$$
$$= f_n - \sum_{k=1}^{2} \begin{Vmatrix} E_k & F_k \\ G_k & I_k \end{Vmatrix} \lambda_k^n f_{-n}. \qquad (9.67)$$

After rather lengthy but elementary calculations we find

$$\mathrm{Det}\left(\begin{Vmatrix} 1+iA & -iC \\ iB & 1-iA \end{Vmatrix} - \sum_{k=1}^{2} \begin{Vmatrix} E_k, & F_k \\ G_k, & I_k \end{Vmatrix} \lambda_k^n \sum_{k=1}^{2} \begin{Vmatrix} \tilde{N}_k & \tilde{M}_k \\ \tilde{L}_k & \tilde{H}_k \end{Vmatrix} \tilde{\lambda}_k^n \right) =$$
$$= (1 + A^2 - BC)\Delta_n, \qquad (9.68)$$

where Δ_n is defined by (9.52). Solving equation (9.67),

$$X_n = \frac{1}{(1+A^2-BC)\Delta_n} \begin{Vmatrix} 1-iA & iC \\ -iB & 1+iA \end{Vmatrix} D_n \left[f_n - \sum_{k=1}^{2} \begin{Vmatrix} E_k & F_k \\ G_k & I_k \end{Vmatrix} \lambda_k^n f_{-n} \right],$$

where D_n is given by (9.55). Substituting the obtained values of X_0, X_n, X_{-n} first in (9.63), and then inserting the value of $\varphi(\omega_0)$ into (9.58), we obtain

$$u(x) = f_0 + 2\,\mathrm{Re} \sum_{k=1}^{2} \sum_{n=1}^{\infty} \begin{Vmatrix} E_k & F_k \\ G_k & I_k \end{Vmatrix} \frac{\tilde{D}_n}{\Delta_n} \left[f_{-n} - \sum_{k=1}^{2} \begin{Vmatrix} \tilde{E}_k & \tilde{F}_k \\ \tilde{G}_k & \tilde{I}_k \end{Vmatrix} \tilde{\lambda}_k^n \tilde{f}_n \right] (t_{k1}^n + t_{k2}^n). \qquad (9.57')$$

This expression coincides with (9.57), which was derived before by using regular equations.

Case of a circular plate. Setting $a=b$, we obtain the solution of the first boundary-value problem for an anisotropic disk. This surprisingly makes for no great simplifications, so that the solutions of the elliptic and circular problems present essentially the same difficulties. Choosing the Hooke constants appropriately, one may obtain from the solution given in this section the solution of the first problem for an isotropic disk and ellipse. For details the reader may consult /1a/.

§ 4. Solution of the second boundary-value problem for an anisotropic disk and ellipse

This problem also may be solved by regular, as well as singular equations. We first consider the solution by means of regular equations.

1°. Solution by regular equations. Let us look for a solution in the form of a single-layer potential of the second kind

$$u(x)=\frac{1}{\pi}\int_l M(x,\ y)\varphi(y)\,ds_y, \tag{9.69}$$

where the matrix $M(x,\ y)$ is defined by (8.14),

$$M(x,\ y)=\operatorname{Im}\sum_{k=1}^{2}\begin{Vmatrix} A_k' & B_k' \\ C_k' & D_k' \end{Vmatrix}\ln\sigma_k. \tag{9.70}$$

Applying T to the single-layer potential of the second kind, we obtain in view of (8.34)

$$\mathsf{T}u(x)=\frac{1}{\pi}\operatorname{Im}\sum_{k=1}^{2}\begin{Vmatrix} e_k & g_k \\ h_k & f_k \end{Vmatrix}\int_l \varphi(y)\frac{\partial}{\partial s_y}\ln\sigma_k\,ds_y, \tag{9.71}$$

where the constants $e_k,\ g_k,\ h_k,\ f_k$ are defined by (8.33). By (8.36), $\varphi(y)$ satisfies the Fredholm equations

$$-\varphi(x_0)+\frac{1}{\pi}\operatorname{Im}\sum_{k=1}^{2}\begin{Vmatrix} e_k & g_k \\ h_k & f_k \end{Vmatrix}\int_l \varphi(y)\frac{\partial}{\partial s_y}\ln\sigma_k\,ds_y=F(x_0), \tag{9.72}$$

where $F(x_0)$ is a continuous vector function given on l. From the equation of the ellipse we find

$$\frac{\partial}{\partial s_x}\ln\sigma_k=\frac{2\,(\alpha_k\cos(nx_1)-\cos(nx_2))}{(a-i\alpha_k b)\,(t_{k1}-t_{k2})}\left(\frac{t_{k2}}{e^{i\omega}-t_{k2}}-\frac{t_{k1}}{e^{i\omega}-t_{k1}}\right), \tag{9.73}$$

where t_{k1} and t_{k2} were defined in the beginning of § 3.

Equation (9.72) may be written in the form

$$-\psi(\omega_0)+X_0+2\operatorname{Re}\sum_{k=1}^{2}\sum_{n=1}^{\infty}\begin{Vmatrix} e_k & g_k \\ h_k & f_k \end{Vmatrix}\lambda_k^n e^{-in\omega_0}X_{-n}=f(\omega_0), \tag{9.74}$$

where

$$\psi(\omega)=\varphi(\omega)\sqrt{a^2\sin^2\omega+b^2\cos^2\omega},\quad f(\omega)=F(\omega)\sqrt{a^2\sin^2\omega+b^2\cos^2\omega} \tag{9.75}$$

and $X_0,\ X_n,\ X_{-n}$ are defined by (9.46). Repeating the arguments applied in § 3 to derive $X_0,\ X_n,\ X_{-n}$, we obtain

$$-X_0+X_0=\frac{1}{2\pi}\int_0^{2\pi}f(\omega)\,d\omega=\frac{1}{2\pi}\int_0^{2\pi}F(y)\,ds_y, \tag{9.76}$$

$$\begin{aligned} -X_n+\sum_{k=1}^{2}\begin{Vmatrix} e_k & g_k \\ h_k & f_k \end{Vmatrix}\lambda_k^n X_{-n}&=f_n,\\ -X_{-n}+\sum_{k=1}^{2}\begin{Vmatrix} \tilde{e}_k & \tilde{g}_k \\ \tilde{h}_k & \tilde{f}_k \end{Vmatrix}\tilde{\lambda}_k^n X_n&=f_{-n}. \end{aligned} \tag{9.77}$$

The condition

$$\int_0^{2\pi}F(y)\,ds_y=0. \tag{9.78}$$

is necessary for the determination of X_0 from (9.76). Taking this for granted, we may consider X_0 to be an arbitrary constant; X_0, as it will appear below, does not occur in the expression for the stress vector.

Eliminating X_{-n} between equations (9.77),

$$\left(-E+\sum_{k=1}^{2}\begin{Vmatrix} e_k & g_k \\ h_k & f_k \end{Vmatrix}\lambda_k^n\sum_{k=1}^{2}\begin{Vmatrix} \tilde{e}_k & \tilde{g}_k \\ \tilde{h}_k & \tilde{f}_k \end{Vmatrix}\tilde{\lambda}_k^n\right)X_n=f_n+\sum_{k=1}^{2}\begin{Vmatrix} e_k & g_k \\ h_k & f_k \end{Vmatrix}\lambda_k^n f_{-n}. \tag{9.79}$$

After elementary calculations we get

$$\operatorname{Det}\left(-E+\sum_{k=1}^{2}\begin{Vmatrix} e_k & g_k \\ h_k & f_k \end{Vmatrix}\lambda_k^n \sum_{k=1}^{2}\begin{Vmatrix} \tilde{e}_k & \tilde{g}_k \\ \tilde{h}_k & \tilde{f}_k \end{Vmatrix}\tilde{\lambda}_k^n\right)=$$

$$=(1-\lambda_1^n\tilde{\lambda}_1^n)(1-\lambda_2^n\tilde{\lambda}_2^n)-\frac{(1-\lambda_1\tilde{\lambda}_1)(1-\lambda_2\tilde{\lambda}_2)}{(\lambda_1-\lambda_2)(\tilde{\lambda}_1-\tilde{\lambda}_2)}(\lambda_1^n-\lambda_2^n)(\tilde{\lambda}_1^n-\tilde{\lambda}_2^n)=\Delta_n. \qquad (9.80)$$

Obviously, $\Delta_1=0$ for $n=1$; it may also be shown easily that $\Delta_n\neq 0$ for $n\geqslant 2$. X_1 may be derived from (9.79) for $n=1$ only provided that the resultant moment of the external forces vanishes, i. e.,

$$\int_l [y_1F_2(y)-y_2F_1(y)]\,dS_y=\int_l [a\cos\omega\cdot f_2(\omega)-b\sin\omega\cdot f_1(\omega)]\,d\omega=0, \qquad (9.81)$$

For $n\geqslant 2$, we have from (9.79)

$$X_n=\frac{D_n}{\Delta_n}\left[f_n+\sum_{k=1}^{2}\begin{Vmatrix} e_k & g_k \\ h_k & f_k \end{Vmatrix}\lambda_k^n f_{-n}\right], \qquad (9.82)$$

where

$$D_n=\begin{Vmatrix} -1+\sum\limits_{k,s}^{2}(h_k\tilde{g}_s+f_k\tilde{f}_s)\lambda_k^n\tilde{\lambda}_s^n & -\sum\limits_{k,s}^{2}(e_k\tilde{g}_s+g_k\tilde{f}_s)\lambda_k^n\tilde{\lambda}_s^n \\ -\sum\limits_{k,s}^{2}(h_k\tilde{e}_s+f_k\tilde{h}_s)\lambda_k^n\tilde{\lambda}_s^n & -1+\sum\limits_{k,s}^{2}(e_k\tilde{e}_s+g_k\tilde{h}_s)\lambda_k^n\tilde{\lambda}_s^n \end{Vmatrix}. \qquad (9.83)$$

Substituting the values of X_0 and X_{-n} in (9.74) and then inserting the obtained $\psi(\omega_0)$ into (9.71), we obtain for the stress vector

$$\mathbf{T}u(x)=F_{-1}e^{i\omega}+F_1e^{-i\omega}+$$

$$+2\operatorname{Im}\sum_{k=1}^{2}\sum_{n=2}^{\infty}\begin{Vmatrix} e_k & g_k \\ h_k & f_k \end{Vmatrix}(t_{k2}^n-t_{k1}^n)\frac{(\alpha_k\cos(n,x_1)-\cos(n,x_2))}{\sqrt{z_k^2-(a^2+\alpha_k^2b^2)}}X_{-n}, \qquad (9.84)$$

where

$$X_{-n}=\frac{\tilde{D}_n}{\Delta_n}\left[f_{-n}+\sum_{k=1}^{n}\begin{Vmatrix} \tilde{e}_k & \tilde{g}_k \\ \tilde{h}_k & \tilde{f}_k \end{Vmatrix}\tilde{\lambda}_k^n f_n\right].$$

In particular, for $a=b$ we have $f(\omega)=aF(\omega)$; there can be therefore no further simplifications in the case of a disk.

In order to obtain the displacement vector it is evidently sufficient to substitute the value of $\psi(\omega_0)$ in (9.69). The solution is determined up to an additive rigid displacement; the displacements are uniquely determined if the net external force vanishes.

2°. **Solution by singular equations.** Let us look for a solution in the form of a single-layer potential of the first kind

$$u(x)=\frac{1}{\pi}\int_l \Gamma(x,y)\,\varphi(y)\,dS_y, \qquad (9.85)$$

then, as we already know,

$$\mathbf{T}u(x)=\frac{1}{\pi}\operatorname{Im}\sum_{k=1}^{2}\begin{Vmatrix} N_k & L_k \\ M_k & H_k \end{Vmatrix}\int_l \frac{\partial}{\partial s_x}\ln\sigma_k\cdot\varphi(y)\,ds_y, \qquad (9.86)$$

and, by (8.36), we obtain for $\varphi(y)$ the singular integral equations

$$-\varphi(x_0)+\frac{1}{\pi}\operatorname{Im}\sum_{k=1}^{2}\begin{Vmatrix} N_k & L_k \\ M_k & H_k \end{Vmatrix}\int_l \frac{\partial}{\partial s_{x_0}}\ln\sigma_k\cdot\varphi(y)\,ds_y=F(x_0). \qquad (9.87)$$

Since

$$-\frac{e^{i\omega_0}}{e^{i\omega}-e^{i\omega_0}}=\frac{1}{2}+\frac{i}{2}\operatorname{ctg}\frac{\omega-\omega_0}{2},$$

the representation (9.73) and the arguments of § 3 enable us to write (9.87) in the form

$$\mathsf{K}\psi(\omega_0) = -\psi(\omega_0) + \frac{1}{2\pi}\begin{Vmatrix} A & B \\ -C & -A \end{Vmatrix}\int_0^{2\pi} \operatorname{ctg}\frac{\omega-\omega_0}{2}\psi(\omega)\,d\omega +$$

$$+ X_0 + 2\,\mathrm{Re}\sum_{k=1}^{2}\sum_{n=1}^{\infty}\begin{Vmatrix} N_k & L_k \\ M_k & H_k \end{Vmatrix}\lambda_k^n e^{-in\omega_0} X_{-n} = f(\omega_0), \tag{9.88}$$

where ψ and f are defined by (9.75), and X_0 and X_{-n} by (9.46). We choose the regularizing operator as

$$\mathsf{M}\chi(\omega_0) = -\chi(\omega_0) - \frac{1}{2\pi}\begin{Vmatrix} A & B \\ -C & -A \end{Vmatrix}\int_0^{2\pi} \operatorname{ctg}\frac{\omega-\omega_0}{2}\chi(\omega)\,d\omega \tag{9.89}$$

and (exactly as in § 3) find

$$\mathsf{MK}\psi \equiv (1 + A^2 - BC)[\psi(\omega_0) - X_0] -$$

$$- 2\,\mathrm{Re}\sum_{k=1}^{2}\sum_{n=1}^{\infty}\begin{Vmatrix} 1-iA & -iB \\ iC & 1+iA \end{Vmatrix}\begin{Vmatrix} N_k & L_k \\ M_k & H_k \end{Vmatrix}\lambda_k^n e^{-in\omega_0} X_{-n} = Mf(\omega_0) \tag{9.90}$$

which gives the following equations for the constants X_0, X_n, X_{-n}

$$(1 + A^2 - BC)(X_0 - X_0) = \frac{1}{2\pi}\int_0^{2\pi} Mf\,d\omega = -\frac{1}{2\pi}\int_0^{2\pi} f\,d\omega = -\frac{1}{2\pi}\int_l F(y)\,ds_y, \tag{9.91}$$

$$-\begin{Vmatrix} 1+iA & iB \\ -iC & 1-iA \end{Vmatrix} X_n + \sum_{k=1}^{2}\begin{Vmatrix} N_k & L_k \\ M_k & H_k \end{Vmatrix}\lambda_k^n X_{-n} = f_n,$$

$$-\begin{Vmatrix} 1-iA & -iB \\ iC & 1+iA \end{Vmatrix} X_{-n} + \sum_{k=1}^{2}\begin{Vmatrix} \tilde{N}_k & \tilde{L}_k \\ \tilde{M}_k & \tilde{H}_k \end{Vmatrix}\tilde{\lambda}_k^n X_n = f_{-n}. \tag{9.92}$$

The vanishing of the net external force is, as mentioned before, necessary for the determination of X_0; X_0 is then an arbitrary constant vector.

To determine X_n and X_{-n} we multiply the second of equations (9.92) on the left by the matrix

$$\sum_{k=1}^{2}\begin{Vmatrix} e_k & g_k \\ h_k & f_k \end{Vmatrix}\lambda_k^n,$$

which is regular, since

$$\mathrm{Det}\sum_{k=1}^{2}\begin{Vmatrix} e_k & g_k \\ h_k & f_k \end{Vmatrix}\lambda_k^n = \lambda_1^n\lambda_2^n \neq 0,$$

and apply the identity

$$\begin{Vmatrix} N_k & L_k \\ M_k & H_k \end{Vmatrix} = \begin{Vmatrix} e_k & g_k \\ h_k & f_k \end{Vmatrix}\begin{Vmatrix} 1-iA & -iB \\ iC & 1+iA \end{Vmatrix},$$

which may be easily verified. Adding now the two relations (9.92), we obtain

$$\left(-\begin{Vmatrix} 1+iA & iB \\ -iC & 1-iA \end{Vmatrix} + \sum_{k=1}^{2}\begin{Vmatrix} e_k & g_k \\ h_k & f_k \end{Vmatrix}\lambda_k^n \sum_{k=1}^{2}\begin{Vmatrix} \tilde{N}_k & \tilde{L}_k \\ \tilde{M}_k & \tilde{H}_k \end{Vmatrix}\tilde{\lambda}_k^n\right) X_n =$$

$$= f_n + \sum_{k=1}^{2}\begin{Vmatrix} e_k & g_k \\ h_k & f_k \end{Vmatrix}\lambda_k^n f_{-n}. \tag{9.93}$$

2109

Simple calculations give

$$\operatorname{Det}\left(-\left\|\begin{matrix}1+iA & iB \\ -iC & 1-iA\end{matrix}\right\|+\sum_{k=1}^{2}\left\|\begin{matrix}e_k & g_k \\ h_k & f_k\end{matrix}\right\|\lambda_k^n\sum_{k=1}^{2}\left\|\begin{matrix}\tilde{N}_k & \tilde{L}_k \\ \tilde{M}_k & \tilde{H}_k\end{matrix}\right\|\tilde{\lambda}_k^n\right)=(1+A^2-BC)\Delta_n, \quad (9.94)$$

where Δ_n is given by (9.80).

As $\Delta_1=0$, the possibility of determining $(X_1)_1$ and $(X_1)_2$ from (9.93), depends on the vanishing of the resultant moment of the external forces.

For $n\geqslant 2$, we have from (9.93)

$$X_n=\frac{D_n}{(1+A^2-BC)\Delta_n}\left\|\begin{matrix}1-iA & -iB \\ iC & 1+iA\end{matrix}\right\|\left[f_n+\sum_{k=1}^{2}\left\|\begin{matrix}e_k & g_k \\ h_k & f_k\end{matrix}\right\|\lambda_k^n f_{-n}\right]. \quad (9.95)$$

Substituting the values of X_0, X_1, X_n, X_{-n} in (9.90) we similarly conclude from (9.86) that the stress vector is represented by the same formula (9.84), but now it is necessary to take into account that

$$\frac{1}{1+A^2-BC}\left\|\begin{matrix}N_k & L_k \\ M_k & H_k\end{matrix}\right\|\left\|\begin{matrix}1+iA & iB \\ -iC & 1-iA\end{matrix}\right\|=\left\|\begin{matrix}e_k & g_k \\ h_k & f_k\end{matrix}\right\|.$$

§ 5. Solution of the first boundary-value problem for an infinite anisotropic plane with a circular or elliptic aperture

This problem is somewhat simpler than the preceding one, because the functions t_{k1} and t_{k2} are single valued in the external domain and it is possible to avoid some transformations which were necessary in order to effect a uniformization of many-valued expressions that appeared in the internal problems.

We are looking for a solution of the form

$$u(x)=\frac{1}{\pi}\operatorname{Im}\sum_{k=1}^{2}\left\|\begin{matrix}E_k & F_k \\ G_k & I_k\end{matrix}\right\|\int_l\left[\frac{\partial}{\partial s_y}\ln\sigma_k-\left(\frac{1}{2}+\frac{t_{k2}}{e^{i\omega}-t_{k2}}\right)\frac{i}{\sqrt{a^2\sin^2\omega+b^2\cos^2\omega}}\right]\varphi(y)\,ds_y, \quad (9.96)$$

where ω is the parameter of point y on the ellipse and the coordinate origin lies at the center of the ellipse. Applying the discontinuity relation for a double-layer potential of the second kind, we get from the boundary condition the following regular Fredholm equation for $\varphi(y)$:

$$-\varphi(x_0)+\frac{1}{\pi}\operatorname{Im}\sum_{k=1}^{2}\left\|\begin{matrix}E_k & F_k \\ G_k & H_k\end{matrix}\right\|\int_l\left[\frac{\partial}{\partial s_y}\ln\sigma_k-\right.$$
$$\left.-\left(\frac{1}{2}+\frac{t_{k2}}{e^{i\omega}-t_{k2}}\right)\frac{i}{\sqrt{a^2\sin^2\omega+b^2\cos^2\omega}}\right]\varphi(y)\,ds_y=f(x_0), \quad (9.97)$$

where $f(x_0)$ is a continuous vector function given on l.

It follows from the considerations of § 3 that when x_0 and y lie on l (the ellipse) then

$$\operatorname{Im}\sum_{k=1}^{2}\left\|\begin{matrix}E_k & F_k \\ G_k & I_k\end{matrix}\right\|\int_l\left[\frac{\partial}{\partial s_y}\ln\sigma_k-\right.$$
$$\left.-\left(\frac{1}{2}+\frac{t_{k2}}{e^{i\omega}-t_{k2}}\right)\frac{i}{\sqrt{a^2\sin^2\omega+b^2\cos^2\omega}}\right]ds_y=0$$

while by (9.97)

$$\varphi(x_0)=-f(x_0).$$

Inserting this value of $\varphi(y)$ in (9.96), we obtain after some transformations the following representation for the solution

$$u(x)=\frac{1}{2\pi}\operatorname{Re}\sum_{k=1}^{2}\left\|\begin{matrix}E_k & F_k\\ G_k & I_k\end{matrix}\right\|\int_0^{2\pi}\frac{1+t_{k1}^{-1}e^{i\omega}}{1-t_{k1}^{-1}e^{i\omega}}f(\omega)\,d\omega. \tag{9.98}$$

If x lies in the external domain, then $|t_{k1}^{-1}|<1$.

Solution by singular equations. Let us look for a solution of the form

$$u(x)=\frac{1}{\pi}\operatorname{Re}\sum_{k=1}^{2}\left\|\begin{matrix}N_k & M_k\\ L_k & H_k\end{matrix}\right\|\int_0^{2\pi}\left(\frac{1}{2}+\frac{t_{k1}}{e^{i\omega}-t_{k1}}\right)\varphi(\omega)\,d\omega. \tag{9.99}$$

Applying the discontinuity relations for a double-layer potential of the first kind, we obtain

$$\mathbf{K}\varphi\equiv-\varphi(\omega_0)-\frac{1}{2\pi}\left\|\begin{matrix}A & -C\\ B & -A\end{matrix}\right\|\int_0^{2\pi}\operatorname{ctg}\frac{\omega-\omega_0}{2}\varphi(\omega)\,d\omega=f(\omega_0). \tag{9.100}$$

We choose the regularizing operator

$$\mathbf{M}\chi\equiv-\chi(\omega_0)+\frac{1}{2\pi}\left\|\begin{matrix}A & -C\\ B & -A\end{matrix}\right\|\int_0^{2\pi}\operatorname{ctg}\frac{\omega-\omega_0}{2}\chi(\omega)\,d\omega,$$

and obtain, as before,

$$\mathbf{MK}\varphi\equiv(1+A^2-BC)\varphi(\omega_0)-(A^2-BC)X_0=\mathbf{M}f(\omega_0). \tag{9.101}$$

Hence

$$X_0=-f_0,$$

and the solution of (9.101) is representable in the form

$$\varphi(\omega_0)=\frac{1}{1+A^2-BC}[\mathbf{M}f(\omega_0)-(A^2-BC)f_0]. \tag{9.102}$$

Substituting this value of $\varphi(y)$ in (9.99), we obtain for the solution

$$u(x)=-\frac{1}{2\pi}\operatorname{Re}\sum_{k=1}^{2}\left\|\begin{matrix}N_k & M_k\\ L_k & H_k\end{matrix}\right\|\int_0^{2\pi}\frac{1+t_{k1}^{-1}e^{i\omega}}{1-t_{k1}^{-1}e^{i\omega}}\frac{\mathbf{M}f(\omega)-(A^2-BC)f_0}{1+A^2-BC}d\omega. \tag{9.103}$$

It may be shown that (9.103) reduces to (9.98).

§ 6. Solution of the second boundary-value problem for an infinite anisotropic plane with a circular or elliptic aperture

We are looking for a solution of this problem in the form of the following modified single-layer potential of the second kind

$$u(x)=\frac{1}{\pi}\operatorname{Im}\sum_{k=1}^{2}\left\|\begin{matrix}e_k & g_k\\ h_k & f_k\end{matrix}\right\|\int_0^{2\pi}\ln(e^{i\omega}-t_{k1})\varphi(\omega)\,d\omega. \tag{9.104}$$

Then

$$\mathbf{T}u(x)=\frac{1}{\pi}\operatorname{Im}\sum_{k=1}^{2}\left\|\begin{matrix}A_k & C_k\\ B_k & D_k\end{matrix}\right\|\frac{\alpha_k\cos(n,x_1)-\cos(n,x_2)}{\sqrt{z_k^2-(a^2+b^2\alpha_k^2)}}\int_0^{2\pi}\frac{t_{k1}}{t_{k1}-e^{i\omega}}\varphi(\omega)\,d\omega. \tag{9.105}$$

Applying the discontinuity relations for a single-layer potential of the second kind, we obtain

$$\varphi(\omega_0)+\frac{1}{\pi}\operatorname{Im}\sum_{k=1}^{2}\left\|\begin{matrix}A_k & C_k\\ B_k & D_k\end{matrix}\right\|\frac{\alpha_k\cos(n,x_1)-\cos(n,x_2)}{\sqrt{z_k^2-(a^2+b^2\alpha_k^2)}}\int_0^{2\pi}\frac{t_{k1}}{t_{k1}-e^{i\omega}}\varphi(\omega)\,d\omega=F(\omega_0). \tag{9.106}$$

where

$$\varphi(\omega_0)=\psi(\omega_0)\sqrt{a^2\sin^2\omega_0+b^2\cos^2\omega_0},$$
$$f(\omega_0)=F(\omega_0)\sqrt{a^2\sin^2\omega_0+b^2\cos^2\omega_0}.$$

After some elementary transformations, (9.106) becomes

$$\varphi(\omega_0)+\frac{1}{2\pi}\int_0^{2\pi}\varphi(\omega)\,d\omega=f(\omega_0).$$

On account of the boundedness of the single-layer potential at infinity

$$\int_0^{2\pi}\varphi(\omega)\,d\omega=0,$$

and we find that

$$\varphi(\omega_0)=f(\omega_0).$$

Substituting this value of $\varphi(\omega)$ in (9.105),

$$\mathbf{T}u(x)=\frac{1}{\pi}\,\mathrm{Im}\sum_{k=1}^{2}\begin{Vmatrix}A_k & C_k\\ B_k & D_k\end{Vmatrix}\frac{\alpha_k\cos(n,x_1)-\cos(n,x_2)}{\sqrt{z_k^2-(a^2+b^2\alpha_k^2)}}\int_0^{2\pi}\frac{t_{k1}f(\omega)}{t_{k1}-e^{i\omega}}\,d\omega, \tag{9.107}$$

where we have made use of

$$\int_0^{2\pi}\varphi(\omega)\,d\omega=\frac{1}{2}\int_l F(y)\,ds_y=0.$$

Therefore (9.107) is valid only when the net external force vanishes.

This problem too may be solved by means of singular integral equations. Setting here and in the preceding section $a=b$ gives the corresponding solutions for a circular aperture.

§ 7. Other explicitly solvable problems

It is possible to solve boundary-value problems for contours related to a circle or an ellipse. It is reasonable to expect that the problems for the Pascal limaçon, the epitrochoid, the hypotrochoid and other curves might be solved explicitly. It would be interesting to prove the assumption that it is possible to obtain explicit solutions for simple domains which may be mapped onto a disk by means of rational functions. Perhaps it will prove possible to obtain "visible" solutions for certain concentric domains. All these problems require further investigation.

§ 8. Isotropic plane with an elastic isotropic circular or elliptic insert of a different material

For the static problem we have (IV, 2) the functional equations for $x\in S_i$

$$2\pi\mu_a l u(x)=m\int_{S_i}u(y)\,\mathrm{grad\,div}\,\Gamma_{(a)}(x,\ y)\,dS_y+ \\ +\mu_a\int_S u_i(y)\,\mathbf{T}^*\Gamma_{(a)}\,dS_y+2\pi\mu_a E(x;\ x_*); \tag{9.108$_i$}$$

for $x\in S_a$

$$2\pi\mu_a u(x)=m\int_{S_i}u(y)\,\mathrm{grad\,div}\,\Gamma_{(a)}(x,\ y)\,dS_y+ \\ +\mu_a\int_S u_i(y)\,\mathbf{T}^*\Gamma_{(a)}\,ds_y+2\pi\mu_a E(x;\ x_*). \tag{9.108$_a$}$$

with

$$\Gamma_{(a)}(x, y)=\left\|\begin{matrix} \frac{\lambda_a+3\mu_a}{2\mu_a(\lambda_a+2\mu_a)}\ln r-\frac{\lambda_a+\mu_a}{2\mu_a(\lambda_a+2\mu_a)}\left(\frac{\partial r}{\partial x_1}\right)^2 & -\frac{\lambda_a+\mu_a}{2\mu_a(\lambda_a+2\mu_a)}\frac{\partial r}{\partial x_1}\frac{\partial r}{\partial x_2} \\ -\frac{\lambda_a+\mu_a}{2\mu_a(\lambda_a+2\mu_a)}\frac{\partial r}{\partial x_1}\frac{\partial r}{\partial x_2} & \frac{\lambda_a+3\mu_a}{2\mu_a(\lambda_a+2\mu_a)}\ln r-\frac{\lambda_a+\mu_a}{2\mu_a(\lambda_a+2\mu_a)}\left(\frac{\partial r}{\partial x_2}\right)^2 \end{matrix}\right\|,$$

while the other symbols have the same meaning as in (IV,2) and in § 1 of the present chapter. Assuming the Poisson's ratios of the two adjoining media to be equal, and passing to the limit in (9.108_i) for $x\to x_0$ $(x_0\in S)$, we obtain the integral equation

$$u_i(x_0)+\frac{1}{\pi}\frac{\mu_a-\mu_i}{\mu_a+\mu_i}\int\limits_S u_i(y)\,\mathrm{T}_y^{(a)}\Gamma_{(a)}(x_0, y)dS_y=\frac{\mu_a}{\mu_i+\mu_a}E(x_0;\ x_*).$$

This equation does not differ from (9.60) and may be solved explicitly; the solution differs from (9.57) only in the values of constant coefficients.

We insert the $u_i(y)$ thus obtained in (9.108_i); this yields the value of $u(x)$ in S_i; then we obtain the value of $u(x)$ in S_a from (9.108_a). In the general case (without the assumption of equal Poisson's ratios) the solution is obtained in the form of the series (7.25), in which all the terms $u^{(k)}(x)$ $(k=1, 2, 3, \dots)$ satisfy the same integral equation (more accurately, integral equations differing from each other only in the (given) right members $F(x)$)

$$2\pi\varkappa(x)v(x)-\mu_a\int\limits_S v(y)\,\mathrm{T}^*\Gamma_{(a)}(x, y)\,dS_y=F(x),\qquad x\in S_i,$$

which is also an equation of the type (9.60) and may be solved explicitly. Since the series (7.25) is now actually constructed one may verify the convergence conditions directly.

§ 9. Orthotropic plane with an elastic circular or elliptic insert of a different material

By the arguments of (IV,2) and (VIII, 7) it may be shown that the static problem here reduces to the system of functional equations

for $x\in S_i$

$$\alpha_{kk}^{ia}u_k(x)=$$
$$=(A_{12}^i+A_{33}^i)\int\limits_{S_i}\left[u_1\left(\tau_1\frac{\partial^2\Gamma_{1(a)}^{(k)}}{\partial y_1^2}+\tau_2\frac{\partial^2\Gamma_{1(a)}^{(k)}}{\partial y_2^2}\right)+u_2\left(\frac{\partial^2\Gamma_{2(a)}^{(k)}}{\partial y_1^2}+\tau_3\frac{\partial^2\Gamma_{2(a)}^{(k)}}{\partial y_2^2}\right)\right]dS_y+$$
$$+\int u(y)\,\mathrm{T}^*\Gamma_{(a)}^{(k)}(x, y)\,dS_y+E(x;\ x_*);\qquad (9.109_i)$$

for $x\in S_a$

$$\alpha_{kk}^{a}u_k(x)=$$
$$=(A_{12}^i+A_{33}^i)\int\limits_{S_i}\left[u_1\left(\tau_1\frac{\partial^2\Gamma_{1(a)}^{(k)}}{\partial y_1^2}+\tau_2\frac{\partial^2\Gamma_{1(a)}^{(k)}}{\partial y_2^2}\right)+u_2\left(\tau_2\frac{\partial^2\Gamma_{2(a)}^{(k)}}{\partial y_1^2}+\tau_3\frac{\partial^2\Gamma_{2(a)}^{(k)}}{\partial y_2^2}\right)\right]dS_y+$$
$$+\int\limits_S u(y)\,\mathrm{T}^*\Gamma_{(a)}^{(k)}dS_y+E(x;\ x_*).\qquad (9.109_a)$$

Assuming first the constants τ_1, τ_2, τ_3 to be zero and passing to the limit in (9.109_i) as x approaches the boundary point x_0, we obtain the equation

$$\frac{\alpha_{kk}^a}{2}\,\frac{A_{12}^a+A_{33}^a+A_{12}^i+A_{33}^i}{A_{12}^a+A_{33}^a}(u_k(x_0))_i-$$
$$-\frac{A_{12}^a+A_{33}^a-A_{12}^i-A_{33}^i}{A_{12}^a+A_{33}^a}\int\limits_S u_i(y)\,T^{(a)}\Gamma_{(a)}^{(k)}(x_0, y)\,dS_y=E(x_0;\ x_*).$$

This equation does not differ much from (9.60), and like the latter may be solved explicitly; the solution has the form (9.57).

Substituting this value of $(u_k(y))_i$ in (9.109$_i$), we obtain $u_k(x)$ in S_i; inserting this into (9.109$_a$), we obtain $u_k(x)$ in S_a. If, however, the Poisson's ratios are not assumed equal, the solution is sought in the form of a power series in the parameters τ_1, τ_2, τ_3, and the method of undetermined coefficients then leads, as in (VII,4), to a set of recurrence relations which differ from each other only in the known right members. These equations are of the type (9.60), and likewise may be solved explicitly, as in § 3 of the present chapter.

§ 10. Plane problems of pressed components. Anisotropic elliptic plate with a press-fitted or soldered-in elastic insert

Let a hole of any shape with contour γ be cut in an undeformed anisotropic plate, bounded by the ellipse l. Let then an anisotropic plate of the same material and shape but slightly larger in size be inserted in this hole. Applying the arguments of (IV, 7) and of § 7 of the present chapter, and assuming that the boundary conditions of the first problem are fulfilled along the ellipse, we find the following representation for the solution of the static problem

$$\boldsymbol{u}(x)=\frac{1}{2\pi}\int\limits_{\gamma}\boldsymbol{g}(y)\,\mathrm{T}G(x,\ y)\,dS_y+\int\limits_{l}\boldsymbol{f}(y)\,\mathrm{T}G(x,\ y)\,dl_y, \qquad (9.110)$$

where $\boldsymbol{g}(y)$ is a vector function prescribed on γ, and $G(x, y)$ is Green's tensor of the first problem for the elliptic domain (of an anisotropic body). The construction of the tensor $G(x, y)$ reduces to solving the first boundary-value problem for the ellipse; this problem was explicitly solved in § 3 of the present chapter. Substituting the expression for Green's tensor in (9.110), we obtain the explicit solution of the first problem for a pressed anisotropic elliptic plate. If not the displacement but the stresses are prescribed on the external boundary of the ellipse, we have the second problem for a pressed anisotropic elliptic plate. The solution of this problem reduces to deriving the second Green's tensor for an anisotropic ellipse. This in turn amounts to solving the second boundary-value problem for the ellipse, which was also done in § 3. We shall not go into other plane problems of pressed components; let us only remark that whenever the corresponding Green's tensors can be obtained explicitly, so will the solutions, as we have seen in the above examples.

§ 11. Solution of some three-dimensional problems of pressed components

These problems were considered briefly in (IV, 7). Let us now consider them in greater detail. We assume that a hollow cavity, bounded by the surface S, exists before the deformation within an isotropic body B_a having an arbitrarily shaped boundary S_a; into this cavity is now inserted another body B_i of the same shape S but slightly larger in size. In mechanical engineering, in designing cannon barrels, and in other technical problems, it is necessary to calculate stratified tubes, pipes, wheels, etc.; this amounts to calculating the deformations of variously shaped bodies, sectionally-pressed by homogeneous or inhomogeneous materials. Explicit solutions may be obtained by our method in those cases when the conditions at the interface between the pressed parts reduce to stress continuity across it, and the given discontinuity of displacements:

$$u_i - u_a = g(y), \quad (\mathrm{T}^{(i)} u(y))_i = (\mathrm{T}^{(a)} u(y))_a, \quad y \in S,$$

where $g(y)$ is a vector function prescribed on the interface. Assuming first the insert be small in comparison with the main body, we may apply the method of solving Problem (A) in (IV,2) and obtain the equations

$$4\pi\varkappa(x)\, u(x) = \omega^2 (\mu_a - \mu_i) \int_{B_i} u(y)\, \Gamma_{(a)}(x, y)\, dv_y +$$
$$+ m \int_{B_i} u(y) \operatorname{grad} \operatorname{div} \Gamma_{(a)}(x, y)\, dv_y + \mu_a \int_S u_i(y)\, \mathrm{T}^* \Gamma_{(a)}(x, y)\, dS_y +$$
$$+ \mu_a \int_S g(y)\, \mathrm{T}^{(a)} \Gamma_{(a)}(x, y)\, dS_y + 4\pi\mu_a E(x; x_0), \tag{9.111}$$

$$\varkappa(x) = \begin{cases} \mu_a l & \text{for} \quad x \in B_i, \\ \mu_a & \text{for} \quad x \in B_a. \end{cases}$$

For the static problem $\omega = 0$; the deformation is caused by the size difference between the original hole and the one distended by the squeezed-in body, i. e., there is no source of external deformation (located by the definition of Problem (A) at the point x_*), and so the corresponding equation has the form

$$4\pi\varkappa(x)\, u(x) = m \int_{B_i} u(y) \operatorname{grad} \operatorname{div} \overset{0}{\Gamma}_{(a)}(x, y)\, dv_y +$$
$$+ \mu_a \int_S u_i(y)\, \mathrm{T}^* \overset{0}{\Gamma}_{(a)}(x, y)\, dS_y + \mu_a \int_S g(y)\, \mathrm{T}^{(a)} \overset{0}{\Gamma}_{(a)}(x, y)\, dS_y. \tag{9.112}$$

Solving equations (9.111) and (9.112), we obtain the solutions of the dynamic and static problems.

1°. **Insert of the same material.** In one practically important case these solutions may be obtained without integral equations, namely, when the insert is made of the same material as the main body. Then we have

$$\lambda_i = \lambda_a = \lambda, \quad \mu_i = \mu_a = \mu; \quad m = 0, \quad l = 1, \quad \varkappa(x) = \mu_a = \mu;$$
$$\mathrm{T}^* = \mathrm{T}^{(a)} - \mathrm{T}^{(i)} = 0, \quad \Gamma_{(a)}(x, y) = \Gamma(x, y); \quad \Delta^* E + \omega^2 E = 0, \tag{*}$$

and (9.111) gives for the dynamic problem

$$4\pi u(x) = \int_S g(y)\, \mathrm{T}\Gamma(x, y)\, dS_y + 4\pi E(x; x_*), \tag{9.113}$$

while (9.112) gives for the static problem

$$4\pi u(x) = \int_S g(y)\, \mathrm{T}\overset{0}{\Gamma}(x, y)\, dS_y. \tag{9.114}$$

That (9.113) and (9.114) are indeed solutions of the above problems evidently follows from the general theory developed above, but it may also be demonstrated directly. Let us do this in the case of (9.113); the proof for (9. 114) is similar.

Formulas (*) imply that in B_i and in B_a

$$\Delta^* u + \omega^2 u = \mu \Delta u + (\lambda + \mu) \operatorname{grad} \operatorname{div} u + \omega^2 u = 0. \tag{9.115}$$

Since the integral on the right-hand side of (9.113) is a double-layer potential (of the first kind), we have by (2.1)

$$u_a - u_i = g(y), \quad y \in S. \tag{9.116}$$

We now apply the generalized Lyapunov-Tauber theorem; the double-layer potential has a continuous T-transform, if its density is twice differentiable*. Applying T to (9.113) and passing to the limit as x approaches the boundary from the inside and from the outside, we obtain

$$(\mathsf{T}u(x))_i = (\mathsf{T}u(x))_a. \tag{9.117}$$

It is clear from (9.113) that the solution possesses the required singularity at x_*. The relations (9.115)–(9.117) show therefore that (9.113) is indeed a solution of the dynamic problem for such a pressed body.

2°. **Many-layered pressed body.** Let the insert B_i, pressed in B_a, itself contain a hole of the shape S_1, into which another insert of the same material and the same shape S_1 but slightly bigger, is then pressed. The deformed state of such a body is described by the vector field

$$4\pi u(x) = \int_S g(y)\,\mathsf{T}\overset{0}{\Gamma}(x, y)\,dS_y + \int_{S_1} g_1(y)\,\mathsf{T}\overset{0}{\Gamma}(x, y)\,dS_{1y}, \tag{9.118}$$

where $g_1(y)$ is a vector function prescribed given at the points of contact along the surface S_1.

The proof is the same as the preceding one. The solution for an n-layered pressed body is evidently

$$4\pi u(x) = \sum_{k=0}^{n} \int_{S_k} g_k(y)\,\mathsf{T}\overset{0}{\Gamma}(x, y)\,dS_{ky}; \tag{9.119}$$

where $g_k(y)$ are vector functions prescribed on the surfaces of contact S_k, $k = 1, 2, \ldots, n$ and $S_0 = S$.

3°. **Pressed body of finite size.** Let B_a be a finite body, bounded by the closed surface S_a; let B_a have n cavities, bounded by nonintersecting surfaces S_k, $k = 1, 2, \ldots, n$; let these cavities contain pressed inserts of the same material as B_a, so that the following conditions hold on S_k, $k = 1, 2, \ldots, n$,

$$u_a - u_i = g_k(y), \quad (\mathsf{T}u(y))_i = (\mathsf{T}u(y))_a, \quad y \in S_k \quad (k = 1, 2, \ldots, n);$$

here $g_k(y)$, $k = 1, 2, \ldots, n$ are vector functions given on S_k. We further assume that either (a) the displacements or (b) the stresses, which we denote by $f(x)$, are given on S_a.

Repeating the arguments of IV, 4, we now obtain in case (a)

$$4\pi u(x) = \sum_{k=1}^{n} \int_{S_k} g_k(y)\,\mathsf{T}\overset{0}{G}(x, y)\,dS_y + \int_{S_a} f(y)\,\mathsf{T}\overset{0}{G}(x, y)\,dS_y \tag{9.120}$$

and in case (b)

$$4\pi u(x) = \sum_{k=1}^{n} \int_{S_k} g_k(y)\,\mathsf{T}\overset{0}{H}(x, y)\,dS_y - \int_{S_k} f(y)\,\overset{0}{H}{}^*(x, y)\,dS_y, \tag{9.121}$$

where $\overset{0}{G}(x, y)$ and $\overset{0}{H}(x, y)$ are respectively the static first and second Green's tensors for the entire domain B, bounded by the surface S_a.

Thus, whenever the corresponding Green's tensor is known for the domain B, formulas (9.120) and (9.121) furnish solutions of the stated problems.

It is well known that Green's tensors may actually be derived explicitly

* This condition is sufficient.

for plane problems of many contours of practical importance, and the relations (9.120) and (9.121) which remain valid in the plane case may then be used to deduce explicit solutions for problems of pressed plane components.

4°. **Half-space with pressed inserts.** Consider the particular case of the preceding problem when the surface S_a coincides with the plane $x_3=0$. It was shown in (IV, 5) that the first and second Green's tensors for a half-space are respectively of the form

$$\overset{0}{G}{}^{(k)}(x,\ y)=\overset{0}{\Gamma}{}^{(k)}_{(a)}(x,\ y)+\frac{1}{2\pi}\int_{-\infty}^{+\infty}\overset{0}{\Gamma}_{\text{II}}(x,\ x')\overset{0}{\Gamma}{}^{(k)}_{(a)}(x';\ y)\,dS_{x'},$$

and

$$\overset{0}{H}{}^{(k)}(x,\ y)=\overset{0}{\Gamma}{}^{(k)}_{(a)}(x,\ y)+\frac{1}{2\pi}\int_{-\infty}^{+\infty}M_{(a)}(x,\ x')\,\mathrm{T}_{x'}\overset{0}{\Gamma}{}^{(k)}_{(a)}(x';\ y)\,dS_{x'},$$

$$(k=1,\ 2,\ 3).$$

Consequently, formulas (9.120) and (9.121) provide in this case solutions in a closed form for deformation problems of a half-space with pressed inserts. It may be verified directly that this method actually yields solutions for the two boundary-value problems.

Let us apply the operator $\mu\Delta+(\lambda+\mu)\,\text{grad div}$ to (9.120) and (9.121); in virtue of the properties of Green's tensors (IV, 3 and 4), and since $\Delta^*\mathrm{T}H(x,\ y)=0$ (VII, 9), we obtain

$$\Delta^* u(x)=0. \tag{9.122}$$

If the stresses are given on S_a we must also use here the solvability condition (VII, 9). Further, since each of the integrals over the surfaces S_k, $k=1,\ 2,\ \ldots,\ n$, appearing in (9.120) and (9.121), is a double-layer potential, then by the theorem on boundary discontinuities of such potentials and by the Lyapunov-Tauber theorem, we have on S_k, $k=1,\ 2,\ \ldots,\ n$,

$$u_a-u_i=g_k(y),\quad (\mathrm{T}u(x))_i \underset{x\to y}{=}(\mathrm{T}u(x))_a\quad y\in S_k\quad (k=1,\ 2,\ \ldots,\ n). \tag{9.123}$$

Let us check the conditions on the external boundary. When x approaches the point y_0 on S_a, we find that by the properties of Green's tensors (IV, 3, 4)

$$\lim_{x\to y_0\in S_a}\overset{0}{G}(x,\ y)=0,\qquad \lim_{x\to y_0\in S_a}\mathrm{T}_x\overset{0}{H}(x,\ y)=0,\qquad y\,\overline{\in}\,S_a;$$

and further (VI, 7)

$$\lim_{x\to y_0}\int_{S_a}f(y)\,\mathrm{T}_y\overset{0}{G}(x,\ y)\,dS_y=4\pi f(y_0),$$

$$\lim_{x\to y_0}\mathrm{T}_x\int_{S_a}f(y)\,\overset{0}{H}{}^*(x,\ y)\,dS_y=-4\pi f(y_0).$$

After passing to the limit in (9.120) and (9.121)* for $x\to y_0\in S_a$, we obtain in view of the above formulas

$$\lim_{x\to y_0}u(x)=f(y_0),$$

$$\lim_{x\to y_0\in S_a}Tu(x)=f(y_0). \tag{9.124}$$

The last relations show that the boundary conditions of the first and second problems are fulfilled on S_a. Formulas (9.122)–(9.124) thus prove that (9.120) and (9.121) are indeed solutions of the first and second problems of strain of an elastic finite body, pressed by n elastic inserts.

* First applying the T-operator.

§ 12. The method of successive approximations

Some of the foregoing functional equations associated with general problems may be solved by the method of successive approximations. This applies, for instance, to the equations of the static Problems (A) and (B_1) in the case of equal Poisson's ratios; these equations have, as shown in (VII, 2) the form

$$\varkappa(x)\,\boldsymbol{u}(x)=\frac{1}{4\pi}(\mu_a-\mu_i)\int\limits_S \boldsymbol{u}_i(y)\,\mathrm{T}_y^{(a)}\overset{0}{\Gamma}_{(a)}(x,\,y)\,dS_y+\mu_a E(x;\,x_*) \tag{9.125}$$

and

$$\varkappa(x)\,\boldsymbol{u}(x)=\frac{1}{4\pi}(\mu_a-\mu_i)\int\limits_S \boldsymbol{u}_i(y)\,\mathrm{T}_y^{(a)}\overset{0}{G}(x,\,y)\,dS_y+\frac{\mu_a}{4\pi}\int\limits_{S_a} f(y)\,\mathrm{T}_y^{(a)}\overset{0}{G}(x,y)\,dS_y. \tag{9.126}$$

Passing to the limit for $x\in B_i$ approaching the point y_0 on S we obtain the integral equations

$$\boldsymbol{u}_i(y_0)-\frac{\varkappa}{2\pi}\int\limits_S \boldsymbol{u}_i(y)\,\mathrm{T}_y^{(a)}\overset{0}{\Gamma}_{(a)}(y_0,\,y)\,dS_y=\frac{2\mu_a}{\mu_a+\mu_i}E(y_0;\,x_*) \tag{9.125'}$$

and

$$\boldsymbol{u}_i(y_0)-\frac{\varkappa}{2\pi}\int\limits_S \boldsymbol{u}_i(y)\,\mathrm{T}_y^{(a)}\overset{0}{G}(y_0,\,y)\,dS_y=\frac{\mu_a}{2\pi(\mu_i+\mu_a)}\int\limits_{S_a} f(y)\,\mathrm{T}_y^{(a)}\overset{0}{G}(y_0,\,y)\,dS_y, \tag{9.126'}$$

where the parameter $\varkappa$ is

$$\varkappa=\frac{\mu_a-\mu_i}{\mu_a+\mu_i}. \tag{9.127}$$

The kernels of the integral equations (9.125') and (9.126') obviously depend only on the parameters λ_a and μ_a, not on λ_i and μ_i. Assuming the first to be fixed, we may state that the considered kernels do not depend on $\varkappa$. In order to obtain solutions of the functional eqautions (9.125) and (9.126) it is sufficient, by Theorem 4 of (VII, 2) to solve the integral equations (9.125') and (9.126'). It follows from Ch. V that these singular equations are generally solvable only when $\varkappa$ is not a pole of the resolvent. The resolvent may be represented by the ratio of two everywhere convergent power series in $\varkappa$, and a pole of the resolvent may only be a zero of the power series in the denominator. By Theorem 2 of (VI, 1) and Theorem 2' of (VII, 2) the eigenvalues of (9.125') and (9.126'), i. e., the zeros of the denominator of the resolvent, cannot be smaller then one in absolute value; since (9.127) implies that $|\varkappa|<1$, these are certainly no eigenvalues. Therefore the resolvents of (9.125') and (9.126') represent power series in $\varkappa$, which converge within the circle $|\varkappa|<1$ of the complex $\varkappa$-plane. Accordingly we may look for solutions in the form of series converging in that circle,

$$u_i(y_0)=\sum_{k=0}^{\infty}\varkappa^k\varphi^{(k)}(y_0), \tag{9.128}$$

where $\varphi^{(k)}(y_0)$ $(k=0,\,1,\,2,\,\ldots)$ are unknown vectors. The uniqueness of solution, of which Ch. VII assures us here, implies that (9.128) is also a solution of a Fredholm equation, which may be constructed as explained in Ch. V and which is equivalent to (9.125') and (9.126'). Substitution of the power series (9.128) in that Fredholm equation would give again the known recurrence relations for $\varphi^{(k)}(y_0)$ $(k=0,\,1,\,\ldots)$. However, the equivalent Fredholm equation is not given explicitly, so that this will lead us nowhere. We apply instead the following simple and convenient method. It is clear from the discussion of the recurrence relations obtained from the Fredholm equation, that the vectors $\varphi^{(k)}(y_0)(k=0, 1, \ldots)$ belong to class H. Writing (9.125') and (9.126') in the form

$$u_i(y_0) - \frac{\varkappa}{2\pi}\int\limits_S \left\{\sum_{k=0}^{\infty} \varkappa^k [\varphi^{(k)}(y) - \varphi^{(k)}(y_0)]\right\} \overset{0}{\mathrm{T}_y^{(a)}\Gamma_{(a)}}(y_0, y)\, dS_y -$$

$$-\frac{\varkappa}{2\pi} u_i(y_0) \int\limits_S \overset{0}{\mathrm{T}_y^{(a)}\Gamma_{(a)}}(y_0, y)\, dS_y = \frac{2\mu_a}{\mu_a+\mu_i} E(y_0, x_*),$$

$$u_i(y_0) - \frac{\varkappa}{2\pi}\int\limits_S \left\{\sum_{k=0}^{\infty} \varkappa^k [\varphi^{(k)}(y) - \varphi^{(k)}(y_0)]\right\} \overset{0}{\mathrm{T}_y^{(a)}G}(y_0, y)\, dS_y -$$

$$-\frac{\varkappa}{2\pi} u_i(y_0) \int\limits_S \overset{0}{\mathrm{T}_y^{(a)}G}(y_0, y)\, S_y = \frac{\mu_a}{2\pi(\mu_i+\mu_a)} \int\limits_{S_a} f(y)\, \overset{0}{\mathrm{T}_y^{(a)}G}(y_0, y)\, dS_y,$$

which is permissible because the singular integrals

$$\int\limits_S \overset{0}{\mathrm{T}_y^{(a)}\Gamma_{(a)}}(y_0, y)\, dS_y, \quad \int\limits_S \overset{0}{\mathrm{T}_y^{(a)}G}(y_0, y)\, dS_y$$

exist, we reverse the order of summation and integration (the first terms converge absolutely), and hence obtain

$$\sum_{k=0}^{\infty} \varkappa^k \varphi^{(k)}(y_0) - \frac{1}{2\pi}\sum_{k=0}^{\infty} \varkappa^{k+1} \int\limits_S \varphi^{(k)}(y)\, \overset{0}{\mathrm{T}_y^{(a)}\Gamma_{(a)}}(y_0, y)\, dS_y =$$

$$= \frac{2\mu_a}{\mu_a+\mu_i} E(y_0, x_*),$$

$$\sum_{k=0}^{\infty} \varkappa^k \varphi^{(k)}(y_0) - \frac{1}{2\pi}\sum_{k=0}^{\infty} \varkappa^{k+1} \int\limits_S \varphi^{(k)}(y)\, \overset{0}{\mathrm{T}_y^{(a)}G}(y_0, y)\, dS_y =$$

$$= \frac{\mu_a}{2\pi(\mu_i+\mu_a)} \int\limits_{S_a} f(y)\, \overset{0}{\mathrm{T}_y^{(a)}G}(y_0, y)\, dS_y.$$

Equating now the coefficients of equal powers of $\varkappa$, we obtain successively all the $\varphi^k(y_0)$ $(k=1, 2, \ldots)$. It is not necessary to prove the convergence of (9.128) separately, since the above discussion shows that it follows from the existence and uniqueness theorems.

Chapter X

APPROXIMATE SOLUTIONS

The functional equations which we have used in proving existence theorems may also be applied to obtain approximate numerical solutions /15/. We shall use for this purpose a method, based on replacing the integral (functional) equations by systems of linear algebraic equations which are in a certain sense equivalent to the original equations, (§§ 1–19), and also the method of generalized Fourier expansions in certain complete sets of functions (§§ 20–37).

Let us first mention some known facts. Consider a Fredholm integral equation of the second kind

$$\varphi(x)+\int_a^b K(x, y)\varphi(y)\,dy=f(x), \tag{10.1}$$

where $K(x, y)$ and $f(x)$ are differentiable up to a certain order; we assume that a unique solution of this equation exists within some class of functions. Applying a quadrature formula, we bring (10.1) to the form

$$\varphi(x)+\sum_{i=1}^{N} A_i^{(N)} K(x, y_i)\varphi(y_i)+\delta(x; \varphi)=f(x), \tag{10.2}$$

where N is the number of subdivisions of the interval (a, b) by the basic points y_i; $A_i^{(N)}$ and y_i are numbers, fixed for the given integration interval and the chosen quadrature formula, and $\delta(x; \varphi)$ is the quadrature error. Usually

$$A_i^{(N)} \geqslant 0, \quad \sum_{i=1}^{N} A_i^{(N)}=b-a.$$

Thus for rectangular quadrature

$$y_1=a, \quad y_2=a+\frac{b-a}{N}, \ \ldots, \ y_N=a+(N-1)\frac{b-a}{N}, \quad A_i=\frac{b-a}{N};$$

for Gaussian quadrature

$$y_i=a+(b-a)\,y_i^{(N)}, \quad A_i^{(N)}=(b-a)\,C_i^{(N)}, \tag{10.3}$$

where $y_i^{(N)}$ are the Gaussian points (roots of a Legendre polynomial), and $C_i^{(N)}$ the Gaussian coefficients for the interval (0, 1). The rectangular quadrature error is estimated by

$$|\delta(x; \varphi)| \leqslant \frac{M(b-a)^3}{24N^2},$$

where

$$M > \left|\{K(x, y)\varphi(y)\}''_{y=\eta}\right|, \quad a \leqslant \eta \leqslant b,$$

while for the Gaussian error

$$|\delta(x;\varphi)| < \frac{(b-a)^{2N+1}(N!)^4 M}{(2N+1)[(2N)!]^3}, \tag{10.4}$$

where

$$M > \left|\{K(x, y)\varphi(y)\}^{(2N)}_{y=\eta}\right|, \quad \eta \in (a, b). \tag{10.4'}$$

Equation (10.2) holds for any value of x in the interval (a, b), in particular for $x_i = y_i$, $i = 1, 2, \ldots, N$, and the values $\delta(x_i; \varphi)$ are bounded. Assuming them to be small for sufficiently large N, we may replace (10.2) by the system of equations in $\tilde{\varphi}(y_j)$, $j = 1, 2, \ldots, N$,

$$\tilde{\varphi}(y_j) + \sum_{i=1}^{N} A_i^{(N)} K(y_j, y_i)\tilde{\varphi}(y_i) = f(y_j) \qquad (j = 1, 2, \ldots, N) \tag{10.5}$$

and consider the latter as an approximate representation of the integral equation (10.1). Here $\tilde{\varphi}(y_k)$ denotes an approximate value of the function $\varphi(y)$ at the point y_k.

Let Δ_{kl} be the cofactor of the element in the k-th row and l-th column of the determinant, Δ, of the system (10.5). The deviations of the values of the exact solution at y_k from the approximate values there are obtained by comparing the solutions of (10.2) and (10.5),

$$|\varphi(y_k) - \tilde{\varphi}(y_k)| = \left| \frac{\sum_{l=1}^{N} \Delta_{kl}\delta(x_l, \varphi)}{\Delta} \right|. \tag{10.5'}$$

The unknown φ appears on the right-hand side; expressing it in terms of known quantities with the aid of the solution of (10.1), one may deduce the constant M which appears in the error formulas, so that (10.5') becomes a quite convenient estimate of the approximation error for a given N.

Thus, if the kernel and the right-hand member of (10.1) possess the degree of smoothness required for the above reduction, the solution reduces to solving a system of N linear algebraic equations in N unknowns. Unfortunately, this method meets with basic difficulties when applied to the integral equations of mathematical physics; in most cases the kernels are not only not differentiable but not even continuous, and it is not possible to set up the system (10.5). The integral equations of the theory of elasticity are in this sense typical. However, as we shall see later, the theory of boundary-value problems developed in Ch. IV–VII, enables us to arrive at functional equations which admit approximate solution by the above method. Let us now examine a few examples.

§ 1. Diffraction of elastic waves

Let B_i be a finite plane or three-dimensional domain with a closed Lyapunov boundary S, which is empty of matter. Let B_a be the infinite domain which complements B_i to make up the entire space, and let it be occupied by an elastic medium with the Lamé constants λ_a, μ_a. A source of time-periodic elastic oscillations of frequency ω, which differs from that of any normal mode of B_i, is located at the point $x_* \in B_a$. Let $\boldsymbol{E}(x; x_*)$ be the displacement field caused by this source in the infinite homogeneous space characterized by the constants λ_a, μ_a; this field is easily derived and may be considered as given; clearly

$$\overset{*}{\Delta}_{(a)}\boldsymbol{E} + \omega^2\boldsymbol{E} = 0, \quad x \in B_i + B_a, \quad x \neq x_*. \tag{10.6}$$

The problem of the diffraction of the steady field around the cavity B_i reduces to finding the vector function $\boldsymbol{u}(x)$ from the conditions

1°. $$\overset{*}{\Delta}_{(a)}\boldsymbol{u}(x)+\omega^2\boldsymbol{u}(x)=0, \quad x\in B_a.$$

2°. $$(\mathrm{T}^{(a)}\boldsymbol{u}(x_0))_a=0, \quad x_0\in S.$$

3°. The difference $\boldsymbol{u}(x)-\boldsymbol{E}(x;\ x_*)$ must be a regular vector function in B_a.

For a start we will obtain the existence theorem for this problem. We represent the solution in the form

$$\boldsymbol{u}(x)=\frac{1}{2\pi}\int_S \varphi(y)\Gamma(x,\ y)\,dS_y+\boldsymbol{E}(x;\ x_*), \quad x\in B_a; \tag{10.7}$$

then, using the boundary condition 2°, we obtain by Theorem 4 of (II,1) and in virtue of the continuity of $\mathrm{T}\boldsymbol{E}(x;\ x_*)$ on S, the following integral equation for $\varphi(y)$

$$\varphi(y_0)-\frac{1}{2\pi}\int_S \varphi(y)\,\mathrm{T}_{y_0}\Gamma(y_0,\ y)\,dS_y=\mathrm{T}_{y_0}\boldsymbol{E}(y_0;\ x_*). \tag{10.8}$$

This singular equation was studied in (VI, 12); it is uniquely solvable and provides a solution for a problem of the type (10.7) which satisfies the required conditions.

Equation (10.8) is not directly reducible to a system of linear algebraic equations by the above quadrature method because its kernel, represented by the matrix $\mathrm{T}_{y_0}\Gamma(y_0,\ y)$, has a pole at $y=y_0$, and the diagonal coefficients of (10.5) are then meaningless. We therefore proceed in another way. We first assume that B_i is not empty but occupied by an elastic medium with the Lamé constants $\lambda_i,\ \mu_i$, and that this medium is coupled to the external medium in the domain B_a through free contact along the surface S. The field of the point source, as we have seen in (IV, 7) is then described by a system of functional equations of the type

$$\begin{aligned}\varkappa(x)\boldsymbol{u}(x)=\ &\omega^2(\mu_a-\mu_i)\int_{B_i}\boldsymbol{u}(y)\Gamma_{(a)}(x,\ y)\,dv_y+\\ &+m\int_{B_i}\boldsymbol{u}(y)\,\mathrm{grad\,div}\,\Gamma_{(a)}(x,\ y)\,dv_y+\mu_a\int_S \boldsymbol{u}_i(y)\,\overset{*}{\mathrm{T}}_y\Gamma_{(a)}(x,\ y)\,dS_y+\\ &+\mu_a\int_S\varphi(y)\,\mathrm{T}_y^{(a)}\Gamma_{(a)}(x,\ y)\,dS_y+4\pi\mu_a\boldsymbol{E}(x,\ x_*),\end{aligned} \tag{10.9}$$

where φ denotes the difference

$$\boldsymbol{u}_a-\boldsymbol{u}_i;$$

the other notations have the same meaning as in (IV, 7); in particular

$$\varkappa(x)=\begin{cases}\dfrac{4}{3}\pi\left(2\mu_i+\dfrac{\lambda_i+2\mu_i}{\lambda_a+2\mu_a}\mu_a\right) & \text{for} \quad x\in B_i,\\ 4\pi\mu_a \quad \text{for} \quad x\in B_a.\end{cases}$$

We have seen in Ch. VII that (10.9) has a unique solution for sufficiently small values of the parameter $|m|$,

$$|m|=|\lambda_i\mu_a-\lambda_a\mu_i|.$$

This solution is simultaneously a solution, in the ordinary or generalized sense of the elastic problem

a) $\overset{*}{\Delta}_{(i)}\boldsymbol{u}(x)+\omega^2\boldsymbol{u}(x)=0, \quad x\in B_i,$ (10.10$_1$)

b) $\overset{*}{\Delta}_{(a)}\boldsymbol{u}(x)+\omega^2\boldsymbol{u}(x)=0, \quad x\in B_a,$ (10.10$_2$)

c) $\boldsymbol{u}_a(x)-\boldsymbol{u}_i(x)=\varphi(x), \quad x\in S,$ (10.10$_3$)

d) $(\mathrm{T}^{(i)}u(x))_i=(\mathrm{T}^{(a)}u(x))_a, \quad x\in S,$ (10.10$_4$)

e) $u(x)-E(x;\,x_*)$, $x\in B_a$, is a solution of (10.6), regular in B_a.

Let us now assume that $\lambda_i=\mu_i=0$; then $m=0$, and the existence theorem for equation (10.9) is valid. Condition (10.10$_1$) implies that $u(x)=0$ in B_i, and consequently $u_i(x)=0$ on S; therefore

$$\varphi(x)=u_a(x) \text{ for } x\in S, \tag{10.11}$$

by (10.10$_3$), and

$$(\mathrm{T}^{(a)}u(x))_a=0 \text{ for } x\in S, \tag{10.12}$$

by (10.10$_4$), and finally (10.9) itself becomes

$$u(x)=\frac{1}{4\pi}\int_S \varphi(y)\,\mathrm{T}_y^{(a)}\Gamma_{(a)}(x,\,y)\,dS_y+E(x;\,x_*), \qquad x\in B_a, \tag{10.13$_1$}$$

$$0=\frac{1}{4\pi}\int_S \varphi(y)\,\mathrm{T}_y^{(a)}\Gamma_{(a)}(x,\,y)\,dS_y+E(x;\,x_*), \qquad x\in B_i. \tag{10.13$_2$}$$

This result may also be obtained directly. Indeed, our diffraction problem must have, in view of the above discussion, a solution of the form (10.7). It follows that the vector function

$$D(x;\,x_*)=u(x)-E(x;\,x_*),$$

where $u(x)$ is the solution in question, is a solution of the equation $\overset{*}{\Delta}_{(a)}D+\omega^2 D=0$, which is regular in B_a. We have seen in (III, 3) that the Betti relation applies to solutions of the equations of elasticity that are regular in B_a. Assuming the point x to lie first in B_a, and then in B_i, and applying in turn the Betti relation to $D(y;\,x_*)$ and $\Gamma_{(a)}(x,\,y)$, we obtain

$$4\pi D(x)=\int_S \left[D_a(y)\,\mathrm{T}_y^{(a)}\Gamma_{(a)}(x,\,y)-\Gamma_{(a)}(x,\,y)(\mathrm{T}^{(a)}D(y))_a\right]dS_y, \qquad x\in B_a,$$

$$0=\int_S \left[D_a(y)\,\mathrm{T}_y^{(a)}\Gamma_{(a)}(x,\,y)-\Gamma_{(a)}(x,\,y)(\mathrm{T}^{(a)}D(y))_a\right]dS_y, \qquad x\in B_i.$$

Taking into account the boundary condition 2° and the equalities

$$0=\int_S E(y;\,x_*)\,\mathrm{T}_y^{(a)}\Gamma_{(a)}(x,\,y)\,dS_y-\int_S \Gamma_{(a)}(x,\,y)\,\mathrm{T}_y^{(a)}E(y;\,x_*)\,dS_y, \qquad x\in B_a,$$

$$4\pi E(x;\,x_*)=\int_S E(y;\,x_*)\,\mathrm{T}_y^{(a)}\Gamma_{(a)}(x,\,y)\,dS_y-\int_S \Gamma_{(a)}(x,\,y)\,\mathrm{T}_y^{(a)}E(y;\,x_*)\,dS_y, \qquad x\in B_i,$$

which result from applying the Betti relation in B_i (but now with the operator $\overset{*}{\Delta}_{(a)}$) to $E(y;\,x_*)$ and $\Gamma_{(a)}(x,\,y)$, we obtain (10.13$_1$) and (10.13$_2$). Thus, if $\varphi(y)$ is derived from (10.13$_2$), then the $u(x)$ defined by (10.13$_1$) satisfies, on account of (10.10$_2$), the equation

$$\overset{*}{\Delta}_{(a)}u(x)+\omega^2 u(x)=0, \qquad x\in B_a,$$

and, on account of (10.12), the boundary condition 2° on S; (10.13$_1$) also ensures that condition e) is fulfilled. It follows that (10.13$_1$) and (10.13$_2$) indeed represent the solution of our problem. This may also be inferred directly from the general theory of Ch. VII — one may show that a $u(x)$ which satisfies (10.13$_1$) and (10.13$_2$) exists, is unique, and satisfies the conditions 1°, 2°, 3°.

A vector function $\varphi(y)$ of class H, defined for the points $y \in S$ and independent of x, is called a solution of the functional equation (10.13_2) if on substituting it this equation is satisfied identically for all $x \in B_i$.

Functional equations of the type (10.13_2), in which $\varphi(y)$ appears only under the integral sign, and the domains of the variables x and y do not coincide, will be called canonical functional equations.

Passing to the limit in (10.13_2) as the x of B_i tends to y_0 on S, we have by Theorem 2 of (II, 1)

$$\varphi(y_0) - \frac{1}{2\pi}\int_S \varphi(y)\, T_y^{(a)}\Gamma(y_0, y)\, dS_y = 2E(y_0; x_*). \tag{10.14}$$

This is a singular equation corresponding to problem (D_i) with the boundary value of the unknown vector equal to $-2E(y_0; x_*)$. Equation (10.14) is solvable (cf. VI, 8) because ω is assumed not to be an eigenvalue of (D_i^0), and the solution is uniquely determined by means of Fredholm's first theorem (V, 9). We shall show that this is also a unique solution of the functional equation (10.13_2). Substituting the solution of (10.14) $\varphi(y)$ into (10.13_2),

$$v(x) = \frac{1}{4\pi}\int_S \varphi(y)\, T_y^{(a)}\Gamma_{(a)}(x, y)\, dS_y + E(x; x_*), \quad x \in B_i.$$

Evidently

$$\overset{*}{\Delta}_{(a)} v(x) + \omega^2 v(x) = 0, \quad x \in B_i,$$
$$v_i(y_0) = 0, \quad y_0 \in S,$$

and by Theorem 9 of Ch. VI, $v(x) = 0$ for $x \in B_i$, since ω is not an eigenfrequency of the homogeneous internal problem (D_i^0), which proves the existence of solution. The uniqueness follows from the fact that the homogeneous equation

$$\frac{1}{2\pi}\int_S \varphi(y)\, T_y^{(a)}\Gamma_{(a)}(x, y)\, dS_y = 0, \quad x \in B_i \tag{10.15}$$

possesses only a trivial solution. Indeed, suppose $\varphi_0(y)$ is a nontrivial solution of the homogeneous functional equation (10.15); then the double-layer potential

$$W(x; \varphi_0) = \frac{1}{2\pi}\int_S \varphi_0(y)\, T^{(a)}\Gamma_{(a)}(x, y)\, dS_y$$

vanishes identically in B_i, and therefore also

$$(T^{(a)} W(y_0; \varphi_0))_i = 0.$$

But the Lyapunov-Tauber theorem (VI, 9) now gives

$$(T^{(a)} W(y_0; \varphi_0))_a = 0,$$

and by Theorem 1 of (III, 4) $W(x; \varphi_0)$ vanishes identically also in B_a, because it is a regular solution of the equations of elasticity in this domain. By Theorem 2 of (II, 1) we now have $\varphi_0(y) = 0$, which proves the uniqueness. To prove c) note that the validity of conditions 1° and 3° follows directly from the form of (10.13_1), on account of (10.6). To prove the property 2°, note that (10.13_2) implies the existence of the inner limit

$$\left(T^{(a)}\int_S \varphi(y)\, T_y^{(a)}\Gamma_{(a)}(x, y)\, dS_y\right)_i;$$

the analogous outer limit also exists by the Lyapunov-Tauber theorem, and the two limits are equal. Applying the $T^{(a)}$-operator to (10.13_1) and (10.13_2), and forming the difference between the limiting values on S, we obtain (10.12), which is identical with 2°. This completes the proof of a), b), c). We now write

$$K(x, y) = \frac{1}{4\pi} T_x^{(a)} \Gamma_{(a)}(x, y),$$

so that (10.13_1) and (10.13_2) become

$$u(x) = \int_S \varphi(y) K(y, x)\, dS_y + E(x; x_*), \qquad x \in B_a, \qquad (10.13_1')$$

$$0 = \int_S \varphi(y) K(y, x)\, dS_y + E(x; x_*), \qquad x \in B_i. \qquad (10.13_2')$$

This system lends itself to the algebraic method of approximate solution. Indeed, replacing the integral in ($10.13'_2$) by one of the quadrature formulas, we obtain

$$\sum_{l=1}^{N} A_l^{(N)} \varphi(y_l) K(y_l, x) = -E(x; x_*) \qquad x \in B_i, \qquad (10.16)$$

where $A_l^{(N)}$ and y_l are parameters of the chosen formula, $\varphi(y_l)$ ($l = 1, 2, \ldots, N$) are approximate values of the $\varphi(y)$ at the points y_l, and

$$K(y_l, x) = \begin{Vmatrix} K_{11}(y_l, x) & K_{12}(y_l, x) \\ K_{21}(y_l, x) & K_{22}(y_l, x) \end{Vmatrix} \qquad (l = 1, 2, \ldots, N)$$

is a given matrix*. Since the approximate equality (10.16) holds for all x in B_i, these values may be chosen arbitrarily from the internal points of B_i, and thus

$$\sum_{l=1}^{N} A_l^{(N)} \varphi(y_l) K(y_l, x_j) = -E(x_j; x_*) \quad (j = 1, 2, \ldots, N) \quad x_j \in B_i \qquad (10.17)$$

or in component form

$$\sum_{l=1}^{N} \sum_{m=1}^{2} A_l^{(N)} \varphi_m(y_l) K_{m1}(y_l, x_j) = -E_1(x_j; x_*),$$
$$\sum_{l=1}^{N} \sum_{m=1}^{2} A_l^{(N)} \varphi_m(y_l) K_{m2}(y_l; x_j) = -E_2(x_j; x_*). \qquad (10.17')$$

The possibility of choosing the points x_j ($j = 1, 2, \ldots, N$) strictly from the interior of B_i ensures the boundedness of the coefficients in (10.17); the fact that a free term containing $\varphi(x)$ is absent in ($10.13'_2$) indicates that the number of unknowns in this system is equal to the number of equations.

The approximate solution of the diffraction problem is now obtained from ($10.13_1'$),

$$u(x) = \sum_{l=1}^{N} A_l^{(N)} \varphi(y_l) K(y_l, x) + E(x; x_*) \qquad x \in B_a, \qquad (10.18)$$

where $\varphi(y_l) = (\varphi_1(y_l), \varphi_2(y_l))$ ($l = 1, 2, \ldots, N$) is the solution of the system of linear algebraic equations (10.17'). Leaving the question of convergence open, we note that the departure of the approximate solution (10.18) from the exact one depends on the chosen points $x_1, x_2, \ldots, x_N$ and may be evaluated by means of the error formula (10.5') for the method of quadrature used, which depends on x_j ($j = 1, 2, \ldots, N$) as parameters (cf. formulas (10.3) and (10.4)).

* Here we confine ourselves for simplicity to the plane case; the three-dimensional problem is not essentially different.

General arguments and numerical examples presented below give reason to assume that there exists for any given problem an optimal domain of x, from which it is most convenient to choose the x_j $(j=1, 2, \ldots, N)$. This problem, as well as the problem of convergence have not been investigated sufficiently in the general case.

§ 2. Solution of Problem (D_i)

Let the domain B_i be occupied by an elastic medium with the constants λ, μ. Problem (D_i) reduces, as known, to finding a solution $\boldsymbol{u}(x)$, regular in B_i, for the equation

$$\mu \Delta \boldsymbol{u}(x) + (\lambda+\mu) \operatorname{grad} \operatorname{div} \boldsymbol{u}(x) + \omega^2 \boldsymbol{u}(x) = 0, \qquad x \in B_i,$$

that satisfies the boundary condition

$$\boldsymbol{u}_i(y_0) = \boldsymbol{f}(y_0), \qquad y_0 \in S.$$

The vector function $\boldsymbol{f}(y)$ will be assumed to possess second continuous derivatives. General arguments analogous to those used in the preceding section, or the Betti relation (1.63) of (I, 6) show that a solution of this problem will also solve the system of functional equations

$$\boldsymbol{u}(x) = \frac{1}{2\pi} \int_S \Gamma(x, y) \boldsymbol{\varphi}(y) \, dS_y - \frac{1}{4\pi} \int_S \Gamma_{\mathrm{I}}(x, y) \boldsymbol{f}(y) \, dS_y, \qquad x \in B_i, \qquad (10.19_1)$$

$$0 = \frac{1}{2\pi} \int_S \Gamma(x, y) \boldsymbol{\varphi}(y) \, dS_y - \frac{1}{4\pi} \int_S \Gamma_{\mathrm{I}}(x, y) \boldsymbol{f}(y) \, dS_y \qquad x \in B_a, \qquad (10.10_2)$$

where $\boldsymbol{\varphi}(y)$ is an auxiliary vector function which must be determined from (10.19_2). We first assume that this equation has a solution in Hölder's class. Since the right-hand member of (10.19_1) contains single- and double-layer potentials constructed by means of the solution $\Gamma(x, y)$,

$$\mu \Delta \boldsymbol{u}(x) + (\lambda+\mu) \operatorname{grad} \operatorname{div} \boldsymbol{u}(x) + \omega^2 \boldsymbol{u}(x) = 0.$$

In order to verify the boundary condition, we take the difference of the inner and outer limiting values of (10.19_1) and (10.19_2), respectively, and apply the theorems on the continuity of a single-layer potential and the discontinuity of a double-layer potential at the surface S (Theorems 1, 2 of II, 1); we thus find that

$$\boldsymbol{u}_i(x) = \boldsymbol{f}(x), \qquad x \in S.$$

This proves our statement. Let us now show that (10.19_2) has a unique solution of class H. We apply the T-operator to (10.19_2) and pass to the limit as x approaches $x_0 \in S$ from the outside. The restriction on $\boldsymbol{f}(y)$ guarantees the existence of the limit of the T-transform of the double-layer potential of (10.19_2), and by Theorem 4 of (II, 1) we have

$$\boldsymbol{\varphi}(x_0) - \frac{1}{2\pi} \int_S (\mathrm{T}_{x_0} \Gamma(x_0, y)) \boldsymbol{\varphi}(y) \, dS_y = -(\mathrm{T}_{x_0} \boldsymbol{W}(x_0; \boldsymbol{f}))_a, \qquad (10.20)$$

where

$$\boldsymbol{W}(x; \boldsymbol{f}) = \frac{1}{4\pi} \int_S \Gamma_{\mathrm{I}}(x, y) \boldsymbol{f}(y) \, dS_y.$$

Equation (10.20) is the integral equation associated with problem (T_a); if ω

is not an eigenfrequency (frequency of a normal mode of oscillations) of (D_i^0), which we assume as in § 1, then equation (10.20) has by Theorem 12 of (VI, 10) a unique solution which can be determined from Fredholm's first theorem. It remains to show that this solution is at the same time a solution of the functional equation (10.19_2). Let us first consider the three-dimensional case and suppose that the assertion is wrong; introducing the notation

$$\boldsymbol{v}(x) = \frac{1}{2\pi}\int_S \Gamma(x, y)\boldsymbol{\varphi}(y)\, dS_y - \frac{1}{4\pi}\int_S \Gamma_{\text{I}}(x, y)\boldsymbol{f}(y)\, dS_y, \quad x \in B_a, \tag{10.21}$$

where $\boldsymbol{\varphi}(y)$ is the solution of the integral equation (10.20), we have

$$\boldsymbol{v}(x) \not\equiv 0, \quad x \in B_a.$$

On the other hand

$$\Delta^* \boldsymbol{v}(x) + \omega^2 \boldsymbol{v}(x) = 0, \quad x \in B_a,$$
$$(\mathbf{T}\boldsymbol{v}(x))_a = 0, \quad x \in S;$$

which may be easily verified; $\boldsymbol{v}(x)$ further satisfies the radiation condition at infinity; now by Theorem 1 of (III,4)

$$\boldsymbol{v}(x) \equiv 0, \quad x \in B_a.$$

This contradiction proves our assertion.

The proof for the plane problems requires some modifications. In this case, the form of the vector $\boldsymbol{v}(x)$ analogous to expression (10.21), namely

$$\boldsymbol{v}(x) = \frac{1}{\pi}\int_S \Gamma(x, y)\boldsymbol{\varphi}(y)\, dS_y - \frac{1}{2\pi}\int_S \Gamma_{\text{I}}(x, y)\boldsymbol{f}(y)\, dS_y, \quad x \in B_a,$$

does not, generally speaking, imply that it satisfies the radiation condition, because a plane single-layer potential tends asymptotically to infinity; in order to suppress this we only need to impose the condition

$$\int_S \boldsymbol{\varphi}(y)\, dS_y = 0. \tag{10.22}$$

Let us show that in our case this condition is actually satisfied. We replace the coefficient $\frac{1}{2\pi}$ of the integral in (10.20) by $\frac{1}{\pi}$, multiply by dS_{x_0} and integrate over S; keeping in mind that

$$\int_S \Gamma_{\text{I}}(x_0, y)\, dS_y = -\pi \quad \text{for} \quad x_0 \in S,$$

we obtain

$$\int_S \boldsymbol{\varphi}(x_0)\, dS_{x_0} = -\frac{1}{2}\int_S (\mathbf{T}_{x_0}\boldsymbol{W}(x_0; \boldsymbol{f}))_a\, dS_{x_0}. \tag{10.23}$$

The existence of the limit $(\mathbf{T}_x \boldsymbol{W}(x, \boldsymbol{f}))_a$ implies by the Lyapunov-Tauber theorem the existence of $(\mathbf{T}_x \boldsymbol{W}(x, \boldsymbol{f}))_i$ and

$$(\mathbf{T}\boldsymbol{W}(x; \boldsymbol{f}))_i = (\mathbf{T}\boldsymbol{W}(x; \boldsymbol{f}))_a. \tag{10.24}$$

We apply the Betti relation in the domain B_i to the vectors $\boldsymbol{i}_k$ $(k = 1, 2, 3)$ (unit basis vectors) and to the double-layer potential $\boldsymbol{W}(x, \boldsymbol{f})$; this is permitted on account of the restrictions on $\boldsymbol{f}(x)$. We get

$$0 = \int_{B_i} (\boldsymbol{i}_k \Delta^* \boldsymbol{W} - \boldsymbol{W}\Delta^* \boldsymbol{i}_k)\, d\sigma = \int_S \{\boldsymbol{i}_k (\mathbf{T}\boldsymbol{W})_i - \boldsymbol{W}_i \mathbf{T}\boldsymbol{i}_k\}\, dS$$

and, consequently,

$$\int_S (\mathbf{T}W(x;\ f))_i\, dS = 0;$$

hence from (10.24)

$$\int_S (\mathbf{T}W(x;\ f))_a\, dS_x = 0,$$

and (10.22) is proved. We then proceed as in the three-dimensional case.

It remains to demonstrate that the solution is unique. Let the functional equation (10.19_2) have two distinct solutions of class H, φ_1 and φ_2; the difference $\varphi_0 = \varphi_1 - \varphi_2$ satisfies

$$\frac{1}{2\pi}\int_S \Gamma(x,\ y)\,\varphi_0(y)\, dS_y = 0, \qquad x \in B_a.$$

From the continuity of a single-layer potential and Theorem 1 of (III, 4)

$$\frac{1}{2\pi}\int_S \Gamma(x,\ y)\,\varphi_0(y)\, dS_y = 0, \qquad x \in B_i,$$

and by Theorem 4 of (II, 1) these two equalities give

$$\varphi_0(y) \equiv 0.$$

The functional equation (10.19_2), for which we have just proved the existence and uniqueness theorems, is of the canonical type (in the sense of § 2), so we may apply the method of approximate solution of § 1.

The approximate solution of problem (D_i) has the form

$$u(x) = \frac{1}{2\pi}\sum_{i=1}^{N} A_i^{(N)}\Gamma(x;\ y_i)\,\varphi(y_i) - \frac{1}{4\pi}\int_S \Gamma_1(x,\ y)\,f(y)\, dS_y, \qquad x \in B_i,$$

where

$$\varphi(y_1),\ \varphi(y_2),\ \ldots,\ \varphi(y_N)$$

are values of the approximate solution of (10.19_2) at the points $y_1,\ y_2,\ \ldots,\ y_N$, obtained by solving the system of linear equations

$$\sum_{i=1}^{N} A_i^{(N)}\Gamma(x_j,\ y_i)\,\varphi(y_i) = \frac{1}{2}\int_S \Gamma_1(x_j,\ y)\,f(y)\, dS_y,$$

$$x_j \in B_a, \quad y_i \in S \qquad (j = 1,\ 2,\ \ldots,\ N).$$

§ 3. Approximate solution of the static Problem (T_i)

It is required to find a vector $u(x)$ such that

$$\mu\,\Delta u(x) + (\lambda + \mu)\,\mathrm{grad\,div}\, u(x) = 0, \qquad x \in B_i;$$

$$(\mathbf{T}u(x))_i = f(x), \qquad x \in S, \qquad (T_i)$$

where $f(x)$ is a vector of class H, given on the surface S. This problem has a solution, by Theorem 7 of (VI, 5) only provided that

$$\int_S f(x)\, dS_x = 0, \quad \int_S f(x) \times r(x)\, dS_x = 0, \qquad (10.25)$$

where $r(x)$ is the radius-vector of point x. Let us assume that conditions (10.25) are fulfilled. The solution of (T_i), in analogy with the preceding, is represented by the solution of the system of functional equations

$$0 = \frac{1}{4\pi}\int_S \overset{0}{\Gamma}(x,\ y)\,f(y)\, dS_y + \frac{1}{2\pi}\int_S \overset{0}{\Gamma}_1(x,\ y)\,\varphi(y)\, dS_y, \qquad x \in B_a, \qquad (10.26_1)$$

$$u(x)=\frac{1}{4\pi}\int\limits_S \overset{0}{\Gamma}(x,\ y)f(y)\,dS_y+\frac{1}{2\pi}\int\limits_S \overset{0}{\Gamma}_{\rm I}(x,\ y)\varphi(y)\,dS_y,\quad x\in B_i. \qquad (10.26_2)$$

To prove this, we first assume that (10.26_1) has a solution of class H. The existence of the limit of a T-transform of the single-layer potential

$$\frac{1}{4\pi}\int\limits_S \overset{0}{\Gamma}(x,\ y)f(y)\,dS_y$$

as the point x approaches the point $x_0\in S$ from the outside implies the existence of such an external limit for the T-transform of the double-layer potential

$$\frac{1}{2\pi}\int\limits_S \overset{0}{\Gamma}_{\rm I}(x,\ y)\varphi(y)\,dS_y,\quad x\in B_a.$$

But the Lyapunov-Tauber theorem then implies the existence of

$$\left(\frac{1}{2\pi}\mathrm{T}_x\int\limits_S \overset{0}{\Gamma}_{\rm I}(x,\ y)\varphi(y)\,dS_y\right)_i$$

and

$$\left(\mathrm{T}_x\int\limits_S \overset{0}{\Gamma}_{\rm I}(x,\ y)\varphi(y)\,dS_y\right)_i=\left(\mathrm{T}_x\int\limits_S \overset{0}{\Gamma}_{\rm I}(x,\ y)\varphi(y)\,dS_y\right)_a.$$

Carrying out the T-operation on both sides of (10.26_1) and (10.26_2) and taking the difference of their external and internal limiting values, respectively, we obtain by Theorem 4 of (II, 1)

$$(\mathrm{T}u(x))_i=f(x),\quad x\in S.$$

It is also plain from the form of (10.26_2) that

$$\Delta^* u(x)=0,\quad x\in B_i.$$

This proves our statement. It remains to show the existence of solution of the functional equation (10.26_1). Going to the limit as $x\to x_0\in S$ from the outside, we find from Theorems 2 and 1 of (II, 1)

$$\varphi(x_0)+\frac{1}{2\pi}\int\limits_S \overset{0}{\Gamma}_{\rm I}(x_0,\ y)\varphi(y)\,dS_y=-\frac{1}{4\pi}\int\limits_S \overset{0}{\Gamma}(x_0,\ y)f(y)\,dS_y. \qquad (10.27)$$

This is the integral equation associated with problem (D_a), and according to (VI, 5) the necessary and sufficient conditions for its solvability are

$$\int\limits_S \psi^{(s)}(x_0)\left(\int\limits_S \overset{0}{\Gamma}(x_0,\ y)f(y)\,dS_y\right)dS_{x_0}=0,\quad (s=1,\ 2,\ \ldots,\ 6) \qquad (10.28)$$

where $\psi^{(s)}(x_0)$ $(s=1,\ 2,\ 3,\ \ldots,\ 6)$ is a complete system of linearly independent solutions of

$$\psi(x_0)+\frac{1}{2\pi}\int\limits_S \mathrm{T}_{x_0}\overset{0}{\Gamma}(x_0,\ y)\psi(y)\,dS_y=0. \qquad (T_i^0)$$

The solutions of this problem have the form

$$V(x;\ \psi^{(s)})=\frac{1}{2\pi}\int\limits_S \overset{0}{\Gamma}(x,\ y)\psi^{(s)}(y)\,dS_y,\quad x\in B_i\quad (s=1,\ 2,\ \ldots,\ 6)$$

and, as we know (cf. VI, 3) represent rigid displacements. We therefore have from the conditions (10.25)

$$\int_S \psi^{(s)}(x_0)\, dS_{x_0} \int_S \overset{0}{\Gamma}(x_0, y) f(y)\, dS_y =$$

$$= \int_S \left(\int_S \psi^{(s)}(x_0) \overset{0}{\Gamma}(x_0, y)\, dS_{x_0} \right) f(y)\, dS_y =$$

$$= 2\pi \int_S V(y; \psi^{(s)}) f(y)\, dS_y = 0,$$

so that the solvability conditions (10.28) are fulfilled. Let us show that the solutions of the integral equation (10.27) also solve the functional equation (10.26_1). We construct the vector

$$v(x) = \frac{1}{4\pi} \int_S \overset{0}{\Gamma}(x, y) f(y)\, dS_y + \frac{1}{2\pi} \int_S \overset{0}{\Gamma}_1(x, y) \varphi(y)\, dS_y, \quad x \in B_a, \qquad (10.29)$$

where $\varphi(y)$ is a solution of (10.27). Obviously $\Delta^* v(x) = 0$ for $x \in B_a$, and $v_a(x) = 0$ for $x \in S$, and since $v(x)$ satisfies the regularity conditions at infinity, Theorem 5 of (III,4) shows that $v(x) = 0$ for $x \in B_a$. This proves our assertion. The proof of the dimensional case requires some modification at this point. Then $v(x)$ does not vanish at infinity but grows boundlessly, but the proof may be carried through nonetheless with the aid of the solvability conditions (10.25). In the plane case $\overset{0}{\Gamma}(x, y)$ is the matrix (9.2) defined in (IX,1); therefore, terms of the type

$$\int_S f_k(y) \ln r(x, y)\, dS_y \text{ and } \int_S f_k(y) \frac{\partial r(x, y)}{\partial x_l} \frac{\partial r(x, y)}{\partial x_j}\, dS_y$$

$$(k = 1, 2;\ l, j = 1, 2), \qquad (10.30)$$

appear in the single-layer potential which should be shown to vanish at infinity. Let $x'(x'_1, x'_2)$ be an arbitrary fixed point in B_i; we introduce the distance $r(x', x)$ and rewrite (10.30) as follows

$$\int_S f_k(y) \ln r(x, y)\, dS_y =$$

$$= \int_S f_k(y) \ln \frac{r(x, y)}{r(x', x)}\, dS_y + \ln r(x', x) \int_S f_k(y)\, dS_y, \qquad (10.31_1)$$

$$\int_S f_k(y) \frac{\partial r}{\partial x_l} \frac{\partial r}{\partial x_j}\, dS_y =$$

$$= \int_S f_k(y) \left[\frac{(x_l - y_l)(x_j - y_j)}{r^2(x, y)} - \frac{(x_l - x'_l)(x_j - x'_j)}{r^2(x', x)} \right] dS_y +$$

$$+ \frac{\partial r(x', x)}{\partial x_l} \frac{\partial r(x', x)}{\partial x_j} \int_S f_k(y)\, dS_y = \int_S \frac{f_k(y)}{r^2(x, y)\, r^2(x', x)} \{(x_l x_j -$$

$$- x_l y_j - x_j y_l + y_l y_j)[(x_1 - x'_1)^2 + (x_2 - x'_2)^2] -$$

$$- (x_l x_j - x_l x'_j - x_j x'_l - x'_l x'_j)[(x_1 - y_1)^2 + (x_2 - y_2)^2]\}\, dS_y +$$

$$+ \frac{\partial r(x', x)}{\partial x_l} \frac{\partial r}{\partial x_j} \int_S f_k(y)\, dS_y. \qquad (10.31_2)$$

The last terms of both expressions vanish on account of (10.25); as to the first terms, we have in (10.31_1) for x tending to infinity

$$\lim \ln \frac{r(x, y)}{r(x', x)} = 0,$$

and in (10.31_2) this term is of the order $O\left(\frac{1}{r(x, y)}\right)$, which ensures the vanishing at infinity. Thus the $v(x)$ determined by (10.29) satisfies the regularity condition also in the plane problem. The remaining steps are as in the three-dimensional case. The solution of equation (10.26_1) is not unique, because the homogeneous functional equation

$$\frac{1}{2\pi}\int_S \overset{0}{\Gamma}_1(x,\ y)\,\varphi(y)\,dS_y = 0, \qquad x\in B_a, \tag{10.32}$$

is solved by any arbitrary rigid displacement vector, as it follows from the integral equation obtained from (10.32) upon transition to the limit as the point x of B_a approaches x_0 on S. The integral equation derived in this way corresponds to the homogeneous problem (D_a) and, as was shown in (VI, 3) is satisfied solely by a rigid displacement and therefore has six linearly independent solutions. Consequently, the solution of (10.26_1) is determined to within an additive rigid displacement, and it is therefore possible to impose additional conditions to exclude a rigid displacement. The system of algebraic equations corresponding to the functional equation (10.26_1),

$$\sum_{l=1}^{N} A_l^{(N)}\overset{0}{\Gamma}_1(x_j,\ y_l)\,\varphi(y_l) = -\frac{1}{2}\int_S \overset{0}{\Gamma}(x_j,\ y)\,f(y)\,dS_y \quad (j=1,\ 2,\ \ldots,\ N),$$
$$x_j\in B_a,\quad y_l\in S \tag{10.33}$$

may be solved for sufficiently large N, although its homogeneous system has six linearly independent nontrivial solutions so that the matrix of coefficients is of rank $(3N-6)$; assigning any fixed values to six of the unknowns, according to the number of linearly independent solutions of the homogeneous system, we express the remaining unknowns by means of the first six, and thus solve (10.33). The approximate solution of our problem is represented by

$$u(x) = \frac{1}{2\pi}\sum_{l=1}^{N} A_l^{(N)}\overset{0}{\Gamma}_1(x,\ y_l)\,\varphi(y_l) + \frac{1}{4\pi}\int_S \overset{0}{\Gamma}(x,\ y)\,f(y)\,dS_y, \qquad x\in B,$$

where $\varphi(y_l)$ $(l=1,\ 2,\ \ldots,\ N)$ are solutions of the system (10.33). We have gone into the static problem precisely because of this situation. The dynamic problem is uniquely solvable when ω is not an eigenfrequency, exactly as in the case of problem (D_i).

§ 4. Solution of Problem (D_a)

This problem consists in finding a regular vector $u(x)$ in B_a such that

$$(\Delta^* + \omega^2)\,u(x) = 0 \quad x\in B_a;\qquad u_a(x) = f(x) \quad x\in S.$$

We assume that the vector $f(x)$ has second continuous derivatives. It was shown in (VI, 12) that problem (D_a) possesses unique solutions for any value of the frequency ω; in some cases (indicated in Theorem 13 of VI, 12), the solution is represented by a double-layer potential, in others — by a combination of double- and single-layer potentials. Let us now look for a solution in the form of a solution of the system of functional equations

$$u(x) = \frac{1}{4\pi}\int_S \Gamma_1(x,\ y)\,f(y)\,dS_y + \frac{1}{2\pi}\int_S \Gamma(x,\ y)\,\varphi(y)\,dS_y, \qquad x\in B_a, \tag{10.34$_1$}$$

$$0 = \frac{1}{4\pi}\int_S \Gamma_1(x,\ y)\,f(y)\,dS_y + \frac{1}{2\pi}\int_S \Gamma(x,\ y)\,\varphi(y)\,dS_y, \qquad x\in B_i. \tag{10.34$_2$}$$

We first consider the static case. Let (10.34_2) have a solution of class H. From (10.34_1)

$$\Delta^* u(x) = 0, \quad x \in B_a.$$

Next, taking the difference of the internal and external limits of (10.34_1) and (10.34_2) at S, we obtain by virtue of Theorems 2 and 1 of (II, 1)

$$u_a(x) = f(x), \quad x \in S.$$

Thus, if a solution of the functional equation (10.34_2) exists, then (10.34_1) solves (D_a).

We first show that the functional equation (10.34_2) may have no more than one solution. Assuming the opposite, we find that the homogeneous functional equation

$$\frac{1}{2\pi} \int_S \overset{0}{\Gamma}(x, y) \varphi(y) dS_y = 0 \quad x \in B_i, \tag{10.35}$$

possesses a nontrivial solution. Let this solution be $\varphi_0(y)$; now for the single-layer potential

$$V(x; \varphi_0) = \frac{1}{2\pi} \int_S \overset{0}{\Gamma}(x, y) \varphi_0(y) dS$$

we know that $V(x; \varphi_0) = 0$, $x \in B_i$; and $0 = V_i(x_0; \varphi_0) = V_a(x, \varphi_0)$; this potential is a regular solution of the equations of elasticity in B_a (here we consider the three-dimensional case), and therefore $V(x; \varphi_0) = 0$, $x \in B_a$, by Theorem 5 of (III,4). Consequently, $\varphi_0(x_0) = 0$ by Theorem 4 of (II,1) and the asserted uniqueness of solution of (10.34_2) follows. In order to show that such a solution exists, consider the limiting value of a T-transform of (10.34_2) for $x \to x_0 \in S$

$$\varphi(x_0) + \frac{1}{2\pi} \int_S \left[\mathrm{T}_{x_0} \overset{0}{\Gamma}(x_0, y) \right] \varphi(y) dS_y = -\frac{1}{4\pi} \mathrm{T} \int_S \Gamma_{\mathrm{I}}(x_0, y) f(y) dS_y. \tag{T_i}$$

This is the integral equation of problem (T_i); according to Theorem 7 of (VI, 5) the necessary and sufficient conditions for its solvability are

$$\int_S (\mathrm{T}_x W(x; f)) \mathfrak{A}^{(k)}(x) dS_x = 0,$$
$$W(x; f) = \frac{1}{4\pi} \int_S \Gamma_{\mathrm{I}}(x, y) f(y) dS_y) \tag{10.36}$$
$$(k = 1, 2, 3, \ldots, 6),$$

where $\mathfrak{A}^{(k)}(x)$, $k = 1, 2, 3, \ldots, 6$ is a complete system of linearly independent solutions of the adjoint homogeneous equation; this system of solutions may be represented by the rigid displacement vectors

$$\mathfrak{A}^{(1)}(a, 0, 0), \mathfrak{A}^{(2)}(0, b, 0), \mathfrak{A}^{(3)}(0, 0, c), \mathfrak{A}^{(4)}(qx_3, 0, -qx_1),$$
$$\mathfrak{A}^{(5)}(-rx_2, rx_1, 0), \mathfrak{A}^{(6)}(0, -px_3, px_2).$$

Conditions (10.36) are in fact fulfilled automatically, which may be verified by applying the Betti formula in the domain B_i to the vector function $W(x; f)$ and to each of the $\mathfrak{A}^{(k)}(x)$, $k = 1, 2, \ldots, 6$. This may be done because of the restriction imposed on $f(x)$. Let $\varphi_*(x)$ be some particular solution of (T_i). We assert that $\varphi(x) = \varphi_*(x) + \psi(x)$, where $\psi(x)$ is an arbitrary solution of the homogeneous equation

$$\psi(x_0) + \frac{1}{2\pi} \int_S \left(\mathrm{T}_{x_0} \overset{0}{\Gamma}(x_0, y) \right) \psi(y) dS_y = 0, \tag{10.37}$$

solves the functional equation (10.34_2). Indeed, substituting $\varphi(x)=\varphi_*(x)+\psi(x)$ in (10.34_2),

$$v(x)=\frac{1}{4\pi}\int_S \Gamma_I(x, y)f(y)\,dS_y+\frac{1}{2\pi}\int_S \Gamma(x, y)\varphi_*(y)\,dS_y+\frac{1}{2\pi}\int_S \Gamma(x, y)\psi(y)\,dS_y. \quad (10.38)$$

The sum of the first two terms on the right, as readily follows from (T_i), is some rigid displacement $A+B(x)$, where A is a constant vector and $B(x)$ has the components qx_3-rx_2, rx_1-px_3, px_2-qx_1; here A, p, q, r are fully determined constants; but now for the third term we may choose $\psi(x)$ such that this term becomes equal to $-[A+B(x)]$, and we get $v(x)=0$, which proves our assertion.

Equation (10.34_2) is a canonical functional equation, so that approximate solution by reduction to a system of linear equations is possible. The approximate solution of the problem is, on account of (10.34_1), of the form

$$u(x)=\frac{1}{2\pi}\sum_{i=1}^{N} A_i^{(N)}\Gamma(x, y_i)\varphi(y_i)+\frac{1}{4\pi}\int_S \Gamma_I(x, y)f(y)\,dS_y, \quad y_i\in S,$$

where $\varphi(y_1), \varphi(y_2), \ldots, \varphi(y_N)$ is a solution of the system

$$\sum_{i=1}^{N} A_i^{(N)}\Gamma(x_j, y_i)\varphi(y_i)=-\frac{1}{2}\int_S \Gamma_I(x_j, y)f(y)\,dS_y$$

$$(j=1, 2, \ldots, N) \quad x_j\in B_i, \quad y_j\in S.$$

Problem (D_a) may be treated analogously, provided that ω is not an eigenvalue.

§ 5. Solution of Problem (T_a)

It is required to find in B_a a regular solution which satisfies

$$\Delta^* u(x)+\omega^2 u(x)=0, \quad x\in B_a; \quad (\mathrm{T}u(x))_a=f(x), \quad x\in B_a, \quad (T_a)$$

where $f(x)$ is a vector-function of class H, prescribed on S. The solution of this problem may be represented by

$$u(x)=-\frac{1}{4\pi}\int_S \Gamma(x, y)f(y)\,dS_y+\frac{1}{2\pi}\int_S \Gamma_I(x, y)\varphi(y)\,dS_y, \quad (10.39_1)$$

$$x\in B_a,$$

provided $\varphi(y)$ satisfies the functional equation

$$0=-\frac{1}{4\pi}\int_S \Gamma(x, y)f(y)\,dS_y+\frac{1}{2\pi}\int_S \Gamma_I(x, y)\varphi(y)\,dS_y, \; x\in B_i. \quad (10.39_2)$$

In fact, the $u(x)$ determined by (10.39_1) solves the equation of elasticity in B_a and turns out to be regular, and the difference of the limiting values at S of the T-transforms of the two sides of (10.39_1) and (10.39_2) gives, by Theorem 4 of (II, 1) and Theorem 10 of (VI, 9)

$$(\mathrm{T}u(x))_a=f(x), \quad x\in S. \quad (10.39_3)$$

This completes the proof of our statement. The existence of solution of equation (10.39_2) is demonstrated in the following way. In the limit, when x approaches x_0 on S from the inside, (10.39_2) becomes

$$\varphi(x_0)-\frac{1}{2\pi}\int_S \Gamma_I(x_0, y)\varphi(y)\,dS_y=-\frac{1}{4\pi}\int_S \Gamma(x_0, y)f(y)\,dS_y. \quad (10.40)$$

But this is the integral equation associated with problem (D_i), and if, as we assume, ω is not an eigenvalue, it admist a unique solution. The solution of equation (10.40) also solves the functional equation (10.39_2). In fact, constructing the potential

$$v(x)=\frac{1}{2\pi}\int_S \Gamma_1(x,\ y)\varphi(y)\,dS_y-\frac{1}{4\pi}\int_S \Gamma(x,\ y)f(y)\,dS_y,\qquad x\in B_i,$$

where the solution of equation (10.40) serves as density distribution, we get

$$\Delta^* v(x)+\omega^2 v(x)=0,\qquad x\in B_i;\qquad v_i(x)=0,\qquad x\in S, \tag{D_i^0}$$

and since ω is not eigenvalue of (D_i^0), we have

$$v(x)\equiv 0,\ x\in B_i.$$

This proves our assertion*. Let us show that the obtained solution of (10.39_2) is unique. Suppose it is not. Then the functional equation

$$W(x;\ \varphi)=\frac{1}{2\pi}\int_S \Gamma_1(x,\ y)\varphi(y)\,dS_y=0,\qquad x\in B_i, \tag{10.41}$$

must possess a nontrivial solution. From (10.41)

$$(\mathbf{T}W(x;\ \varphi))_i=0,\qquad x\in S,$$

and hence, by the Lyapunov-Tauber theorem,

$$(\mathbf{T}W(x;\ \varphi))_a=0,\qquad x\in S.$$

$W(x;\ \varphi)$ satisfies the radiation condition at infinity, and therefore

$$W(x;\ \varphi)\equiv 0,\qquad x\in B_a$$

This identity together with (10.41) imply $\varphi(x)=0$, which proves our statement. The functional equation (10.39_2) is canonical, and the approximate solution of the problem has the form

$$u(x)=\frac{1}{2\pi}\sum_{l=1}^{N} A_l^{(N)}\Gamma_1(x,\ y_l)\varphi(y_l)-\frac{1}{4\pi}\int_S \Gamma(x,\ y)f(y)\,dS_y,\qquad x\in B_a,$$

where $\varphi(y_1),\ \varphi(y_2),\ \ldots,\ \varphi(y_n)$ is the solution of the system of equations

$$\sum_{l=1}^{N} A_l^{(N)}\Gamma_1(x_j,\ y_l)\varphi(y_l)=\frac{1}{2}\int_S \Gamma(x_j,\ y)f(y)\,dS_y\qquad (j=1,\ 2,\ \ldots,\ N),$$

where $x_j\in B_i,\ y_j\in S.$

§ 6. Concerning the approximate construction of Green's tensors

The existence proof for the first and second Green's tensors amounts (see Ch. VI) to the solution of (D_i) and (T_i) for the domain B_i. Therefore in view of §§ 2, 3, approximate values of these tensors may be obtained by solving the systems of algebraic equations derived from the canonical functional equations.

* The additional condition

$$\int_S f(y)\,dS_y=0 \tag{*}$$

is necessary in the case of the plane problem, in order to ensure that $u(x)$ vanish at infinity.

§ 7. Solution of some particular problems for doubly-connected domains

Let the domain B_a be bounded by two nonintersecting closed Lyapunov surfaces (curves) S_1 and S_2. Let S_1 be the internal, S_2 the external boundary. The interior of S_1 will again be denoted by B_i. An elastic medium with the constants λ, μ occupies B_a; it is required to find a vector function $\boldsymbol{u}(x)$ such that

1°. $\Delta^* \boldsymbol{u}(x) + \omega^2 \boldsymbol{u}(x) = 0, \quad x \in B_a$.
2°. $(\mathbf{T}\boldsymbol{u}(x)) = 0, \quad x \in S_1$.
3°. $\boldsymbol{u}(x) = \boldsymbol{f}(x), \quad x \in S_2$

or alternatively

1°′. $\Delta^* \boldsymbol{u}(x) + \omega^2 \boldsymbol{u}(x) = 0, \quad x \in B_a$.
2°′. $(\mathbf{T}\boldsymbol{u}(x)) = 0, \quad x \in S_1$.
3°′. $(\mathbf{T}\boldsymbol{u}(x)) = \boldsymbol{f}(x), \quad x \in S_2$.

In order to obtain the functional equations suitable for an approximate solution of these problems, we proceed as in § 1. Let us first assume that B_i is occupied by an elastic medium with the Lamé constants λ_i, μ_i; the Lamé constants of B_a will now be denoted by λ_a, μ_a. Consider the case of free contact between domains B_i and B_a. The functional equations for this case when the displacement vector is prescribed on S_2 are, according to (IV,3,7), *

$$\varkappa(u)\boldsymbol{u}(x) = \omega^2(\mu_a - \mu_i)\int_{B_i} \boldsymbol{u}(y) G(x, y)\, dv_y + \\ + m\int_{B_i} \boldsymbol{u}(y)\, \mathrm{grad\, div}\, G(x, y)\, dv_y + \mu_a \int_{S_1} \boldsymbol{u}_i(y)\, \mathbf{T}_y^* G(x, y)\, dS_y + \\ + \mu_a \int_{S_1} \boldsymbol{\varphi}(y)\, \mathbf{T}_y^{(a)} G(x, y)\, dS_y + \mu_a \int_{S_2} \boldsymbol{f}(y)\, \mathbf{T}_y^{(a)} G(x, y)\, dS_y, \tag{10.42}$$

where $G(x, y)$ is the dynamic first Green's tensor for the domain $B = \bar{B}_i + B_a$. Other symbols retain their meaning, in particular, $\boldsymbol{f}(x_0) = \lim_{x \to x_0 \in S_2} \boldsymbol{u}(x)$. If, however, it is the forces that are prescribed on S_2,

$$\boldsymbol{f}(x_0) = \lim_{x \to x_0 \in S_2} \mathbf{T}\boldsymbol{u}(x),$$

and the functional equations are

$$\varkappa(u)\boldsymbol{u}(x) = \omega^2(\mu_a - \mu_i)\int_{B_i} \boldsymbol{u}(y) H^*(x, y)\, dv_y + \\ + m\int_{B_i} \boldsymbol{u}(y)\, \mathrm{grad\, div}\, H^*(x, y)\, dv_y + \mu_a \int_{S_1} \boldsymbol{u}_i(y)\, \mathbf{T}_y^* H(x, y)\, dS_y + \\ + \mu_a \int_{S_1} \boldsymbol{\varphi}(y)\, \mathbf{T}_y^{(a)} H(x, y)\, dS_y - \mu_a \int_{S_2} \boldsymbol{f}(y)\, H^*(x, y)\, dS_y, \tag{10.43}$$

where $H(x, y)$ is the dynamic second Green's tensor for B, and H^* the associated tensor. It follows from the existence and equivalence theorems, proved for these equations in Ch. VIII, that the solutions of (10.42) and (10.43) also constitute respectively ordinary or generalized solutions of

* It is assumed that ω is not an eigenfrequency of the domain $B = \bar{B}_i + B_a$ in the homogeneous Problem (D_i^0).

the problems

(a) $\overset{*}{\Delta}_{(i)}u(x)+\omega^2u(x)=0, \quad x\in B_i;$

(b) $\overset{*}{\Delta}_{(a)}u(x)+\omega^2u(x)=0, \quad x\in B_a;$

(c) $u_a(x)-u_i(x)=\varphi(x), \quad x\in S_1;$

(d) $(\mathrm{T}u(x))_i=(\mathrm{T}u(x))_a, \quad x\in S_1;$

(e) $\lim\limits_{x\to x_0\in S_2} u(x)=f(x_0)$ in the first case;

(e') $\lim\limits_{x\to x_0\in S_2} \mathrm{T}u(x)=f(x_0)$ in the second case.

We now set

$$\lambda_i=\mu_i=0,$$

which, exactly as in § 1, turns (10.42) and (10.43) into

$$u(x)=\frac{1}{4\pi}\int_{S_1}\varphi(y)\,\mathrm{T}_y^{(a)}G(x, y)\,dS_y+$$
$$+\frac{1}{4\pi}\int_{S_2}f(y)\,\mathrm{T}_y^{(a)}G(x, y)\,dS_y, \quad x\in B_a; \tag{10.44$_1$}$$

$$0=\frac{1}{4\pi}\int_{S_1}\varphi(y)\,\mathrm{T}_y^{(a)}G(x, y)\,dS_y+$$
$$+\frac{1}{4\pi}\int_{S_2}f(y)\,\mathrm{T}_y^{(a)}G(x, y)\,dS_y, \quad x\in B_i, \tag{10.44$_2$}$$

and

$$u(x)=\frac{1}{4\pi}\int_{S_1}\varphi(y)\,\mathrm{T}_y^{(a)}H^*(x, y)\,dS_y-$$
$$-\frac{1}{4\pi}\int_{S_2}f(y)\,H^*(x, y)\,dS_y, \quad x\in B_a; \tag{10.45$_1$}$$

$$0=\frac{1}{4\pi}\int_{S_1}\varphi(y)\,\mathrm{T}_y^{(a)}H^*(x, y)\,dS_y-$$
$$-\frac{1}{4\pi}\int_{S_2}f(y)\,H^*(x, y)\,dS_y, \quad x\in B_i. \tag{10.45$_2$}$$

Although it follows from the general theory that the solutions of these equations respectively satisfy the conditions 1°, 2°, 3° and 1°', 2°', 3°', set down at the beginning of this section, we shall demonstrate this directly by an elementary argument. We have by definition of the dynamic first Green's tensor

$$\overset{*}{\Delta}_{(a)}G(x, y)+\omega^2G(x, y)=0, \quad (x, y)\in B, \quad x\neq y;$$
$$\lim_{x\to x_0\in S_2} G(x, y)=0, \quad y\in B;$$

and

$$(\overset{*}{\Delta}_{(a)}+\omega^2)\int_S\psi(y)\,\mathrm{T}_y^{(a)}G(x, y)\,dS_y=0, \quad x\bar{\in} S,$$

and in virtue of the property proved in (VI, 7)

$$\lim_{x\to x_0\in S_2}\int_{S_2}\psi(y)\,\mathrm{T}_y^{(a)}G(x, y)\,dS_y=4\pi\psi(x_0).$$

Keeping in mind these properties of the Green's tensor and applying $(\overset{*}{\Delta}_{(a)}+\omega^2)$ to (10.44$_1$), we obtain

$$\overset{*}{\Delta}_{(a)}u(x)+\omega^2u(x)=0, \quad x\in B_a. \tag{10.46$_1$}$$

Passing to the limit in the same equation (10.44$_1$) for $x\to x_0\in S_2$, we get

$$\lim_{x\to x_0} u(x)=f(x_0). \tag{10.46$_2$}$$

Turning now to equation (10.44_2), we note that the existence of the limit

$$\lim_{x\to x_0}\left(\mathsf{T}_x^{(a)}\int_{S_2} f(y)\,\mathsf{T}_y^{(a)}G(x,\ y)\,dS_y\right),\qquad x\in B_i,\qquad x_0\in S_1,$$

at S_1 implies the existence of

$$\lim_{x\to x_0}\left(\mathsf{T}_x^{(a)}\int_{S_1} \varphi(y)\,\mathsf{T}_y^{(a)}G(x,\ y)\,dS_y\right),\qquad x\in B_i,\qquad x_0\in S_1;$$

but then, by the Lyapunov-Tauber theorem, the external limit exists as well and

$$\lim_{B_a\ni x\to x_0\in S_1}\mathsf{T}_x^{(a)}\left(\int_{S_1}\varphi(y)\,\mathsf{T}_y^{(a)}G(x,\ y)\,dS_y\right)=\lim_{B_i\ni x\to x_0\in S_1}\mathsf{T}_x^{(a)}\left(\int_{S_1}\varphi(y)\,\mathsf{T}_y^{(a)}G(x,\ y)\,dS_y\right).$$

Applying now $\mathsf{T}^{(a)}$ to (10.44_1) and (10.44_2), and letting x approach the x_0 on S_1 from the outside and the inside, respectively, we form their difference, and obtain

$$(\mathsf{T}u(x))_a=0,\qquad x\in S_1. \tag{10.46$_3$}$$

The relations (10.46_1), (10.46_2) and (10.46_3) prove our statement concerning the system (10.44). Our proof refers to the dynamic case; but since $\omega=0$ is not an eigenvalue of the dynamic problem (D_i^0), the proof holds good also in the static case. It may be proved in an exactly the same way that if $\omega\neq 0$ the solution of (10.45) satisfies the above conditions (a), (b), (c), (d), (e'). In the static case, however, the proof requires some modification because $\omega=0$ is an eigenvalue of the dynamic problem (T_i^0). We know from (VII, 9) that the static boundary-value problem with the condition (e'), that is, surface tractions prescribed, is only solvable if

$$\int_{S_2} f(x)\,\mathfrak{A}^{(s)}(x)\,dS_x=0\qquad (s=1,\ 2,\ 3,\ \ldots,\ 6). \tag{10.47}$$

Taking these for granted, we get from (10.45_1) after applying $\overset{*}{\Delta}_{(a)}$ and making use of Lemma C^0 of VII, 9

$$\overset{*}{\Delta}_{(a)}u(x)=-\frac{1}{4\pi}\int_{S_2} f(y)\,\overset{*}{\Delta}_a\overset{0}{H}{}^*(x,\ y)\,dS_y,\qquad x\in B_a. \tag{10.48}$$

But from (4.15_a) (IV, 4)

$$\overset{*}{\Delta}_{(a)}\overset{0}{H}{}^{(k)}(x,\ y)=4\pi\sum_{s=1}^{6}\mathfrak{B}^{(s,\ k)}(x,\ y),$$

and further

$$\begin{aligned}\frac{1}{4\pi}f(y)\,\overset{*}{\Delta}_{(a)}H^*(x,\ y)&=\frac{1}{4\pi}\overset{*}{\Delta}_{(a)}H(x,\ y)\,f(y)=\\ &=\sum\left(\mathfrak{A}^{(s)}(x)*\mathfrak{A}^{(s)}(y)\right)f(y)=\sum i_1\mathfrak{A}_1^{(s)}(x)\,\mathfrak{A}^{(s)}(y)\cdot f(y)+\\ &\quad+i_2\mathfrak{A}_2^{(s)}(x)\,\mathfrak{A}^{(s)}(y)\cdot f(y)+i_3\mathfrak{A}_3^{(s)}(x)\,\mathfrak{A}^{(s)}(y)\cdot f(y)=\\ &=\sum\mathfrak{A}^{(s)}(x)\left(\mathfrak{A}^{(s)}(y)\cdot f(y)\right)\quad (s=1,\ 2,\ \ldots,\ 6).\end{aligned}$$

It follows on account of (10.47) and (10.48) that

$$\overset{*}{\Delta}_{(a)}u(x)=0,\qquad x\in B_a. \tag{10.49$_1$}$$

Further, making use of (6.44) and the following property of the second Green's tensor

$$\lim_{x\to x_0\in S_2}\mathsf{T}_x\overset{0}{H}(x,\ y)=0,$$

we apply $T^{(a)}$, pass to the limit for x of B_a approaching x_0 on S_2, and obtain from (10.45_1)

$$\lim_{x \to x_0 \in S_2} (\mathbf{T}\boldsymbol{u}(x)) = \boldsymbol{f}(x_0). \qquad (10.49_2)$$

It remains to verify that the boundary condition on S_1 is satisfied. It follows from (10.45_2) that the following internal limit at S_1 exists

$$\lim_{x \to x_0 \in S_1} \mathbf{T}_x^{(a)} \left(\int_{S_1} \boldsymbol{\varphi}(y)\, \mathbf{T}_y^{(a)} \overset{0}{H}{}^* (x, y)\, dS_y \right), \qquad x \in B_i, \quad x_0 \in S_1;$$

hence, applying $T^{(a)}$ to (10.45_1) and (10.45_2), passing to the internal and external limits and forming their difference, we obtain with the help of the Lyapunov-Tauber theorem

$$\lim_{x \to x_0} \mathbf{T}\boldsymbol{u}(x) = 0, \qquad x \in B_a, \quad x_0 \in S_1. \qquad (10.49_3)$$

Relations (10.49_1), (10.49_2) and (10.49_3) prove our assertion about the system (10.45) for the case $\omega = 0$.

It now remains to prove the existence of solutions of the functional equations (10.44_1) and (10.45_2). This will be done for the case $\omega = 0$. We approach in (10.44_2) a point on S_1 from the inside and obtain from the discontinuity formulas for a double-layer potential

$$\boldsymbol{\varphi}(x_0) - \frac{1}{2\pi} \int_{S_1} \boldsymbol{\varphi}(y)\, \mathbf{T}_y^{(a)} \overset{0}{G}(x_0; y)\, dS_y = \frac{1}{2\pi} \int_{S_2} \boldsymbol{f}(y)\, \mathbf{T}_y^{(a)} \overset{\text{U}}{G}(x_0, y)\, dS_y. \qquad (10.50)$$

The corresponding homogeneous equation has only trivial solutions. Indeed, otherwise the associated equation

$$\boldsymbol{\psi}(x_0) - \frac{1}{2\pi} \int_{S_1} \mathbf{T}_{x_0}^{(a)} \overset{\text{U}}{G}(x_0, y)\, \boldsymbol{\psi}(y)\, dS_y = 0$$

would also possess a nontrivial solution, and taking such a solution for density distribution of the single-layer potential

$$\boldsymbol{u}(x) = \frac{1}{2\pi} \int_{S_1} \overset{0}{G}(x, y)\, \boldsymbol{\psi}(y)\, dS_y, \qquad (10.51)$$

we would get

$$\lim_{x \to x_0} (\mathbf{T}\boldsymbol{u}(x)) = 0 \qquad (10.52)$$

as x approaches $x_0 \in S_1$ from B_a. On the other hand, when x approaches the point x_0 on S_2 from B_a we have by the properties of the first Green's tensor

$$\lim \boldsymbol{u}(x) = 0. \qquad (10.53)$$

But formula (1.9') gives for these conditions

$$\boldsymbol{u}(x) \equiv 0, \qquad x \in B_a. \qquad (10.54)$$

It follows that $\boldsymbol{u}(x) = 0$ also in B_i; finally, these two facts imply that $\boldsymbol{\psi}(x) = 0$, which completes the uniqueness proof for a solution of (10.50). This solution is at the same time a unique solution of the functional equation (10.44_2). The proof of this last property resembles the procedure which was repeatedly applied in the preceding sections.

§ 8. Solution of the first fundamental boundary-value problem for a doubly-connected domain

A solution of the equations of elasticity which is regular in B_a, assumes on S_1 the values $f^{(1)}(x)$ and on S_2 the values $f^{(2)}(x)$ with prescribed twice differentiable $f^{(1)}(x)$ and $f^{(2)}(x)$, may be sought among the solutions of the system of functional equations*

$$u(x)=\frac{1}{4\pi}\int_{S_1} f^{(1)}(y)\,\mathsf{T}_y^{(a)}\overset{0}{G}(x,\,y)\,dS_y+\frac{1}{4\pi}\int_{S_2} f^{(2)}(y)\,\mathsf{T}_y^{(a)}\overset{0}{G}(x,\,y)\,dS_y+$$

$$+\frac{1}{2\pi}\int_{S_1}\overset{0}{G}(x,\,y)\,\varphi(y)\,dS_y,\qquad x\in B_a, \tag{10.55$_1$}$$

$$0=\frac{1}{4\pi}\int_{S_1} f^{(1)}(y)\,\mathsf{T}_y^{(a)}\overset{0}{G}(x,\,y)\,dS_y+\frac{1}{4\pi}\int_{S_2} f^{(2)}(y)\,\mathsf{T}_y^{(a)}\overset{0}{G}(x,\,y)\,dS_y+$$

$$+\frac{1}{2\pi}\int_{S_1}\overset{0}{G}(x,\,y)\,\varphi(y)\,dS_y,\qquad x\in B_i. \tag{10.55$_2$}$$

This proposition can be proved in exactly the same manner as before.

To show that (10.55_2) has a solution, we apply $\mathsf{T}^{(a)}$ to it and let x approach from B_i the point x_0 on S_1; we get

$$\varphi(x_0)+\frac{1}{2\pi}\int_{S_1}\left(\mathsf{T}_{x_0}^{(a)}\overset{0}{G}(x_0,\,y)\right)\varphi(y)\,dS_y=-\frac{1}{4\pi}\left\{\mathsf{T}_{x_0}^{(a)}\sum_{l=1}^{2}\int_{S_l} f^{(l)}(y)\,\mathsf{T}_y^{(a)}\overset{0}{G}(x_0;\,y)\,dS_y\right\}_i. \tag{10.56}$$

Consider the corresponding homogeneous equation

$$\varphi(x_0)+\frac{1}{2\pi}\int_{S_1}\left(\mathsf{T}_{x_0}^{(a)}\overset{0}{G}(x_0,\,y)\right)\varphi(y)\,dS_y=0, \tag{10.57}$$

and its associated homogeneous equation

$$\psi(x_0)+\frac{1}{2\pi}\int_{S_1}\psi(y)\,\mathsf{T}_y^{(a)}\overset{0}{G}(y,\,x_0)\,dS_y=0. \tag{10.58}$$

Equation (10.58) is solved by the rigid displacements $\mathfrak{A}^{(i)}(x)$ $(i=1,\,2,\,3,\,\ldots,\,6)$. To show this, recall that the first Green's tensor for the domain $B=\bar{B}_i+B_a$ (bounded by the surface S_2) has the form $\overset{0}{G}(x,\,y)=\overset{0}{\Gamma}(x,\,y)-\overset{0}{v}(x,\,y)$, where $\overset{0}{v}(x,\,y)$ is a regular solution of the equations of elasticity for any x and y in B; we rewrite (10.58) as

$$\psi(x_0)+\frac{1}{2\pi}\int_{S_1}\psi(y)\,\mathsf{T}_y^{(a)}\overset{0}{\Gamma}_{(a)}(y,\,x_0)\,dS_y-\frac{1}{2\pi}\int_{S_1}\psi(y)\,\mathsf{T}_y^{(a)}\overset{0}{v}(y,\,x_0)\,dS_y=0.$$

But (cf. VI, 3)

$$\mathfrak{A}^{(k)}(x_0)+\frac{1}{2\pi}\int_{S_1}\mathfrak{A}^{(k)}(y)\,\mathsf{T}_y^{(a)}\overset{0}{\Gamma}_{(a)}(y,\,x_0)\,dS_y=0\qquad(k=1,\,2,\,\ldots,\,6). \tag{10.59}$$

On the other hand,

$$\int_{S_1}\mathfrak{A}^{(k)}(y)\,\mathsf{T}_y^{(a)}\overset{0}{v}(y,\,x_0)\,dS_y=0\qquad(k=1,\,2,\,3,\,\ldots,\,6). \tag{10.59$'$}$$

hold identically because of the mentioned property of $\overset{0}{v}(x,\,y)$. To verify this, it is sufficient to apply the Betti relation in B_i to the vectors $\mathfrak{A}^{(k)}(x)$ $(k=1,\,2,\,\ldots,\,6)$ and $\overset{0}{v}{}^{(s)}(y,\,x)$ $(s=1,\,2,\,3)$, where $\overset{0}{v}{}^{(s)}(y,\,x)$ is the s-th column of the

* The positive direction is taken along the inward normal. The form of these equations displays their connection with Green's formulas. In this section we shall consider the static problem which is of special interest.

matrix $\overset{0}{v}(x, y)$. The identity (10.59') follows since $\overset{*}{\Delta}_a \overset{0}{v}^{(s)}(x, y) = 0$, $\overset{*}{\Delta}_a \mathfrak{A}^{(k)}(x) = 0$, $\mathbf{T}\mathfrak{A}^{(k)}(x) = 0$. The $\mathfrak{A}^{(k)}(x) (k = 1, 2, \ldots, 6)$ thus satisfy equation (10.58). Let us show that these solutions of (10.58) constitute a complete set. Consider the solutions $\varphi^{(k)}(x)$ of (10.57). It is clear from the preceding that at least six of them are linearly independent. These must constitute a complete set of solutions of (10.57). For otherwise let $\varphi_*(x)$ be a solution of (10.57) which is not linearly dependent on $\varphi^{(k)}(x)$ $(k = 1, 2, \ldots, 6)$. The single-layer potentials

$$V(x; \varphi^{(k)}) = \frac{1}{2\pi} \int_{S_1} \varphi^{(k)}(y) \overset{0}{G}(x, y) \, dS_y, \quad x \in B_i, \tag{10.60}$$

being solutions of the equations of elasticity which satisfy the boundary conditions

$$(\mathbf{T}V(x_0; \varphi^{(k)}))_i = 0, \quad x_0 \in S_1 \quad (k = 1, 2, 3, \ldots, 6),$$

are rigid displacements in B_i. They are linearly independent, for if

$$\sum_{k=1}^{6} C_k V(x; \varphi^{(k)}) = 0, \quad x \in B_i,$$

were identically fulfilled for any x of B_i, and not all the C_k vanished, then the single-layer potential

$$V(x; \psi_*) = \frac{1}{2\pi} \int_{S_1} \psi_*(y) \overset{0}{G}(x, y) \, dS_y,$$

where

$$\psi_*(y) = \sum_{k=1}^{6} C_k \varphi^{(k)}(y), \quad y \in S_1,$$

would possess the boundary property

$$\lim_{B_a \ni x \to x_0 \in S_1} V(x; \psi_*) = 0, \tag{10.61$_1$}$$

in virtue of the continuity of this potential, and on account of the identity

$$V(x; \psi_*) \equiv 0, \quad x \in B_i. \tag{10.62$_1$}$$

On the other hand, by the properties of the first Green's tensor

$$\lim_{x \to x_0 \in S_2} V(x; \psi_*) = 0. \tag{10.61$_2$}$$

Relations (10.61$_1$) and (10.61$_2$) imply

$$V(x; \psi_*) = 0 \quad x \in B_a. \tag{10.62$_2$}$$

It follows exactly as in the previous section that $\psi_*(y) = 0$. This proves the linear independence of $V(x; \varphi^{(k)})$ $(k = 1, 2, \ldots, 6)$. But these vectors constitute in that case a complete system of rigid displacement vectors, and any other such vector can be expressed as their linear combination; consequently and since $V(x; \varphi_*)$, $x \in S_1$, represents a rigid displacement, $\varphi^*(x)$ cannot depend linearly on $\varphi^{(k)}(x)$ $(k = 1, 2, \ldots, 6)$ (cf. VI, 3)*.

So (10.57) has only six linearly independent solutions. Therefore (10.58) has by Fredholm's second theorem also six linearly independent solutions; these solutions are obviously

$$\mathfrak{A}^{(k)}(x) \quad (k = 1, 2, 3, \ldots 6), \quad x \in S_1.$$

* The behavior of the tensor $G(x, y)$ in the neighborhood of and at the surface S_2 is used here instead of the condition at infinity.

We may now state that the equalities

$$\int_{S_1} \mathfrak{A}^{(k)}(y)\,\mathrm{T}_y^{(a)} \sum_{i=1}^{2} W(f^{(i)};\ y)\,dS_y = 0 \qquad (k = 1,\ 2,\ \ldots,\ 6), \tag{10.63}$$

where

$$W(f^{(i)};\ x) = \frac{1}{2\pi} \int_{S_i} f^{(i)}(y)\,\mathrm{T}_y^{(a)}\,G(x,\ y)\,dS_y. \qquad (i = 1,\ 2)$$

are necessary and sufficient conditions for the solvability of (10.56). But the conditions (10.63) are actually fulfilled. To verify this it is sufficient to apply the Betti relation in B_i to $\mathfrak{A}^{(k)}(x)\ (k = 1,\ 2,\ \ldots,\ 6)$ and $W(f^{(i)};\ x)\ (i = 1,\ 2)$. This may be done in view of the restrictions imposed on the $f^{(i)}(x)$. The conditions (10.63) readily follow. It now remains to prove the solvability of the functional equation (10.55_2). Let $\varphi^*(x)$ be a particular solution of (10.56), and $\psi^*(x)$ some fully determined (by a method to which we shall presently come) solution of the homogeneous equation (10.57). Replacing $\varphi(y)$ in (10.55_2) by the vector $\varphi^*(y)$, we obtain

$$v(x) = \frac{1}{4\pi} \int_{S_1} f^{(1)}(y)\,\mathrm{T}_y^{(a)} \overset{0}{G}(x,\ y)\,dS_y +$$
$$+ \frac{1}{4\pi} \int_{S_2} f^{(2)}(y)\,\mathrm{T}_y^{(a)} \overset{0}{G}(x,\ y)\,dS_y + \frac{1}{2\pi} \int_{S_1} \overset{0}{G}(x,\ y)\,\varphi^*(y)\,dS_y, \qquad x \in B_i,$$

which satisfies the conditions

$$\overset{*}{\Delta}_{(a)} v = 0, \quad x \in B_i; \quad (\mathrm{T} v(x))_i = 0, \quad x_0 \in S_1,$$

and thus represents a rigid displacement $A + B(x)$ in B_i. Choosing $\psi^*(x)$ so that

$$\frac{1}{2\pi} \int_{S_1} \overset{0}{G}(x,\ y)\,\psi^*(y)\,dS_y = -[A + B(x)],$$

we find that $\varphi^* + \psi^*$ is a solution of (10.55_2). To prove its uniqueness, let us show that the functional equation

$$V(x;\ \varphi^{(0)}) = \frac{1}{2\pi} \int_{S_1} \varphi^{(0)}(y)\,\overset{0}{G}(x,\ y)\,dS_y = 0, \qquad x \in B_i,$$

only has a trivial solution. Suppose $\varphi^{(0)}(y)$ is a nontrivial solution. Then

$$\lim_{x \to x_0} (\mathrm{T} V(x;\ \varphi^{(0)})) = 0, \qquad x_0 \in S_1. \tag{10.64$_1$}$$

The continuity of the single-layer potential $V(x;\ \varphi^{(0)})$ and the vanishing of tensor $\overset{0}{G}(x,\ y)$ on S_2 imply

$$\lim_{x \to x_0} V(x;\ \varphi^{(0)}) = 0, \quad x \in B_a, \quad x_0 \in S_1;$$
$$\lim_{x \to x_0} V(x;\ \varphi^{(0)}) = 0, \quad x \in B_a, \quad x_0 \in S_2;$$

whence, as above,

$$V(x;\ \varphi^{(0)}) \equiv 0, \quad x \in B_a. \tag{10.64$_2$}$$

Relations (10.64_1) and (10.64_2) imply that $\varphi^{(0)}(x) \equiv 0$, which proves the uniqueness.

Since (10.55_2) is canonical, reduction to a system of linear algebraic equations by means of quadrature formulas is possible. The approximate

2109

solution has the form

$$u(x)=\frac{1}{2\pi}\sum_{i=1}^{N}A_i^{(N)}G(x,\ y_i)\varphi(y_i)+\frac{1}{2}\sum_{i=1}^{2}W(f^{(i)};\ x),\quad x\in B_a,$$

where $\varphi(y_1),\ \varphi(y_2),\ \ldots,\ \varphi(y_N)$ is the solution of the system

$$\sum_{i=1}^{N}A_i^{(N)}G(x_j,\ y_i)\varphi(y_i)=-\pi\sum_{i=1}^{2}W(f^{(i)};\ x_j)\quad (j=1,\ 2,\ \ldots,\ N),$$

and

$$x_j\in B_i,\quad y_i\in S_1.$$

§ 9. Solution of the second fundamental boundary-value problem for a doubly-connected domain

Let the values of $\mathrm{T}u(x)$ be prescribed on S_1 and S_2

$$\lim \mathrm{T}u(x)=f_1(x_0),\quad x_0\in S_1,\quad x\in B_a;$$
$$\lim \mathrm{T}u(x)=f_2(x_0),\quad x_0\in S_2,\quad x\in B_a,$$

and let

$$\int_{S_1}f_1(y)\,\mathfrak{A}^{(k)}(y)\,dS_y+\int_{S_2}f_2(y)\,\mathfrak{A}^{(k)}(y)\,dS_y=0. \tag{*}$$

Then the system of functional equations

$$4\pi u(x)=-\int_{S_1}\overset{0}{H}(x,\ y)f_1(y)\,dS_y-\int_{S_2}\overset{0}{H}(x,\ y)f_2(y)\,dS_y+$$
$$+\int_{S_1}\varphi(y)\,\mathrm{T}_y^{(a)}\overset{0}{H^*}(x,\ y)\,dS_y,\quad x\in B_a, \tag{10.65$_1$}$$

$$0=-\int_{S_1}\overset{0}{H}(x,\ y)f_1(y)\,dS_y-\int_{S_2}\overset{0}{H}(x,\ y)f_2(y)\,dS_y+$$
$$+\int_{S_1}\varphi(y)\,\mathrm{T}_y^{(a)}\overset{0}{H^*}(x,\ y)\,dS_y,\quad x\in B_i, \tag{10.65$_2$}$$

is solved by the solution, in the ordinary or generalized sense, of

$$\overset{*}{\Delta}_{(a)}u(x)+\omega^2u(x)=0,\quad x\in B_a;\quad \lim_{x\to x_0}\mathrm{T}u(x)=f_1(x_0),\ x_0\in S_1;$$
$$\lim_{x\to x_0}\mathrm{T}u(x)=f_2(x_0),\ x_0\in S_2. \tag{10.66}$$

The proof of this assertion is based on the condition (*) and resembles the foregoing proofs of analogous statements.

Let us prove the existence theorem for the functional equation (10.65$_2$). In the internal limit at S_1, this becomes

$$\varphi(x_0)-\frac{1}{2\pi}\int_{S_1}\varphi(y)\,\mathrm{T}_y^{(a)}\overset{0}{H^*}(x_0,\ y)\,dS_y=\frac{1}{2\pi}\int_{S_1}\overset{0}{H}(x_0,\ y)f_1(y)\,dS_y+\frac{1}{2\pi}\int_{S_2}\overset{0}{H}(x_0,\ y)f_2(y)\,dS_y. \tag{10.67}$$

The corresponding homogeneous equation

$$\varphi_0(x_0)-\frac{1}{2\pi}\int_{S_1}\varphi_0(y)\,\mathrm{T}_y^{(a)}\overset{0}{H^*}(x_0,\ y)\,dS_y=0 \tag{10.68}$$

will now be shown to possess none but a trivial solution. Assuming the opposite, let $\varphi_0(x_0)$ be a nontrivial solution. The double-layer potential

$$W(x;\ \varphi_0)=\frac{1}{2\pi}\int_{S_1}\varphi_0(y)\,\mathrm{T}_y^{(a)}\overset{0}{H^*}(x,\ y)\,dS_y$$

is by Lemma C^0 of (VII, 9) a solution of the $\overset{*}{\Delta}_{(a)}u=0$ (in B_i as well as in B_a); hence

$$W(x;\ \varphi_0)=0, \quad x\in B_i; \tag{10.69}$$

and by the Lyapunov-Tauber theorem

$$\lim_{x\to x_0} \mathrm{T}W(x;\ \varphi_0)=0, \quad x\in B_a, \quad x_0\in S_1.$$

On the other hand, by the properties of the second Green's tensor

$$\lim_{x\to x_0} \mathrm{T}W(x;\ \varphi_0)=0, \quad x\in B_a, \quad x_0\in S_2.$$

It follows from the last two relations and from the fact that $\overset{*}{\Delta}_{(a)}W=0$ in B_a, that $\varphi_0(x_0)$ is a rigid displacement in B_a. This together with (10.69) implies that

$$\varphi_0(x_0)=\sum_{k=1}^{6}\alpha_k\mathfrak{A}^{(k)}(x_0).$$

Thus, if equation (10.68) has a nontrivial solution, the latter can only be a rigid displacement, and

$$\sum_{k=1}^{6}\alpha_k\mathfrak{A}^{(k)}(x_0)-\frac{1}{2\pi}\sum_{k=1}^{6}\alpha_k\int_{S_1}\mathfrak{A}^{(k)}(y)\,\mathrm{T}_y^{(a)}\overset{0}{H}{}^*(x_0,\ y)\,dS_y=0.$$

Since for the second Green's tensor $\overset{0}{H}{}^*(x_0,\ y)=\overset{0}{H}(y,\ x_0)$ (cf. VI, 7) the last equality becomes

$$\sum_k\alpha_k\mathfrak{A}^{(k)}(x_0)-\frac{1}{2\pi}\sum_k\alpha_k\int_{S_1}\mathfrak{A}^{(k)}(y)\,\mathrm{T}_y^{(a)}\overset{*}{\Gamma}(y,\ x_0)\,dS_y-\frac{1}{2\pi}\sum_k\alpha_k\int_{S_1}\mathfrak{A}^{(k)}(y)\,\mathrm{T}_y^{(a)}\overset{0}{W}(y,\ x_0)\,dS_y=0.$$

But the integrals

$$\int_{S_1}\mathfrak{A}^{(k)}(y)\,\mathrm{T}_y^{(a)}\overset{0}{W}(y,\ x_0)\,dS_y \qquad (k=1,\ 2,\ \ldots,\ 6)$$

may be shown to vanish by applying the Betti relation to the vectors $\mathfrak{A}^{(k)}(y)$ and the matrix $\overset{0}{W}(y,\ x)$ in B_i, where $\mathfrak{A}^{(k)}(x)$ and $\overset{0}{W}(x,\ y)$ are regular solutions of the equations of elasticity; the last relation therefore becomes

$$\sum_{k=1}^{6}\alpha_k\left\{\mathfrak{A}^{(k)}(x_0)-\frac{1}{2\pi}\int_{S_1}\mathfrak{A}^{(k)}(y)\,\mathrm{T}_y^{(a)}\overset{*}{\Gamma}(y,\ x_0)\,dS_y\right\}=0. \tag{10.70}$$

Using the notations of (VI, 7) we may now write down

$$\int_{S_1}\mathfrak{A}^{(s)}(x)\,\mathrm{T}_x^{(a)}\overset{*}{\Gamma}(x,\ y)\,dS_x=\int_{S_1}\mathfrak{A}^{(s)}(x)\,\mathrm{T}_x^{(a)}\overset{0}{\Gamma}(x,\ y)\,dS_x-$$
$$-\int_{S_1}\mathfrak{A}^{(s)}(x)\,\mathrm{T}_x^{(a)}[L(x,\ y)+M(x,\ y)-N(x,\ y)]\,dS_x, \tag{10.71}$$

where $L(x,\ y)$, $M(x,\ y)$, $N(x,\ y)$ are matrices with the following k-th column-vectors $(k=1,\ 2,\ 3)$, respectively,

$$\left.\begin{aligned}
&\sum_{s=1}^{6}\mathfrak{A}^{(s)}(x)\left(\int_B\overset{0}{\Gamma}(y,\ \xi)\,\mathfrak{A}^{(s)}(\xi)\,dv_\xi\right)_{x_k},\\
&\sum_{s=1}^{6}\left(\int_B\overset{0}{\Gamma}(x,\ \eta)\,\mathfrak{A}^{(s)}(\eta)\,dv_\eta\right)\mathfrak{A}_k^{(s)}(y),\\
&\sum_{s=1}^{6}\sum_{q=1}^{6}\gamma_{sq}\mathfrak{A}^{(s)}(x)\,\mathfrak{A}_k^{(q)}(y),
\end{aligned}\right\} \tag{10.72}$$

where B is the entire domain $B_i + B_a$ for which $H(x, y)$ is the second Green's tensor. It is clear that the matrix $H(x, y)$ is fully determined in any domain entirely contained within B, and B_i in particular. For any closed Lyapunov surface

$$\int_{S_1} \mathfrak{A}^{(s)}(x)\, T_x^{(a)} \overset{0}{\Gamma}(x, y)\, dS_x = -2\pi \mathfrak{A}^{(s)}(y). \tag{10.73}$$

Using (10.72) and the identity

$$T_x \mathfrak{A}^{(s)}(x) = 0,$$

we get for the component along the x_k-axis

$$\int_{S_1} \mathfrak{A}^{(s)}(x)\, T_x^{(a)} L^{(k)}(x, y)\, dS_x = \\ = \int_{S_1} \mathfrak{A}^{(s)}(x)\, T_x^{(a)} N^{(k)}(x, y)\, dS_x = 0. \tag{10.74}$$

For the term

$$J_k^{(s)} = -\int_{S_1} \mathfrak{A}^{(s)}(x)\, T_x^{(a)} M^{(k)}(x, y)\, dS_x \qquad (k = 1, 2, 3),$$

we obtain

$$J_k^{(s)} = -\int_{S_1} \mathfrak{A}^{(s)}(x)\, dS_x T_x^{(a)} \left[\sum_{p=1}^{6} \left(\int_B \overset{0}{\Gamma}(x, \eta)\, \mathfrak{A}^{(p)}(\eta)\, dv_\eta \right) \mathfrak{A}_k^{(p)}(y) \right] = \\ = -\sum_{p=1}^{6} \left\{ \int_B \left(\int_{S_1} \mathfrak{A}^{(s)}(x)\, T_x^{(a)} \overset{0}{\Gamma}(x, \eta)\, dS_x \right) \mathfrak{A}^{(p)}(\eta)\, dv_\eta \right\} \mathfrak{A}_k^{(p)}(y),$$

or in view of (10.73)

$$J_k^{(s)} = 2\pi \sum_{p=1}^{6} \left(\int_B \mathfrak{A}^{(s)}(\eta)\, \mathfrak{A}^{(p)}(\eta)\, dv_\eta \right) \mathfrak{A}_k^{(p)}(y) \qquad (k = 1, 2, 3).$$

The orthonormality relations (6.31) give

$$J_k^{(s)} = 2\pi \mathfrak{A}_k^{(s)}(y). \tag{10.75}$$

Substituting (10.73), (10.74) and (10.75) in (10.71), we obtain

$$\int_{S_1} \mathfrak{A}^{(s)}(x)\, T_x^{(a)} \overset{*}{\Gamma}(x, y)\, dS_x = 0 \qquad (s = 1, 2, 3, 4, 5, 6). \tag{10.76}$$

Inserting this into (10.70), we find that we have a contradiction with the linear independence of the $\mathfrak{A}^{(s)}(x)$, $s = 1, 2, 3, \ldots, 6$. This contradiction proves that equation (10.68) has only a trivial solution; this also goes for the associated equation, and consequently (10.67) is solvable. We state that its solution satisfies the functional equation (10.65_2). For otherwise, forming the potential

$$v(x) = -\int_{S_1} \overset{0}{H}(x, y) f_1(y)\, dS_y - \int_{S_2} \overset{0}{H}(x, y) f_2(y)\, dS_y + \\ + \int_{S_1} \varphi(y)\, T_y^{(a)} \overset{0}{H}{}^*(x, y)\, dS_y, \quad x \in B_i,$$

we must have

$$\overset{*}{\Delta}_{(a)} v(x) = 0, \quad x \in B_i.$$

What we get is

$$\overset{*}{\Delta}_{(a)} v(x) = -\int_{S_1} \left(\overset{*}{\Delta}_{(a)} \overset{0}{H}(x, y)\right) f_1(y)\, dS_y - \int_{S_2} \left(\overset{*}{\Delta}_{(a)} \overset{0}{H}(x, y)\right) f_2(y)\, dS_y + \\ + \overset{*}{\Delta}_{(a)} \int_{S_1} \varphi(y)\, T_y^{(a)} \overset{0}{H}{}^{*}(x, y)\, dS_y;$$

The last term vanishes by Lemma C^0 of (VII, 9); in order to prove that the first two terms on the right also vanish, we note that in virtue of (4.15_a) (IV, 4)

$$\overset{*}{\Delta}_{(a)} \overset{0}{H}(x, y) = \left\{ \overset{*}{\Delta}_{(a)} \overset{0}{H}{}^{(1)},\ \overset{*}{\Delta}_{(a)} \overset{0}{H}{}^{(2)},\ \overset{*}{\Delta}_{(a)} \overset{0}{H}{}^{(3)} \right\} =$$

$$= 4\pi \sum_{s=1}^{6} \left\| \begin{matrix} \mathfrak{A}_1^{(s)}(x)\, \mathfrak{A}_1^{(s)}(y) & \mathfrak{A}_1^{(s)}(x)\, \mathfrak{A}_2^{(s)}(y) & \mathfrak{A}_1^{(s)}(x)\, \mathfrak{A}_3^{(s)}(y) \\ \mathfrak{A}_2^{(s)}(x)\, \mathfrak{A}_1^{(s)}(y) & \mathfrak{A}_2^{(s)}(x)\, \mathfrak{A}_2^{(s)}(y) & \mathfrak{A}_2^{(s)}(x)\, \mathfrak{A}_3^{(s)}(y) \\ \mathfrak{A}_3^{(s)}(x)\, \mathfrak{A}_1^{(s)}(y) & \mathfrak{A}_3^{(s)}(x)\, \mathfrak{A}_2^{(s)}(y) & \mathfrak{A}_3^{(s)}(x)\, \mathfrak{A}_3^{(s)}(y) \end{matrix} \right\|;$$

consequently

$$\int_{S_1} \left(\overset{*}{\Delta}_{(a)} \overset{0}{H}(x, y)\right) f_1(y)\, dS_y = 4\pi \sum_{s=1}^{6} \mathfrak{A}^{(s)}(x) \int_{S_1} \boldsymbol{\mathfrak{A}}^{(s)}(y) f_1(y)\, dS_y$$

and

$$\int_{S_2} \left(\overset{*}{\Delta}_{(a)} \overset{0}{H}(x, y)\right) f_2(y)\, dS_y = 4\pi \sum_{s=1}^{6} \boldsymbol{\mathfrak{A}}^{(s)}(x) \int_{S_2} \boldsymbol{\mathfrak{A}}^{(s)}(y) f_2(y)\, dS_y,$$

and the solvability condition (*) secures the required result. On the other hand, it is plain that

$$\lim_{x \to x_0} v(x) = 0, \quad x \in B_i, \quad x_0 \in S_1,$$

so that

$$v(x) = 0, \quad x \in B_i.$$

Thus, the solution of (10.67) indeed satisfies the functional equation (10.65_2). Its uniqueness may also be easily proved. Equation (10.65_2) is a canonical functional equation and therefore algebraization through use of quadrature formulas is feasible.

§ 10. The mixed problem for a doubly-connected domain

Let now the stresses be prescribed on one of the boundaries, say, S_1, and the displacements on the other, S_2. The solution may be obtained by solving the system

$$0 = -\frac{1}{4\pi} \int_{S_1} \overset{0}{G}(x, y) f_1(y)\, dS_y + \frac{1}{4\pi} \int_{S_2} f_2(y)\, T_y^{(a)} \overset{0}{G}(x, y)\, dS_y + \\ + \frac{1}{2\pi} \int_{S_1} \varphi(y)\, T_y^{(a)} \overset{0}{G}(x, y)\, dS_y, \quad x \in B_i, \qquad (10.76_1)$$

$$u(x) = -\frac{1}{4\pi} \int_{S_1} \overset{0}{G}(x, y) f_1(y)\, dS_y + \frac{1}{4\pi} \int_{S_2} f_2(y)\, T_y^{(a)} \overset{0}{G}(x, y)\, dS_y + \\ + \frac{1}{2\pi} \int_{S_1} \varphi(y)\, T_y^{(a)} \overset{0}{G}(x, y)\, dS_y, \quad x \in B_a. \qquad (10.76_2)$$

This follows from the fact that $G(x, y)$ and $T_y^{(a)} G(x, y)$ satisfy the equations of elasticity with respect to the point x (by definition of the first Green's tensor and by Theorem 1 of (I,3)). To show the solvability of (10.76_1) we again form the internal limit at S_1, which by Theorem 2 of (II, 1) as

$$\varphi(x_0)-\frac{1}{2\pi}\int\limits_{S_1}\varphi(y)\,\mathrm{T}_y^{(a)}\overset{0}{G}(x_0,\,y)\,dS_y=$$

$$=-\frac{1}{4\pi}\int\limits_{S_1}\overset{0}{G}(x_0,\,y)\,f_1(y)\,dS_y+\frac{1}{4\pi}\int\limits_{S_2}f_2(y)\,\mathrm{T}_y^{(a)}\overset{0}{G}(x_0,\,y)\,dS_y. \tag{10.77}$$

The corresponding homogeneous equation admits only a trivial solution; for, if $\varphi_*(x_0)$ is a nontrivial solution, the double-layer potential

$$W(\varphi_*,\,x)=\frac{1}{2\pi}\int\limits_{S_1}\varphi_*(y)\,\mathrm{T}_y^{(a)}G(x,\,y)\,dS_y,$$

being a solution of the equations of elasticity which vanishes in the internal limit at S_1, must vanish identically in B_i; therefore

$$(\mathrm{T}W(\varphi_*;\,x_0))_i=0,\qquad x_0\in S_1,$$

and by the Lyapunov-Tauber theorem

$$(\mathrm{T}W(\varphi_*;\,x_0))_a=0,\qquad x_0\in S_1. \tag{10.78}$$

On the other hand, by the properties of the first Green's tensor

$$\lim_{B\ni x\to x_0\in S_2} G(x,\,y)=0,$$

hence

$$\lim_{B_a\ni x\to x_0\in S_2} W(\varphi_*;\,x)=0. \tag{10.79}$$

Relations (10.78) and (10.79) imply that

$$W(\varphi_*;\,x)=0,\qquad x\in B_a;$$

and so

$$\varphi_*(x_0)=0,\qquad x_0\in S_1.$$

This proves the solvability of (10.77). The solution of (10.77) is also a solution of the functional equation (10.76_1); the proof of this is obvious. Equation (10.76_1) is canonical and may be solved approximately by algebraization using quadrature formulas.

§ 11. The problem of sound scattering

The method which we have thus far used to obtain approximate solutions of various boundary-value problems of elasticity, may also be used for approximate solution of many other problems of mathematical physics. By way of illustration, consider the problem of scattering of sound by a rigid obstacle. This problem requires us to solve the scalar wave equation

$$\Delta u+k^2u=0 \tag{10.80}$$

in the infinite domain B_a, enclosing an absolutely rigid body with the surface S, at which the following boundary condition is fulfilled

$$\frac{\partial u}{\partial n}=f(y),\qquad y\in S\quad (n\text{-normal}).$$

Here $k=\frac{\omega}{a}$, ω is the frequency of the incident wave, $a=\sqrt{\gamma\frac{h}{\rho}}$ is the velocity of sound, γ the adiabatic index, h and ρ the pressure and density of the undisturbed medium filling B_a, and $u(p)$ is the pressure of the scattered wave.

The Sommerfeld radiation condition must be satisfied at infinity. The solution of the problem is of the form

$$u(x)=-\frac{1}{4\pi}\int_S f(y)\frac{e^{ikr}}{r(x,y)}dS_y+\frac{1}{2\pi}\int_S \varphi(y)\frac{\partial}{\partial n_y}\frac{e^{ikr}}{r(x,y)}dS_y,\quad x\in B_a; \qquad (10.81_1)$$

whereas

$$0=-\frac{1}{4\pi}\int_S f(y)\frac{e^{ikr}}{r}dS_y+\frac{1}{2\pi}\int_S \varphi(y)\frac{\partial}{\partial n_y}\frac{e^{ikr}}{r(x,y)}dS_y,\quad x\in B_i. \qquad (10.81_2)$$

The integrals

$$\frac{1}{2\pi}\int_S \varphi(y)\frac{e^{ikr}}{r(x,y)}dS_y \quad\text{and}\quad \frac{1}{2\pi}\int_S \varphi(y)\frac{\partial}{\partial n_y}\frac{e^{ikr}}{r(x,y)}dS_y$$

are the single- and double-layer potential solutions of the scalar equation (10.80), and they possess the properties of elastic potentials established in Ch. II. In particular, the existence of one of the limits

$$\left(\frac{\partial}{\partial n_x}\int_S \varphi(y)\frac{\partial}{\partial n_y}\frac{e^{ikr}}{r(x,y)}dS_y\right)_i \quad\text{or}\quad \left(\frac{\partial}{\partial n_x}\int_S \varphi(y)\frac{\partial}{\partial n_y}\frac{e^{ink}}{r(x,y)}dS_y\right)_a$$

implies the existence of the other, and if they exist they are equal.

We first assume that equation (10.81_2) has a solution; then the internal limit

$$\left(\frac{\partial}{\partial n_x}\int_S \varphi(y)\frac{\partial}{\partial n_y}\frac{e^{ikr}}{r(x,y)}dS_y\right)_i,$$

exists, and therefore so does the external limit and is equal to the first. Forming the difference of the normal derivatives of (10.81_1) and (10.81_2), we infer from the properties of a single-layer potential and the Lyapunov-Tauber theorem that

$$\frac{\partial u}{\partial n}=f(x_0),\qquad x_0\in S.$$

Thus, $u(x)$ as defined by (10.81_1) indeed satisfies the given boundary condition; the choice of the kernels of the potentials ensures that the radiation condition is fulfilled too.

That the functional equation (10.81_2) has a solution follows from the form of its internal limit at S

$$\varphi(x_0)-\frac{1}{2\pi}\int_S \varphi(y)\frac{\partial}{\partial n_y}\frac{e^{ikr}}{r(x_0,y)}dS_y=-\frac{1}{4\pi}\int_S f(y)\frac{e^{ikr}}{r(x_0,y)}dS_y.$$

This is the integral equation (D_i) (for (10.80)), and if ω is not an eigenvalue of the problem, the corresponding homogeneous equation admits only a trivial solution (cf. /13a/). The uniqueness proof is easy. Equation (10.81_2) is a canonical functional equation and it may be solved approximately by using quadratures.

This method of solution may evidently be applied to other problems of electromagnetic or acoustic diffraction, which by and large amount to a Dirichlet or a Neumann problem, or a combination of both, in a medium containing various inclusions.

§ 12. Proof of existence of the inverse operator

The fact that the approximate solution reduces to the treatment of canonical functional equations is very important; this guarantees that the number of equations is equal to the number of unknowns and also ensures the boundedness of the coefficients of the linear algebraic equations, derived from the functional equations of the problem by means of quadrature formulas. We shall consider this system here and in the following sections, and show that

(a) it is solvable and the solution may be obtained by the method of successive approximations /15/,

(b) the error of approximation may be estimated and depends on the classes of surfaces and the boundary values of the given functions.

Let us for simplicity investigate these questions in the case of the plane Dirichlet problem for the Laplace equation and a domain bounded by a simple closed Lyapunov curve S.

The solution of the internal Dirichlet problem with a given boundary-value function $f(x)$ on S has the form

$$u(x)=\frac{1}{2\pi}\int_S f(y)\frac{\partial}{\partial n_y}\ln r(x, y)\,dS_y+\frac{1}{\pi}\int_S \varphi(y)\ln r(x, y)\,dS_y, \quad x\in B_i, \qquad (10.82_1)$$

where $\varphi(y)$ is the solution of the functional equation

$$0=\frac{1}{2\pi}\int_S f(y)\frac{\partial}{\partial n_y}\ln r(x, y)\,dS_y+\frac{1}{\pi}\int_S \varphi(y)\ln r(x, y)\,dS_y, \quad x\in B_a. \qquad (10.82_2)$$

Let $f(x)$ possess first derivatives of class H with respect to the coordinates; we shall show that this assumption ensures that (10.82_2) is solvable. Differentiating (10.82_2) along the normal and letting x approach from the outside the point x_0 on S,

$$\varphi(x_0)+\frac{1}{\pi}\int_S \varphi(y)\frac{\partial}{\partial n_{x_0}}\ln r(x_0, y)\,dS_y=\left(\frac{\partial F(x_0)}{\partial n_{x_0}}\right)_a, \qquad (10.83)$$

where

$$F(x)=\frac{1}{2\pi}\int_S f(y)\frac{\partial}{\partial n_y}\ln r(x, y)\,dS_y.$$

The existence of the limit on the right-hand side of (10.83) is guaranteed by the restriction imposed on the function $f(y)$, viz., that it be the density of a double-layer potential. Equation (10.83) is the integral equation for the exterior Neumann problem and is known to be solvable. Its solution is at the same time the unique solution of the functional equation (10.82_2). Replacing the integral in (10.82_2) by a quadrature formula, we obtain

$$\sum_{i=1}^{N} A_i^{(N)}\varphi(y_i)\ln r(x_k, y_i)=-\pi F(x_k) \qquad (k=1, 2, \ldots, N), \qquad (10.84)$$

where $y_k\in S$, $x_k\in B_a$.

We now show that the x_k $(k=1, \ldots, N)$ may be chosen in B_a so that the system (10.84) is solvable and the solution may be approached by iteration. Let us draw in B_a a curve S' parallel to S at a distance δ from the latter and consider the points x_k $(k=1, 2, \ldots, N)$ on S' which lie on the normal to S through the point y_k (i.e., on n_{y_k}). Since N is finite, the number δ may be chosen so small that the following inequality holds

$$\max_k \left(\frac{1}{|A_k^{(N)} \ln r(x_k, y_k)|} \sum_{l=1\,(l \neq k)}^{N} |A_l^{(N)} \ln r(x_k, y_l)| \right) = q < 1 \qquad (10.85)$$

$$(k = 1, 2, \ldots, N).$$

We now introduce the notation

$$\left.\begin{aligned} a_{lk} &= \begin{cases} -\dfrac{1}{A_k^{(N)} \ln r(x_k, y_k)} A_l^{(N)} \ln r(x_k, y_l) & (l \neq k), \\ 0 & (l = k), \end{cases} \\ \psi_k &= \frac{-\pi F(x_k)}{A_k^{(N)} \ln r(x_k, y_k)}, \\ \varphi(y_k) &= \varphi_k \end{aligned}\right\} \qquad (10.86)$$

and the vectors $\varphi = (\varphi_1, \varphi_2, \ldots, \varphi_N)$, $\psi = (\psi_1, \psi_2, \ldots, \psi_N)$; the system (10.84) may now be written in the form

$$\varphi - A\varphi = \psi. \qquad (10.87)$$

The operator A represents a linear transformation defined by the matrix

$$\|a_{lk}\|_{lk=1, 2, \ldots, N}.$$

This transformation maps the N-dimensional vector space m_N

$$\xi = (\xi_1, \xi_2, \ldots, \xi_N)$$

with the norm

$$\|\xi\| = \max_l |\xi_l| \qquad (l = 1, 2, \ldots, N)$$

onto itself, and the norm of the operator A equals

$$\|A\| = \max_k \sum_{l=1}^{N} |a_{lk}| \qquad (k = 1, 2, \ldots, N).$$

In view of (10.86) and the inequality (10.85),

$$\|A\| = q < 1.$$

By Banach's theorem, *if* $\|A\| = q < 1$, *then the equation* $\varphi - A\varphi = \psi$ *has a unique solution for any* ψ, *and it may be obtained by successive approximations beginning with an arbitrary* $\varphi^{(0)}$; *in other words, if the condition* $\|A\| = q < 1$ *is satisfied, the operator* $(I - A)$ *has an inverse*

$$B \equiv (I - A)^{-1}$$

and further

$$\|B\| = \|(I - A)^{-1}\| \leqslant \frac{1}{1-q}.$$

Indeed, equation (10.87) formally gives

$$\varphi = (I - A)^{-1}\psi = B\psi = I\psi + A\psi + A^2\psi + \ldots;$$

but the series

$$B\psi = I\psi + A\psi + A^2\psi + \ldots$$

converges, since

$$\|A^k\psi\| < \|A\|^k \|\psi\| \leqslant q^k \|\psi\|.$$

and, consequently,

$$\|B\psi\| \leqslant \frac{1}{1-q} \|\psi\|.$$

On the other hand

$$\varphi = B\psi = I\psi + A\psi + A^2\psi + \dots$$

is a solution of (10.87), since

$$(I-A)\varphi = (I-A)B\psi = \psi + A\psi + A^2\psi + \dots - A\psi - A^2\psi - \dots = \psi$$

and

$$\varphi(I-A) = B\psi(I-A) = \psi(I-A) + A[\psi(I-A)] + A^2[\psi(I-A)] + \dots = \psi.$$

Thus, we have proved that a solution exists, and may be approached by the iterations

$$\varphi^{(1)} = A\varphi^{(0)} + \psi, \quad \varphi^{(2)} = A\varphi^{(1)} + \psi = A^{(2)}\varphi^0 + \psi + A\psi,$$
$$\varphi^{(n)} = A\varphi^{(n-1)} + \psi = A^n\varphi^0 + \psi + A\psi + A^2\psi + \dots + A^{n-1}\psi,$$

for since $\lim A^n\varphi^0 = 0$ for $n \to \infty$,

$$\lim_{n\to\infty} \varphi^{(n)} = B\psi.$$

Banach's theorem gives only sufficient conditions for the existence of the inverse operator. It sometimes turns out that a more convenient choice of the auxiliary points x_k in B_a than that made above will also satisfy the requirement. The examples considered below make clear this point.

§ 13. Evaluation of error

As is known /25/, there exist quadrature formulas for which the error is of the order $O(N^{-\alpha})$ if the unknown function is of class H with exponent α, and of the order $O(N^{-n})$ if this function is $(n-1)$ times continuously differentiable and has a piecewise-continuous n-th derivative. Therefore in view of (10.5') the deviation of the approximate from the exact values is estimated by

$$|\varphi(y_k) - \tilde{\varphi}(y_k)| < \frac{\sum_{i=1}^{N} \Delta_{ki}}{\Delta} O(N^{-\alpha}) \tag{10.88}$$

in the first case, and by

$$|\varphi(y_k) - \tilde{\varphi}(y_k)| < \frac{\sum_{i=1}^{N} \Delta_{ki}}{\Delta} O(N^{-n}) \tag{10.89}$$

in the second. Solving equation (10.83), we get

$$\varphi(x_0) = \Phi(x_0) + \int_S R(x_0, y)\Phi(y)\,dS_y, \tag{10.90}$$

where

$$R(x_0, y) = K(x_0, y) + K^{(2)}(x_0, y) + R_*^{(2)}(x_0, y)[1 + K^2(x_0, y)],$$

$$K(x_0, y) = \frac{1}{\pi}\frac{\partial}{\partial n_y}\ln r(x_0, y),$$

$$\Phi(x_0) = \frac{1}{2\pi}\frac{\partial}{\partial n_{x_0}}\int_S f(y)\frac{\partial}{\partial n_y}\ln r(x_0, y)\,dS_y,$$

where $K^{(2)}(x_0, y)$ is the iterated kernel, and $R_*^{(2)}(x_0, y)$ is the (continuous) resolvent of this kernel. It is known from potential theory that if the surface S, which bears the attracting masses, and the density distribution on it are differentiable up to a certain order, then also the double-layer potential formed by that distribution is differentiable to a certain order on S. The proof of this statement may be found, for example, in /8/ (cf. also /5c/). The two terms on the right-hand side of (10.90) are obviously double-layer potentials and, consequently, if S and $f(y)$ are differentiable up to some order then the unknown function is also differentiable to some order. In this case the product $K(x, y)\varphi(y)$ for $x \in B_a$ has the same number of derivatives and one may apply the estimate (10.89).

§ 14. Various remarks. Use of the method of least squares

(a) When the auxiliary points x_k, $k=1, 2, \ldots, N$ are chosen close to the contour S, as was done in § 12, the error of the quadrature formulas increases; this is evident from formulas (10.4) and (10.4'). However, it may be shown that for any choice of N points x_k in B_a the determinant Δ of the system is different from zero with a probability as close as desired to one. Some allied and more general theorems will be presented in § 19 (cf. /15/).

(b) Choosing arbitrarily in B_a a sufficiently large number of points

$$x_1, x_2, \ldots, x_{N-1}, x_N, x_{N+1}, \ldots, x_M \qquad (M \gg N),$$

we may expect to find among them at least one set of N points for which $\Delta \neq 0$ and the rank of the matrix of coefficients of the system of M equations in N unknowns

$$\sum_{l=1}^{N} A_l^{(N)} \ln r(x_k, y_l)\varphi(y_l) = -\frac{1}{2}F(x_k) \quad (k=1, 2, 3, \ldots, M) \tag{10.91}$$

equals N. Let

$$P_k^{(l)} = A_l^{(N)} \ln r(x_k, y_l).$$

Consider the system of N vectors in an M-dimensional space $P^{(l)}$, $l=1, 2, 3, \ldots, N$, with the components

$$(P_1^{(l)}, P_2^{(l)}, \ldots, P_M^{(l)}).$$

These vectors are linearly independent, for otherwise

$$\sum_{l=1}^{N} C_l P^{(l)} = 0, \tag{10.92}$$

where not all the constants C_l, $l=1, 2, \ldots, N$ vanish. Projecting on the coordinate axes, we obtain

$$\sum_{l=1}^{N} C_l P_k^{(l)} = 0 \qquad (k=1, 2, \ldots, M).$$

The rank of the matrix of coefficients of this system is N. Picking out the appropriate N equations and considering them separately, we get

$$C_l = 0 \quad (l=1, 2, \ldots, N).$$

Let us try to fit a solution to the system (10.91) by the method of least squares. It is required to determine $\varphi(y_1)\ \varphi(y_2) \ldots \varphi(y_N)$ that minimize

$$\sum_{k=1}^{M}\left(X_k - \sum_{l=1}^{N} P_k^{(l)}\varphi_l\right)^2,$$

where

$$X_k = -\frac{1}{2}F(x_k), \qquad \varphi_l = \varphi(y_l).$$

Differentiating with respect to φ_s and equating the derivatives to zero,

$$\sum_{k=1}^{M}\left(X_k-\sum_{l=1}^{N}P_k^{(l)}\varphi_l\right)P_k^{(s)}=0 \qquad (s=1,\,2,\,\ldots,\,N).$$

or

$$\sum_{l=1}^{N}\left(\sum_{k=1}^{M}P_k^{(l)}P_k^{(s)}\right)\varphi_l=\sum_{k=1}^{M}P_k^{(s)}X_k.$$

Indicating scalar products by brackets, we may write

$$\sum_{l=1}^{N}(P^{(l)}P^{(s)})\varphi_l=(XP^{(s)}) \qquad (s=1,\,2,\,\ldots,\,N).$$

The determinant of this system

$$\begin{vmatrix} (P^{(1)}P^{(1)}) \ldots (P^{(N)}P^{(1)}) \\ \cdot\;\cdot\;\cdot\;\cdot\;\cdot\;\cdot\;\cdot\;\cdot\;\cdot\;\cdot \\ (P^{(1)}P^{(N)}) \ldots (P^{(N)}P^{(N)}) \end{vmatrix}$$

is the Gram's determinant of the vector set $P^{(s)}$, $s=1,\,2,\,\ldots,\,N$, and does not vanish because of their linear independence.

§ 15. Numerical examples. Approximate solution of the Gaussian functional equation

The simplest, but sufficiently typical functional canonical equation is

$$\frac{1}{2\pi}\int_S \varphi(y)\frac{\cos(xy,\,n_y)}{r(x,\,y)}\,dS_y=1, \qquad x\in B_i, \tag{10.93}$$

where S is the unit circle, $(xy,\,n_y)$ the angle between the normal to S at point y and the direction xy, $r(x,\,y)$ the distance between x and y, with x lying in the internal domain B_i (the unit disk); $\varphi(y)$ is a continuous function of the contour points which satisfies equation (10.93) identically for any x in B_i. Equation (10.93) will be called the Gaussian functional equation. It is obviously satisfied by $\varphi\equiv 1$, since for this value of φ the equation reduces to the Gauss integral

$$\frac{1}{2\pi}\int_S \frac{\cos(xy,\,n_y)}{r(x,\,y)}\,dS_y=1, \qquad x\in B_i.$$

It may be also shown easily that $\varphi\equiv 1$ is a unique solution. Assuming the opposite and taking the difference of two different solutions, we obtain, after passing to the limit at the contour from the inside, the known Fredholm integral equation for the internal homogeneous Dirichlet problem, which has only a trivial solution.

To solve the Gaussian functional equation approximately we apply two numerical integration formulas of different accuracy, the rectangular formula and the Gaussian formula. In order to consider typical cases, we assume the points x_k to be located in B_i on concentric circles of radius ρ, ρ being close to one or zero.

Applying the rectangular formula, we divide the interval $(0,\,2\pi)$ by the points y_k into N equal subintervals; we have the approximate equality

$$\frac{1}{2\pi}\int_S \varphi(y)\frac{\cos(xy,\,n_y)}{r(x,\,y)}\,dS_y=\frac{1}{N}\sum_{l=1}^{N}\varphi(\alpha_l)\frac{\cos(xy_l,\,n_{y_l})}{r(x,\,y_l)},$$

where $\alpha_i = i\frac{2\pi}{N}$, $i = 1, 2, \ldots, N$. It is easily verified that

$$\frac{\cos(x_k y_i,\, n_{y_i})}{r(x_k,\, y_i)} = \frac{1-\rho\cos(i-k)\,\omega}{1+\rho^2-2\rho\cos(i-k)\,\omega}$$
$$\left(\omega = \frac{2\pi}{N};\quad i,\, k = 1, 2, 3, \ldots, N\right),$$

and hence we have the system of equations

$$\sum_{i=1}^{N} \frac{1-\rho\cos(i-k)\,\omega}{1+\rho^2-2\rho\cos(i-k)\,\omega}\,\varphi(y_i) = N \qquad (k = 1, 2, \ldots, N), \tag{10.94}$$

where each point x_k lies on a concentric circle of radius ρ at the nearest position to the point y_k on S.

We present the results of calculations for five different sets of the auxiliary points x_k $(k = 1, 2, 3, \ldots, N)$, with $N = 40$.

1°. $\rho = 0.95$, $N = 40$, $\omega = 9°$,

$$\sum_{i=1}^{40} \frac{1-0.95\cos(i-k)\,\omega}{1.9025-1.9\cos(i-k)\,\omega}\,\varphi_i = 40 \qquad (k = 1, 2, \ldots, 40).$$

The determinant of the system is

$$\begin{vmatrix} a_1 & a_2 & a_3 & \ldots & a_{40} \\ a_2 & a_1 & a_3 & \ldots & a_{39} \\ a_3 & a_2 & a_1 & \ldots & a_{38} \\ \cdot & \cdot & \cdot & \cdots & \cdot \\ a_{40} & a_{39} & a_{38} & \ldots & a_1 \end{vmatrix},$$

where

$a_1 = 20$	$a_{11} = 0.525624$	$a_{21} = 0.512820$	$a_{31} = 0.525624$
$a_2 = 2.382804$	$a_{12} = 0.522161$	$a_{22} = 0.512899$	$a_{32} = 0.530368$
$a_3 = 1.010510$	$a_{13} = 0.519581$	$a_{23} = 0.513141$	$a_{33} = 0.537061$
$a_4 = 0.732599$	$a_{14} = 0.517630$	$a_{24} = 0.513558$	$a_{34} = 0.546878$
$a_5 = 0.633427$	$a_{15} = 0.516146$	$a_{25} = 0.514173$	$a_{35} = 0.562045$
$a_6 = 0.587209$	$a_{16} = 0.515018$	$a_{26} = 0.515018$	$a_{36} = 0.587209$
$a_7 = 0.562045$	$a_{17} = 0.514173$	$a_{27} = 0.516146$	$a_{37} = 0.633427$
$a_8 = 0.546878$	$a_{18} = 0.513558$	$a_{28} = 0.517630$	$a_{38} = 0.732599$
$a_9 = 0.537061$	$a_{19} = 0.513141$	$a_{29} = 0.519581$	$a_{39} = 0.010510$
$a_{10} = 0.530368$	$a_{20} = 0.512899$	$a_{30} = 0.522161$	$a_{40} = 2.382804$

It may be easily verified that

$$\varphi_1 = \varphi_2 = \ldots = \varphi_{40} = \varphi$$

and

$$\varphi = \frac{40}{\sum_{i=1}^{40} a_i} = 0.87. \tag{10.95}$$

2°. $\rho = 0.90$, $N = 40$, $\omega = 9°$,

$$\sum_{i=1}^{40} \frac{1-0.9\cos(i-k)\,\omega}{1.81-1.8\cos(i-k)\,\omega}\,\varphi_i = 40.$$

$a_1 = 10$	$a_{11} = 0.552486$	$a_{21} = 0.526315$	$a_{31} = 0.552486$
$a_2 = 3.453882$	$a_{12} = 0.545420$	$a_{22} = 0.526478$	$a_{32} = 0.562155$
$a_3 = 1.468416$	$a_{13} = 0.540148$	$a_{23} = 0.526974$	$a_{33} = 0.575771$
$a_4 = 0.960743$	$a_{14} = 0.536160$	$a_{24} = 0.527828$	$a_{34} = 0.595687$
$a_5 = 0.768536$	$a_{15} = 0.533123$	$a_{25} = 0.529085$	$a_{35} = 0.626332$
$a_6 = 0.676840$	$a_{16} = 0.530816$	$a_{26} = 0.530816$	$a_{36} = 0.676840$
$a_7 = 0.626332$	$a_{17} = 0.529085$	$a_{27} = 0.533123$	$a_{37} = 0.768536$
$a_8 = 0.595687$	$a_{18} = 0.527828$	$a_{28} = 0.536160$	$a_{38} = 0.960743$
$a_9 = 0.575577$	$a_{19} = 0.526974$	$a_{29} = 0.540148$	$a_{39} = 1.468416$
$a_{10} = 0.562155$	$a_{20} = 0.526478$	$a_{30} = 0.545420$	$a_{40} = 3.453882$

Substituting these values of the coefficients in (10.95), we get

$$\varphi = 0.91.$$

3°. $\rho = 0.1,\ N = 40,\ \omega = 9°$,

$$\sum_{i=1}^{40} \frac{1 - 0.1\cos(i-k)\,\omega}{1.01 - 0.2\cos(i-k)\,\omega}\,\varphi_i = 40.$$

$a_1 = 1.11111$	$a_{11} = 0.90909$	$a_{21} = 0.90900$	$a_{31} = a_{11}$
$a_2 = 1.10926$	$a_{12} = 0.909925$	$a_{22} = a_{20}$	$a_{32} = a_{10}$
$a_3 = 1.10381$	$a_{13} = 0.91243$	$a_{23} = a_{19}$	$a_{33} = a_9$
$a_4 = 1.09509$	$a_{14} = 0.91660$	$a_{24} = a_{18}$	$a_{34} = a_8$
$a_5 = 1.08359$	$a_{15} = 0.91242$	$a_{25} = a_{17}$	$a_{35} = a_7$
$a_6 = 1.06990$	$a_{16} = 0.92990$	$a_{26} = a_{16}$	$a_{36} = a_6$
$a_7 = 1.05466$	$a_{17} = 0.93900$	$a_{27} = a_{15}$	$a_{37} = a_5$
$a_8 = 1.038151$	$a_{18} = 0.94967$	$a_{28} = a_{14}$	$a_{38} = a_4$
$a_9 = 1.02204$	$a_{19} = 0.96184$	$a_{29} = a_{13}$	$a_{39} = a_3$
$a_{10} = 1.00577$	$a_{20} = 0.97537$	$a_{30} = a_{12}$	$a_{40} = a_2$

Substituting these values of the coefficients in (10.95), we get the approximation

$$\varphi = 1.00002.$$

Finally, we consider the case of a still larger distance of the auxiliary points from the contour.

4°. $\rho = 0.01.\ N = 40,\ \omega = 9°$,

$$\sum_{i=1}^{40} \frac{1 - 0.01\cos(i-k)\,\omega}{1.0001 - 0.02\cos(i-k)\,\omega}\,\varphi_i = 40.$$

$a_1 = 1.01010$	$a_{11} = 0.99990$	$a_{21} = 0.99010$	$a_{31} = 0.99990$
$a_2 = 1.00997$	$a_{12} = 0.99834$	$a_{22} = 0.99022$	$a_{32} = 1.00147$
$a_3 = 1.00959$	$a_{13} = 0.99683$	$a_{23} = 0.99057$	$a_{33} = 1.00301$
$a_4 = 1.00897$	$a_{14} = 0.99540$	$a_{24} = 0.99115$	$a_{34} = 1.00448$
$a_5 = 1.00812$	$a_{15} = 0.99409$	$a_{25} = 0.99194$	$a_{35} = 1.00584$
$a_6 = 1.00707$	$a_{16} = 0.99293$	$a_{26} = 0.99293$	$a_{36} = 1.00707$
$a_7 = 1.00584$	$a_{17} = 0.99194$	$a_{27} = 0.99409$	$a_{37} = 1.00812$
$a_8 = 1.00448$	$a_{18} = 0.99115$	$a_{28} = 0.99540$	$a_{38} = 1.00897$
$a_9 = 1.00301$	$a_{19} = 0.99057$	$a_{29} = 0.99683$	$a_{39} = 1.00959$
$a_{10} = 1.00147$	$a_{20} = 0.99022$	$a_{30} = 0.99834$	$a_{40} = 1.00997$

The approximation is in this case even better and formula (10.95) gives

$$\varphi = 1.000005.$$

5°. Instead of the rectangular formula we now use the Gaussian five-point formula; the auxiliary points x_k, $k=1, 2, \ldots, 5$ are chosen as follows

$$x_{1,2}=\pm 0.2, \quad x_3=0, \quad x_{4,5}=\pm 0.1.$$

Then the values of the unknowns fall in the interval (0.99–1.101). This simple case allows us to draw a few conclusions of which the most important is, that *the solution of the algebraic system of linear equations obtained from a canonical functional equation by means of quadrature formulas approximates quite well to the solution of the original equation, and the degree of accuracy depends, for a given number of basic points and a given quadrature formula, on the choice of the auxiliary points.*

It is readily seen from our example that when the auxiliary points are taken on a contour which lies close to the original circle the approximation is worse than when this contour is located further away. The maximum error connected with the use of any quadrature formula is limited by the corresponding remainder term. This remainder term has in the case of the rectangular formula for interval (a, b) the form

$$R_N=\frac{(b-a)^3}{24N^2}M, \quad M>|f''(\xi)|, \ a\leqslant\xi\leqslant b. \tag{10.96}$$

In the Gaussian formula it is given by

$$R_N=\frac{(b-a)^{2N+1}(N!)^4 f^{(2N)}(\xi)}{(2N!)^3(2N+1)}.$$

Choosing the points x_k, as in cases 1° and 2°, close to the contour, namely at the distance of 0.05 and 0.1 respectively, we substitute the values of the second derivatives of the function $\ln r(x, y)$ at the minimum values of $r(x_k, y_l)$ into (10.96); in the cases considered these are obviously large numbers, which in view of (10.96) spoils the accuracy of the approximation. On the other hand, it should be noted that if the contour of auxiliary points is sufficiently close to the original circle the solution may be obtained by the method of successive approximations, as shown in § 14.

While a far position of the contour of auxiliary points is seen to provide higher accuracy, it should be kept in mind that the determinant of the system is usually of small modulus, which is the source of distortions due to the rounding errors inescapable in numerical calculations. The effect of rounding errors is negligible in the above examples, because the symmetry of the configuration allows us to derive the solution of the system directly from (10.95). Besides that, one should keep in mind that the existence of the inverse operator does not follow in this case from the considerations of § 14 and must be proved separately.

§ 16. Numerical example. Approximate solution of the Dirichlet problem for the ellipse

Let us consider the Dirichlet problem for the ellipse; this furnishes an adequate illustration of the method discussed.

It is required to find a harmonic function $u(x)$ in the interior of the ellipse

$$x_1=a\cos t, \quad x_2=b\sin t$$

for the boundary condition on S

$$u(x)=f(x), \quad x\in S.$$

In order to obtain a numerical result which it would be convenient to compare with the exact solution, we assign the following values

$$a=1, \quad b=0.5; \quad f(x)=0.5(x_1^2+x_2^2). \tag{10.97}$$

It may be verified easily that the exact solution is

$$u(x_1, x_2)=0.2+0.3(x_1^2-x_2^2). \tag{10.98}$$

Let us now work out an approximate solution. Proceeding as before, we find that we have to solve the system of functional equations

$$u(x)=\frac{1}{2\pi}\int_S f(y)\frac{\cos(xy, n_y)}{r(x, y)}dS_y+\frac{1}{\pi}\int_S \varphi(y)\ln r(x, y)dS_y, \quad x\in B_i, \tag{10.99$_1$}$$

$$0=\frac{1}{2\pi}\int_S f(y)\frac{\cos(xy, n_y)}{r(x, y)}dS_y+\frac{1}{\pi}\int_S \varphi(y)\ln r(x, y)dS_y, \quad x\in B_a. \tag{10.99$_2$}$$

We use the Gaussian 16-point formula in the interval $(-1, +1)$ for (10.99_2). The coefficients and the basic points are in this case

$$A_1^{(16)}=A_{16}^{(16)}=0.027152459; \qquad A_2^{(16)}=A_{15}^{(16)}=0.062253524;$$
$$A_3^{(16)}=A_{14}^{(16)}=0.097158512; \qquad A_4^{(16)}=A_{13}^{(16)}=0.12462897;$$
$$A_5^{(16)}=A_{12}^{(16)}=0.14959599; \qquad A_6^{(16)}=A_{11}^{(16)}=0.16915652;$$
$$A_7^{(16)}=A_{10}^{(16)}=0.18260342; \qquad A_8^{(16)}=A_9^{(16)}=0.18945061;$$

$$\alpha_1^{(16)}=-\alpha_{16}^{(16)}=0.98940093; \qquad \alpha_2^{(16)}=-\alpha_{15}^{(16)}=0.94457502;$$
$$\alpha_3^{(16)}=-\alpha_{14}^{(16)}=0.86563120; \qquad \alpha_4^{(16)}=-\alpha_{13}^{(16)}=0.75540441;$$
$$\alpha_5^{(16)}=-\alpha_{12}^{(16)}=0.61787624; \qquad \alpha_6^{(16)}=-\alpha_{11}^{(16)}=0.45801678;$$
$$\alpha_7^{(16)}=-\alpha_{10}^{(16)}=0.28160355; \qquad \alpha_8^{(16)}=-\alpha_9^{(16)}=0.09501251.$$

The position of the point y on S in equation (10.99_2) is determined by the parameter t which varies in the interval $(0, 2\pi)$; introducing the new variable $t=(1+\alpha)\pi$, changes the interval to $(-1, +1)$ and (10.99_2) becomes

$$\int_{-1}^{+1}\varphi(\alpha)\ln\sqrt{[a\cos(1+\alpha)\pi-x_1]^2+[b\sin(1+\alpha)\pi-x_2]^2}\,d\alpha=$$
$$=-\frac{1}{2}\int_{-1}^{+1} f(\alpha)\left[\frac{d}{dt}\operatorname{arctg}\frac{b\sin t-x_2}{a\cos t-x_1}\right]_{t=(1+\alpha)\pi}d\alpha. \tag{10.100}$$

To simplify the calculations we take advantage of the freedom of choosing the points x in B_a; in this case it is convenient to locate the $x^{(k)}$ $(k=1, 2, 3, \ldots, 16)$ on the confocal ellipse; then, in view of

$$x_1=a_1\cos\tau, \quad x_2=b_1\sin\tau \tag{10.101}$$

so that the Gaussian ordinates corresponding to these points would coincide with the basic points $y^{(k)}$ $(k=1, 2, 3, \ldots, 16)$ on the main ellipse; then, in view of

$$\frac{\cos(xy, n_y)}{r(x, y)}=\frac{d}{dt}\operatorname{arctg}\frac{b\sin t-b_1\sin\tau}{a\cos t-a_1\cos\tau}=$$
$$=\frac{ab-a_1b\cos t\cos\tau-ab_1\sin t\sin\tau}{r^2(x, y)}$$

TABLE A

$\varphi(y_1)$	$\varphi(y_2)$	$\varphi(y_3)$
$0.7056690 \cdot 10^{-5}$	$0.225080 \cdot 10^{-2}$	$0.192227 \cdot 10^{-1}$
$-0.777287 \cdot 10^{-3}$	$0.437733 \cdot 10^{-3}$	$0.164132 \cdot 10^{-1}$
$-0.445645 \cdot 10^{-2}$	$-0.814582 \cdot 10^{-2}$	$0.266067 \cdot 10^{-2}$
$-0.106619 \cdot 10^{-1}$	$-0.235192 \cdot 10^{-1}$	$-0.274808 \cdot 10^{-1}$
$-0.154312 \cdot 10^{-2}$	$-0.446667 \cdot 10^{-2}$	$-0.136913 \cdot 10^{-1}$
$0.256990 \cdot 10^{-1}$	$0.580715 \cdot 10^{-1}$	$0.821648 \cdot 10^{-1}$
$0.4742860 \cdot 10^{-1}$	0.1080855	0.1601319
$0.5830134 \cdot 10^{-1}$	0.1331035	0.1990737

$\varphi(y_4)$	$\varphi(y_5)$	$\varphi(y_6)$
$0.704409 \cdot 10^{-1}$	0.159167	0.2648224
$0.669288 \cdot 10^{-1}$	0.155506	0.2613435
$0.5915418 \cdot 10^{-1}$	0.136775	0.2435480
$0.140368 \cdot 10^{-2}$	$0.830037 \cdot 10^{-1}$	0.1923034
$-0.361374 \cdot 10^{-1}$	$-0.238976 \cdot 10^{-1}$	$-0.176667 \cdot 10^{-1}$
$0.832118 \cdot 10^{-1}$	$0.386139 \cdot 10^{-1}$	$-0.452015 \cdot 10^{-1}$
0.1910762	0.1827931	0.116503
0.2447090	0.2540837	0.211360

$\varphi(y_7)$	$\varphi(y_8)$	b
0.3574148	0.4109894	0.0129680
0.3541655	0.4078786	0.0130195
0.3375693	0.3920035	0.0130689
0.2899972	0.3466244	0.1025823
0.185959	0.2479454	-0.0141866
$0.213925 \cdot 10^{-2}$	$0.710876 \cdot 10^{-1}$	-0.0314054
$-0.340888 \cdot 10^{-2}$	$-0.730354 \cdot 10^{-1}$	0.0063592
0.112886	$0.3371127 \cdot 10^{-2}$	0.0130801

we obtain from (10.100) upon applying the Gaussian formula

$$\sum_{i=1}^{16} A_i^{(16)}\varphi(\alpha_i)\ln\left\{[a\cos(1+\alpha_i)\pi - a_1\cos(1+\alpha_j)\pi]^2 + [b\sin(1+\alpha_i)\pi - b_1\sin(1+\alpha_j)\pi]^2\right\}^{\frac{1}{2}} = -\frac{1}{4}\sum_{i=1}^{16} A_i^{(16)}\left[a^2\cos^2(1+\alpha_i)\pi + b^2\sin^2(1+\alpha_i)\pi\right]\frac{ab - a_1 b\cos(1+\alpha_i)\pi\cos(1+\alpha_j)\pi - ab_1\sin(1+\alpha_i)\pi\sin(1+\alpha_j)\pi}{r^2(x_j, y_i)} \tag{10.101'}$$

$$(j = 1, 2, 3, \ldots, 16).$$

Let us first consider the case when the auxiliary ellipse (10.101) is close to the principal one; (let, say, $a_1=2,\ b_1=1$); then for $a=1,\ b=\frac{1}{2}$,

$$\sum_{i=1}^{16} A_i^{(16)}\varphi(\alpha_i)\ln\Big\{[\cos(1+\alpha_i)\pi-2\cos(1+\alpha_j)\pi]^2+$$

$$+[0.5\sin(1+\alpha_i)\pi-\sin(1+\alpha_j)\pi]^2\Big\}^{\frac{1}{2}}=-\frac{1}{4}\sum_{i=1}^{16}A_i^{(16)}\big[\cos^2(1+\alpha_i)\pi+$$

$$+0.25\sin^2(1+\alpha_i)\pi\big]\frac{0.5-\cos[(1+\alpha_i)\pi-(1+\alpha_j)\pi]}{r^2(x_j,\ y_i)}\quad (j=1,\ 2,\ \ldots,\ 16). \tag{10.102}$$

In virtue of the special choice of the points $x^{(k)}$ (for simplicity let us write x_k instead of $x^{(k)}$) we have

$$r(x_i,\ y_j)=r(x_j,\ y_i),$$

and as is readily seen

$$\varphi(y_i)=\varphi(y_{17-i})\qquad (i=1,\ 2,\ \ldots,\ 16), \tag{10.103}$$

on account of which the system of 16 equations (10.102) reduces to a system of 8 equations. The coefficients of $\varphi(y_i)$ $(i=1,\ 2,\ \ldots,\ 8)$ and the right-hand sides (b) are listed in Table A.

The solution of the system is

$$\varphi(y_1)=20.0201504,\qquad \varphi(y_2)=-12.7255234$$
$$\varphi(y_3)=3.33231100,\qquad \varphi(y_4)=-1.01333008,$$
$$\varphi(y_5)=0.40868940,\qquad \varphi(y_6)=0.070016210,$$
$$\varphi(y_7)=0.05396402,\qquad \varphi(y_8)=-0.13162008.$$

The values of $\varphi(y_9)\ldots\varphi(y_{16})$ are obtained from (10.103).

We represent the function $u(x)$ defined by (10.99_1) by means of the Gaussian 16-point formula, using the values of $\varphi(y_i)$ just derived. The approximate value of $u(x)$ at any point within the ellipse is given by

$$u(x)=\frac{1}{4}\sum_{i=1}^{16}A_i^{(16)}\big[\cos^2(1+\alpha_i)\pi+$$

$$+0.25\sin^2(1+\alpha_i)\pi\big]\frac{0.5-0.5x_1\cos(1+\alpha_i)\pi-x_2\sin(1+\alpha_i)\pi}{r^2(x,\ y^{(i)})}+$$

$$+\sum_{i=1}^{16}A_i^{(16)}\varphi(\alpha_i)\ln r(x,\ y^{(i)}). \tag{10.104}$$

Substituting here the coordinates of the point x of B_i and performing simple calculations, we obtain an approximate value of the solution at x. In the table below we list the approximate values $\tilde{u}(x)$ at four different points within the ellipse, as calculated by means of formula (10.104), side-by-side with the exact values (10.98), and the absolute error.

x	$\tilde{u}(x)$	$u(x)$	$\lvert\tilde{u}(x)-u(x)\rvert$
0.01; 0	0.19993	0.20003	0.00010
0.1; 0	0.199247	0.20300	0.00371
0.5; 0	0.28309	0.27500	0.00809
0.9; 0	0.405242	0.44200	0.03775

Let us now place the contour of auxiliary points farther away, say, at the ellipse

$$x_1=5\cos t,\qquad x_2=3\sin t;$$

then we have instead of (10.102)

$$\sum_{i=1}^{16} A_i^{(16)} \varphi(\alpha_i) \ln \Big\{[\cos(1+\alpha_i)\pi - 5\cos(1+\alpha_j)\pi]^2 +$$

$$+ [0.5 \sin(1+\alpha_i)\pi - 3\sin(1+\alpha_j)\pi]^2\Big\}^{\frac{1}{2}} = -\frac{1}{4}\sum_{i=1}^{16} A_i^{(16)} \left[\cos^2(1+\alpha_i)\pi + \right.$$

$$\left. + 0.25 \sin^2(1+\alpha_i)\pi\right] \frac{0.5 - 2.5\cos(1+\alpha_i)\pi\cos(1+\alpha_j)\pi - 3\sin(1+\alpha_i)\pi\sin(1+\alpha_j)\pi}{r^2(x_j, y_i)}$$

$$(j = 1, 2, \ldots, 16).$$

This system of 16 equations reduces by symmetry considerations to a system of 8 equations. The coefficients and right-hand sides are listed in Table B.

TABLE B

$\varphi(y_1)$	$\varphi(y_2)$	$\varphi(y_3)$	$\varphi(y_4)$	$\varphi(y_5)$
0.0752699	0.1730547	0.2681332	0.3631916	0.4604444
0.0747264	0.1718091	0.26623310	0.3607252	0.4575569
0.0720349	0.1656363	0.2567916	0.3484000	0.4430299
0.0653164	0.1501869	0.2328661	0.3163336	0.4040258
0.0580352	0.1331898	0.2046733	0.2727523	0.3413289
0.0665271	0.1522498	0.2306135	0.2949523	0.3401015
0.0848429	0.1942006	0.2943752	0.3767454	0.4318289
0.0958882	0.2195407	0.3333182	0.4284564	0.4953056

$\varphi(y_6)$	$\varphi(y_7)$	$\varphi(y_8)$	b
0.5547294	0.6320834	0.6760895	—0.0019034
0.5516019	0.6288618	0.6728463	—0.0018967
0.5357863	0.6125266	0.6563853	—0.0018337
0.4923138	0.5670684	0.6103583	—0.0013162
0.4132172	0.4788839	0.5188632	—0.0018202
0.3696079	0.3949311	0.4144059	—0.00445297
0.4543481	0.4510483	0.4414421	—0.00085351
0.5274618	0.5287958	0.5182005	—0.00187779

The solution of this system is

$$\begin{aligned} \varphi(y_1) &= -0.1428199, & \varphi(y_2) &= -0.3384742, \\ \varphi(y_3) &= -0.0327377, & \varphi(y_4) &= -0.0282381, \\ \varphi(y_5) &= 0.1189288, & \varphi(y_6) &= 0.14184350, \\ \varphi(y_7) &= 0.03063215, & \varphi(y_8) &= -0.1243106. \end{aligned} \qquad (10.105)$$

We insert the values $\varphi(y_i)$ from (10.105) into the formula (10.104) which gives the approximate values of $u(x)$ at any point x within the ellipse, and keep in mind that

$$x_1 = 5\cos(t), \quad x_2 = 3\sin(t).$$

The approximate values $\tilde{u}(x)$ obtained from (10.104) and the exact values calculated from (10.98) are listed in the following table for seven different points in the interior of the ellipse; the absolute error is also listed.

This table shows a considerable improvement in accuracy even for a small displacement of the ellipse of auxiliary points away from the main ellipse. As we know, the auxiliary points may be chosen arbitrarily and thus it is probably possible to attain a still better accuracy for a given number of basic points and a given quadrature formula.

x		$\tilde{u}(x)$	$u(x)$	$\lvert\tilde{u}(x)-u(x)\rvert$
0.01;	0	0.19993	0.20003	0.00010
0.1;	0	0.20290	0.20300	0.00010
0.5;	0	0.27486	0.27500	0.00014
0.9;	0	0.44282	0.44300	0.00017
0.2;	−0.2	0.20010	0.20000	0.00010
0;	0.3	0.17257	0.17300	0.00043
0.8;	0.1	0.38860	0.38900	0.00039

To demonstrate this we have further tried the following parameters

$$a_1 = 3, \quad b_1 = 1.5;$$

and

$$a_1 = 4, \quad b_1 = 2$$

$$a_1 = 7, \quad b_1 = 3.5.$$

The corresponding determinants and right-hand sides are listed below.

TABLE C

$a_1 = 3,\ b_1 = 1.5$

$\varphi(y_1)$	$\varphi(y_2)$	$\varphi(y_3)$	$\varphi(y_4)$	$\varphi(y_5)$
$0.7526011 \cdot 10^{-1}$	0.1745802	0.2818152	0.4165566	0.5893938
$0.7377617 \cdot 10^{-1}$	0.1711861	0.2766964	0.4101329	0.5823205
$0.6638950 \cdot 10^{-1}$	0.1542674	0.2510312	0.3776196	0.5462728
$0.4814593 \cdot 10^{-1}$	0.1121586	0.1850473	0.2894817	0.4447045
$0.3661240 \cdot 10^{-1}$	$0.8366170 \cdot 10^{-1}$	0.1265848	0.1709528	0.2569628
$0.7733745 \cdot 10^{-1}$	0.1760815	0.2596753	0.3064286	0.2928396
0.1237079	0.2826170	0.4241774	0.5272195	0.5643688
0.1475896	0.3375149	0.5092041	0.6426415	0.7128290

$\varphi(y_6)$	$\varphi(y_7)$	$\varphi(y_8)$	b
0.7804797	0.9462359	1.0423776	$-0.2175468 \cdot 10^{-1}$
0.7733356	0.9392726	1.0355696	$-0.2188336 \cdot 10^{-1}$
0.7368488	0.9037093	1.0008112	$-0.2228166 \cdot 10^{-1}$
0.6326348	0.8019363	0.9013891	$-0.1963791 \cdot 10^{-1}$
0.4151936	0.5836528	0.6870789	$0.2031618 \cdot 10^{-1}$
0.2430581	0.2755580	0.3486804	$0.6273127 \cdot 10^{-1}$
0.5148092	0.3974565	0.3047832	$-0.1531830 \cdot 10^{-1}$
0.6998007	0.6106538	0.5125636	$-0.2209416 \cdot 10^{-1}$

TABLE D

$a_1 = 4,\ b_1 = 2$

$\varphi(y_1)$	$\varphi(y_2)$	$\varphi(y_3)$	$\varphi(y_4)$	$\varphi(y_5)$
0.1192883	0.2748023	0.4297982	0.5948556	0.7773952
0.1178791	0.2715788	0.4249299	0.5886897	0.7704471
0.1107854	0.2553446	0.4003544	0.5574234	0.7350634
0.9211774	0.2124976	0.3346410	0.4717101	0.6356957
$0.7070599 \cdot 10^{-1}$	0.1623435	0.2503948	0.3404511	0.4534192
$0.9958654 \cdot 10^{-1}$	0.2274045	0.3405744	0.4217119	0.4551168
0.1465274	0.3353572	0.5062894	0.6403666	0.7148042
0.1716788	0.3929098	0.5951590	0.7599801	0.8659264

TABLE D (continued)

$\varphi(y_6)$	$\varphi(y_7)$	$\varphi(y_8)$	b
0.9644514	1.1222204	1.2129659	$-0.1200486 \cdot 10^{-1}$
0.9572263	1.1150097	1.2058270	$-0.1208226 \cdot 10^{-1}$
0.9203521	1.0781916	1.1693772	$-0.1235026 \cdot 10^{-1}$
0.8154628	0.9730379	1.0652039	$-0.1123376 \cdot 10^{-1}$
0.6024533	0.7513576	0.8432376	$0.1018639 \cdot 10^{-1}$
0.4570063	0.4869380	0.5342380	$0.3671170 \cdot 10^{-1}$
0.7148036	0.6567247	0.6010951	$-0.9140302 \cdot 10^{-2}$
0.8978073	0.8642387	0.8147520	$-0.1221528 \cdot 10^{-1}$

TABLE E

$a_1 = 7,\ b_1 = 3.5$

$\varphi(y_1)$	$\varphi(y_2)$	$\varphi(y_3)$	$\varphi(y_4)$	$\varphi(y_5)$
0.1945633	0.4467118	0.6875753	0.9165759	1.1438488
0.1942516	0.4437088	0.6830180	0.9107206	1.1270636
0.1865981	0.4284742	0.6598843	0.8809577	1.0925119
0.1683188	0.3865892	0.5960635	0.7982160	0.9954875
0.1392820	0.3197231	0.4917547	0.6555539	0.8157245
0.1496218	0.3425712	0.5200706	0.6691179	0.7791161
0.1958901	0.4486045	0.6817290	0.8787012	1.0221028
0.2225185	0.5097276	0.7757032	1.0036874	1.1763909

$\varphi(y_6)$	$\varphi(y_7)$	$\varphi(y_8)$	b
1.3305995	1.4852525	1.5714454	$-0.3857165 \cdot 10^{-2}$
1.3232816	1.4777089	1.5638384	$-0.3883625 \cdot 10^{-2}$
1.2859653	1.4392146	1.5250124	$-0.3981773 \cdot 10^{-2}$
1.1803082	1.3297231	1.4143866	$-0.3710540 \cdot 10^{-2}$
0.9721584	1.1061113	1.1850845	$0.2929478 \cdot 10^{-2}$
0.8528505	0.9066793	0.9420934	$0.1242199 \cdot 10^{-1}$
1.1017112	1.1260646	1.1343579	$-0.3114384 \cdot 10^{-2}$
1.2826390	1.3273836	1.3457654	$-0.3930370 \cdot 10^{-2}$

Table 1 below lists the exact values of the solution at the points (0.1; 0), (0.9; 0), (0.5; 0), (0.01; 0), (0; 0.3), (0.2; 0.2) (first row) and the approximate values corresponding to the different values of a_1 and b_1.

TABLE 1

	x_1, x_2					
$a_1 b_1$	(0.1; 0)	(0.9; 0)	(0.5; 0)	(0.01; 0)	(0; 0.3)	(0.2; 0.2)
	0.20300	0.44300	0.27500	0.20003	0.17300	0.20000
(2; 1)	0.19925	0.40524	0.28309	0.19711	0.17257	0.20010
(3; 1.5)	0.20433	0.45700	0.27287	0.20072	0.12715	0.15780
(4; 2)	0.20347	0.44096	0.27427	0.20028	0.12720	0.15298
(5; 3)	0.20290	0.44282	0.27486	0.19993	0.17257	0.20010
(7; 3.5)	0.18188	0.02032	0.23679	0.19274	0.15417	0.06980

The corresponding errors $\varepsilon_i(x^{(1)}, x^{(2)})$ are listed in Table 2.

TABLE 2

$a_1 b_1$	$\varepsilon_i(x_1, x_2)$							
	$\varepsilon_1(0.1;\ 0)$	$\varepsilon_2(0.9;\ 0)$	$\varepsilon_3(0.01;\ 0)$	$\varepsilon_4(0;\ 0.3)$	$\varepsilon_5(0.2;\ 0.2)$	$\varepsilon_6(0.5;\ 0)$	$\sum_{i=1}^{6} \varepsilon_i$	$\frac{1}{6}\sum_{i=1}^{6} \varepsilon_i$
(2; 1)	0.00375	0.03776	0.00292	0.00043	0.00010	0.00809	0.05305	0.00884
(3; 1.5)	0.00133	0.01400	0.00069	0.04585	0.04220	0.00213	0.10620	0.017700
(4; 2)	0.00047	0.00204	0.00025	0.04580	0.04702	0.00073	0.09631	0.016052
(5; 3)	0.00010	0.00018	0.00010	0.00043	0.00010	0.00014	0.00105	0.00017
(7; 3.5)	0.02112	0.42268	0.00729	0.01883	0.13020	0.03821	0.63833	0.10638

The error ε of an approximate solution of the functional equation (10.99_2) is estimated as follows

$$\|\varepsilon\| \leqslant \|L^{-1}\|\,\|R\|,$$

where L is the operator corresponding to the system (10.101'), and R is the vector of remainder terms (the norms are taken in the space in which ε is to be evaluated). It is readily seen that R may be made as small as desired by moving the points x_k away from the main boundary S, but at the same time the determinacy of the matrix L deteriorates and vice versa — when the points x_k move nearer to S it improves but $\|R\| \to \infty$. It is therefore natural to assume that there is some optimal location of the points x_k. Let $\varepsilon^{(j)}$ be the error vector when the values of the parameter x are taken on the curve S_j. Then S_k is said to be the optimal curve with respect to the metric A, of all families of curves S_j $(j = 1, 2, \ldots, N)$, if

$$\|\varepsilon^{(k)}\|_A = \min_j \|\varepsilon^{(j)}\|_A.$$

The optimal curve in our case $(N = 6)$ with respect to Euclidean space and also with respect to C-space, is, according to Table 2, the ellipse with the semi-axes $a_1 = 5$; $b_1 = 3$.

§ 17. Numerical example. The Dirichlet problem for a doubly-connected domain

It is required to find a function, harmonic in B_i, which vanishes on the internal circle S_1 of radius $R(S_1) = 1$, and assumes the value $\ln 2$ on the external circle S_2 of radius $R(S_2)$. It is readily seen that the exact solution is $\ln r(x_0, x)$, where x_0 is the common center of the two circles. With these boundary conditions the functional equations for our problem become

$$u(x) = -\ln 2 - \frac{1}{2\pi}\int_{S_1} \ln r(x, y)\,\varphi(y)\,dS_y - \frac{1}{2\pi}\int_{S_2} \ln r(x, y)\,\varphi(y)\,dS_y, \qquad x \in B_i;$$

$$0 = -\frac{1}{2\pi}\int_{S_1} \ln r(x, y)\,\varphi(y)\,dS_y - \frac{1}{2\pi}\int_{S_2} \ln r(x, y)\,\varphi(y)\,dS_y + \frac{1}{2\pi}\int_{S_1+S_2} f(y)\frac{\partial}{\partial n_y}\ln r(x, y)\,dS_y, \qquad x \in B_a. \tag{A}$$

In order to solve (A) we take the values of the parameter x on the concentric circles S_3 and S_4 of radii $R(S_3)=3$ and $R(S_4)=\frac{1}{2}$ centered at x_0

$$x_j^{(1)} = 3\cos j\frac{360}{N_3}, \qquad x_j^{(2)} = 3\sin j\frac{360}{N_3} \qquad (j=1, 2, \ldots, N_3).$$

$$x_{N_3+p}^{(1)} = \frac{1}{2}\cos p\frac{360}{N_4}, \quad x_{N_3+p}^{(2)} = \frac{1}{2}\sin p\frac{360}{N_4} \quad (p=1, 2, \ldots, N_4).$$

Here $x_j^{(1)}$ and $x_j^{(2)}$ denote the coordinates of x_j.

Expressing the integrals in (A) by means of the rectangular formula (in this case the rectangular and the trapezoidal formulas coincide), we obtain

$$\frac{1}{2\pi}\frac{2\pi}{N_1}\sum_{l=1}^{N_1}\ln r(x_j, y_l)\varphi(y_l)+\frac{1}{2\pi}\frac{4\pi}{N_2}\sum_{k=1}^{N_2}\ln r(x_j, y_{N_1+k})\varphi(y_k)=0$$

for $x_j \in S_3$,

$$\frac{1}{2\pi}\frac{2\pi}{N_1}\sum_{l=1}^{N_1}\ln r(x_{N_3+p}, y_l)\varphi(y_l)+\frac{1}{2\pi}\frac{4\pi}{N_2}\sum_{k=1}^{N_2}\ln r(x_{N_3+p}, y_{N_1+k})\varphi(y_k)=\ln 2$$

for $x_{N_3+p} \in S_4$,

where

$$y_l^{(1)} = \cos l\frac{360}{N_1}, \qquad y_l^{(2)} = \sin l\frac{360}{N_1} \qquad (l=1, 2, \ldots, N_1),$$

$$y_{N_1+k}^{(1)} = 2\cos k\frac{360}{N_2}, \qquad y_{N_1+k}^{(2)} = 2\sin k\frac{360}{N_2} \quad (k=1, 2, \ldots, N_2)$$

$$(N_1+N_2=N_3+N_4).$$

The following values were taken: $N_1=N_2=N_3=N_4=N=$ 5, 10, 20, 40. This gives rise to systems of 10, 20, 40 and 80 equations. The determinant $\Delta^{(N)}$ of the system

$$\sum_{l=1}^{N}\log_{10} r^2(x_j, y_l)\varphi(y_l)+2\sum_{k=1}^{N}\log_{10} r^2(x_j, y_{N+k})\varphi(y_l)=0 \quad (x_j \in S_3),$$

$$\sum_{l=1}^{N}\log_{10} r^2(x_{N+p}, y_l)\varphi(y_l)+2\sum_{k=1}^{N}\log_{10} r^2(x_{N+p}, y_{N+k})\varphi(y_k)=2\log_{10} 2$$

$$(x_{N+p} \in S_4)$$

has the form

$$\Delta^{(N)} = \begin{vmatrix} A_1^{(N)} & A_3^{(N)} \\ A_2^{(N)} & A_4^{(N)} \end{vmatrix},$$

where all the matrices $A_l^{(N)}$ are symmetric and

$$A_l^{(N)} = \begin{vmatrix} a_1^{(l,N)} & a_2^{(l,N)} & a_3^{(l,N)} & \ldots & a_N^{(l,N)} \\ & a_1^{(l,N)} & a_2^{(l,N)} & \ldots & a_{N-1}^{(l,N)} \\ & & a_1^{(l,N)} & \ldots & a_{N-2}^{(l,N)} \\ & & \cdot\cdot\cdot & \cdot\cdot\cdot & \cdot\cdot\cdot \\ & & & & a_1^{(l,N)} \end{vmatrix},$$

while $a_k^{(l,N)} = a_{N-k+2}^{(l,N)}$ $(k \geqslant 2)$. We accordingly list the following elements

$a_1^{(1,40)} = 0.6020600$ $\quad a_8^{(1,40)} = 0.8618961$ $\quad a_{15}^{(1,40)} = 1.1311922$

$a_2^{(1,40)} = 0.6100072$ $\quad a_9^{(1,40)} = 0.9109390$ $\quad a_{16}^{(1,40)} = 1.1535905$

$a_3^{(1,40)} = 0.6328278$ $\quad a_{10}^{(1,40)} = 0.9571950$ $\quad a_{17}^{(1,40)} = 1.1718464$

$a_4^{(1,40)} = 0.6678227$ $\quad a_{11}^{(1,40)} = 1.0000000$ $\quad a_{18}^{(1,40)} = 1.1859963$

$a_5^{(1,40)} = 0.7114611$ $\quad a_{12}^{(1,40)} = 1.0389620$ $\quad a_{19}^{(1,40)} = 1.1960750$

$a_6^{(1,40)} = 0.7602234$ $\quad a_{13}^{(1,40)} = 1.0738686$ $\quad a_{20}^{(1,40)} = 1.2021102$

$a_7^{(1,40)} = 0.8111249$ $\quad a_{14}^{(1,40)} = 1.1046218$ $\quad a_{21}^{(1,40)} = 1.2041200$

$a_1^{(2,40)}=-0.6020600$	$a_1^{(3,40)}=0$	$a_1^{(4,40)}=0.7043650$
$a_2^{(2,40)}=-0.5811824$	$a_2^{(3,40)}=0.1196874$	$a_2^{(4,40)}=0.7138190$
$a_3^{(2,40)}=-0.5244109$	$a_3^{(3,40)}=0.4013300$	$a_3^{(4,40)}=0.7413544$
$a_4^{(2,40)}=-0.4449134$	$a_4^{(3,40)}=0.7264422$	$a_4^{(4,40)}=0.7846858$
$a_5^{(2,40)}=-0.3555782$	$a_5^{(3,40)}=1.0348658$	$a_5^{(4,40)}=0.8405606$
$a_6^{(2,40)}=-0.2652856$	$a_6^{(3,40)}=1.3092614$	$a_6^{(4,40)}=0.9053470$
$a_7^{(2,40)}=-0.1790012$	$a_7^{(3,40)}=1.5485340$	$a_7^{(4,40)}=0.9755292$
$a_8^{(2,40)}=-0.0990818$	$a_8^{(3,40)}=1.7561370$	$a_8^{(4,40)}=1.0480178$
$a_9^{(2,40)}=-0.0264182$	$a_9^{(3,40)}=1.9361994$	$a_9^{(4,40)}=1.1202836$
$a_{10}^{(2,40)}=0.0388448$	$a_{10}^{(3,40)}=2.0924272$	$a_{10}^{(4,40)}=1.1903596$
$a_{11}^{(2,40)}=0.0969100$	$a_{11}^{(3,40)}=2.2278868$	$a_{11}^{(4,40)}=1.2567778$
$a_{12}^{(2,40)}=0.1481195$	$a_{12}^{(3,40)}=2.3450432$	$a_{12}^{(4,40)}=1.3184760$
$a_{13}^{(2,40)}=0.1928508$	$a_{13}^{(3,40)}=2.4458596$	$a_{13}^{(4,40)}=1.3747072$
$a_{14}^{(2,40)}=0.2314672$	$a_{14}^{(3,40)}=2.5318932$	$a_{14}^{(4,40)}=1.4249594$
$a_{15}^{(2,40)}=0.2642947$	$a_{15}^{(3,40)}=2.6043770$	$a_{15}^{(4,40)}=1.4688908$
$a_{16}^{(2,40)}=0.2916145$	$a_{16}^{(3,40)}=2.6642822$	$a_{16}^{(4,40)}=1.5062792$
$a_{17}^{(2,40)}=0.3136599$	$a_{17}^{(3,40)}=2.7123656$	$a_{17}^{(4,40)}=1.5369852$
$a_{18}^{(2,40)}=0.3306180$	$a_{18}^{(3,40)}=2.7492062$	$a_{18}^{(4,40)}=1.5609244$
$a_{19}^{(2,40)}=0.3426312$	$a_{19}^{(3,40)}=2.7752310$	$a_{19}^{(4,40)}=1.5780486$
$a_{20}^{(2,40)}=0.3497996$	$a_{20}^{(3,40)}=2.7907316$	$a_{20}^{(4,40)}=1.5883314$
$a_{21}^{(2,40)}=0.3521825$	$a_{21}^{(3,40)}=2.7958800$	$a_{21}^{(4,40)}=1.5917000$

The elements of the matrices $A_l^{(N)}$ for $N=5,\ 10,\ 20$ are obtained from the tabulated elements of the matrix $A_l^{(40)}$ by*

$$a_j^{(l,\,N)}=a^{(l,\,40)}_{\frac{40\,(j-1)}{N}+1}.$$

It is readily seen that the solution of the functional equation (A) is

$$\varphi(y)=\begin{cases}-1, & y\in S_1,\\ \frac{1}{2}, & y\in S_2.\end{cases}$$

The algebraic system may be solved in either of two ways: (1) Solve the two equations (with $x\in S_3$ and $x\in S_4$), assuming that $\varphi|_{S_1}=C_1$, $\varphi|_{S_2}=C_2$, where C_1 and C_2 are constants to be determined. (2) Solve the obtained system directly.

N	$c_1^{(N)}$	$c_2^{(N)}$	$u^{(N)}(x_0)$	$\varepsilon_1^{(N)}$	$\varepsilon_2^{(N)}$	$\varepsilon_3^{(N)}$
5	−0.9666646	0.4957121	0.3049905	0.0333354	0.0042879	0.1004747
10	−0.9982690	0.4999297	0.3971241	0.0017310	0.0000703	0.0083411
20	−0.9999863	0.4999999	0.4052856	0.0000137	0.0000001	0.0001796
40	−1.0000000	0.4999999	0.4054650	0.0000000	0.0000001	0.0000002

* Here and in the other examples we write down explicitly the complete matrices, because the matrices of all the numerical examples considered here may be used for the solution of problems with different boundary conditions. Thus, for instance, the matrix tabulated above may be used for the solution of the Dirichlet problem for the same annulus with any boundary values $U|_{S_1}=f_1(S)$, $U|_{S_2}=f_2(S)$. In other words, the elements of the determinant depend for fixed values of the parameter x on the geometry of the domain, while the right-hand sides depend on the boundary values. This allows us to construct tables for domains commonly met in practice so as to simplify the solution of boundary-value problems for them once and for all.

Comparing the results obtained by these two methods, it is possible to judge the determinacy of the matrix $A^{(N)}$.

The preceding table lists the values of $C_1^{(N)}$ and $C_2^{(N)}$ derived by the first method, the values of solution $u(x)$ of the Dirichlet problem at the point $x(x_0^{(1)}, x_0^{(2)})$, where $x_0^{(1)}=1.5$ and $x_0^{(2)}=0$, and the corresponding errors $|-1-C_1^{(N)}|=\varepsilon_1^{(N)}$, $\left|\frac{1}{2}-C_2^{(N)}\right|=\varepsilon_2^{(N)}$, $|u(x_0)-u^{(N)}(x_0)|=\varepsilon_3^{(N)}$.

The following solutions were obtained by machine computation for the systems of 10 ($N=5$) and 20 ($N=10$) equations:

$N=5$

$\varphi(y_1)=-0.966664518$	$\varphi(y_6)=0.495712068$
$\varphi(y_2)=-0.966664516$	$\varphi(y_7)=0.495712068$
$\varphi(y_3)=-0.966664520$	$\varphi(y_8)=0.495712070$
$\varphi(y_4)=-0.966664510$	$\varphi(y_9)=0.495712068$
$\varphi(y_5)=-0.966664518$	$\varphi(y_{10})=0.495712070$

$N=10$

$\varphi(y_1)=-0.998268836$	$\varphi(y_{11})=0.499929796$
$\varphi(y_2)=-0.998268468$	$\varphi(y_{12})=0.499929706$
$\varphi(y_3)=-0.998269560$	$\varphi(y_{13})=0.499929706$
$\varphi(y_4)=-0.998267464$	$\varphi(y_{14})=0.499929748$
$\varphi(y_5)=-0.998269428$	$\varphi(y_{15})=0.499929706$
$\varphi(y_6)=-0.998268544$	$\varphi(y_{16})=0.499929700$
$\varphi(y_7)=-0.998268928$	$\varphi(y_{17})=0.499929796$
$\varphi(y_8)=-0.998268852$	$\varphi(y_{18})=0.499929798$
$\varphi(y_9)=-0.998268574$	$\varphi(y_{19})=0.499929794$
$\varphi(y_{10})=-0.998268894$	$\varphi(y_{20})=0.499929796$

These results give $u^{(5)}(x_0)=0.3049905$ and $u^{(10)}(x_0)=0.3971240$.

The exact solution at this point is $u(x_0)=0.4054652$. This numerical example serves to get some idea about the determinacy of the systems encountered in solution of the functional equations. It is clear from the above comparison that the determinant of the system is well-defined for $N=5$ and $N=10$.

Let us also remark that though $\log 2=0.3010300$ was taken accurate to seven decimal places the final errors were small, especially for $N=20$ and $N=40$.

§ 18. Numerical example. Approximate solution of the first fundamental problem for an isotropic elastic disk

Let us consider the case $\omega=0$. Let the components of the displacement $(f(y))$ be prescribed at the points y of the circumference S $(y \in S)$:

$$u_1(y)=-1+4y_1^2+6y_1y_2=f_1(y),$$

$$u_2(y)=2-2y_1^2+2y_1y_2=f_2(y).$$

We take the radius equal to one and denote the polar coordinates of point y by $(1, \psi)$; these conditions then become

$$u_1(1, \psi)=1+2\cos 2\psi+3\sin 2\psi=f_1(\psi),$$
$$u_2(1, \psi)=1-\cos 2\psi+\sin 2\psi=f_2(\psi). \qquad (10.106)$$

It is required to find the solution, regular within the circle, of the equation of the plane static problem

$$\Delta^* u(x)=0,$$

which satisfies the boundary conditions (10.106). The exact solution of this problem is*

$$\left.\begin{aligned} u_1(x)&=\frac{2(2\lambda+3\mu)}{\lambda+3\mu}+\frac{(3\mu-\lambda)}{\lambda+3\mu}x_1^2-\frac{5\lambda+9\mu}{\lambda+3\mu}x_2^2+6x_1x_2,\\ u_2(x)&=\frac{5\lambda+7\mu}{\lambda+3\mu}-\frac{5\lambda+7\mu}{\lambda+3\mu}x_1^2-\frac{3\lambda+\mu}{\lambda+3\mu}x_2^2+2x_1x_2. \end{aligned}\right. \qquad (10.107)$$

Let us work out the approximate solution and compare it with the exact one (10.107). Let $\lambda=2$, $\mu=1$. Then (10.107) becomes

$$\left.\begin{aligned} u_1(x)&=2.8+0.2x_1^2-3.8x_2^2+6x_1x_2,\\ u_2(x)&=3.4-3.4x_1^2-1.4x_2^2+2x_1x_2. \end{aligned}\right\} \qquad (10.108)$$

The approximate solution is (§ 2) derived from the system of functional equations (10.19_1), (10.19_2) which now become

$$u(x)=\frac{i}{\pi}\int_S \overset{0}{\Gamma}(x,y)\varphi(y)\,dS_y-\frac{1}{2\pi}\int_S \overset{0}{\Gamma}_1(x,y)f(y)\,dS_y,\quad x\in B_i, \qquad (10.19_1^1)$$

$$0=\frac{1}{\pi}\int_S \overset{0}{\Gamma}(x,y)\varphi(y)\,dS_y-\frac{1}{2\pi}\int_S \overset{0}{\Gamma}_1(x,y)f(y)\,dS_y,\quad x\in B_a, \qquad (10.19_2^1)$$

where (cf. IX, 1)

$$\overset{0}{\Gamma}(x,y)=\left\|\begin{matrix} n\ln r(x,y)-m\left(\dfrac{\partial r}{\partial x_1}\right)^2 & -m\dfrac{\partial r}{\partial x_1}\dfrac{\partial r}{\partial x_2}\\ -m\dfrac{\partial r}{\partial x_1}\dfrac{\partial r}{\partial x_2} & n\ln r-m\left(\dfrac{\partial r}{\partial x_2}\right)^2 \end{matrix}\right\|,$$

$$n=\frac{\lambda+3\mu}{2\mu(\lambda+2\mu)},\qquad m=\frac{\lambda+\mu}{2\mu(\lambda+2\mu)},$$

* This problem may be solved in many different ways. One of the simplest is based on the application of the double-layer potential of the second kind (cf. Ch. IX); the problem is by this reduced to an easily solvable system of regular Fredholm integral equations. This problem (as well as some others) was solved by this method by N. S. Kakhniashvili /11/. Using the same double-layer potentials, M. Basheleishvili represented the solution in the following form

$$u(x)=\frac{1}{2\pi}\int_0^{2\pi}\left\{AI\frac{R^2-\rho^2}{r}-\right.$$

$$-2B\left\|\begin{matrix}(\rho\cos\psi-R\cos\varphi_0)^2 & (\rho\cos\psi-R\cos\varphi_0)(\rho\sin\psi-R\sin\varphi_0)\\ (\rho\cos\psi-R\cos\varphi_0)(\rho\sin\psi-R\sin\varphi_0) & (\rho\sin\psi-R\sin\varphi_0)^2\end{matrix}\right\|\frac{\rho^2-r^2-R^2}{r^4}+$$

$$\left.+B\left\|\begin{matrix}\dfrac{\rho\cos(\psi+\varphi_0)}{R}-1 & \dfrac{\rho\sin(\psi+\varphi_0)}{R}\\ \dfrac{\rho\sin(\psi+\varphi_0)}{R}-1 & -\dfrac{\rho\cos(\psi+\varphi_0)}{R}\end{matrix}\right\|\right\}f(\psi)\,d\psi,$$

where R is the radius, (ρ, φ_0) the polar coordinates of the point x, $A=\frac{2\mu}{\lambda+3\mu}$, $B=\frac{\lambda+\mu}{\lambda+3\mu}$, I the unit matrix, $f(\psi)$ the vector-function giving the boundary values of u. This formula is a generalization of the Poisson integral in the theory of elasticity. In the particular case $\lambda=-\mu=-1$ it reduces to the familiar Poisson formula

$$u(\rho,\varphi_0)=\frac{1}{2\pi}\int_0^{2\pi}\frac{R^2-\rho^2}{r^2}f(\psi)\,d\psi.$$

$$\overset{0}{\Gamma}_1(x, y)=\begin{Vmatrix} a\frac{\partial}{\partial n_y}\ln r+2b\left(\frac{\partial r}{\partial y_1}\right)^2\frac{\partial}{\partial n_y}\ln r & a\frac{\partial}{\partial S_y}\ln r+2b\frac{\partial r}{\partial y_1}\frac{\partial r}{\partial y_2}\frac{\partial}{\partial n_y} \\ -a\frac{\partial}{\partial S_y}\ln r+2b\frac{\partial r}{\partial y_1}\frac{\partial r}{\partial y_2}\frac{\partial}{\partial n_y}\ln r & a\frac{\partial}{\partial n_y}\ln r+2b\left(\frac{\partial r}{\partial y_2}\right)^2\frac{\partial}{\partial n_y}\ln r \end{Vmatrix}, \quad a=\frac{\mu}{\lambda+2\mu}, \quad b=\frac{\lambda+\mu}{\lambda+2\mu}.$$

$$\frac{\partial}{\partial n_y}=\frac{\partial}{\partial y_1}\cos(n_y, \xi_1)+\frac{\partial}{\partial y_2}\cos(n_y, \xi_2),$$

$$\frac{\partial}{\partial S_y}=\frac{\partial}{\partial y_2}\cos(n_y, \xi_1)-\frac{\partial}{\partial y_1}\cos(n_y, \xi_2).$$

Substituting the values of $f_1(\psi)$ and $f_2(\psi)$ from (10.106), we evaluate the integral

$$W(x, f)=\frac{1}{2\pi}\int_S \overset{0}{\Gamma}_1(x, y)f(y)\,dS_y \qquad (x\in B_a),$$

and obtain

$$\begin{aligned} W_1(x, f)=-\Big[&\frac{(2\lambda+3\mu)\cos 2\varphi_0+(3\lambda+5\mu)\sin 2\varphi_0}{2\rho^2(\lambda+2\mu)}+ \\ &+\frac{\lambda+\mu}{2(\lambda+2\mu)}\frac{(\rho^2-1)(\cos 4\varphi_0+2\sin 4\varphi_0)}{\rho^4}\Big], \\ W_2(x, f)=-\Big[&\frac{(\mu-\lambda)\cos 2\varphi_0+\lambda\sin 2\varphi_0}{2\rho^2(\lambda+2\mu)}+ \\ &+\frac{\lambda+\mu}{2(\lambda+2\mu)}\frac{(\rho^2-1)(\sin 4\varphi_0-2\cos 4\varphi_0)}{\rho^4}\Big], \end{aligned} \qquad (10.109)$$

and the functional equation for $\varphi(y)$ may be written

$$\begin{aligned} &\int_0^{2\pi}\Big[\overset{0}{\Gamma}{}_1^{(1)}(x, y)\varphi_1(y)+\overset{0}{\Gamma}{}_1^{(2)}(x, y)\varphi_2(y)\Big]d\psi=\pi W_1(x; f), \\ &\int_0^{2\pi}\Big[\overset{0}{\Gamma}{}_2^{(1)}(x, y)\varphi_1(y)+\overset{0}{\Gamma}{}_2^{(2)}(x, y)\varphi_2(y)\Big]d\psi=\pi W_2(x; f). \end{aligned} \qquad (10.110)$$

To solve this equation we use the Gaussian 12-point formula. The Gaussian points and corresponding coefficients are

$$\begin{aligned} &-x_1^{(12)}=+x_{12}^{(12)}=0.9815606 \\ &\qquad A_1^{(12)}=A_{12}^{(12)}=0.0471753 \quad A_4^{(12)}=A_9^{(12)}=0.2031674 \\ &-x_2^{(12)}=+x_{11}^{(12)}=0.9041172 \\ &-x_3^{(12)}=+x_{10}^{(12)}=0.7699027 \\ &\qquad A_2^{(12)}=A_{11}^{(12)}=0.1069393 \quad A_5^{(12)}=A_8^{(12)}=0.2334925 \\ &-x_4^{(12)}=+x_9^{(12)}=0.5873179 \\ &-x_5^{(12)}=+x_8^{(12)}=0.3678315 \\ &\qquad A_3^{(12)}=A_{10}^{(12)}=0.1600783 \quad A_6^{(12)}=A_7^{(12)}=0.2491471 \\ &-x_6^{(12)}=+x_7^{(12)}=0.1252334 \end{aligned}$$

Equations (10.110) are approximated by

$$\begin{aligned} &\sum_{i=1}^{12}A_i^{(12)}\Big[\overset{0}{\Gamma}{}_1^{(1)}(x, y_i)\varphi_1(y_i)+\overset{0}{\Gamma}{}_1^{(2)}(x, y_i)\varphi_2(y_i)\Big]=\pi W_1(x; f), \\ &\sum_{i=1}^{12}A_i^{(12)}\Big[\overset{0}{\Gamma}{}_2^{(1)}(x, y_i)\varphi_1(y_i)+\overset{0}{\Gamma}{}_2^{(2)}(x, y_i)\varphi_2(y_i)\Big]=\pi W_2(x; f) \end{aligned} \quad (x\in B_a). \qquad (10.110')$$

We take the auxiliary points $x_k(\rho_k, \varphi_{0,k})$, $k=1, 2, \ldots, 12$ on the concentric circle of radius 6 so that the point x_j lies on the radius through the point y_j; we then get a system of 12 linear algebraic equations

$$\begin{aligned} &\sum_{i=1}^{12}A_i^{(12)}\Big[\overset{0}{\Gamma}{}_1^{(1)}(x_k, y_i)\varphi_1(y_i)+\overset{0}{\Gamma}{}_1^{(2)}(x_k, y_i)\varphi_2(y_i)\Big]=\pi W_1(x_k; f), \\ &\sum_{i=1}^{12}A_i^{(12)}\Big[\overset{0}{\Gamma}{}_2^{(1)}(x_k, y_i)\varphi_1(y_i)+\overset{0}{\Gamma}{}_2^{(2)}(x_k, y_i)\varphi_2(y_i)\Big]=\pi W_2(x_k; f). \end{aligned} \qquad (10.111)$$

The coefficients of this system and its right-hand sides are obtained, with the chosen coefficients and Gaussian points, from the expression for the elements of the matrix $\overset{0}{\Gamma}(x, y)$ and from formulas (10.109).

Solving the system (10.111), we obtain

$$
\begin{aligned}
\varphi_1(y_1) &= -3.2898639 & \varphi_2(y_1) &= 0.3048392\\
\varphi_1(y_2) &= -4.8003739 & \varphi_2(y_2) &= -0.1237495\\
\varphi_1(y_3) &= -4.7148752 & \varphi_2(y_3) &= -0.7438623\\
\varphi_1(y_4) &= 0.0943634 & \varphi_2(y_4) &= -0.7585132\\
\varphi_1(y_5) &= 5.1369463 & \varphi_2(y_5) &= 0.3207615\\
\varphi_1(y_6) &= 1.1388360 & \varphi_2(y_6) &= 0.8489420\\
\varphi_1(y_7) &= -5.0928226 & \varphi_2(y_7) &= -0.2840868\\
\varphi_1(y_8) &= -1.3594572 & \varphi_2(y_8) &= -0.8604027\\
\varphi_1(y_9) &= 4.6837652 & \varphi_2(y_9) &= 0.0759234\\
\varphi_1(y_{10}) &= 4.0164068 & \varphi_2(y_{10}) &= 0.8436435\\
\varphi_1(y_{11}) &= 0.1862522 & \varphi_2(y_{11}) &= 0.7829098\\
\varphi_1(y_{12}) &= -2.2725934 & \varphi_2(y_{12}) &= 0.4897975
\end{aligned}
$$

These values of $\varphi_k(y_i)$ may also be obtained in this case without actually solving the system (10.111). Using the fact that $(\mathbf{T}u)_i = 2\varphi$, as is evident from (10.19_1^i) and (10.19_2^i), we construct from the displacement field given by (10.108) the stress vector $\mathbf{T}u(x)$ for $\rho = 1$. We calculate to this end the elements of the stress tensor

$$
\begin{aligned}
\tau_{11} &= \frac{4\mu}{\lambda+3\mu}\left[(2\lambda+3\mu)x_1+(7\lambda+9\mu)x_2\right],\\
\tau_{12} &= \frac{4\mu}{\lambda+3\mu}\left[(\mu-\lambda)x_1-(2\lambda+3\mu)x_2\right],\\
\tau_{22} &= \frac{4\mu}{\lambda+3\mu}\left[(4\lambda+3\mu)x_1+(\lambda-\mu)x_2\right],
\end{aligned}
$$

and hence

$$
\begin{aligned}
\mathbf{T}_1 u(y) &= \frac{4\mu}{\lambda+3\mu}\left[(2\lambda+3\mu)\cos 2\psi+(3\lambda+5\mu)\sin 2\psi\right] = 2\varphi_1(y),\\
\mathbf{T}_2 u(y) &= \frac{4\mu}{\lambda+3\mu}\left[(\mu-\lambda)\cos 2\psi+\lambda\sin 2\psi\right] = 2\varphi_2(y).
\end{aligned}
$$

Substituting here the angles ψ_i which correspond to the Gaussian points, we obtain the values of $\varphi_1(y_i)$ and $\varphi_2(y_i)$, in agreement with those listed above up to seven decimal places.

It remains to substitute the $\varphi_1(y_i)$ and $\varphi_2(y_i)$ in (10.19_1^i); the approximate values of $u(x)$ at any internal point of the disk are then given by

$$
u(x) = \frac{1}{\pi}\sum_{i=1}^{12} A_i^{(12)}\overset{0}{\Gamma}(x, y_i)\varphi(y_i) - W(x; f), \qquad x \in B_i. \tag{10.112}
$$

The following table gives, for three different points in the interior of the circle (a) approximate values of φ_1 and φ_2 calculated by (10.112); (b) the exact values calculated by (10.108); (c) the errors.

φ	Coordinates of x	Approximate φ_1 and φ_2	Exact φ_1 and φ_2	Absolute error
$\varphi_1(x)$	0; 0.1	2.763	2.762	0.001
$\varphi_2(x)$	0; 0.1	3.385	3.386	0.001
$\varphi_1(x)$	0.5; 0.5	3.450	3.40	0.050
$\varphi_2(x)$	0.5; 0.5	2.730	2.70	0.03
$\varphi_1(x)$	0.5; 0	2.851	2.850	0.001
$\varphi_2(x)$	0.5; 0	2.549	2.550	0.001

A certain loss of accuracy in comparison with the results of the preceding chapters is due to the fact that here we have used the Gaussian formula with a smaller number of points (12); furthermore, the problem itself is, from the computational point of view, considerably more complicated than the simple Dirichlet problem, and therefore the effect of rounding errors becomes more important. However, even the accuracy obtained here with 12 ordinates is quite satisfactory, at least from the point of view of the applied theory of elasticity, and gives an idea of what may be expected in practical computational work.

§ 19. Concluding remarks about the method of canonical equations

In §§ 12–14 we have already dealt with some theoretical problems related to the convergence of our method. Now that we have seen in several numerical examples that the method is reassuringly accurate*, let us return to these problems and have a closer look at them /15/. Take for simplicity the interior Dirichlet problem, but (unlike § 12) the three-dimensional case. Instead of (10.84) we have

$$L\varphi \equiv \sum_{i=1}^{N} \frac{A_i^{(N)}}{r(x_k, y_i)} \varphi_i = -\pi F_k \qquad (k = 1, 2, 3, \ldots, N), \tag{10.112'}$$

where $x_1, x_2, \ldots, x_N$ are N different values of the parameter x; N is the number of basic points $y_1, y_2, \ldots, y_N$, in the chosen cubature formula, $A_i^{(N)}$ the corresponding coefficients of the formula, φ_i the approximate value of the unknown function at the basic point y_i. Here we have dropped the remainder term $R(x_k, N, \varphi)$.

Let h be the minimal distance between the basic points y_i. *It may be proved that for any* N *and* $h > 0$, *there exist such values* x_k *of the parameter* x *that the system (10.112') is solvable and the solution may be obtained by the method of successive approximations starting from any vector* φ_0. This theorem was already proved in § 12; let us now consider it somewhat more carefully. We write the system (10.112') in vector form

$$\varphi - H\varphi = E,$$

where the elements of the matrix H are

$$H_{i,k} = \begin{cases} -A_k^{(N)} \left(A_i^{(N)}\right)^{-1} r(x_i, y_i)\left[r(x_k, y_i)\right]^{-1}, & i \neq k, \\ 0, & i = k, \end{cases}$$

and $E_i = -\pi \left(A_i^{(N)}\right)^{-1} F_i r(x_i, y_i)$.

We consider H as an operator which maps the space m_N (cf. 12) onto itself. We then have for the form $\|H\|$

$$\|H\|_{m_N} = \max_i \left| \frac{r(x_i, y_i)}{A_i^{(N)}} \right| \sum_{k=1\ (k \neq i)}^{N} \left| \frac{A_k^{(N)}}{r(x_k, y_i)} \right|. \tag{10.113}$$

* By the time this book was in the press other typical problems had been worked out approximately by the same method at the Computing Center AN GruzSSR, in all cases with satisfactory accuracy. In particular, the Dirichlet problem for a square with discontinuous boundary values was solved (in this case the sufficient conditions for the applicability of our method are obviously not fulfilled), and a satisfactory approximation was obtained even with a small number of points. The results agree with those quoted by Young, D. ORDVAC solutions of the Dirichlet problem. — Journal of the Association for Computing Machinery, 2, No. 3: 137–161. 1955.

$r(x_i, y_i)$ may obviously be made as small as desired since the sum on the right-hand side of (10.113) remains for $h>0$ bounded by the number $\frac{1}{h}\sum_{\substack{k=1\\k\neq i}}^{N}|A_k^{(N)}|$. The points x_i, $i=1, 2, \ldots, N$, may therefore be chosen such that

$$\|H\|_{m_N} \leqslant q < 1. \tag{10.114}$$

Banach's theorem (§ 12) applies here, since m_N is a Banach space. The following estimate is obtained under condition (10.114) for the inverse operator $(I-H)^{-1}$, where I is the unit matrix:

$$\|(I-H)^{-1}\|_{m_N} \leqslant \frac{1}{1-q}. \tag{10.115}$$

The error δ caused by neglecting the remainder terms in (10.112') satisfies the same system of equations with the remainders appearing on the right side, viz., $\delta - H\delta = R$, where $R_i = \frac{r(x_i, y_i)}{A_i^{(N)}} R(x_i, N, \varphi)$. We therefore obtain for δ, on account of (10.115),

$$\|\delta\|_{m_N} = \max_i |\delta_i| = (I-H)^{-1}R \leqslant \frac{1}{1-q}\max_i R_i \qquad (i=1, 2, \ldots, N), \tag{10.116}$$

where $\delta_i = \varphi(y_i) - \varphi_i$. However this estimate does not imply the convergence of the process, i. e., we can not yet state that $\|\delta\| \to 0$ as $N\to\infty$. This is so because the points x_k approach the basic points y_k as $N\to\infty$ and the integrand $\varphi(y)[r(x, y)]^{-1}$, as well as its derivatives appearing in the remainder terms $R(x_k, N, \varphi)$, increase boundlessly. It was made evident in the examples considered in §§ 15–18 that in practice it is more convenient to choose the values of the parameter x not too near to the boundary S. The following proposition has an interesting bearing on this point: *in any neighborhood $\varepsilon(x_k)$ of arbitrary points x_k there exist new points $\bar{x}_k$ (in particular, they may coincide with x_k) such that the determinant of the system (10.112') does not vanish for any cubature formula.* Let us prove this assertion. We denote the top-left $k\times k$ minor of (10.112') by $H_k(x_1, x_2, \ldots, x_k)$. Obviously, $H_1(x_1) = A_1^{(N)}[r(x_1, y_1)]^{-1} \neq 0$, since $A_1^{(N)} \neq 0$, y_1 being a basic point of the cubature formula and $r(x_k, y_i) < \infty$ for all k, $i=1, 2, \ldots, N$. Let us now show that if $H_k(\bar{x}_1, \bar{x}_2, \ldots, \bar{x}_k) \neq 0$, then there exists in any neighborhood $\varepsilon(x_{k+1})$ of any point x_{k+1} a point $\bar{x}_{k+1}$ such that $H_{k+1}(\bar{x}_1, \bar{x}_2, \ldots, \bar{x}_{k+1}) \neq 0$; this would prove our assertion. We expand $H_{k+1}(\bar{x}_1, \bar{x}_2, \ldots, \bar{x}_k, x_{k+1})$ with respect to the $(k+1)$-th row

$$H_{k+1}(\bar{x}_1, \bar{x}_2, \ldots, \bar{x}_k, x_{k+1}) = H_k(\bar{x}_1, \bar{x}_2, \ldots, \bar{x}_k) A_{k+1}^{(N)}[r(x_{k+1}, y_{k+1})]^{-1} + W, \tag{10.117}$$

where $\bar{x}_1, \bar{x}_2, \ldots, \bar{x}_k$ are the points at which $H_k(\bar{x}_1, \bar{x}_2, \ldots, \bar{x}_k) \neq 0$, and x_{k+1} some point of $\varepsilon(x_{k+1})$, and

$$W = \sum_{i=1}^{k} A_i^{(N)}[r(x_{k+1}, y_i)]^{-1} H_{k+1, i},$$

where $H_{k+1,i}$ are the adjoints of the elements of the $(k+1)$-th row. Let S_{k+1} be a closed surface, entirely contained within $\varepsilon(x_{k+1})$, and B_{k+1} the volume enclosed by this surface. Let us show that a point $\bar{x}_{k+1} \in S_{k+1}$ exists, such that $H_{k+1}(\bar{x}_1, \bar{x}_2, \ldots, \bar{x}_{k+1}) \neq 0$. We assume the opposite

$$H_{k+1}(\bar{x}_1, \bar{x}_2, \ldots, \bar{x}_k, x_{k+1}) = 0$$

for any point $x_{k+1} \in S_{k+1}$. Since $H_{k+1}(\bar{x}_1, \bar{x}_2, \ldots, x_{k+1})$ is harmonic in x_{k+1}, $H_{k+1} = 0$

for any point $x_{k+1} \in B_{k+1}$ and $H_{k+1}=0$ in the entire domain of analyticity. Let x_{k+1} approach y_{k+1}. Then $[r(x_{k+1}, y_{k+1})]^{-1} \to \infty$, and since $A_{k+1}^{(N)} H_k \neq 0$, the first term in (10.117) tends to infinity while the second term W remains bounded. This contradiction proves our assertion. We note that the proof is essentially based on the fact that it is possible to choose the values of x arbitrarily in B_a. If however the values x_k are fixed, then the determinant of the system (10.112')

$$\det(I - H)$$

is a function of the N variables y (basic points of the cubature formula), which assume on S, generally speaking, arbitrary values. $\det(I-H)$ depends on the basic points directly (the terms $[r(x_x, y_i)]^{-1}$) as well as indirectly through $A_i^{(N)}$, since the basic points of a cubature formula determine in a known way the coefficients of this formula. Let us consider the $2N$-dimensional Euclidean space and let $J(y_1, y_2, \ldots, y_{2N})$ be a point of this space, where y_{2k-1} and y_{2k} determine the k-th basic point of the cubature formula. The subset of points $J(y_1, y_2, \ldots, y_{2N})$ of R_{2N} on which $\det(I-H)=0$, obviously has zero $2N$-dimensional measure. In fact, the equation $\det(I-H)=0$ defines a hypersurface in R_{2N} and the $2N$-dimensional measure of its point is zero. Therefore, if we take random basic points, the determinant of the system (10.112') will vanish with a probability almost equal to one. Analogously, assigning fixed values to the basic points y_k, the determinant of the system (10.112') becomes a function of N variables x which assume arbitrary values in the domain B_a. Let $E(x_1, x_2, \ldots, x_{3N})$ be a point of the $3N$-dimensional Euclidean space, where $x_{3k-2}, x_{3k-1}, x_{3k}$ belong to the k-th point x. The subset of points $E(x_1, x_2, \ldots, x_{3N})$ of R_{3N} for which $\det(I-H)=0$ is obviously of zero $3N$-dimensional measure. This means that if the values of the parameter x are taken at random then $\det(I-H)$ will almost with probability one differ from zero.

The cubature process

$$\int_S f(y)\, dS_y \approx \sum_{i=1}^{N} A_i^{(N)} f(y_i^{(N)}) \qquad (N \to \infty)$$

will be said to be of general type if the asymptotic relations

$$A_i^{(N)} = O\left(\frac{1}{N}\right) \qquad (i=1, 2, \ldots, N;\ N \to \infty) \tag{10.118}$$

are valid. The cubature processes most frequently applied in practice are as a rule of this general type. Thus, for example, relations (10.118) are valid if the integral in the canonical equation is replaced by a Riemann sum. Let us now prove the following assertion:

If

$$0 < \alpha \leqslant \left[r(x_k^{(N)}, y_i^{(N)})\right]^{-1} \leqslant \mu < \infty; \quad k, i=1, 2, \ldots, N;\ N \to \infty, \tag{10.119}$$

and the canonical equation is solved by means of a general cubature process, then the smallest eigenvalue λ_1 *of the matrix* L, *corresponding to the system (10.112'), satisfies the asymptotic inequality*

$$\lambda_1 \leqslant O(N^{-1/2}). \tag{10.120}$$

If, however, the matrix L *is positive for (10.119), (10.120) is replaced by*

$$\lambda_1 \leqslant O(N^{-1}). \tag{10.120'}$$

Let us first prove (10.120). Consider the double sum

$$\sum_{i=1}^{N}\sum_{k=1}^{N}(A_k^{(N)}[r(x_k^{(N)}, y_i^{(N)})]^{-1})^2.$$

By definition of the general cubature process and (10.119)

$$\sum_{i=1}^{N}\sum_{k=1}^{N}(A_i^{(N)}[r(x_k^{(N)}, y_i^{(N)})]^{-1})^2 \leqslant M, \tag{10.121}$$

where M is a constant independent of N. Applying the well-known Schur inequality to (10.112') and using (10.121), we obtain

$$\sum_{i=1}^{N}|\lambda_i|^2 \leqslant M, \tag{10.122}$$

where $(\lambda_1, \lambda_2, \ldots, \lambda_N)$ is the eigenvalue spectrum of the matrix L. It follows directly from (10.122) that $N|\lambda_1|^2 \leqslant M$ or $\lambda_1 = O(N^{-1/2})$. Let us now prove (10.120'). Consider the trace of the matrix L for (10.112'),

$$\mathrm{Sp}\,\mathrm{L} = \sum_{i=1}^{N} A^{(N)}\frac{1}{r(x_i, y_i)}.$$

From (10.119) we obtain for a general cubature process

$$\mathrm{Sp}\,\mathrm{L} \leqslant M_1, \tag{10.123}$$

where M_1 is a constant independent of N. Since

$$\mathrm{Sp}\,\mathrm{L} = \sum_{i=1}^{N}\lambda_i \tag{10.123'}$$

and the matrix L is positive-definite (eigenvalues all positive), we get from (10.123)

$$\sum_{i=1}^{N}\lambda_i = \sum_{i=1}^{N}|\lambda_i| \leqslant M_1 \quad \text{or} \quad \lambda_1 \leqslant O(N^{-1}).$$

It follows from the assertion just proved that if the matrix L is symmetric then $\|\mathrm{L}^{-1}\|_{R_N} \geqslant O(\sqrt{N})$, and if it is in addition positive-definite then $\|\mathrm{L}\|_{R_N}^{-1} \geqslant O(N)$.

The last statement is based on the fact that if L is symmetric then so is L^{-1}, and the eigenvalues of L^{-1} are λ_i^{-1}, if λ_i are those of L. It is known that for any matrix L^{-1}

$$\|\mathrm{L}^{-1}\|_{R_N} = \sqrt{\lambda_n},$$

where λ_n is the largest eigenvalue of the matrix $\mathrm{L}^{-1}(\mathrm{L}^{-1})^*$, and $(\mathrm{L}^{-1})^*$ is the Hermitian conjugate of L^{-1}, which in our case (L^{-1} real) reduces to the transposed matrix $(\mathrm{L}^{-1})'$. The elements of $\mathrm{L}^*\mathrm{L}$ have the form

$$(\mathrm{L}^*\mathrm{L})_{i,k} = \sum_{j=1}^{N} A_i^{(N)}\frac{1}{r(x_i^{(N)}, y_j^{(N)})} A_j^{(N)}\frac{1}{r(x_j^{(N)}, y_k^{(N)})};$$

and therefore satisfy asymptotically the equality

$$(\mathrm{L}^*\mathrm{L})_{i,k} = O(N^{-1}),$$

and, consequently, the inequality

$$\sum_{i=1}^{N}\sum_{k=1}^{N}[(\mathrm{L}^*\mathrm{L})_{i,k}]^2 \leqslant M_2,$$

$$\mathrm{Sp}\,\mathrm{L}^*\mathrm{L} \leqslant M_3,$$

where M_2 and M_3 are constants independent of N. Applying (10.123') to the matrix (L^*L), which is always positive-definite, we obtain

$$\mu_1 \leqslant O(N^{-1}), \qquad (10.124)$$

where μ_1 is the smallest eigenvalue of L^*L. Since $L^{-1}(L^{-1})^* = L^{-1}(L^*)^{-1} = (L^*L)^{-1}$, it follows from (10.124) that $\lambda_n \geqslant O(N)$. We finally obtain the following result: *the asymptotic inequality*

$$\|L^{-1}\|_{R_N} \geqslant O(\sqrt{N})$$

holds for any matrix L. *If* L *is symmetric and positive-definite then*

$$\|L^{-1}\|_{R_N} \geqslant O(N).$$

Everything established in this section for the Dirichlet problem may be easily extended to all the other problems considered before. But since these results do not solve the problem of convergence of the approximation process, we shall not consider the other problems. Again, the satisfactory results of the above numerical examples suggest that a general convergence proof is attainable. In the next sections we shall outline another method of approximate solution for the problems of interest, which is allied to the first but for which the convergence proof is established.

§ 20. Method of generalized Fourier series. Introductory remarks

The foregoing numerical examples show that the method of canonical functional equations yields approximate solutions of boundary-value problems. However, no general proof of the convergence of the approximation process has been found, and the theorems of § 19 ensure convergence only in particular cases. We shall now present another method of approximate solution of boundary-value problems, for which we have succeeded in proving the convergence. The solutions are here obtained in the form of series expansions in some complete sets of orthogonal functions, and their partial sums approximate to the exact solutions. The representation of solutions of boundary-value problems by series of orthogonal functions is one of the basic and widely applied notions of mathematical physics. A fairly detailed survey of the relevant results and their applications may be found, for example, in the known book by L. V. Kantorovich and V. I. Krylov "Approximate Methods of Higher Analysis" (Priblizhennye metody vysshego analiza.—Gostekhizdat. Moskva-Leningrad. 1949 [English translation.—Interscience Publishers. 1958]). The main difficulty encountered in this method is to choose an appropriate set of functions for the expansion of the required solution so as to guarantee the convergence to its exact value. Moreover it is necessary to know in many cases the Green's function and allied functions, in order to carry through the convergence proof. Additional difficulties appear in problems with multiply-connected domains. The method of generalized Fourier series presented below is, as we shall see, free of these disadvantages. It will be applied in §§ 21–38 to boundary-value problems for a single equation and a system of equations. These results (except those related to mixed problems) were obtained by the author jointly with M. A. Aleksidze /15/ and are presented here with some additions and modifications.

2109

§ 21. Solution of the Dirichlet problem for a simply-connected domain

We consider the three-dimensional case and represent the solution, as before, in the form

$$u(x)=\frac{1}{4\pi}\int_S \frac{\varphi(y)}{r(x, y)}\,dS_y-\frac{1}{4\pi}\int_S f(y)\frac{\partial}{\partial n_y}\frac{1}{r(x, y)}\,dS_y, \quad x\in B_i, \qquad (10.125_1)$$

where $\varphi(y)$ is an unknown function satisfying the canonical functional equation

$$\int_S \frac{\varphi(y)}{r(x, y)}\,dS_y=F(x), \quad x\in B_a, \qquad (10.125_2)$$

and

$$F(x)=\int_S f(y)\frac{\partial}{\partial n_y}\frac{1}{r(x, y)}\,dS_y,$$

and $f(y)$ (the boundary value of the required harmonic function) is sufficiently smooth for the functional equation (10.125_2) to have a solution. Differentiating along the normal and passing to the limit as the point x of B_a tends to $y_0\in S$, we obtain from (10.125_2)

$$-2\pi\varphi(y_0)+\int_S \varphi(y)\frac{\partial}{\partial n_{y_0}}\frac{1}{r(y_0\,y)}\,dS_y=\lim_{x\to y_0}\frac{\partial F(x)}{\partial n_x};$$

this is the integral equation corresponding to the exterior Neumann problem, and is solvable for any continuous right-hand side. The fact that this solution at the same time satisfies the functional equation (10.125_2) follows if we consider the function

$$\Omega(x)=\int_S \frac{\varphi(y)}{r(x, y)}\,dS_y-F(x), \quad x\in B_a,$$

which is harmonic in B_a and vanishes at infinity, and its normal derivative vanishes on the boundary. (In the two-dimensional case this results from the identity $\int_S \varphi(y)\,ds_y=0$, which follows from the integral equation satisfied by $\varphi(y)$ in view of

$$\int_S \frac{\partial}{\partial n_{y_0}}\frac{1}{r(y_0\,y)}\,dS_{y_0}=-2\pi \text{ and } \int_S \frac{\partial F(y_0)}{\partial n_{y_0}}\,dS_{y_0}=0.\Big)$$

The uniqueness of this solution of (10.125_2) is now easily proved. Let S_1 be an arbitrary smooth closed surface, the boundary of a domain B which includes B_i entirely, so that

$$\min r(S,\ S_1)>0,$$

where $\min r(S,\ S_1)$ is the shortest distance from the surface S to S_1. We introduce the functions

$$[r(x_i,\ y)]^{-1}=\omega_i(y) \qquad (i=1, 2, 3, 4, \ldots),$$

where $y\in S$ and the elements of the denumerable set of points $x_i\in S_1$ are everywhere dense on S_1. We now prove the following basic theorem:—

The functions of the set $\{\omega_i(y)\}$ *are linearly independent and the set is complete in the* L_2*-space of square-integrable functions S.*

This means that for any function on S, $\gamma(y)\in L_2$, $\left(\int_S [\gamma(y)]^2\,dS_y<\infty\right)$ and for any

$\varepsilon>0$ there exists a positive number N_0 and a set of coefficients $b_l (l=1,2,3,\ldots)$, such that for any $N>N_0$

$$\left\{\int_S [\gamma(y)-\sum_{l=1}^{N} b_l \omega_l(y)]^2 dS\right\}^{1/2} < \varepsilon. \tag{10.126}$$

Let us assume that not all members of $\{\omega_l(y)\}$ are linearly independent. Then there exist constants C_l $(l=1,2,3,\ldots,n)$, among which at least one, say, C_r, $r\leqslant n$, is not zero, for which

$$\sum_{l=1}^{n} C_l \omega_{k_l}(y)\equiv 0$$

holds for all $y\in S$ and at least for one finite n. This implies that the function $u(y)=\sum C_l \omega_{k_l}(y)$ which is regular and harmonic in B_i vanishes identically there. Hence it obviously vanishes in its entire domain of harmonicity, in particular, in B. Taking y sufficiently close to x_{k_r} of B, we may increase the absolute value of the term $C_r\omega_{k_r}(y)$ as much as desired, while all other terms remain bounded; this contradicts the previously proved vanishing of the function $\sum_1^n C_l\omega_{k_l}(y)$, and thus disproves the assumption of linear dependence among $\omega_l(y)$. To prove the completeness of the set $\{\omega_l(y)\}$ in L_2, it is sufficient to prove it in the space C_{L_2} of continuous functions on S. Completeness in C_{L_2} entails completeness in L_2, for it is known that the set of all continuous functions is everywhere dense in L_2; hence for any function $\gamma(y)\in L_2$ there exists a function $\alpha(y)$ such that

$$\left\{\int_S [\gamma(y)-\alpha(y)]^2 dS_y\right\}^{1/2} < \frac{\varepsilon}{2},$$

where $\varepsilon>0$ is an arbitrarily small number. Now in virtue of the completeness in C_{L_2} it is possible to choose coefficients $a_l (l=1,2,3,\ldots,N)$, such that for sufficiently large N

$$\int_S \left[\alpha(y)-\sum_{l=1}^{N} a_l\omega_{k_l}(y)\right]^2 dS_y < \frac{\varepsilon^2}{4}.$$

The last two preceding inequalities in conjunction with Minkowski's inequality (triangle inequality for the L_2-metric) give

$$\left\{\int_S \left[\gamma(y)-\sum_{l=1}^{N} a_l\omega_{k_l}(y)\right]^2 dS_y\right\}^{1/2} =$$

$$=\left\{\int_S \left[\gamma(y)-\alpha(y)+\alpha(y)-\sum_{l=1}^{N} a_l\omega_{k_l}(y)\right]^2 dS_y\right\}^{1/2} \leqslant$$

$$\leqslant \left\{\int_S [\gamma(y)-\alpha(y)]^2 dS_y\right\}^{1/2} + \left\{\int_S \left[\alpha(y)-\sum_{l=1}^{N} a_l\omega_{k_l}(y)\right]^2 dS_y\right\}^{1/2} < \varepsilon,$$

which completes the proof. To see that set $\{\omega_l(y)\}$ actually is complete in $C_{L_2}(S)$, it is sufficient to show that if $\alpha(y)$ is a continuous function on S and if

$$\int_S \alpha(y)\,\omega_l(y)\,dS_y=0 \qquad (l=1,2,3,\ldots), \tag{10.127}$$

then

$$\alpha(y)\equiv 0, \quad y\in S.$$

This is the property of being closed in $C_{L_2}(S)$.

Let us consider the single-layer potential

$$V(x)=\int_S \frac{\alpha(y)}{r(xy)}\,dS_y$$

with $\alpha(y)$ for density. This potential vanishes, by definition, almost everywhere on S_1, and since it is continuous there, we get

$$V(x)\equiv 0, \quad x\in S_1.$$

On the other hand, $V(x)=0$ at infinity, and the uniqueness of solution of the exterior Dirichlet problem requires that $V(x)\equiv 0$ for $x\in B_a-B$. This implies the vanishing throughout the domain of harmonicity, and thus

$$V(x)\equiv 0, \quad x\in B_a.$$

It follows from the continuity of the single-layer potential and from the uniqueness of solution of the interior Dirichlet problem that

$$V(x)\equiv 0, \quad x\in B_i$$

and hence, finally, $\alpha(y)\equiv 0,\ y\in S$. This proves that the considered set is closed in C_{L_2}, and consequently complete in L_2. The vanishing of the single-layer potential at infinity is essential for this proof. As is well known, this property does not obtain in the two-dimensional case. Therefore the proof for the plane problem requires some modification. Instead of the set $\{\omega_i(y)\}$ $(i=1,2,3,\ldots)$ we consider the set $\{\omega_i(y)\}$ $(i=0,1,2,3,\ldots)$, where $\omega_0(y)$ denotes an arbitrary nonzero constant, and prove the following theorem: —

The set $\{\omega_i(y)\}_i=0,1,2,3,\ldots$ *is linearly independent and closed in* C_{L_2}.

The first part is proved as before. The closedness if proved by noticing that all the arguments used to prove it in C_{L_2} for the three-dimensional case apply here as well, since now we have in addition to (10.127) the condition

$$\int_S \alpha(y)\,\omega_0(y)\,dS_y=\text{const}\int_S \alpha(y)\,dS_y=0$$

which ensures the vanishing at infinity of the logarithmic single-layer potential

$$V(x)=\int_S \alpha(y)\ln r(x,\ y)\,dS_y.$$

Let us now remark that due to the linear independence, $\omega_0(y)$ cannot be represented by a linear combination of a finite number of members of $\{\omega_i(y)\}$ $(i=1,2,3,\ldots)$; but such a representation is possible precisely by means of the infinite sequence $\omega_1(y),\ \omega_2(y),\ \ldots$ To see this, consider the single-layer potential

$$v(y)=\int_{S_1}\psi(x)\ln r(x,\ y)\,dS_x,$$

with a density $\psi(x)$ for which we require that

$$\lim_{B\ni y\to x_0\in S_1}\frac{\partial v}{\partial n}=0.$$

This leads, as is known, to an integral equation with a unique nontrivial solution, and the corresponding single-layer potential is constant in B; we then have*

$$v(y)=\text{const}\ ), \quad x\in B.$$

* Since S_1 is arbitrary, we may assume this constant to be different from zero.

Replacing now the integral by some quadrature formula we obtain

$$\omega_0(y) = \text{const} = \sum_{i=1}^{\infty} A_i \omega_i(y), \text{ where } A_i \text{ are given constants.}$$

The required result follows by virtue of the uniform convergence of the series.

Because of the key part of this theorem in the following we present another proof of it which is also interesting in itself. Theorems analogous to the Weierstrass approximation theorems in a complex domain imply that the harmonic polynomials $p_i(x)$ constitute in the space C a complete set on the contour of an arbitrary simple-connected domain bounded by a rectifiable Jordan curve. Thus, for any function $\gamma(y) \in C$ and any $\varepsilon > 0$ there exists a positive number N_0 and a set of coefficients d_i $(l = 1, 2, \ldots, N)$, such that for any $N > N_0$

$$\max_{y \in S} \left| \gamma(y) - \sum_{i=1}^{N} d_i p_i(y) \right| < \frac{\varepsilon}{2}.$$

Consider the Dirichlet problem

$$\Delta u(x) = 0, \qquad \lim_{x \to y \in S_1} u(x) = \sum_{i=1}^{N} d_i p_i(y), \qquad y \in S_1,$$

for the domain B, and let its contour be sufficiently smooth so that it is possible to express the solution of the problem by the single-layer potential

$$u(x) = \int_{S_1} \psi(y) \ln r(x, y)\, dS_1.$$

It is evident from the uniqueness theorem that

$$u(x) = \sum_{i=1}^{N} d_i p_i(x).$$

Let us consider the value of $u(x)$ for $x \in S$, and replace the integral by a Riemann sum with N_1 terms (or by any quadrature formula with basic points at $\eta_{k_i} \in S_1$) so that

$$\max_{x \in S} \left| \int_{S_1} \psi(y) \ln r(x, y)\, dS_1 - \sum_{i=1}^{N_1} a_i \ln r(x, \eta_{k_i}) \right| < \frac{\varepsilon}{2}.$$

Let $N_2 = \max(N, N_1)$; we then find

$$\max_{y \in S} \left| \gamma(y) - \sum_{i=1}^{N_2} a_i \omega_{k_i}(y) \right| \leqslant$$

$$\leqslant \max_{y \in S} \left| \gamma(y) - \sum_{i=1}^{N_2} d_i p_i(y) \right| + \max_{y \in S} \left| \sum_{i=1}^{N_2} d_i p_i(y) - \sum_{i=1}^{N_2} a_i \omega_{k_i}(y) \right| \leqslant$$

$$\leqslant \frac{\varepsilon}{2} + \max_{y \in S} \left| \int_{S_1} \psi(\eta) \ln r(y, \eta)\, dS_1 - \sum_{i=1}^{N_2} a_i \ln r(y, \eta_{k_i}) \right| < \varepsilon,$$

which completes the proof. This proof may also be applied in the three-dimensional case since any function $\gamma(y)$, continuous on the surface S of a simply connected domain, may be uniformly approximated by harmonic polynomials.

The remaining discussion is identical for three or two dimensions, and we choose the former.

It is known that if $\{\omega_i(y)\}$ if a set of linearly independent elements of a Hilbert space, then it is possible to construct an orthonormal set $\{\varphi_i(y)\}$ such that its elements be linear combinations of the elements of the set $\{\omega_i(y)\}$ and vice versa. Carrying out a Gram-Schmidt orthonormalization, we obtain

$$\varphi_i(y) = \sum_{k=1}^{i} A_{ki}\omega_k(y), \quad \omega_i(y) = \sum_{k=1}^{i} B_{ki}\varphi_k(y).$$

As $\omega_i(y) \in L_2$, we conclude from the basic theorem and from the first of the above relations that the orthonormalized set $\{\varphi_i(y)\}$ is linearly independent, and in view of the second relation it is complete in L_2.

We denote by Φ_i the Fourier coefficients of the function $\varphi(y)$ expanded in a series of the functions $\{\varphi_i(y)\}$

$$\Phi_i = \int_S \varphi(y)\varphi_i(y)\,dS_y \quad i = 1, 2, 3, 4, \ldots$$

Set $x = x_i \in S_1$, $i = 1, 2, 3, \ldots$ in (10.125_2), multiply the first i equations by A_{ki} $(k = 1, 2, \ldots, i)$ and add them together; then

$$\int_S \varphi(y) \sum_{k=1}^{i} A_{ki}\omega_k(y)\,dS_y = \int_S \varphi(y)\varphi_i(y)\,dS_y = \Phi_i = \sum_{k=1}^{i} A_{ki}F(x_k).$$

Since $F(x)$ is a given function, and the coefficients A_{ki} are constructed in the process of orthonormalization, all the coefficients Φ_i of the required function $\varphi(y)$ are defined. But in a complete Hilbert space the Fourier expansion of any element in a complete orthonormal set of basis elements converges to that element. Since L_2 is complete

$$\lim_{N\to\infty} \left\| \varphi(y) - \sum_{i=1}^{N} \varphi_i(y) \sum_{k=1}^{i} A_{ki}F(x_k) \right\|_{L_2} = 0. \tag{10.128}$$

We now write

$$\varphi^{(N)}(y) = \sum_{i=1}^{N} \Phi_i \varphi_i(y),$$

$$u^{(N)}(x) = \frac{1}{4\pi} \int_S \frac{\varphi^{(N)}(y)}{r(x, y)}\,dS_y - \frac{1}{4\pi} F(x).$$

We may now formulate the theorem: —

For any point x in the interior of B_i and for any $\varepsilon > 0$, there exists a number N_0 such that for any $N > N_0$

$$|u(x) - u^{(N)}(x)| < \varepsilon.$$

We denote the minimal distance from x to the boundary S by σ. It is then readily verified that

$$|u(x) - u^{(N)}(x)| = \frac{1}{4\pi} \int_S \frac{1}{r(x, y)} [\varphi(y) - \varphi^{(N)}(y)]\,dS_y \leqslant$$

$$\leqslant \frac{1}{4\pi} \int_S \frac{1}{r(x, y)} |[\varphi(y) - \varphi^{(N)}(y)]|\,dS_y. \tag{10.129}$$

Relation (10.128) allows us to choose N so that

$$\left\{ \int_S [\varphi(y) - \varphi^{(N)}(y)]^2\,dS_y \right\}^{1/2} < \frac{4\pi\varepsilon\sigma}{\sqrt{|S|}},$$

where $|S|$ is the area of the surface S. Applying the Schwarz inequality to (10.129) and using the last inequality, we finally obtain

$$|u(x) - u^{(N)}(x)| \leqslant \frac{1}{4\pi} \left\{ \int_S \left[\frac{1}{r(x, y)}\right]^2 dS_y \right\}^{1/2} \left\{ \int_S [\varphi(y) - \varphi^{(N)}(y)]^2 dS_y \right\}^{1/2} < \frac{1}{4\pi} \frac{\sqrt{|S|}}{\sigma} \frac{4\pi\varepsilon\sigma}{\sqrt{|S|}} = \varepsilon,$$

which proves the theorem. The finite sum on the right-hand side of

$$u(x)=\lim_{N\to\infty}\frac{1}{4\pi}\int_S\frac{1}{r(x,y)}\sum_{i=1}^{N}\Phi_i\varphi_i(y)dS_y-\frac{1}{4\pi}F(x),\quad x\in B_i,$$

obviously constitutes an approximate solution of the problem.

Let us add a few remarks. After the proof of the basic theorem, it is possible to proceed along different lines; thus we may reduce the problem to an infinite regular system of linear (algebraic) equations, or apply the method due to Picone and others. Let us briefly describe Picone's method. We expand the function $f(y)$ (boundary values of the unknown function $u(x)$) in a Fourier series with the basis $\{\varphi_i(y)\}$

$$f(y)\approx\sum_{n=1}^{\infty}f_n\varphi_n(y),\qquad f_n=\int_S f(y)\varphi_n(y)dS_y.$$

Then, in view of the aforementioned completeness in the sense of L_2-metric, we may write down

$$\lim_{N\to\infty}\int_S\left[f(y)-\sum_{n=1}^{N}f_n\varphi_n(y)\right]^2dS_y=0,$$

i. e., the partial sums of this series converge the mean to the function $f(y)$. It may be shown that the series

$$u(x)=\sum_{n=1}^{\infty}f_n\varphi_n(x),\qquad x\in B_i,$$

converges uniformly for any point x within B_i, and represents a solution of the problem. Indeed, let $G(x, y)$ be the Green's function of the Dirichlet problem for the domain B_i. It then follows from the existence theorem that the solution may be represented as

$$u(x)=\int_S f(y)\frac{\partial G}{\partial\nu}dS_y.$$

Writing

$$u^{(N)}(x)=\sum_{n=1}^{N}f_n\varphi_n(x)=\int_S\sum_{n=1}^{N}f_n\varphi_n(y)\frac{\partial G}{\partial\nu}dS_y\qquad x\in B_i,$$

we form the difference

$$|u(x)-u^{(N)}(x)|.$$

Applying the Schwarz inequality and seeing that the integral $\int_S\left[\frac{\partial G}{\partial\nu}\right]^2dS_y$ is finite for $x\in B_i$, we again obtain

$$u(x)=\lim_{N\to\infty}\sum_{i=1}^{N}f_i\varphi_i(x).$$

This proves our statement.

§ 22. Solution of the exterior Dirichlet problem

It is now required to find a function, harmonic in B_a from given boundary values, and the auxiliary surface S_1 should be taken within B_i, as the (10.125_1) and (10.125_2) become

$$u(x)=\frac{1}{4\pi}\int_S\frac{\varphi(y)}{r(x,y)}dS_y+\frac{1}{4\pi}F(x),\quad x\in B_a,$$

$$\int_S\frac{\varphi(y)}{r(x,y)}dS_y+F(x)=0,\quad x\in B_i.$$

Consider the three-dimensional problem. Using the notation of the last section, we shall show that the set of functions $\{r(x_i, y)^{-1}\} = \{\omega_i(y)\}$, where $x_i \in S_1$, (S_1, we remember, is any smooth closed surface entirely contained in B_i) is linearly independent and closed in $C_{L_2}(S)$. Let there exist a set of constants $C_i (i = 1, 2, 3, \ldots)$ among which at least one, say, C_r, differs from zero, such that

$$\sum_{i=1}^{n} C_i \omega_{k_i}(y) \equiv 0, \quad y \in S,$$

identically holds for at least one finite n; then the function

$$v(x) = \sum_{i=1}^{n} C_i \omega_{k_i}(x), \quad x \in B_a,$$

being harmonic and regular in B_a, vanishes there identically by the uniqueness theorem. Therefore it vanishes in its entire domain of harmonicity, and consequently also everywhere in $(B_i - B)$. Taking the variable point x in $(B_i - B)$ sufficiently close to x_{k_r}, we run into a contradiction since the term $C_r \omega_{k_r}(x)$ exceeds in absolute value any arbitrarily large positive number, while the other terms appearing in $v(x)$ remain bounded and the sum cannot vanish. This proves the linear independence of the set $\{r(x_i, y)^{-1}\} = \{\omega_i(y)\}$, $y \in S$, $x_i \in S_i \in B_i$. In order to prove that it is closed in $C_{L_2}(S)$ we assume that the following conditions are fulfilled for any function $\alpha(y)$ continuous on S

$$\int_S \alpha(y)\, \omega_i(y)\, dS_y = 0 \qquad (i = 1, 2, 3, \ldots);$$

and show that $\alpha(y) \equiv 0$, $y \in S$. Actually, the single-layer potential

$$V(x) = \int_S \frac{\alpha(y)}{r(x, y)}\, dS_y$$

vanishes by definition almost everywhere on S_1, and in view of its continuity

$$V(x) \equiv 0, \quad x \in S_1.$$

According to the uniqueness theorem

$$V(x) \equiv 0, \quad x \in B$$

and since this should be satisfied in the entire domain of harmonicity, we get

$$V(x) \equiv 0, \quad x \in B_i.$$

The continuity of a single-layer potential and its vanishing at infinity imply

$$V(x) \equiv 0, \quad x \in B_a,$$

hence, finally

$$\alpha(y) \equiv 0, \quad y \in S,$$

which completes the proof. Constructing the orthonormal set $\{\varphi_i(y)\}$ as in the last section, and repeating the same arguments, we obtain the following theorem: — *For any point in the external domain B_a and for any $\varepsilon > 0$, there exists a number N_0, such that for $N > N_0$*

$$|u(x) - u^{(N)}(x)| < \varepsilon,$$

where $u(x)$ is the exact solution of the exterior Dirichlet problem, and

$$u^{(N)}(x) = \frac{1}{4\pi} \int_S \frac{1}{r(x, y)} \sum_{i=1}^{N} \Phi_i \varphi_i(y)\, dS_y + \frac{1}{4\pi} F(x), \quad x \in B_a$$

which, being a regular solution of the Laplace equation in B_a, represents an approximate solution of this problem.

§ 23. Solution of the Dirichlet problem for a multiply-connected domain

Let B_i be a finite connected domain, bounded by a finite number of closed simple Lyapunov surfaces (contours). Thus, the boundary of B_i now consists of a finite number of closed surfaces (contours) $S_1, S_2, \ldots, S_m, S_{m+1}$, with no common points, one of which, for example S_{m+1} (which we denote by S_0) contains all the others in its interior, while none of the latter encloses another. The domain contained within S_k, $k=1, 2, \ldots, m$ will be denoted by $B_a^{(k)}$, and the external domain with respect to S_0 (infinite domain) by $B_a^{(0)}$. Further let

$$B_a = \sum_{k=0}^{m} B_a^{(k)}, \quad S = \sum_{k=0}^{m} S_k.$$

B_a is obviously the complement of $\bar{B}_i = B_i + S$ to make up the entire space. We define the positive normal to point from B_i into B_a. In the three-dimensional problem we are looking for a solution of the form

$$u(x) = \frac{1}{4\pi}\int_S \frac{\varphi(y)}{r(x, y)}\, dS_y - \frac{1}{4\pi}\int_S f(y)\frac{\partial}{\partial n_y}\frac{1}{r(x, y)}\, dS_y, \quad x \in B_i, \qquad (10.130_1)$$

where $\varphi(y)$ is an unknown function satisfying the functional equation

$$\int_S \frac{\varphi(y)}{r(x, y)}\, dS_y = \int_S f(y)\frac{\partial}{\partial n_y}\frac{1}{r(x, y)}\, dS_y, \quad x \in B_a. \qquad (10.130_2)$$

In this section we assume that the (interior) Dirichlet problem for the domain B_i and the boundary condition $f(y)$ has a (unique) solution to which Green's formula may be applied. Then it is easily verified that the functional equation (10.130_2) also admits a unique solution of class C. It is required to construct an approximate solution of the Dirichlet problem at an internal point of B_i. Let S_k' be an arbitrary smooth closed surface, entirely contained within $B_a^{(k)}$, and S_0' a surface of the same type, enclosing S_0 and entirely contained in $B_a^{(0)}$. Let

$$S' = \sum_{k=0}^{m} S_k'.$$

We arbitrarily fix a denumerable everywhere dense set of points x_k on S' and consider the sequence of functions

$$\{r(x_l, y)^{-1}\} = \{\omega_l(y)\}, \quad x_l \in S', \quad y \in S.$$

The following theorem is valid:—

The set $\{\omega_l(y)\}$ is linearly independent and closed in $C_{L_1}(S)$.

Assuming linear dependence, we form from the $\omega_l(y)$ some linear combination which represents a regular harmonic function in B_i, vanishing on S, and therefore vanishing identically in B_i. Since this expression vanishes throughout its domain of harmonicity, we reach a contradiction, exactly as in § 21. This proves the linear independence. To prove that the set is closed, we show that any continuous function $\alpha(y)$ defined on S, which satisfies the conditions

$$\int_S \alpha(y)\,\omega_l(y)\, dS_y = 0 \quad (l = 1, 2, 3, \ldots)$$

must vanish identically. Consider the single-layer potential with density $\alpha(y)$, given on S,

$$V(x)=\int_S \alpha(y)\frac{dy}{r(x, y)}.$$

This potential vanishes almost everywhere on S' and its continuity shows that

$$V(x)\equiv 0, \quad x\in S'$$

Letting x vary in $B_a^{(0)}$ and noting that the potential vanishes at infinity, we conclude that it vanishes identically in $B_a^{(0)}$ and, consequently, by the continuity

$$\lim_{B_i\ni x\to x_0\in S_0} V(x)=0.$$

Letting x vary in $B_a^{(k)}$ and within S_k', we note that since $V(x)=0$ for $x\in S_k'$, and is a regular harmonic function within S_k', $V(x)\equiv 0$, and as this property must hold throughout the domain of harmonicity, $V(x)\equiv 0$, $x\in B_a^{(k)}$; hence, by the continuity property

$$\lim_{B_i\ni x\to x_0\in S_k} V(x)=0 \quad (k=1, 2, 3, \ldots, m).$$

But then $V(x)\equiv 0$, $x\in B_i$, and therefore $\alpha(y)\equiv 0$, which completes the proof. The remaining arguments coincide with those of § 21 and lead to the following theorem: —

The solution of the interior Dirichlet problem may, at any internal point of a multiply connected domain B_i, *be represented as*

$$u(x)=\lim_{N\to\infty}\left\{\frac{1}{4\pi}\int_S \frac{1}{r(x, y)}\sum_{i=1}^{N}\Phi_i\varphi_i(y)\,dS_y\right\}-\frac{1}{4\pi}F(x), \quad x\in B_i,$$

and the partial sums on the right-hand side approximate to the solution.

§ 24. Solution of the interior Neumann problem for a simply-connected domain

The domain B_i is now simply connected and bounded by a single surface S. We seek a solution of the Laplace equation that satisfies the boundary condition

$$\left.\frac{\partial u}{\partial n}\right|_S=f(y),$$

and is of the form

$$u(x)=\frac{1}{4\pi}\int_S \varphi(y)\frac{\partial}{\partial n_y}\frac{1}{r(x, y)}\,dS_y-\frac{1}{4\pi}\int_S f(y)\frac{dS_y}{r(x, y)}, \quad x\in B_i, \qquad (10.131_1)$$

where $\varphi(y)$ is an unknown function satisfying the functional equation

$$\int_S \varphi(y)\frac{\partial}{\partial n_y}\frac{1}{r(x, y)}\,dS_y=\int_S f(y)\frac{dS_y}{r(x, y)}, \quad x\in B_a. \qquad (10.131_2)$$

As we know,

$$\int_S f(y)\,dS_y=0$$

is a necessary condition for the solvability of the interior problem and the solution is determined up to an additive constant. It is readily seen that this condition also ensures the solvability of (10.131_2). Passing to the limit for x of B_a approaching y_0 on S, we get

$$2\pi\varphi(y_0)+\int_S \varphi(y)\frac{\partial}{\partial n_y}\frac{1}{r(y_0y)}dS_y=\int_S f(y)\frac{dS_y}{r(y_0y)}.$$

We have obtained the integral equation for the exterior Dirichlet problem; the homogeneous equation has, as is known, a unique nontrivial solution, and the single-layer potential with density $\psi(y)$, equal to the solution of the associated homogeneous equation, is constant in $\bar{B}_i$. Therefore the solvability condition for the inhomogeneous equation

$$\int_S \psi(y_0)\left(\int_S f(y)\frac{dS_y}{r(y_0y)}\right)dS_{y_0}=\int_S f(y)\left(\int_S \psi(y_0)\frac{dS_{y_0}}{r(y_0y)}\right)dS_y=C\int_S f(y)\,dS_y=0$$

is fulfilled on account of the solvability condition for the problem. The obtained $\varphi(y)$ satisfies also the functional equation (10.131_2). For, the function

$$\Omega(x)=\int_S \varphi(y)\frac{\partial}{\partial n_y}\frac{1}{r(x,y)}dS_y-\int_S f(y)\frac{dS_y}{r(x,y)},\qquad x\in B_a,$$

harmonic and regular in B_a (the regularity of $\Omega(x)$ is in the two-dimensional case a consequence of the solvability condition of the problem).

We arbitrarily assign an everywhere dense set of points x_l on the surface S_1 (cf. § 21) and consider the set of functions $\{\nu_i(y)\}$ $(i=0,1,2,\ldots)$, such that

$$\nu_0=\text{const}\neq 0,\qquad \nu_i(y)=\frac{\partial}{\partial n_y}\frac{1}{r(x_i,y)},\qquad i=1,2,\ldots,\qquad y\in S.$$

The following theorem is valid:—

The set of functions $\{\nu_i(y)\}$ *is linearly independent and closed in the space* $C_{L_2}(S)$.

Assuming linear dependence, we have identically for $y\in S$

$$-C_0\nu_0+\sum_{i=1}^{n}C_i\nu_{k_i}(y)\equiv 0,$$

where at least one of the constants $C_0, C_1, C_2, \ldots, C_n$ is not zero, and n is an arbitrary (finite) integer. Consider the function

$$v(x)=\sum_{i=1}^{n}C_i\frac{1}{r(x,x_i)},\qquad x\in B_i.$$

Evidently,

$$\lim_{B_i\ni x\to y\in S}\frac{\partial v}{\partial n}=C_0\nu_0.$$

But this is possible only when $C_0=0$, because the integral over S of the left-hand side vanishes, being a surface integral of a normal derivative of a function that is harmonic in B_i, while the integral of the right-hand side differs from zero for $C_0\neq 0$. But then

$$v(x)=\text{const};\qquad x\in B_i.$$

Consider the harmonic function $v_*(x)=v(x)-\text{const}$, which vanishes in B_i and hence vanishes in the entire domain of harmonicity, and certainly in $(B-B_i)$. Taking x in $(B-B_i)$ sufficiently close to x_{k_r}, we reach a contradiction (cf. § 21), which proves the linear independence of $\{\nu_i(y)\}$. In order to prove that this set is closed, consider the double-layer potential

$$W(x)=\int_S \alpha(y)\frac{\partial}{\partial n_y}\frac{1}{r(x,y)}dS_y,$$

where the density $\alpha(y)$ is an arbitrary function continuous on S; we will show that if this function satisfies the conditions

$$\int_S \alpha(y)\,\nu_i(y)\,dS_y = 0 \qquad (i = 0,\ 1,\ 2,\ 3,\ \ldots),$$

then $\alpha(y) \equiv 0$. If these conditions are fulfilled we may write

$$W(x) = 0, \quad x \in S_1;$$

In view of the behavior at infinity, we infer that $W(x) \equiv 0,\ x \in B_a - B$, and then in the entire domain of harmonicity

$$W(x) \equiv 0, \quad x \in B_a.$$

But a double-layer potential which vanishes identically in the external domain has constant density: $\alpha(y) \equiv \text{const}$. The condition

$$\int_S \alpha(y)\,\nu_0\,dS_y = 0$$

now shows that $\alpha(y) \equiv 0$, which proves that $\{\nu_i(y)\}$ is closed. By the orthonormalization process we now construct from the set $\nu_1(y),\ \nu_2(y),\ \nu_3(y),\ \ldots$ a new orthonormal and linearly independent set

$$\{\varphi_i(y)\} \qquad (i = 1,\ 2,\ 3,\ \ldots)$$

and consider the complete orthonormalized set

$$\left(\frac{1}{\sqrt{|S|}},\ \varphi_1(y),\ \varphi_2(y),\ \ldots\right).$$

Let

$$\int_S f(y)\,\frac{dS_y}{r(x,\ y)} = F(x).$$

Let us rewrite (10.131_2) in the form

$$\int_S \varphi(y)\,\frac{\partial}{\partial n_y}\,[r(x,\ y)]^{-1}\,dS_y = F(x),$$

and assign to the point x i various locations on S_1. Multiplying the first $i\,(i = 1,\ 2,\ \ldots)$ equations by A_{ki} $(k = 1,\ 2,\ \ldots,\ i)$ and adding the results together, we obtain the coefficients

$$\Phi_i = \sum_{k=1}^{i} A_{ki}F(x_i) \qquad \Phi_0 = \frac{1}{\sqrt{|S|}} \int_S \varphi(y)\,dS_y$$

We now write

$$\varphi^{(N)}(y) = \sum_{i=0}^{N} \Phi_i\varphi_i(y), \qquad \varphi_0 \equiv 1$$

$$u^{(N)}(x) = \frac{1}{4\pi}\int_S \varphi^{(N)}(y)\,\frac{\partial}{\partial n_y}\,\frac{1}{r(x,\ y)}\,dS_y - \frac{1}{4\pi}F(x), \qquad x \in B_i.$$

It may be shown, exactly as in § 24, that

$$u(x) = \lim_{N\to\infty} u^{(N)}(x).$$

The partial sums of the obtained series evidently give approximate values of the solution at the internal points of B_i. The solution is, as expected, determined to within an additive constant. Using the set $\left\{\frac{1}{\sqrt{|S|}},\ \varphi_i(y)\right\}$ the solution may be obtained (in a somewhat simpler way) by Picone's method (cf. § 21).

§ 25. Solution of the exterior Neumann problem

We now seek a solution (that vanishes at infinity) of the form

$$u(x)=\frac{1}{4\pi}\int_S \varphi(y)\frac{\partial}{\partial n_y}\frac{1}{r(x, y)}dS_y-\frac{1}{4\pi}\int_S \frac{f(y)}{r(x, y)}dS_y, \quad x\in B_a, \qquad (10.132_1)$$

where $\varphi(y)$ is an unknown function satisfying the canonical equation

$$\int_S \varphi(y)\frac{\partial}{\partial n_y}[r(x, y)]^{-1}dS_y=F(x), \quad x\in B_i,$$

$$\left(\int_S f(y)\frac{dS_y}{r(x, y)}=F(x)\right). \qquad (10.132_2)$$

The existence and uniqueness of solution for this equation follows by considering the integral equation

$$-2\pi\varphi(y_0)+\int_S \varphi(y)\frac{\partial}{\partial n_y}\frac{1}{r(y_0 y)}dS_y=F(y_0),$$

which is the limiting form of (10.132_2) for $B_i\ni x\to y_0\in S$. This equation is solvable, being the integral equation of the interior Dirichlet problem, and its solution also satisfies the functional equation (10.132_2). The surface S_1 is now taken, as in § 22, within B_i and the following set of functions on S is considered

$$\nu_i(y)=\frac{\partial}{\partial n_y}[r(x_i y)]^{-1} \qquad (i=1,\ 2,\ 3,\ 4,\ \ldots;\ x_i\in S_1,\ y\in S).$$

Let us prove that this set is linearly independent and closed in $C_{L_2}(S)$.

Let

$$\sum_{i=1}^{n} C_i\nu_{k_i}(y)\equiv 0$$

for all $y\in S$ and C_i not all vanishing. We introduce the following regular function which is harmonic in B_a

$$v(x)=\sum_{i=1}^{n} C_i\frac{1}{r(x, x_i)}, \quad x\in B_a.$$

The uniqueness of a solution of the Neumann problem that vanishes at infinity, implies that $v(x)\equiv 0,\ x\in B_a$. Continuing $v(x)$ into B_i, we get in virtue of the continuity of the function and all its derivatives that $v(x)=0;\ x\in(B_i-B)$. But by bringing x sufficiently close to x_{k_r}, we reach a contradiction; this proves the linear independence. Let $\alpha(y)$ be any continuous function defined on S, and let

$$\int_S \alpha(y)\nu_i(y)dS_y=0 \qquad (i=1,\ 2,\ 3,\ 4,\ \ldots).$$

We show that $\alpha(y)\equiv 0,\ y\in S$. Consider the double-layer potential

$$W(x)=\int_S \alpha(y)\frac{\partial}{\partial n_y}\frac{1}{r(x, y)}dS_y.$$

Now $W(x_i)=0,\ x_i\in S_1$, and by continuity $W(x)\equiv 0,\ x\in S_1$; consequently, for x in B, we conclude that $W(x)=0,\ x\in B$, and hence throughout the domain of harmonicity $W(x)=0,\ x\in B_i$. Writing down the internal limiting value of $W(x)$ on S, and equating it to zero (see above), we obtain the Fredholm integral equation for the interior homogeneous Dirichlet problem, which, as we know, has only a trivial solution; thus $\alpha(y)\equiv 0$, which completes the proof. We replace the set $\{\nu_i(y)\}$ by the equivalent complete orthonormalized set $\{\varphi_i(y)\}$, and denote the coefficients of the Fourier expansion of $\varphi(y)$ in the functions $\{\varphi_i(y)\}$ by Φ_i, i. e.,

$$\Phi_i=\int_S \varphi(y)\varphi_i(y)\,dS_y.$$

These coefficients are derived, as above, from equation (10.132_2). It is sufficient for this to assign to the point x i different values on S_1, multiply the first i $(i=1, 2, 3, \ldots)$ equations by the constants A_{ki} (coefficients in the expression of $\varphi_i(y)$ as a linear combination of $\nu_k(y)$ $(k=1, 2, \ldots, i)$), and add the results together; we then obtain

$$\Phi_i=\sum_{k=1}^{i} A_{ki}F(x_k).$$

Next, using the fact that being closed in C_{L_2} implies completeness in L_2, we get

$$\lim_{N\to\infty}\int_S\left[\varphi(y)-\sum_{k=1}^{N}\Phi_k\varphi_k(y)\right]^2 dS_y=0.$$

This together with (10.132_1) proves that if

$$u^{(N)}(x)=\frac{1}{4\pi}\int_S\left(\sum_{k=1}^{N}\Phi_k\varphi_k(y)\right)\frac{\partial}{\partial n_y}\frac{1}{r(x, y)}dS_y-\frac{1}{4\pi}F(x), \qquad x\in B_a,$$

then there exists for any $\varepsilon>0$ a number N_0, such that for $N>N_0$

$$|u(x)-u^{(N)}(x)|<\varepsilon, \qquad x\in B_a.$$

But since $u^{(N)}(x)$ is a regular harmonic function in B_a, the last result shows that $u^{(N)}(x)$ is an approximate value of the exact solution at any internal point of the external domain B_a. This solution is, as could be expected, unique.

§ 26. Solution of the Neumann problem for a multiply-connected domain

We retain the notation of § 23. We fix arbitrarily an everywhere dense set of points x_k on the surface $S'=\sum_{k=0}^{m}S'_k$, and prove that the set of functions $\{\nu_i(y)\}$ $(i=0, 1, 2, 3, \ldots)$, where

$$\nu_0(y)=\text{const}\neq 0, \quad \nu_k(y)=\frac{\partial}{\partial n_y}[r(x_k, y)]^{-1}, \quad y\in S=\sum_{i=0}^{m}S_i;$$
$$k=1, 2, \ldots$$

is linearly independent and closed in $C_{L_2}(S)$. The linear independence is proved exactly as in the case of the interior Neumann problem for a simply connected domain.

The set will be proved to be closed if it follows from the conditions

$$\int_S \nu_0\alpha(y)\,dS_y=0 \qquad \int_S \alpha(y)\nu_k(y)\,dS_y=0 \qquad k=1, 2, 3, 4, \ldots$$

where $\alpha(y)$ is any continuous function defined on S, that $\alpha(y)\equiv 0$. Consider the double-layer potential

$$W(x)=\int_S \alpha(y)\frac{\partial}{\partial n_y}\frac{1}{r(x,y)}dS_y.$$

The conditions imposed on the density of this potential imply that

$$W(x)=0, \quad x\in S'.$$

In particular, it follows from $W(x)=0,\ x\in S_0'$, and from the behavior of a double-layer potential at infinity that $W(x)\equiv 0,\ x\in B_a^{(0)}$. The condition $W(x)=0$, $x\in S_k'$ $(k=1,2,\ldots,m)$ implies that $W(x)\equiv 0,\ x\in B_a^{(k)}$. By the Lyapunov-Tauber theorem about the continuity of the normal derivative of a double-layer potential and in view of the aforesaid,

$$\lim_{B_i\ni x\to x_0\in S}\left(\frac{\partial W}{\partial n}\right)=0,$$

and since $W(x)$ is a regular harmonic function in B_i,

$$W(x)=\text{const}, \quad x\in B_i.$$

Finally, since

$$W(x)=\begin{matrix}0, & x\in B_a,\\ \text{const}, & x\in B_i,\end{matrix}$$

it follows that

$$\alpha(y)\equiv\text{const}, \quad y\in S.$$

From

$$\nu_0\int_S \alpha(y)\,dS_y=0, \quad \nu_0\neq 0,$$

we may conclude that

$$\alpha(y)\equiv 0,$$

which proves that the set is closed. The remaining arguments are as in § 24 and we obtain, from functional equations of the same type as (10.131_1), (10.131_2), which remain valid in our case, an expression for the approximate solution, completely analogous to those derived in § 24.

§ 27. Solution of the mixed boundary-value problem

The mixed problem is a boundary-value problem in which conditions of the type of the first problem are prescribed on one portion of the boundary, and conditions of the type of the second problem on the remaining portion. In particular, the mixed problem for the Laplace equation consists in finding a function harmonic in B_i that assumes prescribed values on a portion S_1 of the boundary and whose normal derivative assumes prescribed values on the remaining portion $S_2=S-S_1$.

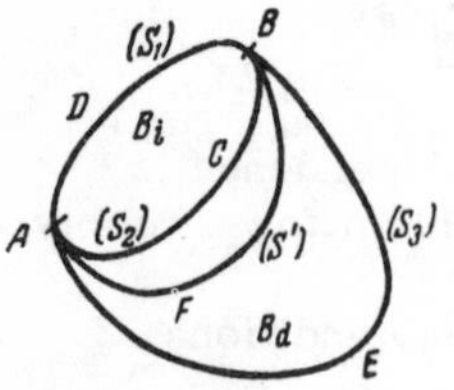

FIGURE 3

Mixed problems have proved less tractable then the first, second and third problems, and not many papers devoted to them are found in the literature. Zaremba has investigated this problem already in 1910 for a harmonic function and proved the existence and uniqueness theorems. But Zaremba's work, apparently because of the complicated and artificial method involved, was not sufficiently developed and extended. Fichera /30/ considered in 1956 the mixed static problem of elasticity. For other works on mixed problems in the theory of elasticity the reader is referred to N. I. Muskhelishvili /24b/. We present below a simple approach to the mixed problem; it is based on an idea of which we have already made some use, and not only affords proof of the existence theorems, but also approximate computation of the solution to any desired accuracy. This method is presented here for the Laplace equation; it might be extended along lines set forth in §§ 32–38 to static problems of plasticity and also dynamic elasticity.

Let (Figure 3) $ACBDA=S$, $ADB=S_1$, $ACB=S_2$ $(S_1+S_2=S)$. $BEA=S_3$ $(ADBEA=S_1+S_3)$, $AFB=S'$. The domains bounded by the closed curves (S_2+S_3) and (S_1+S') are denoted by B_a and B', respectively. We are looking for a harmonic function $u(x)$ in the domain B_i, bounded by the closed curve $S=ACBDA$, which satisfies

$$\lim_{B_i\ni x\to x_0\in S_1} u(x)=f^{(1)}(x_0), \quad \lim_{B_i\ni x\to x_0\in S_2} \frac{\partial u}{\partial n}=f^{(2)}(x_0),$$
$$x_0\neq A, \quad x_0\neq B.$$

The class to which the functions $f^{(1)}(x)$ and $f^{(2)}(x)$ belong will be specified below. We extend the curve $S_1=ADB$ by adding to it $S_3=BEA$ so that the domain B_a, bounded by the closed curve $S_2+S_3=ACBEA$, has no points in common with B_i. Let $G(x, y)$ be the Green's function of the Dirichlet problem for the simply-connected domain $B_i+B_a+S_2$, bounded by the closed curve $S_1+S_3=ADBEA$. We have

a) $\lim\limits_{x\to x_0\in(S_1+S_3)} G(x, y)=0, \quad y\notin(S_1+S_3)$.

b) $\lim\limits_{x\to x_0} \int\limits_{S_1+S_3} f(y)\frac{\partial}{\partial n_y}G(x, y)\,dS_y=2\pi f(x_0)$.

c) $G(x, y)=v(x, y)-\ln r$, where $v(x, y)$ is a regular harmonic function for y not on the boundary.

d) $G(x, y)=G(y, x)$.

Let us first assume that the problem has a solution to which Green's formula may be applied in B_i. Then, taking $G(x, y)$ for a fundamental solution, we represent the solution by means of Green's formula as follows

$$u(x)=\frac{1}{2\pi}\int\limits_S \frac{\partial u}{\partial n}G(x, y)\,dS_y-\frac{1}{2\pi}\int\limits_S u(y)\frac{\partial G}{\partial n}\,dS_y, \quad x\in B_i,$$

and

$$0=\frac{1}{2\pi}\int\limits_S \frac{\partial u}{\partial n}G(x, y)\,dS_y-\frac{1}{2\pi}\int\limits_S u(y)\frac{\partial G}{\partial n}\,dS_y, \quad x\in B_a.$$

On account of the prescribed boundary values of u and $\frac{\partial u}{\partial n}$ and the properties a), d) of the Green's function, we may write

$$u(x)=\frac{1}{2\pi}\int\limits_{S_2} f^{(2)}(y)G(x, y)\,dS_y-\frac{1}{2\pi}\int\limits_{S_1} f^{(1)}(y)\frac{\partial G}{\partial n}\,dS_y-$$
$$-\frac{1}{2\pi}\int\limits_{S_2} u(y)\frac{\partial G}{\partial n}\,dS_y, \quad x\in B_i,$$

$$0=\frac{1}{2\pi}\int\limits_{S_2} f^{(2)}(y)G(x, y)\,dS_y-\frac{1}{2\pi}\int\limits_{S_1} f^{(1)}(y)\frac{\partial G}{\partial n}\,dS_y-$$
$$-\frac{1}{2\pi}\int\limits_{S_2} u(y)\frac{\partial G}{\partial n}\,dS_y, \quad x\in B_a.$$

Let

$$\int_{S_2} f^{(2)}(y)\, G(x, y)\, dS_y - \int_{S_1} f^{(1)}(y) \frac{\partial G}{\partial n} dS_y = F(x).$$

Let us now drop the assumption about the existence of a solution, and look for it in the form

$$u(x) = \frac{1}{2\pi} \int_{S_1} \varphi(y) \frac{\partial G}{\partial n_y} dS_y + \frac{1}{2\pi} F(x), \quad x \in B_i, \qquad (10.133_1)$$

where $\varphi(y)$ is an unknown function, subject to the condition

$$\int_{S_2} \varphi(y) \frac{\partial G}{\partial n_y} dS_y = -F(x), \quad x \in B_a. \qquad (10.133_2)$$

We shall show somewhat later that if this functional equation has a solution $\varphi(y)$, not dependent on x, continuous on the open curve S_2 and admitting at its end-points singularities of order not exceeding 1/2, then its substitution into the expression for $u(x)$ yields the solution of the problem. First let us prove that such a solution exists for (10.133_2). Consider the limiting form of the functional equation

$$\int_{S_2} \varphi(y) \frac{\partial G}{\partial n} dS_y = -F(x), \quad x \in B_a,$$

as x in B_a approaches y_0 and S_2, without coinciding with the end-points. The limiting form is obviously

$$\pi\varphi(y_0) + \int_{S_2} \varphi(y) \frac{\partial G(y_0, y)}{\partial n_y} dS_y = -F(y_0), \quad y_0 \in S_2.$$

We have obtained a Fredholm integral equation. Let us examine the features of the solution of this equation (if it exists) at the integration limits with regard to the properties of the function $F(y_0)$ at these points. Let the given functions $f^{(1)}(y_0)$ and $f^{(2)}(y_0)$ be continuous and bounded on S_1 and S_2, respectively, including the end-points. Then the function $F(y_0)$ obviously takes on at A (say) the singularity of the integrals

$$f^{(2)}(A) \int_{S_2} \ln r(y_0, y)\, dS_y - f^{(1)}(A) \int_{S_1} \frac{\partial}{\partial n_y} \ln r(y_0, y)\, dS_y.$$

These two integrals are bounded at A; consequently, the function $F(y_0)$, under the assumption concerning $f^{(1)}(x)$ and $f^{(2)}(x)$, is bounded at the end-points. Let $R(y_0, y)$ be the resolvent corresponding to the kernel $\frac{\partial G(y_0, y)}{\partial n_y}$; it possesses, as is known, the same singularities as the kernel, and therefore the integral

$$\int_{S_2} F(y)\, R(y_0, y)\, dS_y$$

is also bounded at the integration limits. On the other hand, if the considered Fredholm equation has a solution, it will be of the form

$$\varphi(y_0) = C_1 F(y_0) + C_2 \int_{S_2} F(y)\, R(y_0, y)\, dS_y, \quad (C_1, C_2 \text{ are constants}),$$

and it follows from the preceding that this solution is bounded at the end-points (and continuous on S_2)*. In order to prove the existence of solution,

* It is not difficult also to obtain the sufficient conditions that $f^{(1)}(x)$ and $f^{(2)}(x)$ must satisfy for $\varphi(y_0)$ to possess derivatives of order $l \geqslant 1/8/$.

consider the associated homogeneous equation

$$\pi\psi(y_0)+\int_{S_2}\psi(y)\frac{\partial}{\partial n_{y_0}}G(y_0,\ y)\,dS_y=0.$$

This equation is obtained when it is required to find a harmonic function in B_i, satisfying the boundary conditions

$$\lim_{B_i\ni x\to y_0\in S_1} u(x)=0, \qquad \lim_{B_i\ni x\to x_0\in S_2}\frac{\partial u}{\partial n}=0,$$

and the solution is sought in the form of the single-layer potential

$$\int_{S_2}\psi(y)\,G(x,\ y)\,dS_y.$$

Therefore, assuming that this equation has a nontrivial solution $\psi(y)$, we get for the solution of the auxiliary mixed problem the expression

$$V(x)=\int_{S_2}\psi(y)\,G(x,\ y)\,dS_y;$$

in order to deduce from this result the desired conclusions we must show that

$$V(x)\equiv 0, \quad x\in B_i.$$

This may be easily verified for a harmonic function, continuous in B, by using the Green's formula but we shall now present another uniqueness theorem to which we refer in future and which leads to the required result in all cases encountered here. This theorem was communicated to the author by I. N. Kartsivadze and may be formulated as follows:—

If a function $u(x)$, harmonic in B_i, continuous everywhere in the closed domain $\overline{B}_i$, points A and B excluded, is such that in the neighborhood of these points

$$\lim_{x\to A}|u(x)|\sqrt{r(x,\ A)}=0, \qquad \lim_{x\to B}|u(x)|\sqrt{r(x,\ B)}=0, \tag{10.134}$$

where $r(x,\ A)$ and $r(x,\ B)$ are the distances from x to A and B respectively, then if it satisfies the boundary condition $u=0$ on S_1, and the boundary condition $\frac{\partial u}{\partial n}=0$ on S_2, it vanishes identically in B_i.

The theorem remains valid when the points A and B are simple corners of the curve S, and also in the case when the boundary condition $u=0$ is given on S_2.

We have shown that $\psi(y)$ is bounded at A and B; therefore $V(x)$ fulfills the conditions of the theorem and $V(x)\equiv 0$ $x\in B_i$. Considering $V(x)$ in B_a and using, on the one hand, the continuity of a single-layer potential, and on the other hand property a) of the Green's function, we conclude that $V(x)$ vanishes on the boundary of B_a. Applying again the uniqueness theorem, we get $V(x)\equiv 0$, $x\in B_a$, and finally, $\psi(y)\equiv 0$.

The integral equation obtained as the limiting form of the basic functional equation is thus solvable and has a unique solution which is continuous on S_2 and bounded at the end-points. This result permits us to prove that this solution also satisfies the functional equation itself. To see this, consider

$$\Omega(x)=\int_{S_2}\varphi(y)\frac{\partial G}{\partial n_y}\,dS+F(x), \quad x\in B_a.$$

It is easily seen that this function, which is harmonic in B_a, vanishes on S_2 and S_3. Further, in view of the aforesaid it satisfies the conditions of the uniqueness theorem (with boundary conditions modified correspondingly); therefore $\Omega(x)=0$, $x \in B_a$, and our assertion is proved. The uniqueness of solution is obvious. Finally, it is clear that the derived solution does not depend on the parameter x, is continuous on S_2 and bounded at the end-points. Once $\varphi(y)$ has been found the solution of the problem should be (see above) of the form

$$u(x)=\frac{1}{2\pi}\int_{S_2} \varphi(y)\frac{\partial G}{\partial n_y}\, dS_y+\frac{1}{2\pi}F(x), \qquad x \in B_i.$$

This function is indeed harmonic in B_i. Moreover, properties a) and b) of the Green's function imply

$$\lim_{B_i \ni x \to x_0 \in S_1} u(x)=f^{(1)}(x_0).$$

In order to verify the second boundary condition, we differentiate along the normal and pass to the limit for $B_i \ni x \to x_0 \in S_2$; then

$$\lim_{B_i \ni x \to x_0 \in S_2} \frac{\partial u}{\partial n}=\frac{1}{2\pi}\lim\left(\frac{\partial}{\partial n_x}\int_{S_2} \varphi(y)\frac{\partial G}{\partial n_y}\, dS_y\right)+\frac{1}{2}f^{(2)}(x_0)+$$
$$+\frac{1}{2\pi}\int_{S_2} f^{(2)}(y)\frac{\partial}{\partial n_{x_0}}G(x_0, y)\, dS_y-\lim\left(\frac{\partial}{\partial n_x}\int_{S_1} f^{(1)}(y)\frac{\partial G}{\partial n}\, dS\right)$$

But $\varphi(y)$ was constructed so that

$$0=\frac{1}{2\pi}\lim_{B_a \ni x \to x_0 \in S_2}\left(\frac{\partial}{\partial n_x}\int_{S_2} \varphi(y)\frac{\partial G}{\partial n_y}\, dS_y\right)-\frac{1}{2}f^{(2)}(x_0)+$$
$$+\frac{1}{2\pi}\int_{S_2} f^{(2)}(y)\frac{\partial}{\partial n_{x_0}}G(x_0, y)\, dS_y-\lim_{B_a \ni x \to x_0 \in S_2}\left(\frac{\partial}{\partial n_x}\int_{S_1} f^{(1)}\frac{\partial G}{\partial n}\, dS\right).$$

Consequently

$$\lim_{B_i \ni x \to x_0 \in S_2} \frac{\partial u}{\partial n}=f^{(2)}(x_0).$$

This proves the last statement, and completes the proof of the existence theorem for the considered mixed problem.

Let us turn to the question of approximate solution. We draw a line S' in B_a, as shown on the figure, and fix on it arbitrarily an everywhere dense sequence of points x_k. We now show that

The denumerable set of functions $\left\{\frac{\partial}{\partial n_y}G(x_k, y)\right\}$ *is linearly independent and closed in the space of the functions continuous on* S_2 *and bounded there, the end-points included.*

To prove the first part, we assume that for all $y \in S_2$

$$\sum_{r=1}^{N} C_{k_r}\frac{\partial}{\partial n_y}G(x_{k_r}, y)=0,$$

where at least one of the constants C_{k_r} $(r=1, 2, \ldots, N)$ is not zero. Consider the function

$$v(x)=\sum_{r=1}^{N} C_{k_r}G(x_{k_r}, x).$$

It is easily verified that $v(x)$ is harmonic in B_i, and satisfies all the conditions of the uniqueness theorem. We conclude from the continuity of $v(x)$ together with all its derivatives on S_2, that $v(x)$ also vanishes beyond B_i, in particular in the domain $(B'-B_i)$ between the curves S_2 and S'. Letting x

approach sufficiently close to x_{k_i}, the absolute value of the term $C_{k_i}G(x_{k_i}, x)$ may be made as large as desired while all other terms remain bounded and cannot cancel out. This contradiction proves the linear independence. To prove that the set is closed, we show that the conditions

$$\int_{S_2} \alpha(y) \frac{\partial}{\partial n_y} G(x_k, y)\, dS_y = 0 \qquad (k = 1, 2, 3, 4, \ldots, x_k \in S'),$$

where $\alpha(y)$ is an arbitrary function that is continuous and bounded on all of S_2, imply that $\alpha(y) \equiv 0$. Since almost everywhere on S'

$$W(x_k) = \int_{S_2} \alpha(y) \frac{\partial}{\partial n_y} G(x_k, y)\, dS_y = 0,$$

the function

$$W(x) = \int_{S_2} \alpha(y) \frac{\partial}{\partial n_y} G(x, y)\, dS_y,$$

is continuous on S', and vanishes there

$$W(x) = 0, \quad x \in S'.$$

On the other hand, it follows from property a) of Green's function that $W(x) = 0$, $x \in S_3$, and since $W(x)$ satisfies the uniqueness theorem (behavior in the neighborhood of points A and B, and vanishing at all other points of the boundary) in the domain bounded by the closed curve $S' + S_3 = AFBEA$, then $W(x) = 0$ within the considered domain. It follows by continuity, as above, that $W(x) = 0$ in the domain $(B' - B_i)$ between S' and S_2. By the Lyapunov-Tauber theorem

$$\lim_{B_i \ni x \to x_0 \in S_2} \frac{\partial}{\partial n} W(x) = 0$$

and by property a) of the Green's function

$$\lim_{B_i \ni x \to x_0 \in S_1} W(x) = 0.$$

Applying again Kartsivadze's theorem in B_i, we get $W(x) = 0$, $x \in B_i$, and $\alpha(y) \equiv 0$, which completes the proof. Making use of the linear independence of the set $\left\{ \frac{\partial}{\partial n_y} G(x_k, y) \right\}$ we replace it by the orthonormalized (equivalent) set

$$\varphi_k(y) = \sum_{s=1}^{k} A_{k,s} \frac{\partial}{\partial n_y} G(x_s, y).$$

Now, exactly as in the preceding sections, we derive from the equation

$$\int_{S_2} \varphi(y) \frac{\partial G}{\partial n_y} dS_y = -F(x)$$

the Fourier coefficients

$$\Phi_k = \int_{S_2} \varphi(y) \varphi_k(y)\, dS = -\sum_{s=1}^{k} A_{k,s} F(x_s)$$

and write

$$\varphi^{(N)}(y) = \sum_{k=1}^{N} \Phi_k \varphi_k(y)$$

and

$$u^{(N)}(x) = \frac{1}{2\pi} \int_{S_2} \frac{\partial G(x, y)}{\partial n_y} \sum_{k=1}^{N} \Phi_k \varphi_k(y)\, dS_y + \frac{1}{2\pi} F(x), \quad x \in B_i.$$

Applying Schwarz's inequality, as before, we verify that

$$\lim_{N\to\infty} u^{(N)}(x) = u(x).$$

Another approach to mixed problems is outlined in §§ 32–37.

§ 28. Application of the method of generalized Fourier series to problems of the theory of elasticity. Solution of Problem (D_i) for a simply-connected domain

The solution of Problem (D_i), according to (X, 2) is given by the solution of the functional equations (10.19_1) and (10.19_2). For the plane problem these equations become*

$$u(x) = \frac{1}{2\pi}\int_S \Gamma(x, y)\varphi(y)\,dS_y - \frac{1}{2\pi}\int_S \Gamma_{\mathrm{I}}(x, y) f(y)\,dS_y, \quad x \in B_i, \tag{10.135_1}$$

$$0 = \frac{1}{2\pi}\int_S \Gamma(x, y)\varphi(y)\,dS_y - \frac{1}{2\pi}\int_S \Gamma_{\mathrm{I}}(x, y) f(y)\,dS_y, \quad x \in B_a\,, \tag{10.135_2}$$

where

$$\Gamma(x, y) = \{\Gamma^{(1)}(x, y), \Gamma^{(2)}(x, y)\} = \left\| \begin{matrix} n\ln r(x, y) - m\left(\frac{\partial r}{\partial \xi_1}\right)^2 & -m\frac{\partial r}{\partial \xi_1}\frac{\partial r}{\partial \xi_2} \\ -m\frac{\partial r}{\partial \xi_1}\frac{\partial r}{\partial \xi_2} & n\ln r(x, y) - m\left(\frac{\partial r}{\partial \xi_2}\right)^2 \end{matrix} \right\|,$$

(ξ_1, ξ_2) are the coordinates of point x, (η_1, η_2) of point y;

$$m = \frac{\lambda+\mu}{2\mu(\lambda+2\mu)}, \quad n = \frac{\lambda+3\mu}{2\mu(\lambda+2\mu)}$$

and

$$\Gamma_{\mathrm{I}}(x, y) = \{\Gamma_{\mathrm{I}}^{(1)}(x, y), \Gamma_{\mathrm{I}}^{(2)}(x, y)\} =$$

$$= \left\| \begin{matrix} a\frac{\partial}{\partial n_y}\ln r(x, y) + 2b\left(\frac{\partial r}{\partial \eta_1}\right)^2\frac{\partial}{\partial n_y}\ln r, & a\frac{\partial}{\partial s_y}\ln r + 2b\frac{\partial r}{\partial \eta_1}\frac{\partial r}{\partial \eta_2}\frac{\partial}{\partial n_y}\ln r \\ -a\frac{\partial}{\partial s_y}\ln r + 2b\frac{\partial r}{\partial \eta_1}\frac{\partial r}{\partial \eta_2}\frac{\partial}{\partial n_y}\ln r, & a\frac{\partial}{\partial n_y}\ln r + 2b\left(\frac{\partial r}{\partial \eta_2}\right)^2\frac{\partial}{\partial n_y}\ln r \end{matrix} \right\|,$$

$$a = \frac{\mu}{\lambda+2\mu}, \quad b = \frac{\lambda+\mu}{\lambda+2\mu},$$

$$\frac{\partial}{\partial n_y} = \frac{\partial}{\partial \eta_1}\cos(n_y, i_1) + \frac{\partial}{\partial \eta_2}\cos(n_y, i_2),$$

$$\frac{\partial}{\partial s_y} = \frac{\partial}{\partial \eta_2}\cos(n_y, i_1) - \frac{\partial}{\partial \eta_1}\cos(n_y, i_2),$$

i_1, i_2 are unit vectors along the axes.

All other notations are unaltered.

Theorem. *The set of vector-functions* $\{\Gamma^{(i)}(x_k, y)\}$ $(i = 1, 2;\ k = 1, 2, 3, \ldots)$, *where the set of points* x_k *is denumerable and everywhere dense on* S_1, *is linearly independent and complete in the space* L_2 *of square-integrable vector-functions defined on* S.

This theorem states that for any vector-function $\gamma(y) \in L_2$, $\int_S (\gamma\cdot\gamma)\,dS_y < \infty$,

* Here we restrict ourselves to the plane problem. All the arguments extend to the three-dimensional problem without any modifications (some points are even simplified).

Henceforward we omit in the treatment of static problems the 0 symbol above matrices and vectors, whenever this cannot cause any misunderstanding.

given on S, and any $\varepsilon > 0$, there exists a number N_0 and a set of coefficients $b_{l,k}$ $(l=1, 2;\ k=1, 2, 3, \ldots)$, such that for any $N > N_0$

$$\left\{ \int_S \left[\gamma(y) - \sum_{k=1}^{N} b_{l,k}\omega_{lk}(y) \right]^2 dS_y \right\}^{1/2} < \varepsilon,$$

where

$$\Gamma^{(l)}(x_k, y) = \omega_{l,k}(y) \qquad (l=1, 2;\ k=1, 2, 3, \ldots).$$

Let us assume that the set $\{\omega_{l,k}(y)\}$ is linearly dependent. Then there exist constants $C_{l,k}$ $(l=1, 2;\ k=1, 2, 3, \ldots, n)$, among which at least one $C_{l,r}$, $r \leqslant n$, is not zero, such that $\sum_{l=1}^{2}\sum_{s=1}^{n} C_{ls}\omega_{l,k_s}(y) \equiv 0$ for all $y \in S$ and at least one n. But then the solution of the equations of elasticity which is regular in B_l

$$v(x) = \sum_{l=1}^{2}\sum_{s=1}^{n} C_{l,s}\omega_{l,k_s}(x)$$

vanishes identically in B_l. It follows from the continuity of $v(x)$ and all its derivatives that $v(x) \equiv 0$, in particular in $B - B_l$. When x approaches x_{k_r} from $(B - B_l)$ sufficiently closely, we note that the absolute values of the projections on the coordinate axes

$$v_1(x) = \sum_{s=1}^{n} \{C_{1,s}(\omega_{1,k_s}(x))_1 + C_{2,s}(\omega_{2,k_s}(y))_1\},$$

$$v_2(x) = \sum_{s=1}^{n} \{C_{1,s}(\omega_{1,k_s}(y))_2 + C_{2,s}(\omega_{2,k_s}(y))_2\},$$

and therefore of the terms

$$C_{1,r}(\omega_{1,k_r}(x))_1 \text{ and } C_{2,r}(\omega_{2,k_r}(y))_2,$$

increase boundlessly while the other terms remain bounded. This contradicts the above demonstrated vanishing of $v(x)$ in $(B - B_l)$, and proves the linear independence of the set $\{\omega_{l,k}(y)\}$ $(l=1, 2;\ k=1, 2, 3, \ldots)$.

To prove that this set is closed in L_2, it is sufficient, by the same arguments as in § 21, to prove that it is closed in $C_{L_2}(S)$. Let $\alpha(y)$ be an arbitrary continuous vector-function on S, and let

$$\int_S (\alpha \cdot \omega_{l,k})\, dS = 0 \qquad (l=1, 2;\ k=1, 2, 3, \ldots).$$

We will show that $\alpha(y) \equiv 0$, $y \in S$. Consider the elastic single-layer potential

$$V(x) = \int_S \alpha(y)\Gamma(x, y)\, dS_y.$$

The components of V are

$$V_l(x_k) = \int_S \left[\alpha_1(y)\Gamma_1^{(l)}(x_k, y) + \alpha_2(y)\Gamma_2^{(l)}(x_k, y)\right] dS_y =$$

$$= \int_S (\alpha(y), \omega_{l,k}(y))\, dS_y = 0 \qquad (l=1, 2),$$

almost everywhere on S_1. In virtue of the continuity of $V(x)$ on S_1, $V(x) \equiv 0$, $x \in S_1$. Let us now show that the single-layer potential $V(x)$ vanishes at infinity. As we know (cf. X, 3) it is sufficient for this to show that

$$\int \alpha(y)\, dS_y = 0.$$

This condition is in our case a consequence of the conditions of orthogonality to the set $\{\omega_{l,k}(y)\}$, imposed above on $\alpha(y)$. To show this we introduce a new single-layer potential

$$v(y)=\int_{S_1}\psi(x)\Gamma(x, y)\,dS_x$$

with a density $\psi(y)$ such that

$$\lim_{B\ni y\to x_0\in S_1} Tv(y)=0.$$

This, as we know from § 3, leads to an integral (homogeneous and singular) equation which admits three linearily independent solutions (the number of linearly independent solutions in the three-dimensional case is six), and the corresponding single-layer potentials represent rigid displacements in B^*. In particular, we may choose these solutions so that the two rigid displacements $E_1(1, 0)$ and $E_2(0, 1)$ are expressed by means of the single-layer potentials

$$E_1=\int_{S_1}\psi^{(1)}(x)\Gamma(x, y)\,dS_x, \quad E_2=\int_{S_1}\psi^{(2)}(x)\Gamma(x, y)\,dS_x, \qquad y\in B.$$

We replace the integrals on the right-hand sides of these equalities by any quadrature formula, taking the basic points at x_k on S_1; then

$$E_1=\sum_{k=1}^{\infty}a_k\Gamma(x_k, y), \quad E_2=\sum_{k=1}^{\infty}b_k\Gamma(x_k, y),$$

where a_k and b_k are constant vectors determined by the formulas used, and the series converge uniformly. On the other hand, we have

$$V(x_k)=\int_S\alpha(y)\Gamma(x_k, y)\,dS_y=0 \qquad (k=1, 2, 3, \ldots)$$

Multiplying the k-th equality by a_k and adding the results together,

$$\sum_{k=1}^{\infty}\int_S\alpha(y)\,a_k\Gamma(x_k, y)\,dS_y=0.$$

We next multiply the k-th equality by b_k, add the results together and obtain

$$\sum_{k=1}^{\infty}\int_S\alpha(y)\,b_k\Gamma(x_k, y)\,dS_y=0.$$

In virtue of the uniform convergence these relations may be written

$$\int_S\alpha(y)\sum_{k=1}^{\infty}a_k\Gamma(x_k, y)\,dS_y=\int_S\alpha(y)\sum_{k=1}^{\infty}b_k\Gamma(x_k, y)\,dS_y=0,$$

or, in view of the aforesaid,

$$\int_S(\alpha, E_1)\,dS=\int_S(\alpha, E_2)\,dS=0,$$

and consequently,

$$\int_S\alpha(y)\,dS=0,$$

which is the required property of $\alpha(y)$. The last condition ensures, as we know, the vanishing of the plane elastic single-layer potential at infinity,

* These may be assumed different from zero in view of the characteristics of S_1.

and together with the identity

$$V(x) \equiv 0, \quad x \in S_1,$$

which was verified before, gives on applying the uniqueness theorem

$$V(x) \equiv 0, \quad x \in B_a - B.$$

(Note that the three-dimensional problem is simpler here, since the three-dimensional single-layer potential automatically vanishes at infinity and the last step may be omitted.) It follows from the condition $V(x) \equiv 0,\ x \in B_a - B$, on account of the continuity of $V(x)$ and all its derivatives in the neighborhood of S, that

$$V(x) \equiv 0, \quad x \in B_a.$$

This in turn implies by the continuity of the single-layer potential on the "loaded" curve and in virtue of the uniqueness of solution of problem D_i, that $V(x) \equiv 0,\ x \in B_i$, and finally, $\alpha(y) \equiv 0,\ y \in S$. Being closed in $C_{L_1}(S)$ implies completeness in $L_2(S)$ (cf. § 21), and the proof of theorem is completed.

We introduce some new notations

$$\omega_{1,k}(y) = \psi^{(2k-1)}(y), \quad \omega_{2,k}(y) = \psi^{(2k)}(y).$$

We replace the set $\{\psi^{(i)}(y)\}$ by the equivalent set $\{\varphi^{(i)}_{(y)}\}$, obtained from the first by means of the orthonormalization process,

$$\varphi^{(i)}(y) = \frac{1}{|\chi^{(i)}(y)|} \chi^{(i)}(y),$$

where

$$\chi^{(1)}(y) = \psi^{(1)}(y), \quad \chi^{(2)}(y) = \psi^{(2)}(y) - (\psi^2 \cdot \varphi^{(1)})\, \varphi^{(1)}(y),$$

$$\chi^{(3)}(y) = \psi^{(3)}(y) - (\psi^{(3)} \cdot \varphi^{(1)})\, \varphi^{(1)}(y) - (\psi^{(3)} \cdot \varphi^{(2)})\, \varphi^{(2)}(y)$$

$$\cdots\cdots\cdots\cdots\cdots\cdots$$

(remember that $(a \cdot b)$ is the scalar product of the vectors a and b, and $|a|$ the length of the vector a). We get from Schwarz's formulas

$$\varphi^{(s)}(y) = \sum_{k=1}^{s} A_{sk} \psi^{(k)}(y) \qquad (s = 1,\ 2,\ 3,\ 4,\ \ldots),$$

where A_{sk} are given constants. The Fourier coefficients of the unknown vector-function $\varphi(y)$

$$\Phi_s = \int_S (\varphi,\ \varphi^{(s)})\, dS_y$$

may be derived from the functional equation (10.135_2), which we now write as

$$\int_S \Gamma(x,\ y)\, \varphi(y)\, dS_y = F(x), \quad x \in B_a, \qquad (10.135_2)$$

where

$$F(x) = \int_S \Gamma_1(x,\ y) f(y)\, dS_y.$$

Assigning the values $x_1,\ x_2,\ x_3,\ \ldots,\ x_i$, to the variable x, we rewrite (10.135_2) in component form

$$\int_S \{[\varphi_1(y)\, \psi_1^{(1)}(y) + \varphi_2(y)\, \psi_2^{(1)}(y)]\, i_1 + [\varphi_1(y)\, \psi_1^{(2)}(y) + \varphi_2(y)\, \psi_2^{(2)}(y)]\, i_2\}\, dS_y = F(x_1),$$

$$\int_S \{[\varphi_1(y)\, \psi_1^{(3)}(y) + \varphi_2(y)\, \psi_2^{(3)}(y)]\, i_1 + [\varphi_1(y)\, \psi_1^{(4)}(y) + \varphi_2(y)\, \psi_2^{(4)}(y)]\, i_2\}\, dS_y = F(x_2),$$

$$\cdots\cdots\cdots\cdots\cdots\cdots\cdots\cdots\cdots$$

$$\int_S \{[\varphi_1(y)\psi_1^{(2i-1)}(y)+\varphi_2(y)\psi_2^{(2i-1)}(y)]\, i_1+[\varphi_1(y)\psi_1^{(2i)}(y)+\varphi_2(y)\psi_2^{(2i)}(y)]\, i_2\}\, dS_y=F(x_i).$$

In order to obtain the s-th Fourier coefficient, where $s=2l-1$ or $s=2l$, we multiply the first equality by the vector $A_{s,1}=A_{s,1}i_1+A_{s,2}i_2$, the second by $A_{s,2}=A_{s,3}i_1+A_{s,4}i_2$, etc., the l-th equality by $A_{s,s}=A_{s,s}i_1$ for even s and by $A_{ss}=A_{s-1,s}i_1+A_{s,s}i_2$ for odd s. Adding all the l equalities together and in view of the meaning of $\varphi^{(s)}(y)$, we obtain

$$\int_S \left[\varphi_1(y)\sum_{k=1}^{s} A_{s,k}\psi_1^{(k)}(y)+\varphi_2(y)\sum_{k=1}^{s} A_{s,k}\psi_2^{(k)}(y)\right] dS_y=$$

$$=\int_S (\varphi(y), \varphi^{(s)}(y))\, dS_y=\Phi_s=\sum_{k=1}^{l}(A_{s,k}, F(x_k)).$$

Thus, the Fourier expansion of $\varphi(y)$, which converges to it in the mean, has the form

$$\sum_{s=1}^{\infty}\sum_{k=1}^{l}(A_{s,k}, F(x_k))\,\varphi^{(s)}(y) \qquad l=\left[\frac{s+1}{2}\right],$$

where $\left[\frac{s+1}{2}\right]$ stands for the integral part of $\frac{s+1}{2}$. Let us write

$$u^{(N)}(x)=\frac{1}{2\pi}\int_S\left(\sum_{s=1}^{N}\Phi_s\varphi^{(s)}(y)\right)\Gamma(x, y)\, dS_y-\frac{1}{2\pi}F(x), \qquad x\in B_i.$$

Evidently, $u^{(N)}(x)$ is a solution of the equations of elasticity which is regular in B_i, and as $N\to\infty$ it tends to the exact solution of the considered problem. Indeed, forming the difference $u(x)-u^{(N)}(x)$, $x\in B_i$, we have

$$|u_j(x)-u_j^{(N)}(x)|\leqslant\frac{1}{2\pi}\int_S\left|\varphi_1(y)-\sum_{s=1}^{N}\Phi_s\varphi_1^{(s)}(y)\right|\left|\Gamma_1^{(j)}(x, y)\right| dS_y+$$

$$+\frac{1}{2\pi}\int_S\left|\varphi_2(y)-\sum_{s=1}^{N}\Phi_s\varphi_2^{(s)}(y)\right|\left|\Gamma_2^{(j)}(x, y)\right| dS_y \qquad (j=1, 2).$$

Applying Schwarz's inequality,

$$|u_j(x)-u_j^{(N)}(x)|\leqslant$$

$$\leqslant\frac{1}{2\pi}\sqrt{\int_S\left(\varphi_1(y)-\sum_{s=1}^{N}\Phi_s\varphi_1^{(s)}(y)\right)^2 dS_y\int_S|\Gamma_1^{(j)}(x, y)|^2\, dS_y}+$$

$$+\frac{1}{2\pi}\sqrt{\int_S\left(\varphi_2(y)-\sum_{s=1}^{N}\Phi_s\varphi_2^{(s)}(y)\right)^2 dS_y\int_S|\Gamma_2^{(j)}(x, y)|^2\, dS_y}.$$

$$(j=1, 2),$$

in virtue of the convergence in the mean, established above, this completes the proof. We finally have

$$u(x)=\frac{1}{2\pi}\lim_{N\to\infty}\int_S\left(\sum_{s=1}^{N}\Phi_s\varphi^{(s)}(y)\right)\Gamma(x, y)\, dS_y-\frac{1}{2\pi}F(x), \qquad x\in B_i.$$

Note that since the (first) Green's tensor, as shown in (VI, 7) exists for problem D_i, the solution may also be represented by the uniformly convergent series

$$u(x)=\sum_{k=1}^{\infty}f_k\varphi^{(k)}(x), \qquad x\in B_i,$$

where f_k are the Fourier coefficients of the given $f(y)$, $y\in S$, with respect to the complete set $\{\varphi^{(s)}(y)\}$. (Cf. § 38; 2°).

§ 29. Solution of the first boundary-value problem for the external domain

We consider here the three-dimensional case. The functional equations (cf. X, 4) are of the form

$$u(x)=\frac{1}{4\pi}\int_S \Gamma_{\mathrm{I}}(x, y) f(y)\, dS_y+\frac{1}{4\pi}\int_S \Gamma(x, y) \varphi(y)\, dS_y, \qquad x \in B_a;$$

$$0=\frac{1}{4\pi}\int_S \Gamma_{\mathrm{I}}(x, y) f(y)\, dS_y+\frac{1}{4\pi}\int_S \Gamma(x, y) \varphi(y)\, dS_y, \qquad x \in B_i.$$

where (cf. I, 3–4)

$$\Gamma(x, y)=\left\|\Gamma_k^{(i)}(x, y)\right\|, \quad \Gamma_{\mathrm{I}}(x, y)=\left\|\Gamma_{\mathrm{I}, k}^{(i)}\right\| \quad (i, k=1, 2, 3);$$

$$\Gamma_k^{(i)}(x, y)=\frac{1}{2\mu(\lambda+2\mu)}\left[(\lambda+\mu) \frac{\partial r}{\partial \xi_i} \frac{\partial r}{\partial \xi_k}+(\lambda+3\mu) \delta_{ik}\right] \frac{1}{r(x, y)},$$

$$\Gamma_{\mathrm{I}, k}^{(i)}(x, y)=2\mu \frac{\partial \Gamma_k^{(i)}}{\partial n_y}+\frac{\lambda}{\lambda+2\mu} \cos(n_y, i_k) \frac{\partial}{\partial \eta_i} \frac{1}{r(xy)}+$$
$$+\cos(n_y, i_i) \frac{\partial}{\partial \eta_k} \frac{1}{r(xy)}-\delta_{ik} \frac{\partial}{\partial n_y} \frac{1}{r(xy)},$$

$x \equiv (\xi_1, \xi_2, \xi_3)$, $y \equiv (\eta_1, \eta_2, \eta_3)$, i_1, i_2, i_3 — unit vectors along the axes,

$$\delta_{ik}=\begin{matrix} 1, & i=k, \\ 0, & i \neq k \end{matrix} \qquad (i, k=1, 2, 3).$$

This problem is solved by the method of generalized series much like the internal problem considered above. The only difference is that the auxiliary surface must now lie *within* B_i. This gives rise to the following minor modifications. The linear independence of the set

$$\Gamma^{(i)}(x_k, y)=\omega_{i, k}(y) \qquad x_k \in S_1, \ (i=1, 2, 3; k=1, 2, 3, 4, \ldots),$$

where the points lie in B_i, is proved by assuming the opposite. Let the $\omega_{i,k}(y)$ be linearly dependent. Then there exist constants $C_{i,k}$ $(i=1, 2, 3; k=1, 2, 3, 4, \ldots)$, of which at least one, say one of $C_{i,r}$, $r \leqslant n$, is not zero, such that

$$\sum_{i=1}^{3} \sum_{s=1}^{n} C_{is} \omega_{i, k_s}(y) \equiv 0$$

holds identically for all $y \in S$ and for at least one n. But in this case the solution of the equations of elasticity

$$v(x)=\sum_{i=1}^{3} \sum_{s=1}^{n} C_{i, s} \omega_{i, k_s}(x)$$

which is regular in B_a vanishes there throughout. Since it is continuous across S, as are all its derivatives, it follows that $v(x)$ vanishes also in (B_i-B). By letting x of (B_i-B) approach x_{k_r} on S_1, the terms $C_{1,r}(\omega_{1,k_r}(x))_1$ and $C_{2,r}(\omega_{2,k_r}(x))_2$ in the expressions for the projections $v_1(x)$ and $v_2(x)$ can be made as large as desired while all the other terms remain bounded. This contradiction proves the linear independence of $\{\omega_{i,s}(y)\}$. The completeness is also easily shown. Let $\alpha(y)$ be an arbitrary continuous vector-function on S, and let

$$\int_S (\alpha(y), \omega_{i, s}(y))\, dS_y=0 \qquad (i=1, 2, 3; s=1, 2, 3, 4, \ldots).$$

We will show that $\alpha(y) \equiv 0$. Consider the single-layer potential

$$V(x)=\int_S \alpha(y) \Gamma(x, y)\, dS_y.$$

By assumption

$$V(x_k)=0 \quad (x_k \in S_1,\ k=1,\ 2,\ 3,\ 4,\ \ldots),$$

and we know that these hold almost everywhere on S_1. Thus

$$V(x)=0, \quad x \in S_1,$$

and by the uniqueness theorem for the first internal homogeneous problem,

$$V(x)=0, \quad x \in B.$$

From the continuity across S_1 of $V(x)$ and its derivatives, $V(x)=0,\ x \in B_i$, and since a single-layer potential is continuous at the loaded surface and vanishes at infinity, $V(x)=0,\ x \in B_a$. Forming the difference between the inner and outer limits at S of the T-operation applied to the single-layer potential $V(x)$, we obtain $\alpha(y)\equiv 0,\ y \in S$, which proves the completeness in $L_2(S)$. The remaining arguments coincide with those of the last section, and if the old notations are retained we get the following final result

$$u(x)=\frac{1}{4\pi}\lim_{N\to\infty}\int_S\left(\sum_{k=1}^{N}\Phi_k\varphi^{(k)}(y)\right)\Gamma(x,\ y)\,dS_y+$$
$$+\frac{1}{4\pi}\int_S\Gamma_1(x,\ y)f(y)\,dS_y, \quad x \in B_a.$$

§ 30. Solution of Problem (D_i) for a multiply-connected domain

The form of the multiply-connected domain and all the notations are those of § 23. We will now prove the following theorem:—

The set $\{\omega_{i,k}(y)\}$ *is linearly independent and closed in the space* $C^h_{L_2}(S)$.

Assuming linear dependence, there exists some finite linear subset of $\{\omega_{i,k}(y)\}$ which represents in B_i a regular solution of the equations of elasticity and therefore vanishes everywhere in B_i. From the continuity across S of the solution and its derivatives it follows that this solution vanishes also outside B_i, in particular, in the domain between the surfaces S_0 and S_0', and S_k and S_k' $(k=1,\ 2,\ 3,\ \ldots,\ m)$. In the same way as in the last two sections we reach a contradiction, which implies the linear dependence of $\{\omega_{i,k}(y)\}$. Let us prove that any vector function continuous at S in the sense of belonging to class H, which satisfies the conditions

$$\int_S \alpha(y)\,\omega_{i,k}(y)\,dS_y=0 \qquad (i=1,\ 2,\ 3;\ k=1,\ 2,\ 3,\ 4,\ \ldots),$$

vanishes identically. Consider the single-layer potential

$$V(x)=\int_S \alpha(y)\Gamma(x,\ y)\,dS_y.$$

This potential vanishes by assumption almost everywhere on S', and because of its continuity

$$V(x)\equiv 0, \quad x \in S'.$$

Letting x vary in $B_a^{(0)}$ and noting that the potential vanishes at infinity, we conclude that it vanishes in $B_a^{(0)}$. Hence it follows from the continuity that

$$\lim_{B_i\ni x\to x_0\in S_0} V(x)=0.$$

Letting x vary now in $B_a^{(k)}$ $(k=1,\ 2,\ 3,\ \ldots,\ m)$, we note that $V(x)\equiv 0$ in the domains bounded by the surfaces S_k', since $V(x)$ is a regular solution of the equations of elasticity there and since $V(x)$ vanishes for $x \in S_k'$. Since it is continuous along with all its derivatives, $V(x) \equiv 0$, $x \in B_a^{(k)}$, and in view of the continuity of a single-layer potential

$$\lim_{B_i \ni x \to x_0 \in S_k} V(x) = 0 \quad (k = 1, 2, 3, \ldots, m).$$

But then $V(x) \equiv 0$, $x \in B_i$, and consequently, $\alpha(y) \equiv 0$, which completes the proof. All the remaining arguments remain unchanged, and if the solution exists, they lead to the following result: —

The solution of the first interior problem for a multiply-connected finite domain B_i is at any internal point represented by the limit

$$u(x) = \lim \left\{ \frac{1}{4\pi} \int_S \Gamma(x, y) \sum_{i=1}^{N} \Phi_i \varphi^{(i)}(y)\, dS_y \right\} - \\ - \frac{1}{4\pi} \int_S \Gamma_{\mathrm{I}}(x, y) f(y)\, dS_y, \quad x \in B_i,$$

and the partial sums give approximate solutions.

§ 31. Solution of the second internal problem for a simply-connected domain

Here B_i is a simply-connected domain bounded by the surface S. It is required to find a solution of the system of equations

$$\mu \Delta u(x) + (\lambda + \mu) \operatorname{grad} \operatorname{div} u(x) = 0,$$

satisfying the boundary condition

$$\lim_{B_i \ni x \to x_0 \in S} (\mathrm{T} u(x)) = f(x_0),$$

where $f(x_0)$ is a vector-function of class H, prescribed on the surface. This problem, as we know from (VI, 5) is solvable only if

$$\int_S f(y)\, dS_y = 0, \quad \int_S (f(y) \times r(y))\, dS_y = 0,$$

where $r(x)$ is the radius-vector of point x. The solution in this case (cf. § 3) is represented by the solution of the system of functional equations

$$u(x) = \frac{1}{4\pi} \int_S \Gamma_{\mathrm{I}}(x, y) \varphi(y)\, dS_y + \frac{1}{4\pi} F(x), \quad x \in B_i, \tag{10.136$_1$}$$

$$\int_S \Gamma_{\mathrm{I}}(x, y) \varphi(y)\, dS_y = -F(x), \quad x \in B_a, \tag{10.136$_2$}$$

where

$$F(x) = \int_S \Gamma(x, y) f(y)\, dS_y.$$

To facilitate the calculations which we will perform here in detail, we recall the form of the matrix

$$\Gamma_{\mathrm{I}}(x, y) = \begin{Vmatrix} \Gamma_{\mathrm{I},1}^{(1)} & \Gamma_{\mathrm{I},1}^{(2)} & \Gamma_{\mathrm{I},1}^{(3)} \\ \Gamma_{\mathrm{I},2}^{(1)} & \Gamma_{\mathrm{I},2}^{(2)} & \Gamma_{\mathrm{I},2}^{(3)} \\ \Gamma_{\mathrm{I},3}^{(1)} & \Gamma_{\mathrm{I},3}^{(2)} & \Gamma_{\mathrm{I},3}^{(3)} \end{Vmatrix} = \begin{Vmatrix} \mathrm{T}_1\Gamma^{(1)} & \mathrm{T}_2\Gamma^{(1)} & \mathrm{T}_3\Gamma^{(1)} \\ \mathrm{T}_1\Gamma^{(2)} & \mathrm{T}_2\Gamma^{(2)} & \mathrm{T}_3\Gamma^{(2)} \\ \mathrm{T}_1\Gamma^{(3)} & \mathrm{T}_2\Gamma^{(3)} & \mathrm{T}_3\Gamma^{(3)} \end{Vmatrix} = \{\Gamma_{\mathrm{I}}^{(1)}, \Gamma_{\mathrm{I}}^{(2)}, \Gamma_{\mathrm{I}}^{(3)}\}.$$

Equation (10.136_2) may be written

$$\int_S \sum_{k=1}^{3} (\Gamma_{I,(k)} \cdot \varphi) i_k dS_y = -F(x), \quad x \in B_a. \qquad (10.136_2^1)$$

where $\Gamma_{I(k)}(x, y)$ stands for the k-th row-vector of $\Gamma_I(x, y)$. The projections of this vector on the coordinate axes are obviously $\Gamma^l_{I,(k)}$ $(l=1, 2, 3)$; that is,

$$\Gamma^l_{I,(k)} = \Gamma^{(l)}_{I,k},$$

meaning that the projection of the k-th row-vector on the l-th axis equals the projection of the l-th column-vector on the k-th axis. We arbitrarily fix on the surface S_1 an everywhere dense sequence of points and consider the set of vectors

$$\nu_0(y), \ \nu_{k,s}(y) = \Gamma_{I,(k)}(x_s, y) \qquad (k=1, 2, 3; \ s=1, 2, 3, 4, 5, \ldots),$$

where $\nu_0(y)$ represents a rigid displacement, and $\nu_{k,s}(y)$ is the k-th row-vector of $\Gamma_I(x, y)$ at $x = x_s$. We shall now show that this set is linearly independent and closed in the space $C^h_{L_2}(S)$ of H-continuous vector functions defined on S.

To prove the first part, we assume the opposite. Then there exist constants C_0, $C_{1,s}$, $C_{2,s}$, $C_{3,s}$, different from zero, such that

$$-C_0\nu_0 + \sum_{k=1}^{3} \sum_{l=1}^{n} C_{k,s_l} \nu_{k,s_l}(y) = 0, \quad y \in S, \qquad (10.137)$$

at least for one finite n and for all $y \in S$. We introduce the vector function

$$v(x) = \sum_{k=1}^{3} \sum_{l=1}^{n} C_{k,s_l} \Gamma^{(k)}(x_{s_l}, x), \quad x_{s_l} \in S_1.$$

This vector is a regular solution of the equations of elasticity in B_l. Let us first show that $C_0 = 0$; indeed, otherwise we have from (10.137)

$$\mathrm{T}v(y) = C_0\nu_0, \quad y \in S.$$

Multiplying by dS, integrating over S and taking into account that

$$\int_S \mathrm{T}_y \Gamma^{(k)}(x_{s_l}, y) dS_y = 0, \quad x_{s_l} \in S_1 \in B_a.$$

we find that $C_0\nu_0|S| = 0$, where $|S|$ is the area of S. This contradiction shows that if (10.137) holds, it must have the form

$$\sum_{k=1}^{3} \sum_{l=1}^{n} C_{k,s_l} \nu_{k,s_l}(y) = 0, \quad y \in S.$$

But then by the uniqueness theorem for the second problem we have that within B_i

$$v(x) = \nu(x),$$

where $\nu(x)$ represents some rigid displacement. Consider the vector

$$V(x) = v(x) - \nu(x).$$

It vanishes in B_l, and because of its continuity together with all its derivatives across S it also vanishes beyond B_l, in particular in $(B - B_l)$. Projecting on the coordinate axes, we get

$$v_j(x) = \sum_{k=1}^{3} \sum_{l=1}^{n} C_{k,s_l} \Gamma^{(k)}_j(x_{s_l}, x) \qquad (j=1, 2, 3),$$

In view of the nature of the vectors $\Gamma^{(k)}(x_{s_i}, x)$, one of the terms that make up each projection, for example the terms

$$C_{1, s_r}\Gamma_1^{(1)}(x_{s_r}, x),\ C_{2, s_r}\Gamma_2^{(2)}(x_{s_r}, x),\ C_{3, s_r}\Gamma_3^{(3)}(x_{s_r}, x),$$

grow indefinitely in absolute value as the variable point x of $B-B_i$ approaches x_{s_r} on S_1, while all other terms remain bounded. Therefore, if at least one of the numbers C_{1, s_r}, C_{2, s_r}, C_{3, s_r} is not zero, we reach a contradiction which disproves (10.137). This proves the linear independence.

We have now to prove the closedness. Let $\alpha(y)$ be an arbitrary element of the space $C_{L_2}^h(S)$ and let

$$\int_S (\alpha(y)\cdot \nu_0(y))\,dS = \int_S (\alpha(y)\cdot \nu_{k, s}(y))\,dS = 0$$

$$(k=1,\ 2,\ 3;\ s=1,\ 2,\ 3,\ 4,\ 5,\ \ldots).$$

Then $\alpha(y)\equiv 0$; for, the assumption entails

$$\int_S \Gamma_{\text{I}}(x_s, y)\,\alpha(y)\,dS_y = \int_S \sum_{k=1}^{3} (\Gamma_{\text{I},(k)}(x_s, y)\cdot \alpha(y))\,i_k\,dS_y =$$

$$= \int_S \sum_{k=1}^{3} (\alpha(y)\cdot \nu_{k, s}(y))\,i_k\,dS_y = 0 \quad (s=1,\ 2,\ 3,\ 4,\ \ldots).$$

The vector

$$W(x) = \int_S \Gamma_{\text{I}}(x, y)\,\alpha(y)\,dS_y$$

thus vanishes almost everywhere on S_1 and is continuous there, so that $W(x)=0$ everywhere on S_1.

Now, $W(x)$ is an elastic double-layer potential, vanishing at infinity, for which the uniqueness theorem for the first exterior problem shows that

$$W(x)=0, \quad x\in(B_a-B).$$

Since $W(x)$ and all its derivatives are continuous across S_1,

$$W(x)=0, \quad x\in B_a.$$

This double-layer potential thus vanishes in the entire external domain B_a. It follows in view of (VI, 3) that the density function of this potential is a rigid displacement μ_0, i. e., $\alpha(y)=\mu_0(y)$. But the condition

$$\int_S (\alpha(y)\cdot \nu_0(y))\,dS = \int_S (\mu_0(y)\cdot \nu_0(y))\,dS = 0$$

implies in view of the arbitrariness of the rigid displacement $\nu^{(0)}(y)$ that

$$\mu_0(y) = \alpha(y) = 0.$$

This proves that the considered set is closed in $C_{L_2}^h(S)$. The completeness in L_2 is proved as in § 21. Let us introduce the notations

$$\nu_{1, s}(y) = \psi^{(3s-2)}(y), \quad \nu_{2, s}(y) = \psi^{(3s-1)}(y), \quad \nu_{3, s}(y) = \psi^{(3s)}(y).$$

The sequence $\{\psi^{(k)}(y)\}$ is obviously linearly independent. We use it to construct the orthonormalized sequence $\{\varphi^{(s)}(y)\}$

$$\varphi^{(s)}(y) = \sum_{k=1}^{s} B_{sk}\psi^{(k)}(y),$$

where B_{sk} are known constants. We add the normalized vector of rigid displacement $\varphi^{(0)}(y)$, and consider the sequence

$$\{\varphi^{(s)}(y)\} \qquad (s=0,\ 1,\ 2,\ 3,\ 4,\ \ldots).$$

This sequence is complete and orthonormal, for

$$\int_S \varphi^{(0)}(y)\Gamma_1(x,\ y)\,dS_y = \begin{matrix} 0, \ x \in B_a, \\ \text{const}\,\varphi^{(0)}(x) \quad x \in B_i, \end{matrix}$$

which shows that $\varphi^{(0)}(y)$ is orthogonal to all the others.

The functional equation (10.136_2) has a solution of class H (cf. § 3). Therefore

$$\lim_{N\to\infty} \int_S \left(\varphi(y) - \sum_{k=0}^{N} \Phi_k \varphi^{(k)}(y)\right)^2 dS = 0, \qquad (10.138)$$

where Φ_m is the Fourier coefficient of the solution expanded in the complete and orthonormal set $\{\varphi^{(s)}(y)\}$

$$\Phi_m = \int_S (\varphi(y) \cdot \varphi^{(m)}(y))\,dS \quad (m=0,\ 1,\ 2,\ \ldots).$$

These Fourier coefficients may be determined from (10.136_2). As we have seen, this equation is written for the points x_i on S_1 as

$$\int_S \sum_{k=1}^{3} (\Gamma_{1,(k)}(x_i,\ y) \cdot \varphi(y))\,i_k\,dS =$$

$$= \int_S \sum_{k=1}^{3} (\nu_{k,i}(y) \cdot \varphi(y))\,i_k\,dS = -F(x_i) \quad (i=1,\ 2,\ \ldots).$$

To obtain the m-th Fourier coefficient, we write the number m in one of the following possible forms $m=3s-2$, $m=3s-1$, $m=3s$. We multiply the first equation (i. e., that for which $i=1$) scalarly by $B_{m1} = B_{m1}i_1 + B_{m2}i_2 + B_{m3}i_3$, the second equation ($i=2$) by $B_{m2} = B_{m4}i_1 + B_{m5}i_2 + B_{m6}i_3$, etc., the s-th equation by

$$B_{ms} = \begin{cases} B_{m,m}i_1, & \text{if} \quad s = \dfrac{m+2}{3}, \\ B_{m,m-2}i_1 + B_{m,m-1}i_2, & \text{if} \quad s = \dfrac{m+1}{3}, \\ B_{m,m-2}i_1 + B_{m,m-1}i_2 + B_{m,m}i_3, & \text{if} \quad s = \dfrac{m}{3}. \end{cases}$$

Adding these scalar products together, we get

$$\int_S \sum_{k=1}^{3} [B_{m,k}(\nu_{k,1}\varphi) + B_{m,(k+3)}(\nu_{k,2}\cdot\varphi) + \ldots]\,dS_y =$$

$$= \int_S \left\{ \sum_{k=1}^{3} [(B_{m,k}\nu_{k,1} + B_{m,k+3}\nu_{k,2} + \ldots)\cdot\varphi] \right\} dS_y =$$

$$= \int_S \{[(B_{m1}\psi^{(1)}(y) + B_{m2}\psi^{(2)}(y) + B_{m3}\psi^{(3)}(y) +$$

$$+ B_{m4}\psi^{(4)}(y) + B_{m5}\psi^{(5)}(y) + B_{m6}\psi^{(6)}(y) +$$

$$\cdots\cdots\cdots\cdots\cdots\cdots$$

$$+ B_{mm-2}\psi^{(m-2)}(y + B_{mm-1}\psi^{(m-1)}(y) + B_{mm}\psi^{(m)}(y))] \cdot \varphi(y)\}\,dS_y =$$

$$= \int_S (\varphi^{(m)}(y) \cdot \varphi(y))\,dS_y = \Phi_m = -\sum_{i=1}^{s} B_{mi} \cdot F(x_i)).$$

Using these Fourier coefficients of $\varphi(y)$, we set up the vector function

$$u^{(N)}(x)=\frac{1}{4\pi}\int_S \Gamma_{\rm I}(x, y)\,\varphi_*^{(N)}(y)\,dS_y+\frac{1}{4\pi}F(x);$$

$$\varphi_*^{(N)}(y)=\sum_{s=0}^{N}\Phi_s\varphi^{(s)}(y), \qquad x\in B_i.$$

This is obviously a regular solution of the equations of elasticity in B_i. Further, it is readily verified that as N increases its value at the internal points of B_i approximate to the exact solution with any desired accuracy. We recall from § 3 that a solution does exist and is represented by (10.136_1).

Forming the projections on the coordinate axes of the difference

$$|u(x)-u^{(N)}(x)|,$$

we get

$$|u_j(x)-u_j^{(N)}(x)|\leqslant\frac{1}{4\pi}\left\{\left|\int_S \left|\Gamma^1_{\rm I\,(j)}(x, y)\right|\left[\varphi_1(y)-\sum_{s=0}^{N}\Phi_s\varphi_1^{(s)}(y)\right]dS_y\right|+\right.$$

$$+\int_S\left|\Gamma^2_{\rm I\,(j)}(x, y)\left[\varphi_2(y)-\sum_{s=0}^{N}\Phi_s\varphi_2^{(s)}(y)\right]\right|dS_y+$$

$$\left.+\int_S\left|\Gamma^3_{\rm I\,(j)}(x, y)\left[\varphi_3-\sum_{s=0}^{N}\Phi_s\varphi_3^{(s)}\right]\right|dS_y\right\}$$

applying Schwarz's inequality,

$$|u_j(x)-u_j^{(N)}|\leqslant\frac{1}{4\pi}\left\{\sqrt{\int_S\left(\varphi_1-\sum_{s=0}^{N}\Phi_s\varphi_1^{(s)}\right)^2 dS\int_S|\Gamma^1_{\rm I\,(j)}|^2\,dS}+\right.$$

$$+\sqrt{\int_S\left(\varphi_2-\sum_{s=1}^{N}\Phi_s\varphi_2^{(s)}\right)^2 dS\int_S|\Gamma^2_{\rm I\,(j)}|^2\,dS}+$$

$$\left.+\sqrt{\int_S\left(\varphi_3-\sum_{s=1}^{N}\Phi_s\varphi_3^{(s)}\right)^2 dS\int_S|\Gamma^3_{\rm I\,(j)}|^2\,dS}\right\}$$

and finally from (10.138)

$$\lim_{N\to\infty}u^{(N)}(x)=u(x).$$

Thus, if the solvability conditions set down in the beginning of this section are fulfilled, the second internal problem of elasticity has a solution represented by

$$u(x)=\frac{1}{4\pi}\lim_{N\to\infty}\int_S\Gamma_{\rm I}(x, y)\,\varphi_*^{(N)}(y)\,dS_y+4\pi F(x), \qquad x\in B_i.$$

The partial sums of the series on the right-hand side obviously give approximate solutions at the internal points of B_i. We further note that since $\varphi^{(0)}(y)$ is an arbitrary rigid displacement and

$$\int_S\Gamma_{\rm I}(x, y)\,\Phi_0\varphi^{(0)}(y)\,dS_y=\mathrm{const}\cdot\varphi^{(0)}(x), \qquad x\in B_i,$$

the obtained solution is determined to within an additive rigid displacement vector.

The theorem of (VI,7) about the completeness of the set $\{\nu_{k,s}(y)\}$ and the results relating to the properties of the second Green's tensor allow us to apply Picone's method (cf. § 21) and solve the problem in a somewhat different way. Let us see how this is done. We write the generalized Fourier series in the orthogonal system $\{\varphi^{(s)}(y)\}$ corresponding to the given boundary-value vector function $f(y)$

$$f(y) \approx \sum_{s=0}^{\infty} F_s \varphi^{(s)}(y), \tag{10.139}$$

where

$$F_s = \int_S (f(y) \cdot \varphi^{(s)}(y)) \, dS.$$

$\varphi^{(s)}(y)$ may obviously be represented as a linear combination of the $\psi^{(s)}(y)$, and the latter are expressed through $\nu_{k,s}(y)$. Substituting these expressions on the right-hand side of (10.139), we write the partial sum of the first N terms

$$v^{(N)}(y) = \sum_{k=1}^{3} \sum_{s=0}^{N} A_{s,k} \nu_{k,s}(y) \qquad (A_{s,k} \text{ are given constants.})$$

Consider the vector function

$$u^{(N)}(x) = \sum_{k=1}^{3} \sum_{s=0}^{N} A_{s,k} \Gamma^{(k)}(x_s, x), \qquad x \in B_i.$$

Evidently, $\lim\limits_{x \to y} \mathrm{T} u^{(N)}(x) = v^{(N)}(y)$; but $u^{(N)}(x)$ is a solution of the equations of elasticity which is regular in B_i, because it is made up of terms that each posses this property. Considering these terms as solutions of the equations of elasticity, which under a T-operation and passage to the inner limit on S are equal to $\mathrm{T}\Gamma^{(k)}(x_s, y)$, $y \in S$, we assume them to solve the corresponding partial second problems in B_i. Denoting by $H(x, y)$ the second Green's tensor for this domain, we may write down in view of (VI, 7)

$$\Gamma^{(k)}(x_s, x) = \frac{1}{4\pi} \int_S H(x, y) (\mathrm{T}_y \Gamma^{(k)}(x_s, y)) \, dS_y,$$

(apart from a rigid displacement vector) and consequently,

$$u^{(N)}(x) = \frac{1}{4\pi} \int_S H(x, y) \, v^{(N)}(y) \, dS_y.$$

On the other hand, if the solvability conditions are fulfilled, the exact solution of the problem (to within a rigid displacement) has the form

$$u(x) = -\frac{1}{4\pi} \int_S H(x, y) f(y) \, dS_y.$$

Therefore

$$|u(x) - u^{(N)}(x)| \leqslant \frac{1}{4\pi} \left| \int_S H(x, y) \left(f(y) - \sum_{s=0}^{N} F_s \varphi^{(s)}(y) \right) dS_y \right|.$$

As the series (10.139) converges in the mean and the integral

$$\int_S | H_j^{(k)}(x, y) |^2 \, dS_y$$

is bounded at any internal point of B_i, we have

$$u(x) = \lim_{N \to \infty} u^{(N)}(x).$$

The solution is obviously determined up to an additive rigid displacement. In connection with this method see further § 38, 2°.

We have now finished with the interior problem.

2109

The exterior problem is solved by the same method which was applied to the exterior Neumann problem in § 25. The similarity is complete and we shall not go any further into this problem, nor into the case of multiply-connected domains.

§ 32. Mixed (fourth) boundary-value problem for an isotropic elastic body

This section is devoted to the static plane mixed problem. We first prove the existence theorem, and then develop a method of approximate solution.

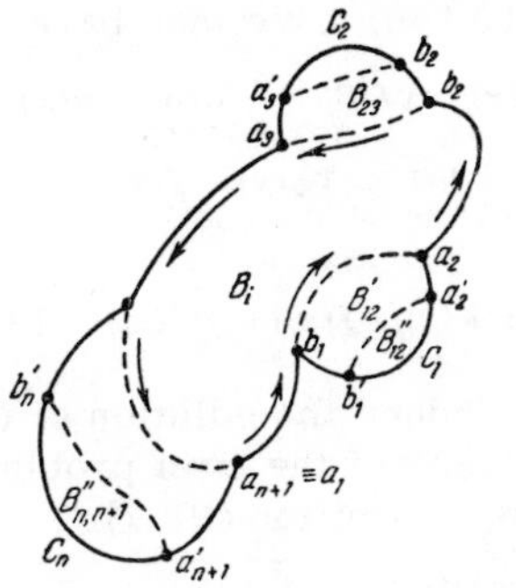

FIGURE 4

Let the body occupy the finite domain B_i bounded by a simple closed smooth contour S. We take on S the arcs $S'_k = a_k b_k$ $(k = 1, 2, 3, \ldots, n)$ (solid lines in Figure 4) which have no common end-points, and the arcs $S''_k = b_k a_{k+1} (k = 1, 2, \ldots, n) (a_{n+1} \equiv a_1)$ (broken lines), which complete the continuous arcs to make up the entire contour S. We shall refer to the set of arcs S'_k following each other in counter-clockwise succession as the index runs through $k = 1, 2, \ldots, n$ as the line S', and to the set of arcs $S''_k (k = 1, 2, 3, \ldots, n)$ as the line S''.

We wish to determine the state of elastic equilibrium of the body B_i from the conditions

$$\left.\begin{aligned} &\Delta^* u(x) = 0 \quad x \in B_i, \quad \lim_{B_i \ni x \to x_0 \in S'} u(x) = f^{(1)}(x_0), \\ &\lim_{B_i \ni x \to x_0 \in S''} \mathrm{T} u(x) = f^{(2)}(x_0), \end{aligned}\right\} \tag{10.140}$$

where $f^{(1)}(x_0)$ and $f^{(2)}(x_0)$ are sufficiently smooth vector functions, prescribed on S' and S'', respectively. We freely join the points b_k and a_{k+1} $(k = 1, 2, 3, \ldots \ldots, n)$ by (solid) lines $b_k c_k a_{k+1}$ $(a_{n+1} \equiv a_1)$ lying entirely outside B, and refer to the set of these arcs, taken in this order, as the line S'_1. We further draw the arcs (broken lines) $b'_k a'_{k+1}$, which have no points in common with S' and S'', and refer to the set of these arcs as S'_2; finally, the sequences of arcs $b'_k c_k a'_{k+1}$ is referred to as S'_3. The disconnected domain bounded by the lines S'' and S'_1 is denoted by B_a and referred to as the external domain; the extended domain $(\bar{B}_i + B_a)$ is denoted by B; the domain (part of B_a)

enclosed between the arcs $b_k a_{k+1}$ and $b'_k a'_{k+1}$ is denoted by $B'_{k,k+1}$, and the domain enclosed between the arcs $b'_k a'_{k+1}$ and $b'_k c_k a'_{k+1}$, by $B''_{k,k+1}$; the disconnected domain obtained by forming the union of the $B'_{k,k+1}$ $(k=1, 2, 3, \ldots, n)$ is denoted by B'_a, and the disconnected domain which is the union of the $B''_{k,k+1}$, by B''_a $(B_a = B'_a + B''_a)$.

The problem is more manageable when the $f^{(1)}(x_0)$ vanishes. The general case may be reduced to this one as follows. Let $\Phi(x)$ be a twice continuously differentiable vector function in B_i with continuous first derivatives at the contour, assuming the values $f^{(1)}(x_0)$ on S'. Let

$$v(x) = u(x) - \Phi(x), \tag{10.141}$$

where $u(x)$ is a solution of (10.140). We then have

$$\left.\begin{aligned} &\Delta^* v(x) = \rho(x), \quad x \in B_i, \quad \lim_{B_i \ni x \to x_0 \in S'} v(x) = 0, \\ &\lim_{B_i \ni x \to x_0 \in S''} \mathrm{T} v(x) = f(x_0), \end{aligned}\right\} \tag{10.142}$$

where

$$\rho(x) = -\Delta^* \Phi(x), \quad f(x_0) = f^{(2)}(x_0) - \mathrm{T}\Phi(x_0).$$

By solving (10.142), we can deduce the solution of (10.140) from (10.141). Let $G(x, y)$ be the Green's tensor of the first problem (first static Green's tensor) for the domain B. By definition (VI, 7)

$$G(x, y) = \Gamma(x, y) - \overset{0}{v}(x, y) \quad (x, y \in B),$$

where in our case of the plane (static) problem

$$\Gamma(x, y) = \left\| \begin{matrix} n \ln r(x, y) + m \dfrac{(x_1 - y_1)^2}{r^2} & m \dfrac{(x_1 - y_1)(x_2 - y_2)}{r^2(x, y)} \\ m \dfrac{(x_1 - y_1)(x_2 - y_2)}{r^2(x, y)} & n \ln r + m \dfrac{(x_2 - y_2)^2}{r^2} \end{matrix} \right\|,$$

(x_1, x_2) and (y_1, y_2) being the coordinates of points x and y in a Cartesian coordinate system, and

$$n = \frac{\lambda + 3\mu}{2\mu(\lambda + 2\mu)}, \quad m = \frac{\lambda + \mu}{2\mu(\lambda + 2\mu)}.$$

Let us recall that

$$\left.\begin{aligned} &\lim_{B \ni x \to x_0 \in S' + S'_1} G(x, y) = 0, \quad (G(x, y))^* = G(y, x), \\ &\Delta^* \int_B G(x, y) \rho(y)\, d\sigma_y = -2\pi\rho(x). \end{aligned}\right\} \tag{10.143}$$

The solution of (10.142) may be sought in the form

$$v(x) = \int_{S''} G(x, y) \varphi(y)\, dS_y - \frac{1}{2\pi} \int_{B_i} G(x, y) \rho(y)\, dy_1\, dy_2, \tag{10.144}$$

where $\varphi(y)$ is an unknown vector function of class H on S'', which admits logarithmic singularities at the end-points of S''. The first two conditions of the problem are fulfilled in view of (10.143), and the last one leads to the following relation for $\varphi(y)$

$$-\pi\varphi(x_0) + \int_{S''} (\mathrm{T}_{x_0} G(x_0, y)) \varphi(y)\, dS_y = f(x_0) + \frac{1}{2\pi} \int_{B_i} (\mathrm{T}_{x_0} G(x_0, y)) \rho(y)\, dy_1\, dy_2. \tag{10.145}$$

This relation amounts to a system of one-dimensional singular integral equation on the disjoint sectional contour. The solvability theory developed in Ch. V for systems of singular integral equations on a closed Lyapunov surface, may in the one-dimensional case be extended to the system (10.145) on a sectional Lyapunov curve, because of its particular character. There exists, however, a general theory of such equations developed by N. P. Vekua and presented in his book "Systems of singular integral equations" (Moscow, 1950).

Consider the associated equation with the homogeneous equation for (10.145)

$$-\pi\psi(x_0)+\int_{S''} G_l(x_0, y)\psi(y)\,dS_y=0. \tag{10.146}$$

$G_l(x_0, y)$ denotes here the matrix obtained from the matrix $(\mathbf{T}_x G(x, y))$ by interchanging rows and columns, as well as the points x and y. It may be shown easily /11/ that this equation may also be written in the form

$$-\pi\psi(x_0)+a\int_{S''} L(x_0, y)\psi(y)\,dS_y+\int_{S''} K_1(x_0, y)\psi(y)\,dS_y=0, \tag{10.146'}$$

where the matrix $L(x, y)$ is

$$L(x, y)=\begin{Vmatrix} 0 & -\frac{1}{r}\frac{dr}{dS_y} \\ \frac{1}{r}\frac{dr}{dS_y} & 0 \end{Vmatrix},$$

and $\frac{d}{dS_y}$ is the tangential derivative at y, $K_1(x_0, y)$ is a Fredholm kernel defined on S'', and

$$a=\frac{\mu}{\lambda+2\mu}. \tag{10.147}$$

If t is the arc-length parameter of the point y, and t_0 of x_0 on S'', then /24b/

$$t_0-t=re^{i\theta},$$

where

$$r=|t_0-t|,\quad \theta=\arg(t_0-t),$$

and, taking the logarithmic derivative with respect to t,

$$\frac{dr}{r}=\frac{dt}{t-t_0}-i\frac{d\theta}{dS_y}dS_y;$$

now since /24b/

$$\frac{d\theta}{dS}=-\frac{d}{dn}\ln r,$$

we finally get

$$\frac{dr}{r}=\frac{dt}{t-t_0}+i\frac{d}{dn}\ln r\,dS_y.$$

Equation (10.146') can now be written

$$-\pi\psi(t_0)+A\int_{S''}\frac{\psi(t)}{t-t_0}dt+\int_{S''} K_2(x_0, y)\psi(y)\,dS_y=0, \tag{10.146''}$$

where

$$A=\begin{Vmatrix} 0 & -a \\ a & 0 \end{Vmatrix}$$

and $K_2(x_0, y)$ is a Fredholm kernel. We introduce two new matrices, defined on the closed line S as

$$K(t_0, t)=\begin{cases} K_2(t_0, t), \\ 0, \end{cases}\quad A(t_0)=\begin{cases} A & (t_0\in S''), \\ 0 & (t_0\in S'). \end{cases}$$

These matrices admit at the points a_k and b_k discontinuities of the first kind.

Consider the following system of integral equations on the closed contour S:

$$-\psi(t_0)+\frac{A(t_0)\,i}{\pi i}\int_S \frac{\psi(t)}{t-t_0}\,dt+\frac{1}{\pi}\int_S K(t_0, t)\,\psi(t)\,dt=0. \qquad (10.148)$$

If this system has a solution of class H with at most logarithmic singularities at a_k and b_k $(k=1, 2, 3, \ldots, n)$, then the solution also satisfies equation (10.146"). As we mentioned before, the general theory of equations of the type (10.148), when the given elements are sufficiently smooth functions of the integration variables, allowing finite jumps at isolated points, had been developed by N. P. Vekua. Equation (10.148), the coefficients of which are piecewise constant functions, is a particular case of this type; accordingly we quote in the following section such results of the general theory of systems of one-dimensional singular integral equations as will be needed for our purpose.

§ 33. Some results of the theory of singular Cauchy-type integral equations with discontinuous coefficients

By a nonfundamental (removable) singularity we mean, as in Ch. V, a pole of order lower than one. If the function $\varphi(t)$ has at point a with arc parameter α a singularity such that the expression $(t-\alpha)^{\varepsilon}\varphi(t)$ belongs for any small positive ε to class H, we say that the singularity at the point a is logarithmic. We now denote the points a_k, b_k $(k=1, 2, \ldots, n)$ by $C_1, C_2, C_3, \ldots, C_q$. We divide these points, according to a certain rule which will be clarified on the example of equation (10.148), into two groups; the points of one group will be called singular, the points of the other—nonsingular. The two groups differ in that at the points of the first (singular) group the solution of the integral equation has a logarithmic singularity, while at the points of the second it may have a removable or a logarithmic singularity, as we require. Let the points $C_1, C_2, \ldots, C_p$ $(p<q)$ be singular, and the remaining $C_{p+1}, C_{p+2}, \ldots, C_q$ nonsingular. We divide the nonsingular points arbitrarily into two groups: $C_{p+1}, C_{p+2}, \ldots, C_r$ $(r<q)$, and $C_{r+1}, C_{r+2}, \ldots, C_q$. A solution is said to belong to class $h(C_{p+1}, C_{p+2}, \ldots, C_r)$ if it is bounded at $C_{p+1}, C_{p+2}, \ldots, C_r$ and admits there only logarithmic singularities (no additional requirements are made in the neighborhood of the other singular or nonsingular points). The following theorems have been established:

A. *For a given inhomogeneous system of singular equations with continuous coefficients to have a solution of class $h(C_{p+1}, C_{p+2}, \ldots, C_r)$ it is necessary and sufficient that its right-hand side be orthogonal to all the linearly independent solutions of the homogeneous associated equation that are of class $h(C_{r+1}, C_{r+2}, \ldots, C_q)$.*

B. *If λ is the number of linearly independent solutions of class $h(C_{p+1}, \ldots, C_r)$ for a given homogeneous system, and μ is the number of linearly independent solutions of class $h(C_{r+1}, \ldots, C_q)$ of the associated homogeneous equation, then $\lambda-\mu=\varkappa$; the number $\varkappa$ is called the (total) index of the system of class $h(C_{p+1}, \ldots, C_r)$, and does not depend on $K(t_0, t)$.*

It is always important to calculate the total index explicitly. It will be shown on the example of equation (10.148) how this is done. If in particular, there are no nonsingular points (in other words, if all discontinuity points of the matrices $A(t_0)$ and $K(t_0, t)$ are singular), then the above theorems obviously refer, not to solutions of class $h(C_{p+1}, C_{p+2}, \ldots, C_r)$ and $h(C_{r+1}, C_{r+2}, \ldots, C_q)$, but to solutions admitting only logarithmic singularities at the points of discontinuity. For further details and an extensive bibliography cf. /24b/.

§ 34. Mixed problem for an isotropic body. Existence theorem

In order to apply the theory of the last section, it is necessary to check which of the discontinuity points of the matrices $A(t_0)$ and $K(t_0, t)$ are singular and which are nonsingular. According to a rule established for this purpose (cf. Vekua's book mentioned in § 32), we proceed as follows. We construct the matrices

$$\sigma(t_0) = -I + A(t_0)\, i = \begin{cases} \begin{Vmatrix} -1 & -ai \\ ai & -1 \end{Vmatrix} & (t_0 \in S''), \\ -I & (t_0 \in S'), \end{cases}$$

$$d(t_0) = -I - A(t_0)\, i = \begin{cases} \begin{Vmatrix} -1 & ai \\ -ai & -1 \end{Vmatrix} & (t_0 \in S''), \\ -I & (t_0 \in S'), \end{cases}$$

where I is the unit matrix. Whence

$$\det \sigma(t_0) = \det d(t_0) = \begin{cases} 1 - a^2 & (t_0 \in S''), \\ 1 & (t_0 \in S'), \end{cases}$$

and since $1 - a^2 \neq 0$ on account of (10.147), $\det \sigma(t_0) = \det d(t_0) \neq 0$ on the entire curve S. We introduce the matrix $g(t_0) = \sigma^{-1}(t_0)\, d(t_0)$:

$$g(t_0) = \begin{cases} \dfrac{1}{1-a^2} \begin{Vmatrix} 1+a^2 & -2ai \\ 2ai & 1+a^2 \end{Vmatrix} & (t_0 \in S''), \\ I & (t_0 \in S'). \end{cases} \tag{10.149}$$

It is easily verified that (cf. Figure 4)

$$g(a_k - 0) = \frac{1}{1-a^2} \begin{Vmatrix} 1+a^2 & -2ai \\ 2ai & 1+a^2 \end{Vmatrix},$$

$$g(a_k + 0) = I \qquad (k = 1, 2, 3, \ldots, n)$$

and

$$g(b_k - 0) = I, \quad g(b_k + 0) = \frac{1}{1-a^2} \begin{Vmatrix} 1+a^2 & -2ai \\ 2ai & 1+a^2 \end{Vmatrix}$$

$$(k = 1, 2, 3, \ldots, n).$$

Let us take the matrices

$$\gamma(a_k) = g^{-1}(a_k + 0)\, g(a_k - 0) = \frac{1}{1-a^2} \begin{Vmatrix} 1+a^2 & -2ai \\ 2ai & 1+a^2 \end{Vmatrix},$$

$$\gamma(b_k) = g^{-1}(b_k + 0)\, g(b_k - 0) = \frac{1}{1-a^2} \begin{Vmatrix} 1+a^2 & 2ai \\ -2ai & 1+a^2 \end{Vmatrix}$$

$$(k = 1, 2, 3, \ldots, n)$$

$$(\gamma(a_1) = \gamma(a_2) = \ldots = \gamma(a_n), \quad \gamma(b_1) = \gamma(b_2), \ldots, \gamma(b_n))$$

and solve the equations

$$\det[\gamma(a_k) - I\nu] = 0, \quad \det[\gamma(b_k) - I\nu] = 0.$$

We have

$$\det[\gamma(a_k) - I\nu] = \left(\frac{1+a^2}{1-a^2} - \nu\right)^2 - \frac{4a^2}{(1-a^2)^2} = 0$$

and similarly for the equation $\det[\gamma(b_k) - I\nu] = 0$. Denoting the roots by ν_1 and ν_2, we get

$$\nu_1 = \frac{1-a}{1+a}, \quad \nu_2 = \frac{1+a}{1-a}.$$

Since (10.147) implies $0 < a < 1$, we conclude that ν_1, ν_2 are positive; this result will be important in the following. We write

$$\rho_j = \frac{1}{2\pi i} \ln \nu_j \qquad (j = 1, 2).$$

The branches of the logarithm may, in view of the positiveness of ν_j, be chosen so that

$$\operatorname{Re} \rho_j = 0 \qquad (j = 1, 2).$$

The discontinuity points which possess this property are called singular points. Those discontinuity points for which the real part of at least one of the ρ_j $(j = 1, 2)$ is not an integer are nonsingular. Thus, all the points of singularity of the solution are singular here and the singularities (of the solution) can not be "stronger" then logarithmic. To obtain the number $\varkappa$ (index of the equation), it is necessary to construct at all points a_k, b_k $(k = 1, 2, 3, \ldots, n)$ the matrices

$$\chi(z) = \begin{Vmatrix} (z - z_0)^{\rho_1} & 0 \\ 0 & (z - z_0)^{\rho_2} \end{Vmatrix},$$

where z_0 is an arbitrary point fixed in B_i. As in our case ρ_1 and ρ_2 are correspondingly constant at a_k and b_k $(k = 1, 2, 3, \ldots, n)$, we get

$$\varkappa = \frac{1}{2\pi} \left\{ \arg \frac{\det g(z)}{[\det \chi(z)]^{2n}} \right\}_S,$$

where $\{\ldots\}_S$ denotes the change in the bracketed expression when the variable point z moves around the closed contour S. We see from (10.149) that $\det g(z) = 1$, and hence $\arg \det g(z)$ remains unaltered. Now since $\rho_1 + \rho_2 = \frac{1}{2\pi i} \ln(\nu_1 \cdot \nu_2) = 0$,

$$\det \chi(z) = 1,$$

and $\arg \det \chi(z)$ is also unaltered. It follows that $\varkappa = 0$, and the theorems of the last section concerning the solvability of (10.148) reduce to the basic Fredholm theorems. We may now prove that equation (10.145) has a unique solution in class H, admitting singularities not "stronger" then logarithmic at the end-points of S'_k and S''_k. Since Fredholm's theorems were shown to be valid for (10.145), it is sufficient to prove that the homogeneous equation admits only a trivial solution. Let the opposite be true and let $\varphi_0(x_0)$ be a nontrivial solution of the homogeneous equation, admitting logarithmic singularities at the end-points. We introduce the single-layer potential

$$v_0(x) = \int_{S''} G(x, y) \varphi_0(y) \, dS_y.$$

The kernel of this potential is the first Green's tensor and has a logarithmic singularity at $x = y$; the density $\varphi_0(y)$ may, by assumption, also have similar singularities at the points a_k and b_k ($k=1, 2, 3, \ldots, n$); then the single-layer potential is obviously bounded everywhere, also at a_k and b_k. Application of the T-operation to a single-layer potential gives, as we saw before, a Cauchy-type integral (plus a completely continuous operator). The behavior of a Cauchy-type integral in the neighborhood of the integration limits (here a_k and b_k) was closely studied /24b/; it was established, in particular, that $\mathrm{T}v_0(x)$ has an integrable singularity at the points a_k and b_k. We therefore apply Betti's relation (1.9') (I, 1) to $v_0(x)$ in the domain $\bar{B}_i$ from which the points a_k and b_k ($k=1, 2, 3, \ldots, n$) have been excluded (by means of small arcs around these points as centers and lying in $\bar{B}_i$), and then pass to the limit as these arcs shrink toward their centers; since $v_0(x)$ vanishes on S' (by definition of $G(x, y)$), and since $Tv_0(x)$ vanished on S'' (by definition of $\varphi_0(y)$) we obtain

$$v_0(x)=0 \qquad (x \in B_i).$$

It follows, by the continuity of a single-layer potential, that

$$\lim_{B_a \ni x \to x_0 \in S''} v_0(x)=0,$$

and in virtue of the properties of the Green's tensor $G(x, y)$

$$\lim_{B_a \ni x \to x_0 \in S_1'} v_0(x)=0.$$

Thus, the elastic single-layer potential $v_0(x)$ vanishes everywhere on the boundary curve $S''+S_1'$ of the finite disconnected domain B_a, in which this potential represents a regular solution of the equations of elasticity. It follows by the uniqueness theorem that $v_0(x)=0$, $x \in B_a$, and consequently, $\varphi_0(y)=0$. This implies, by Theorem B of § 33, the unique solvability of equation (10.145) and hence the existence of solution of (10.142), expressed by (10.144). The solution of (10.140) is given by (10.141). This completes the proof of the existence theorem.

§ 35. Approximate solution of the mixed problem for an isotropic body

By the foregoing existence theorem, the mixed problem may be solved approximately by means of the method of canonical equations, as well as by the method of generalized Fourier series.

Betti's relation, as shown in the last section, may be applied in B_i to the solution of the mixed problem $v(x)$, represented by (10.144). This gives

$$2\pi v(x)= \int_S (\mathrm{T}_y G(x, y))\, v(y)\, dS_y - \int_S G(x, y)\, \mathrm{T}v(y)\, dS_y + \int_{B_i} G(x, y)\, \rho(y)\, d\sigma_y \qquad (x \in B_i), \qquad (10.150_1)$$

$$0 = \int_S (\mathrm{T}_y G(x, y))\, v(y)\, dS_y - \int_S G(x, y)\, \mathrm{T}v(y)\, dS_y + \int_{B_i} G(x, y)\, \rho(y)\, d\sigma_y \qquad (x \in B_a). \qquad (10.150_2)$$

Taking into account the properties of $G(x, y)$ and the boundary values of $v(x)$ and $\mathrm{T}v(x)$, we rewrite the last relations in the form

$$2\pi v(x)= \int_{S''} G_l(x, y)\, v(y)\, dS_y + F(x) \qquad (x \in B_i), \qquad (10.150_1')$$

$$\int_{S''} G_l(x, y)\, v(y)\, dS_y = -F(x) \qquad (x \in B_a), \tag{10.150$_2^1$}$$

where

$$G_l(x, y) = \mathrm{T}_y G(x, y),$$

$$F(x) = \int_{B_i} G(x, y)\, \rho(y)\, d\sigma_y - \int_{S''} G(x, y) f(y)\, dS_y.$$

We now rewrite (10.150$_1^1$) in the form

$$2\pi v(x) = \int_{S''} G_l(x, y)[v(y) - v(C_k)]\, dS_y + v(C_k) \int_{S''} (G_l(x, y))^* dS_y + F(x),$$

where C_k is either a_k, or b_k, and G_l^* is the transpose of G_l, note that $v(x)$ has been shown above to be bounded at a_k and b_k $(k = 1, 2, \ldots, n)$, while the integral $\int_{S''} G_l(x, y)\, dS_y$ is unbounded at these points, and conclude that

$$v(a_k) = 0, \quad v(b_k) = 0 \ (k = 1, 2, 3, \ldots, n).$$

(10.150$_2^1$) may also be written

$$\int_{S''} \sum_{j=1}^{2} (G_{l,(j)} v)\, i_j\, dS_y = -F(x) \qquad (x \in B_a), \tag{10.150$_2^1$}$$

where $G_{l,(j)}$ is the j-th row-vector of $G_l(x, y)$. We arbitrarily fix on S_2' an everywhere dense sequence of points x_k and consider the set of vectors

$$\nu_{j,k}(y) = G_{l(j)}(x_k, y) \qquad (j = 1, 2;\ k = 1, 2, 3, \ldots). \tag{10.151}$$

Here $\nu_{j,k}(y)$ is the value of the j-th row-vector of $G_l(x, y)$ at $x = x_k$. We will prove that the system (10.151) is linearly independent and closed in the space $C^h_{L_2}(S'')$ of H-continuous functions. Assuming linear dependence, there must exist constants C_{1k}, C_{2k}, not all equal to zero, such that

$$\sum_{j=1}^{2} \sum_{i=1}^{n} C_{jk_i} \nu_{j,k_i}(y) = 0$$

holds at least for one finite n and for all y on S.

We define the vector function

$$u(x) = \sum_{j=1}^{2} \sum_{i=1}^{n} C_{jk_i} G^{(j)}(x_{k_i}, x) \qquad (x_{k_i} \in S_2),$$

which represents in B_i a regular solution of the equations of elasticity. It follows from the uniqueness theorem for the second problem and our assumption, that $u(x)$ is some rigid displacement $\nu(x)$ in B_i. Then the vector $u(x) - \nu(x)$, which vanishes in B_i, also vanishes, being continuous across S'' together with all its derivatives, also beyond B_i, in particular in B_a'. Projecting on the coordinate axes, we get

$$u_s(x) = \sum_{j=1}^{2} \sum_{i=1}^{n} C_{jk_i} G_s^{(j)}(x_{k_i}, x) \qquad (s = 1, 2).$$

Letting x in B_a' approach x_{k_r} on S_2', we note that by definition of $G^{(j)}(x_k, x)$, one term in each projection, for example the terms

$$C_{1,k_r} G_1^{(1)}(x_{k_r}, x) \text{ and } C_{2,k_r} G_2^{(2)}(x_{k_r}, x),$$

increase indefinitely while all the other terms remain bounded. Therefore, if at least one of the numbers C_{1,k_r}, C_{2,k_r} is not zero, we reach a contradiction and the assumption of linear dependence of the set $\{\boldsymbol{\nu}_{j,k}(y)\}$ is disproved. To prove that this set is closed we proceed as before. Let $\boldsymbol{\alpha}(y)$ be some element of the space $C^h_{L_2}(S'')$, and let

$$\int_{S''} (\boldsymbol{\alpha}(y)\,\boldsymbol{\nu}_{j,k}(y))\,dS = 0 \qquad (j = 1,\ 2,\ k = 1,\ 2,\ 3,\ \ldots).$$

It is necessary to prove that $\boldsymbol{\alpha}(y) = 0$. It follows from the preceding that

$$\int_{S''} G_I(x_k,\ y)\,\boldsymbol{\alpha}(y)\,dS_y = \int_{S''} \sum_{j=1}^{2} [\boldsymbol{G}_{I,(j)}(x_k,\ y)\,\boldsymbol{\alpha}(y)]\,\boldsymbol{i}_j\,dS =$$

$$= \int_{S''} \sum_{j=1}^{2} [\boldsymbol{\nu}_{j,k}(y)\,\boldsymbol{\alpha}(y)]\,\boldsymbol{i}_j\,dS_y = 0 \qquad (k = 1,\ 2,\ 3,\ \ldots).$$

Consider the vector

$$\boldsymbol{W}(x) = \int_{S''} G_I(x,\ y)\,\boldsymbol{\alpha}(y)\,dS_y.$$

Since this vector vanishes almost everywhere on S_2', it vanishes, by continuity, everywhere on S_2'. On the other hand, $\boldsymbol{W}(x)$ is an elastic double-layer potential defined in B_a'' and vanishing on S_3'; consequently, it vanishes everywhere in B_a''; since it is continuous across S_2' together with all its derivatives, $\boldsymbol{W}(x)$ vanishes everywhere in B_a' up to S''. We therefore have in the outer limit at S''

$$-\pi\boldsymbol{\alpha}(x_0) + \int_{S''} G_I(x_0,\ y)\,\boldsymbol{\alpha}(y)\,dS_y = 0.$$

This is a system of singular integral equations on an open contour, which coincides with (10.146) of § 32. This system has, as shown before, only a trivial solution and thus $\boldsymbol{\alpha}(y) = 0$, which completes the proof. The completeness in $C^h_{L_2}(S'')$ implies completeness in L_2, exactly as in § 21.

We now write

$$\boldsymbol{\nu}_{1,k}(y) = \boldsymbol{\psi}^{(2k-1)}(y), \qquad \boldsymbol{\nu}_{2,k} = \boldsymbol{\psi}^{(2k)}(y).$$

The sequence $\{\boldsymbol{\psi}^{(i)}(y)\}$ is linearly independent. From it we construct the orthonormalized sequence $\{\boldsymbol{\varphi}^{(i)}(y)\}$

$$\boldsymbol{\varphi}^{(s)}(y) = \sum_{i=1}^{S} B_{si}\boldsymbol{\psi}^{(i)}(y),$$

where B_{si} are well-defined constants. Let

$$\sum_{m=1}^{\infty} \Phi_m \boldsymbol{\varphi}^{(m)}(y)$$

be the Fourier expansion of $\boldsymbol{v}(y)$ (solution of the functional equation ($10.150\frac{1}{2}$), which was proved to exist in § 34) in the basis set $\{\boldsymbol{\varphi}^{(i)}(y)\}$. Then

$$\Phi_m = \int_{S''} (\boldsymbol{v}(y),\ \boldsymbol{\varphi}^{(m)}(y))\,dS_y \qquad (m = 1,\ 2,\ \ldots)$$

and

$$\lim_{N\to\infty} \int_{S} \left(\boldsymbol{v}(y) - \sum_{m=1}^{N} \Phi_m \boldsymbol{\varphi}^{(m)}(y)\right)^2 dS_y = 0. \tag{10.152}$$

We turn to ($10.150\frac{1}{2}$) for the derivation of the coefficients Φ_m, and substitute $x = x_k \in S_2'$,

$$\int_{S''} \sum_{j=1}^{2} (G_{I,(j)}(x_k, y), v(y))\, i_j\, dS =$$
$$= \int_{S''} \sum_{j=1}^{2} (\nu_{j,k}(y), v(y))\, i_j\, dS_y = -F(x_k) \quad (k = 1, 2, 3, 4, \ldots). \qquad (10.153)$$

To calculate Φ_m, we write m in one of the forms, $m = 2s - 1$, $m = 2s$. We multiply the first of equations (10.153) (for $k = 1$) scalarly by $B_{m1} = B_{m1} i_1 + + B_{m2} i_2$, the second (for $k = 2$) by $B_{m2} = B_{m3} i_1 + B_{m4} i_2$, etc., the s-th equation $(k = s)$ by

$$B_{ms} = \begin{cases} B_{mm} i_1 & \text{for } s = \frac{m+1}{2}, \\ B_{mm-1} i_1 + B_{mm} i_2 & \text{for } s = \frac{m}{2} \end{cases}$$

and add the results together; we then have

$$\int_{S''} \sum_{j=1}^{2} [B_{m,j}(\nu_{j,1} \cdot v) + B_{m,j+2}(\nu_{j,2} \cdot v) + B_{m,j+4}(\nu_{j3} \cdot v) + \ldots]\, dS_y =$$
$$= \int_{S''} \{[B_{m,1}\varphi^{(1)} + B_{m,2}\varphi^{(2)} + B_{m,3}\varphi^{(3)} + B_{m,4}\varphi^{(4)} + \ldots$$
$$\ldots + B_{m,m-1}\varphi^{(m-1)} + B_{m,m}\varphi^{(m)}] \cdot v\}\, dS_y =$$
$$= \int_{S''} (\varphi^{(m)}(y) \cdot v(y))\, dS_y = \Phi_m = -\sum_{k=1}^{s} (B_{mk} \cdot F(x_k)).$$

Let

$$v^{(N)}(x) = \frac{1}{2\pi} \int_{S''} G_I(x, y) \sum_{m=1}^{N} \Phi_m \varphi^{(m)}(y)\, dS_y + \frac{1}{2\pi} F(x).$$

$v^{(N)}(x)$ is evidently a solution of the equations of elasticity in the domain of definition of $G_I(x, y)$. We shall now show that its values at any point $x \in B_i$ approximate with any desired accuracy to the exact solution at this point. We apply Schwarz's inequality to the projections of the difference $|v(x) - v^{(N)}(x)|$,

$$|v_j(x) - v_j^{(N)}(x)| \leqslant \frac{1}{2\pi} \sqrt{\int_{S''} \left(v_1(y) - \sum_{m=1}^{N} \Phi_m \varphi_1^{(m)}(y)\right)^2 dS_y \int_{S''} |G^1_{I(j)}|^2\, dS_y} +$$
$$+ \frac{1}{2\pi} \sqrt{\int_{S''} \left(v_2 - \sum_{m=1}^{N} \Phi_m \varphi_2^{(m)}(y)\right)^2 dS \int_{S''} |G^2_{I,j}|^2\, dS_y} \quad (j = 1, 2).$$

This proves our assertion, in virtue of (10.152) and because the integrals

$$\int_{S''} |G^l_{I,(j)}(x, y)|^2\, dS_y \qquad (l = 1, 2; \quad j = 1, 2; \quad x \in B_i)$$

are bounded. Thus, by taking partial sums of the series, we have in

$$\frac{1}{2\pi} \int_{S''} G_I(x, y) \sum_{m=1}^{\infty} \Phi_m \varphi^{(m)}(y)\, dS_y + \frac{1}{2\pi} F(x) \qquad (x \in B_i)$$

approximations to the exact solution (in the C-metric).

§ 36. Mixed (fourth) boundary-value problem for an anisotropic body. Existence theorem

The method used above to solve the mixed problem for an isotropic body can be extended to the anisotropic case. It is required to determine the state of equilibrium of the body B_i from the system of differential equations (8.4) of (VIII, 1):

$$\overset{*}{\Delta}_1 u(x) = A_{11}\frac{\partial^2 u_1}{\partial x_1^2} + 2A_{13}\frac{\partial^2 u_1}{\partial x_1 \partial x_2} + A_{33}\frac{\partial^2 u_1}{\partial x_2^2} + \\ + A_{13}\frac{\partial^2 u_2}{\partial x_1^2} + (A_{12}+A_{33})\frac{\partial^2 u_2}{\partial x_1 \partial x_2} + A_{23}\frac{\partial^2 u_2}{\partial x_2^2} = 0,$$

$$\overset{*}{\Delta}_2 u(x) = A_{13}\frac{\partial^2 u_1}{\partial x_1^2} + (A_{12}+A_{33})\frac{\partial^2 u_1}{\partial x_1 \partial x_2} + A_{23}\frac{\partial^2 u_1}{\partial x_2^2} + \\ + A_{33}\frac{\partial^2 u_2}{\partial x_1^2} + 2A_{23}\frac{\partial^2 u_2}{\partial x_1 \partial x_2} + A_{22}\frac{\partial^2 u_2}{\partial x_2^2} = 0$$

and the boundary conditions

$$\lim_{B_i \ni x \to x_0 \in S'} u(x) = f^{(1)}(x_0), \qquad \lim_{B_i \ni x \to x_0 \in S''} \mathrm{T}u(x) = f^{(2)}(x_0).$$

This problem, exactly as in § 32, may be reduced to

$$\left.\begin{aligned} &\Delta^* v(x) = \rho(x) \ (x \in B_i), \quad \lim_{B_i \ni x \to x_0 \in S'} v(x) = 0, \\ &\lim_{B_i \ni x \to x_0 \in S''} \mathrm{T}v(x) = f(x_0), \end{aligned}\right\} \tag{10.154}$$

where Δ^* is a vector differential operator whose components along the axes are $\overset{*}{\Delta}_1$ and $\overset{*}{\Delta}_2$, and

$$\rho(x) = -\Delta^* \Phi(x), \quad f(x_0) = f^{(2)}(x_0) - \mathrm{T}\Phi(x_0).$$

Let $G(x, y)$ be the first Green's tensor for the domain B, which is now occupied by an anisotropic elastic body characterized by six elastic constants. By definition, for the internal points of the domain

$$G(x, y) = \Gamma(x, y) - \overset{0}{v}(x, y), \tag{10.154'}$$

where the matrix $\Gamma(x, y)$ is of the form (VIII, 1)

$$\Gamma(x, y) = \operatorname{Im} \sum_{k=1}^{2} \begin{Vmatrix} A_k & B_k \\ B_k & C_k \end{Vmatrix} \ln \sigma_k,$$

$$\sigma_k = (x_1 - y_1) + \alpha_k (x_2 - y_2),$$
$$A_k = 2a\,(A_{22}\alpha_k^2 + 2A_{23}\alpha_k + A_{33})\,d_k,$$
$$B_k = -2a\,[A_{23}\alpha_k^2 + (A_{12} + A_{33})\,\alpha_k + A_{13}]\,d_k \qquad (k = 1, 2),$$
$$C_k = 2a\,(A_{33}\alpha_k^2 + 2A_{13}\alpha_k + A_{11})\,d_k,$$
$$a = -\frac{1}{A_{22}A_{33} - A_{23}^2}$$

and α_k are the (complex-) roots of the characteristic equation (cf. (8.5))

$$\alpha_k = a_k^* + ib_k^*, \quad \tilde{\alpha}_k = a_k^* - ib_k^* \qquad (k = 1, 2),$$

where we may assume without loss of generality that $b_k^* > 0$ $(k = 1, 2)$, and d_k is the cofactor of the element α_k^3, divided by d in the determinant

$$d = \begin{vmatrix} 1 & \alpha_1 & \alpha_1^2 & \alpha_1^3 \\ 1 & \tilde{\alpha}_1 & \tilde{\alpha}_1^2 & \tilde{\alpha}_1^3 \\ 1 & \alpha_2 & \alpha_2^2 & \alpha_2^3 \\ 1 & \tilde{\alpha}_2 & \tilde{\alpha}_2^2 & \tilde{\alpha}_2^3 \end{vmatrix}$$

The constants

$$A=\frac{\omega\left(a_2^*b_1^*+a_1^*b_2^*\right)}{b_1^*b_2^*\left[\left(a_1^*-a_2^*\right)^2+\left(b_1^*+b_2^*\right)^2\right]},\quad B=\frac{\left[b_1^*\left(a_2^{*2}+b_2^{*2}\right)+b_2^*\left(a_1^{*2}+b_1^{*2}\right)\right]\omega}{b_1^*b_2^*\left[\left(a_1^*-a_2^*\right)^2+\left(b_1^*+b_2^*\right)^2\right]},$$

$$C=\frac{\omega\left(b_1^*+b_2^*\right)}{b_1^*b_2^*\left[\left(a_1^*-a_2^*\right)^2+\left(b_1^*+b_2^*\right)^2\right]},$$

where

$$\omega=b_1^*b_2^*-a_1^*a_2^*-a\left(A_{13}A_{23}-A_{12}A_{13}\right),$$

play an important role in the following (or rather some of their combinations do). From (8.27) and (8.24),

$$BC-A^2=\frac{\omega^2}{b_1^*b_2^*\left[\left(a_1^*-a_2^*\right)^2+\left(b_1^*+b_2^*\right)^2\right]}>0, \tag{10.155}$$

$$1+A^2-BC=\frac{BC-A^2}{a_{11}^2\omega^2\Delta C}\left(A_{22}B+2A_{23}A+A_{33}C\right)>\frac{C}{A_{22}\omega}>0,$$

where

$$a_{11}=\frac{A_{22}A_{33}-A_{23}^2}{\Delta},\quad \Delta=\begin{vmatrix} A_{11} & A_{12} & A_{13}\\ A_{21} & A_{22} & A_{23}\\ A_{31} & A_{32} & A_{33}\end{vmatrix}.$$

These inequalities are due to Basheleishvili and their detailed derivation may be found in his paper /1b/.

We now seek a solution for (10.154) of the form

$$v(x)=\int_{S''}G(x,y)\varphi(y)\,dS_y-\frac{1}{2\pi}\int_{B_l}G(x,y)\rho(y)\,dy_1\,dy_2, \tag{10.156}$$

where $\varphi(y)$ is an unknown vector function of class H, admitting logarithmic singularities at the end-points of the line S''. The first two conditions of the problem are fulfilled in virtue of the nature of Green's tensor, and the last leads to the following equation for $\varphi(y)$

$$-\pi\varphi(x_0)+\int_{S''}\left(\mathrm{T}_{x_0}G(x_0,y)\right)\varphi(y)\,dS_y=f(x_0)+$$

$$+\frac{1}{2\pi}\int_{B_l}\left(\mathrm{T}_{x_0}G(x_0,y)\right)\rho(y)\,dy_1\,dy_2. \tag{10.157}$$

We have met in (VIII, 6) an equation of the type (10.157) and shown there that it constitutes a system of Cauchy-type singular integral equations; but now its domain is a set of open lines, and we must verify that (10.157) is indeed a system of one-dimensional singular integral equations on open contours.

The equation associated with the homogeneous equation of (10.157) is of the form

$$-\pi\psi(x_0)+\int_{S''}G_l(x_0,y)\psi(y)\,dS_y=0, \tag{10.158}$$

where

$$G_l(x_0,y)=\Gamma_l(x_0,y)-v_l(x_0,y)$$

and $\Gamma_l(x_0,y)$ is the transpose of $\mathrm{T}_{x_0}\Gamma(x_0,y)$ with x_0 and y interchanged. The matrix $v_l(x_0,y)$ is obtained analogously from $\mathrm{T}_{x_0}v(x_0,y)$. As we know (cf. VIII, 2),

$$\Gamma_l(x,y)=\operatorname{Im}\sum_{k=1}^{2}\begin{Vmatrix} N_k & M_k\\ L_k & H_k\end{Vmatrix}\frac{\partial}{\partial s_y}\ln\sigma_k,$$

where

$$\sum_{k=1}^{2} N_k = 1 - Ai, \quad \sum_{k=1}^{2} L_k = -Bi, \quad \sum_{k=1}^{2} M_k = Ci, \quad \sum_{k=1}^{2} H_k = 1 + Ai$$

and

$$\frac{\partial}{\partial s_y} \ln \sigma_k = \frac{\partial}{\partial s_y} \ln r(x, y) + \frac{i - \alpha_k}{\sigma_k \sigma} r \cos(r, n_y) - \frac{i \cos(r, n_y)}{r},$$

$$\sigma = (x_1 - y_1) + i(x_2 - y_2).$$

Introducing an arc-parameter for the points x_0 and y on the line S'', and proceeding exactly as in § 32, we can bring equation (10.158) to the form

$$-\psi(t_0) + \frac{1}{\pi i} P \int_{S''} \frac{\psi(t)}{t - t_0} dt + \int_{S''} K_1(t_0, t) \psi(t) dt = 0, \tag{10.158'}$$

where

$$P = \begin{Vmatrix} -Ai & Ci \\ -Bi & Ai \end{Vmatrix} \tag{10.159}$$

and $K_1(t_0, t)$ is a Fredholm kernel on S''. Let us introduce the two new matrices $K(t_0, t)$ and $P(t_0)$, defined on the closed line S:

$$K(t_0, t) = \begin{cases} K_1(t_0, t), \\ 0. \end{cases} \quad P(t_0) = \begin{cases} P & (t_0 \in S''), \\ 0 & (t_0 \in S'); \end{cases}$$

these matrices have first-kind discontinuities at a_k and b_k. Consider the system of singular equations on the closed line S

$$-\psi(t_0) + \frac{P(t_0)}{\pi i} \int_S \frac{\psi(t)}{t - t_0} dt + \int_S K(t_0, t) \psi(t) dt = 0. \tag{10.160}$$

If this system has a solution of class H which admits at a_k and b_k $(k = 1, 2, \ldots, n)$ singularities not "stronger" than logarithmic, then this solution also satisfies (10.158'). We now have to go through the manipulations of § 34 in regard to (10.160). We construct the matrices

$$\sigma(t_0) = -I + P(t_0) = \begin{cases} \begin{Vmatrix} -1 - Ai & Ci \\ -Bi & -1 + Ai \end{Vmatrix} & (t_0 \in S''), \\ -I & (t_0 \in S'), \end{cases}$$

$$d(t_0) = -I - P(t_0) = \begin{cases} \begin{Vmatrix} -1 + Ai & -Ci \\ Bi & -1 - Ai \end{Vmatrix} & (t_0 \in S''), \\ -I & (t_0 \in S'). \end{cases}$$

We find

$$\det \sigma(t_0) = \det d(t_0) = \begin{cases} (1 + A^2 - BC) & (t_0 \in S''), \\ 1 & (t_0 \in S'). \end{cases}$$

Since in view of (10.155) $\delta = 1 + A^2 - BC \neq 0$, we get for all points of S

$$\det \sigma(t_0) = \det d(t_0) \neq 0.$$

Introducing the matrix

$$g(t_0) = \sigma^{-1}(t_0) d(t_0),$$

we find

$$\sigma^{-1}(t_0) = \begin{cases} -\frac{1}{\delta} \begin{Vmatrix} 1 - Ai & Ci \\ -Bi & 1 + Ai \end{Vmatrix} & (t_0 \in S''), \\ -I & (t_0 \in S'). \end{cases}$$

Consequently,

$$g(t_0)=\begin{cases}\dfrac{1}{1+A^2-BC}\begin{Vmatrix}(1-Ai)^2+BC & 2Ci\\ -2Bi & (1+Ai)^2+BC\end{Vmatrix} & (t_0\in S''),\\ I & (t_0\in S').\end{cases}$$

Now take the matrices

$$\gamma(a_k)=g^{-1}(a_k+0)\,g(a_k-0) \text{ and } \gamma(b_k)=g^{-1}(b_k+0)\,g(b_k-0)$$
$$(k=1,2,3,\ldots,n).$$

Noting that the points (a_k+0) and (b_k-0) lie on S', and the points (a_k-0) and (b_k+0) on S'', we conclude that

$$\gamma(a_k)=g(a_k-0)=\frac{1}{1+A^2-BC}\begin{Vmatrix}(1-Ai)^2+BC & 2Ci\\ -2Bi & (1+Ai)^2+BC\end{Vmatrix}$$

and

$$\gamma(b_k)=g^{-1}(b_k+0)=\frac{(1+A^2-BC)}{[(1-Ai)^2+BC][(1+Ai)^2+BC]-4BC}\times$$
$$\times\begin{Vmatrix}(1+Ai)^2+BC & -2Ci\\ 2Bi & (1-Ai)^2+BC\end{Vmatrix}=$$
$$=\frac{1}{1+A^2-BC}\begin{Vmatrix}(1+Ai)^2+BC & -2Ci\\ 2Bi & (1-Ai)^2+BC\end{Vmatrix}.$$

Thus,

$$\gamma(a_1)=\gamma(a_2)=\ldots=\gamma(a_n),\quad \gamma(b_1)=\gamma(b_2)=\ldots=(b_n).$$

Let us consider the equations

$$\det[\gamma(a_k)-I\nu]=\begin{vmatrix}\dfrac{(1-Ai)^2+BC}{\delta}-\nu & \dfrac{2Ci}{\delta}\\ -\dfrac{2Bi}{\delta} & \dfrac{(1+Ai)^2+BC}{\delta}\end{vmatrix}=0,$$

$$\det[\gamma(b_k)-I\nu]=\begin{vmatrix}\dfrac{[(1+Ai)^2+BC]}{\delta}-\nu & -\dfrac{2Ci}{\delta}\\ \dfrac{2Bi}{\delta} & \dfrac{[(1-Ai)^2+BC]}{\delta}-\nu\end{vmatrix}=0$$

We have

$$\det[\gamma(a_k)-I\nu]=\frac{[(1-Ai)^2+BC][(1+Ai)^2+BC]}{\delta^2}-$$
$$-\left[\frac{(1-Ai)^2+BC}{\delta}+\frac{(1+Ai)^2+BC}{\delta}\right]\nu+\nu^2-\frac{4BC}{\delta^2}=$$
$$=1-2\frac{1-A^2+BC}{1+A^2-BC}\nu+\nu^2=0$$

and similarly for the equation $\det[\gamma(b_k)-I\nu]=0$.

Solving this equation for ν, we obtain

$$\nu_{1,2}=\frac{1-A^2+BC}{1+A^2-BC}\pm\sqrt{\left(\frac{1-A^2+BC}{1+A^2-BC}\right)^2-1}=$$
$$=\frac{1-A^2+BC}{1+A^2-BC}\pm\sqrt{\frac{4(BC-A^2)}{(1+A^2-BC)^2}}=\frac{(1+BC-A^2)\pm2\sqrt{BC-A^2}}{1+A^2-BC},$$

and, by (10.155), both roots are positive. We denote them by ν_1 and ν_2; $\nu_1>0$, $\nu_2>0$.

Hence for the numbers

$$\rho_1=\frac{1}{2\pi i}\ln\nu_1 \text{ and } \rho_2=\frac{1}{2\pi i}\ln\nu_2$$

we have

$$\operatorname{Re}\rho_1=0,\quad \operatorname{Re}\rho_2=0.$$

All the discontinuity points of the matrix $P(t_0)$ therefore are singular points of (10.160). To find the index of this equation it is necessary, as shown in § 34, to construct the matrix $\chi(z)$ for all points a_k and b_k $(k=1, 2, 3, \ldots, n)$; since in our case the numbers ρ_1 and ρ_2 are respectively constant at the points a_k and b_k, the matrices $\chi(z)$ retain their form at these points; proceeding as in § 34, we calculate the number

$$\varkappa = \frac{1}{2\pi}\left\{\arg\frac{\det g(z)}{[\det \chi(z)]^{2n}}\right\}_S,$$

i. e., determine the change in argument of the function

$$\frac{\det g(z)}{[\det \chi(z)]^{2n}}$$

around the closed contour S. The expression for $g(z)$ becomes on S''

$$\det g(z) = \frac{[(1-Ai)^2+BC][(1+Ai)^2+BC]}{(1+A^2-BC)^2} = 1.$$

Next, since $\rho_1+\rho_2 = \frac{1}{2\pi i}\ln(\nu_1, \nu_2) = \frac{1}{2\pi i}\ln 1 = 0$, we get

$$\det \chi(z) = (z-z_0)^{\rho_1+\rho_2} = 1.$$

It follows from the above and from

$$\varkappa = \frac{1}{2\pi}[\arg\det g(z) - 2n\arg\det\chi(z)]_S,$$

that $\varkappa=0$. This proves, as shown in §§ 33, 34, that Fredholm's theorems apply to equation (10.160), and we may now prove for (10.157) the uniqueness of solution of class H with logarithmic singularities at the end-points of the lines S' and S'' (more accurately, at the end-points of the arcs S'_k and S''_k). We only need to show that the homogeneous equation for (10.160) has only a trivial solution. We assume the opposite and denote by $\varphi_0(x)$ a non-trivial solution of the homogeneous equation, having logarithmic singularities at the end-points. Let us consider the anisotropic single-layer potential

$$v_0(x) = \int_{S''} G(x, y)\varphi_0(y)\, dS_y,$$

where the kernel $G(x, y)$ is given by (10.154') and, as established in Ch. VIII, has the same analytic singularities (and no others) as the corresponding tensor for the isotropic case. The discussion of § 34, repeated verbatim, again leads to the conclusion that $\varphi_0(y)\equiv 0$. This proves the solvability of (10.157), and that (10.156) yields the solution of the mixed problem for an anisotropic body.

§ 37. Approximate solution of the mixed problem for an anisotropic body

The existence theorem derived in the last section for the mixed problem of an anisotropic body, permits us to obtain an approximate value of the solution at any internal point of the body. This may be done by means of canonical equations as well as by generalized Fourier expansions. The proof can be directly adapted from that of § 35 for the isotropic case. We therefore only give the final result: —

the partial sums

$$\frac{1}{2\pi}\sum_{m=1}^{N}\int_{S''} G_I(x, y)\,\Phi_m\varphi^{(m)}(y)\,dS_y,$$

approximate, in the C*-metric, to the exact values of solution at any internal point of the body with any desired accuracy, provided* N *is made sufficiently large.*

Here $G(x, y)$ is the first Green's tensor for the anisotropic body, introduced in the last section*:

$$G_I(x, y) = \mathrm{T}_y G(x, y),$$

$$\varphi^{(m)}(y) = \sum_{i=1}^{m} B_{mi}\psi^{(i)}(y),$$

$$\psi^{(2k-1)}(y) = \nu_{1,k}(y),\quad \psi^{(2k)}(y) = \nu_{2,k}(y),$$

$$\nu_{j,k}(y) = G_{I,(j)}(x_k, y)\qquad (j = 1, 2;\ k = 1, 2, \ldots;\ x_k \in S_2')$$

and Φ_m are the Fourier coefficients of the boundary-value function $v(x)$ expanded on S'' in the complete and orthonormalized set $\{\varphi^{(i)}(y)\}$; these coefficients arc given by the formula

$$\Phi_m = -\sum_{k=1}^{s}(B_{m,k}\cdot F(x_k))\quad \left(s = \frac{m+1}{2},\quad s = \frac{m}{2}\right),$$

where B_{pq} are well-defined constants (orthonormalization constants associated with the transition from the set $\psi^{(i)}(y)$ to the set $\varphi^{(i)}(y)$),

$$B_{m,1} = B_{m,1}i_1 + B_{m,2}i_2,\quad B_{m,2} = B_{m,3}i_1 + B_{m,4}i_2,\ \ldots,$$

$$B_{m,s} = \begin{cases} B_{m,m}i_1 & \text{for } s = \dfrac{m+1}{2},\\ B_{m,m-1}i_1 + B_{mm}i_2 & \text{for } s = \dfrac{m}{2}\end{cases}$$

and

$$F(x) = \int_{B_i} G(x, y)\,\rho(y)\,d\sigma_y - \int_{S''} G(x, y)\,f(y)\,dS_y.$$

§ 38. Various remarks. Some new problems

1°. **On the convergence to stresses.** The foregoing treatment is based on the basic system of differential equations of the theory of elasticity for the displacements, and the established results, in particular the convergence of the approximations, relate to the displacements. But in applications, as we know, not the displacements but rather the stresses are often of primary interest. It is noteworthy that the methods of approximate solution developed in this chapter allow us to derive approximate values not only for the displacement vector but also for the stresses. This may now be illustrated on the example of the second interior problem dealt with in § 31. The following expression was obtained for the approximate value of the displacement

$$u^{(N)}(x) = \frac{1}{4\pi}\int_S \Gamma_I(x, y)\sum_{k=0}^{N}\Phi_k\varphi^{(k)}(y)\,dS_y + \frac{1}{4\pi}F(x)\qquad (x \in B_i).$$

* The way by which this tensor may be obtained in practice is discussed in § 38, 4°.

The stress vector which corresponds to these displacements is

$$\mathsf{T}\boldsymbol{u}^{(N)}(x)=\frac{1}{4\pi}\int\limits_S(\mathsf{T}\Gamma_I(x,\,y))\sum_{k=0}^{N}\Phi_k\boldsymbol{\varphi}^{(k)}(y)\,dS_y+\frac{1}{4\pi}\,\mathsf{T}\boldsymbol{F}(x).$$

The exact value of the stress vector at x, according to (10.136_1), is

$$\mathsf{T}\boldsymbol{u}(x)=\frac{1}{4\pi}\int\limits_S(\mathsf{T}\Gamma_I(x,\,y))\,\boldsymbol{\varphi}(y)\,dS_y+\frac{1}{4\pi}\,\mathsf{T}\boldsymbol{F}(x).$$

Taking the difference of the projections and estimating their absolute values by means of Schwarz's inequality, we obtain

$$|\,\mathsf{T}_i\boldsymbol{u}(x)-\mathsf{T}_i\boldsymbol{u}^{(N)}(x)\,|<\frac{1}{4\pi}\sum_{k=1}^{3}\left\{\int\limits_S\left(\mathsf{T}_i\Gamma_{\mathrm{I}}^{(k)}(x,\cdot y)\right)^2dS_y\times\right.$$

$$\left.\times\int\limits_S\left(\varphi_k(y)-\sum_{s=0}^{N}\Phi_s\varphi_k^{(s)}(y)\right)^2dS_y\right\}^{\frac{1}{2}}\qquad(i=1,\,2,\,3),$$

where $\mathsf{T}_i\Gamma_{\mathrm{I}}^{(k)}(x,\,y)$ is the x_i-component of $\mathsf{T}\Gamma_{\mathrm{I}}^{(k)}(x,\,y)$, and

$$\varphi_k(y)-\sum_{s=0}^{N}\Phi_s\varphi_k^{(s)}(y)\qquad(*)$$

is the x_k-component of $\boldsymbol{\varphi}(y)-\sum_{s=0}^{N}\Phi_s\boldsymbol{\varphi}^{(s)}(y)$. Since the integrals

$$\int\limits_S\left(\mathsf{T}_i\Gamma_{\mathrm{I}}^{(k)}(x,\,y)\right)^2dS_y\qquad(i=1,\,2,\,3;\;k=1,\,2,\,3)$$

are bounded at any point of a domain B_i' entirely contained within B_i, and in view of the mean-square convergence of the series (*) converges to zero, there exists for an arbitrarily small $\varepsilon>0$ a number N_0, such that for $N>N_0$

$$|\,\mathsf{T}_i\boldsymbol{u}(x)-\mathsf{T}_i\boldsymbol{u}^{(N)}(x)\,|<\varepsilon.$$

This proves the uniform convergence of the approximate stresses to the exact value. This result evidently holds good for all other problems.

2°. **The method of expanding boundary-value functions.** We have seen that on solving approximately problem (D) by means of the method of functional equations we first obtain a generalized Fourier series for the boundary values of the stress vector, and in problem (T) — a Fourier series for the boundary values of the displacement vector, and only then go on to deduce the values of the stress and displacement at any internal point. A similar situation occurs also in solving the mixed problems (cf. §§ 32–37). In practice we meet problems for which these intermediate values are of primary importance, and the method of functional equations is in these cases especially convenient.

The complete systems of vectors, which we have constructed for the approximate solution of various boundary-value problems, may generally be used effectively for the same purpose, together with the familiar procedure of expanding the given boundary-value functions in series. Let us illustrate this on the example of problem (T_i). Let $\boldsymbol{f}(y)$ be the boundary value of the stress vector, which obviously satisfies the solvability condition for problem (T_i). Let

$$\sum_{k=0}^{\infty}F_k\boldsymbol{\varphi}^{(k)}(y),\quad F_k=\int\limits_S(\boldsymbol{f}(y)\cdot\boldsymbol{\varphi}^{(k)}(y))\,dS,\qquad(**)$$

be the expansion of $f(y)$ in the complete and orthonormalized set $\{\varphi^{(k)}(y)\}$ of § 31. Expressing $\varphi^{(k)}(y)$ as a linear combination of the $\psi^{(k)}(y)$, and the latter through the vectors $\nu_{s,k}(y)$, we substitute the results in the last series and form the partial sum of N terms

$$v^{(N)}(y)=\sum_{s=1}^{3}\sum_{k=1}^{N}A_{k,s}\nu_{s,k}(y).$$

The vector

$$u^{(N)}(x)=\sum_{s=1}^{3}\sum_{k=0}^{N}A_{k,s}\Gamma^{(s)}(x_k,x) \qquad (x\in B_i)$$

is obviously a solution of the equations of elasticity, regular in B_i, which satisfies on S the boundary condition

$$\lim_{x\to y\in S}\mathbf{T}u^{(N)}(x)=v^{(N)}(y).$$

Let $H(x,y)$ be the second Green's tensor for the domain B_i (cf. VI, 7). Then

$$u^{(N)}(x)=\frac{1}{4\pi}\int_S H(x,y)\,v^{(N)}(y)\,dS_y+\alpha^{(N)}(x).$$

The exact solution is of the form

$$u(x)=\frac{1}{4\pi}\int_S H(x,y)f(y)\,dS_y+\beta(x),$$

where $\beta(x)$ is some rigid displacement vector. Let $\gamma^{(N)}(x)=\alpha^{(N)}(x)-\beta(x)$. We apply Schwarz's inequality to the difference

$$u(x)-u^{(N)}(x)+\gamma^{(N)}(x)|=\frac{1}{4\pi}\left|\int_S H(x,y)\left(f(y)-\sum_{k=0}^{N}F_k\varphi^{(k)}(y)\right)dS_y\right|;$$

then, in view of the mean-square convergence of the series (**) to $f(y)$ and of the boundedness of the integrals

$$\int_S \{H_j^{(l)}(x,y)\}^2\,dS_y \qquad (l=1,2,3;\ j=1,2,3),$$

we have, at any internal point x of a domain B_i' which is entirely contained within B_i,

$$u(x)=\lim_{N\to\infty}u^{(N)}(x)+\gamma(x),$$

where $\gamma(x)$ is some rigid displacement vector.

The use of this method for approximate solution of mixed problems is of special interest. This involves no real difficulty if the results of §§ 32–37 are utilized and then one proceeds as above; but it is first necessary to construct the Green's tensor for the mixed problem in B_i (cf. 3°).

3°. **On the Green's tensor for mixed problems.** The existence theorems which were proved for the mixed problems in §§ 32–37 may be employed in the derivation of the Green's tensors for these problems. This allows us to consider certain new interesting problems. Thus it is interesting to study boundary-value problems for piecewise-homogeneous bodies with mixed conditions on the external boundary, in which the mentioned Green's tensor plays the role of Green's first and second tensors in problems (B_1) and (B_2) (cf. (IV, 3) and also the remark at the end of 2° above; also 6°).

4°. **Cases of "effective" solution of mixed problems.** The effectiveness of the approximate solution of mixed problems by means of the method presented in §§ 32–37 is somewhat lowered due to the fact that the first Green's tensor of some (though largely arbitrary) domain enters the calculations. One would do well to keep in mind that the first Green's tensor should be constructed as shown in § 2 for problem (D_i). Actually it is possible in the same way to obtain through the approximate solution of some problem of type (D_i) an analytic expression for the Green's tensor which is suitable everywhere in B_i.

It is also interesting to consider mixed problems for arbitrary contours containing a circular arc or a part of any closed curve whose interior can be mapped conformally onto a disk by means of rational functions. If the displacements are prescribed on this particular portion of the contour and the stresses — on the remaining portion, then the problem may "effectively" (approximately) be solved, provided that the "portion with prescribed displacements" may be extended into a closed contour which entirely contains the "portion with prescribed stresses" in its interior. The problem then amounts to deriving the Green's tensor for a domain which may be mapped conformally onto a disk by means of rational functions. This problem /24a/ has been effectively solved.

5°. **On the solution of dynamic problems.** The results of the present chapter indicate that both methods of approximate solution (by canonical equations and by series expansion) apply to dynamic problems (forced oscillations). All the arguments made in the investigation of mixed problems remain valid in the dynamic case, if the oscillation frequency ω is distinct from an eigenfrequency of the body occupying B_i. In particular, this condition is satisfied when ω is complex. This corresponds to damping and ensures the uniqueness of solution.

6°. **Some other mixed problems.** If the domain B_i is bounded by a number of simple closed curves (surfaces) of the type defined in § 23, then the corresponding mixed problem (i. e., the displacements being prescribed on some of these curves (surfaces), and the stresses on the others) is somewhat simpler to solve then the problems considered in §§ 32–37. One case of such a problem was considered above in § 10. More general mixed problems of this type were investigated in the two-dimensional case by T. Burchuladze.

It is of interest to consider mixed problems with boundary conditions of that type instead of those of §§ 32–37. The Green's tensor mentioned in 3° plays an important role in the solution of such problems.

BIBLIOGRAPHY*

1. BASHELEISHVILI, M. O.

a) Effektivnoe reshenie osnovnykh granichnykh zadach statiki anizotropnogo uprugogo tela dlya ellipticheskoi oblasti i beskonechnoi ploskosti s ellipticheskim otverstiem (Effective Solution of the Fundamental Boundary Value Problems of Statics for an Anisotropic Elastic Elliptic Domain and an Infinite Plane with Elliptic Hole). — Trudy Matematicheskogo Instituta AN Gruz. SSR, Vol. 28. 1962;

b) Reshenie ploskikh granichnykh zadach statiki anizotropnogo uprugogo tela (Solution of the Boundary Value Problems of Statics for an Anisotropic Elastic Body). — Trudy Vychislitel'nogo Tsentra AN Gruz. SSR, Vol. 3. 1962;

c) Analog formuly Puassona v teorii uprugosti (Analogue of Poisson's Formula in the Theory of Elasticity). — Ibid., Vol. 1. 1960;

d) Analog formuly Dini v teorii uprugosti (Analogue of Dini's Formula in the Theory of Elasticity). — Ibid., Vol. 4. 1963.

2. BURCHULADZE, T. V.

a) K teorii granichnykh zadach kolebaniya uprugogo tela (Concerning the Theory of Boundary Value Problems of Elastic Oscillations). — Trudy Tbilisskogo Universiteta, Vol. 64. 1957;

b) O nekotorykh ploskikh granichnykh zadachakh dlya anizotropnykh uprugikh tel (On Some Plane Boundary-Value Problems for Anisotropic Elastic Bodies). — Trudy Matematicheskogo Instituta AN Gruz. SSR, Vol. 27. 1960;

c) O fundamental'nykh resheniyakh odnoi sistemy differentsial'nykh uravnenii (On the Fundamental Solutions of a Certain System of Differential Equations). — Soobshcheniya AN Gruz. SSR, Vol. 20, No. 4. 1958;

d) O nekotorykh obobshchennykh potentsialakh dlya anizotropnykh tel (On Some Generalized Potentials for Anisotropic Bodies). — Ibid., Vol. 23, No. 2. 1959;

e) Asimptoticheskie formuly sobstvennykh funktsii nekotorykh granichnykh zadach kolebaniya anizotropnogo uprugogo tela (Asymptotic Expressions for Eigenfunctions of Some Boundary-Value Problems of Oscillations of an Anisotropic Elastic Body). — Ibid., Vol. 23, No. 4. 1959;

f) Ob asimptoticheskom raspredelenii sobstvennykh funktsii kolebaniya uprugogo tela (On the Asymptotic Distribution of Eigenfunctions of an Oscillating Elastic Body). — Ibid., Vol. 15, No. 4. 1954.

* [An explanatory list of abbrevations of Soviet institutions and journals follows the bibliography.]

3. VEKUA, I. N.

a) O metagarmonicheskikh funktsiyakh (On Metaharmonic Functions). — Trudy Matematicheskogo Instituta AN Gruz. SSR, Vol. 12. 1943;

b) Obobshchennye analiticheskie funktsii (Generalized Analytic Functions). — Moscow. 1959. [English translation published by Pergamon Press, Oxford. 1962.]

4. WEYL, H.

a) Das asymptotische Verteilungsgesetz der Eigenschwingungen eines beliebig gestalteten elastischen Körpers. — Rend. Circ. Mat. Palermo, Vol. 39. 1915;

b) Kapazität von Strahlungsfeldern. — Mat. Zeits., Vol. 55, No. 2. 1952.

5. GEGELIYA, T. G.

a) O kompozitsii singulyarnykh yader (On the Composition of Singular Kernels). — DAN SSSR, Vol. 135, No. 4. 1960;

b) O formulakh perestanovki poryadka integrirovaniya v povtornykh singulyarnykh integralakh (On the Change of Order of Integration in Double Singular Integrals). — Trudy Matematicheskogo Instituta AN Gruz. SSR, Vol. 28. 1962;

c) Differentsiyal'nye svoistva nekotorykh integral'nykh preobrazovanii (Differential Properties of Some Integral Transforms). — Ibid., Vol. 26. 1959;

d) Svoistva differentsiruemosti reshenii poverkhnostnykh singulyarnykh integral'nykh uravnenii (Differentiability Properties of Solutions of Surface Singular Integral Equations). — Trudy Gruzinskogo Politekhnicheskogo Instituta im. Lenina, No. 1 (81). 1962;

e) O granichnykh znacheniyakh funktsii tipa potentsiala (On Boundary Values of Potential-like Functions). — Trudy Vychislitel'nogo Tsentra AN Gruz. SSR, Vol. 2. 1961;

f) O nekotorykh prostranstvennykh granichnykh zadachakh teorii uprugosti (On Some Three-Dimensional Problems of the Theory of Elasticity). — Trudy Matematicheskogo Instituta AN Gruz. SSR, Vol. 28. 1962.

6. GOGNIASHVILI, Z. M.

a) O sushchestvovanii resheniya odnoi osnovnoi granichnoi zadachi dlya neodnorodnoi uprugoi sredy (On the Existence of Solution of a Certain Fundamental Boundary Value Problem for an Inhomogeneous Elastic Medium). — Trudy Gruzinskogo Politekhnicheskogo Instituta im. Lenina, No. 1 (81). 1962;

b) O nekotorykh teoremakh sushchestvovaniya v teorii neodnorodnykh uprugikh tel (On Some Existence Theorems in the Theory of Inhomogeneous Elastic Bodies). Dissertation. 1963. Library of the Mathematics Institute of the Academy of Sciences, Georgian SSR.

7. GOURSAT, E. Cours d'analyse mathématique, Vol. 3. 1927.

8. GÜNTER, N. M. Die Potenzialtheorie und ihre Anwendung auf Grundlagen der mathematischen Physik. — Leipzig, Teubner. 1957.

9. ITSKOVICH, I. A. Zadacha ekvivalentnosti v teorii dvumernykh singulyarnykh integral'nykh uravnenii (Equivalence Problem in the Theory of Two-Dimensional Singular Integral Equations). — Uchenye Zapiski Kishinevskogo Gosudarstvennogo Universiteta, Vol. 5. 1952.

10. GIRAUD, G.

a) Equations à intégrales principales, étude suivie d'une application. — Ann. Ec. Norm. (3), Vol. 51, fasc. 3. 1934;

b) Equations à intégrales principales, étude suivie d'une application. — Ann. Ec. Norm. (3), Vol. 51, fasc. 4. 1936;

c) Sur une classe générale d'équations a intégrales principales. — Comptes Rendus, Vol. 202, No. 26. 1936.

11. KAKHNIASHVILI, N. S. Issledovanie ploskikh zadach teorii uprugosti metodom teorii potentsiala (Investigation of Plane Problems of the Theory of Elasticity by Potential-Theoretic Methods). — Trudy Tbilisskogo Universiteta, Vol. 50. 1953.

12. KELLOGG, O. D. Foundations of Potential Theory. — Berlin. 1929.

13. KUPRADZE, V. D.

a) Randwertaufgaben der Schwingungstheorie und Integralgleichungen. — Berlin. 1956;

b) Über das Ausstrahlungsprinzip von A. Sommerfeld. — DAN SSSR, No. 2. 1933;

c) Metod integral'nykh uravnenii v teorii difraktsii (Method of Integral Equations in Diffraction Theory). — Matematicheskii Sbornik, Vol. 41, No. 4. 1934;

d) Granichnye zadachi teorii ustanovivshikhsya uprugikh kolebanii (Boundary Value Problems of the Theory of Forced Elastic Oscillations). — Usp. Matem. Nauk, Vol. 8, No. 3 (53). 1953;

e) Nekotorye novye teoremy ob uravnenii kolebaniya i ikh primeneniya v granichnykh zadachakh (Some New Theorems on Oscillation Equations and Their Application to Boundary Value Problems). — Trudy Tbilisskogo Universiteta, Vol. 25a. 1944;

f) Granichnye zadachi teorii uprugosti dlya kusochno-neodnorodnykh uprugikh tel (Boundary Value Problems of the Theory of Elasticity for Piecewise-Homogeneous Elastic Bodies). — Soobshcheniya AN Gruz. SSR, Vol. 22, No. 2, No. 3. 1959;

g) K teorii granichnykh zadach dlya neodnorodnykh uprugikh tel (Concerning the Theory of Boundary Value Problems for Inhomogeneous Elastic Bodies). — Ibid., Vol. 22, No. 4. 1959;

h) O kraevykh zadachakh teorii uprugosti dlya kusochno-neodnorodnykh tel (On Boundary Value Problems of the Theory of Elasticity for Piecewise-Homogeneous Bodies). — Ibid., Vol. 22, No. 5. 1959.

14. KUPRADZE, V. D., and M. O. BASHELEISHVILI. Novye integral'nye uravneniya anizotropnoi teorii uprugosti i ikh primeneniya dlya resheniya granichnykh zadach (New Integral Equations of the Anisotropic Theory of Elasticity and Their Application to the Solution of Boundary Value Problems). — Soobshcheniya AN Gruz. SSR, Vol. 15, Nos. 6 and 7. 1950.

15. KUPRADZE, V. D., and M. A. ALEKSIDZE. Ob odnom priblizhennom metode resheniya nekotorykh granichnykh zadach (On a Method of Approximate Solution of Some Boundary Value Problems). — Ibid., Vol. 30, No. 5. 1963.

16. KINOSHITA, N., and T. MURA. On Boundary Value Problem of Elasticity. — Resp. Rep. Fac. Eng. Meiji Univ., No. 8. 1956.

17. LEKHNITSKII, S. G. Anizotropnye plastinki (Anisotropic Plates). — Moscow. 1957.

18. LEVI, E. Sulle equazioni lineari totalmente ellitiche alle derivate parziali. — Rend. Circ. Mat. Palermo, 24. 1907.

19. LICHTENSTEIN, L. Über die erste Randwertaufgabe der Elastizitättheorie. — Mat. Zeits., Vol. 20. 1934.

20. MESKHI, K. O granichnykh zadachakh dlya anizotropnykh tel (On Boundary — Value Problems for Anisotropic Bodies). — Trudy Vychislitel'nogo Tsentra AN Gruz. SSR, Vol. 2. 1961.

21. MIRANDA, C. Equazioni alle derivate parziali di tipo ellitico. — Berlin. Springer. 1955.

22. MIKHLIN, S. G.

a) Singulyarnye integral'nye uravneniya (Singular Integral Equations). — Usp. Matem. Nauk, Vol. 3 (25). 1948; [English translation published in American Mathematical Society Translations, Series 1, Vol. 10, p. 84];

b) K teorii mnogomernykh singulyarnykh integral'nykh uravnenii (Concerning the Theory of Many-Dimensional Singular Integral Equations). — Vestnik Leningradskogo Universiteta, No. 1. 1956;

c) Mnogomernye singulyarnye integraly i integral'nye uravneniya (Many-Dimensional Singular Integrals and Integral Equations). — Moscow. 1962;

d) Ploskaya deformatsiya v anizotropnoi srede (Plane Strain in an Anisotropic Medium). — Trudy Seismologicheskogo Instituta AN SSSR, No. 76. 1936.

23. MÜLLER, C.

a) Grundprobleme der mathematischen Theorie elektromagnetischen Schwingungen. — Berlin. 1957;

b) Zur Methode der Strahlungskapazität von Weyl. — Mat. Zeits., Vol. 56, No. 1. 1952.

24. MUSKHELISHVILI, N. I.

a) Nekotorye osnovnye zadachi matematciheskoi teorii uprugosti (Some Basic Problems of the Mathematical Theory of Elasticity). — Moscow. 1954. [English translation published by P. Noordhoff. Groningen.]

b) Singulyarnye integral'nye uravneniya (Singular Integral Equations). — Moscow. 1962. [English translation published by P. Noordhoff. Groningen.]

25. NIKOL'SKII, S. M. Kvadraturnye formuly (Quadrature Formulas). — Moscow. 1958.

26. RELLICH, F. Über das asymptotische Verhalten der Lösungen von $\Delta u + \lambda u = 0$ in unendlichen Gebieten. — Jahresbericht d. Deut. Math. Ver., Vol. 53, p. 1, No. 1.

27. RUKHADZE, Zh. A.

a) O kraevykh zadachakh teorii uprugosti dlya kusochno-neodnorodnykh ortotropnykh tel (On the Boundary Value Problems of the Theory of Elasticity for Piecewise-Homogeneous Orthotropic Bodies). — Soobshcheniya AN Gruz. SSR, Vol. 30, No. 1. 1963.

b) O kraevykh zadachakh teorii uprugosti dlya kusochno-neodnorodnykh ortotropnykh tel. Teorema sushchestvovaniya (On Boundary Value Problems of the Theory of Elasticity for Piecewise-Homogeneous Orthotropic Bodies. Existence Theorem). — Ibid., Vol. 30, No. 6. 1963.

28. SAVIN, G. N. Kontsentratsiya napryazhenii okolo otverstii (Stress Concentration around Holes). — Moscow. 1951.

29. SHERMAN, D. I. Ploskaya zadacha teorii uprugosti dlya anizotropnoi sredy (The Plane Problem of the Theory of Elasticity for an Anisotropic Medium). — Trudy Seismologicheskogo Instituta AN SSSR, No. 86. 1938.

30. FICHERA, G. Sull'esistenza e sul calcolo delle soluzioni dei problemi al contorno, relativi all'equilibrio di un corpo elastica. — Ann. d. Sc. Norm. sup. di Pisa, Vol. IV, ser. III, fasc. I-II. 1950.

EXPLANATORY LIST OF ABBREVIATIONS OF U. S. S. R. INSTITUTIONS AND JOURNALS APPEARING IN THE BIBLIOGRAPHY

Abbreviation	Full name (transliterated)	Translation
AN Gruz. SSR	Akademiya Nauk Gruzinskoi SSR	Academy of Sciences of the Georgian SSR
AN SSSR	Akademiya Nauk SSSR	Academy of Sciences of the U.S.S.R.
DAN	Doklady Akademii Nauk SSSR	Reports of the Academy of Sciences of the U.S.S.R.
Usp. Matem. Nauk	Uspekhi Matematicheskikh Nauk	Advances in Mathematical Sciences

AUTHOR INDEX

SUBJECT INDEX

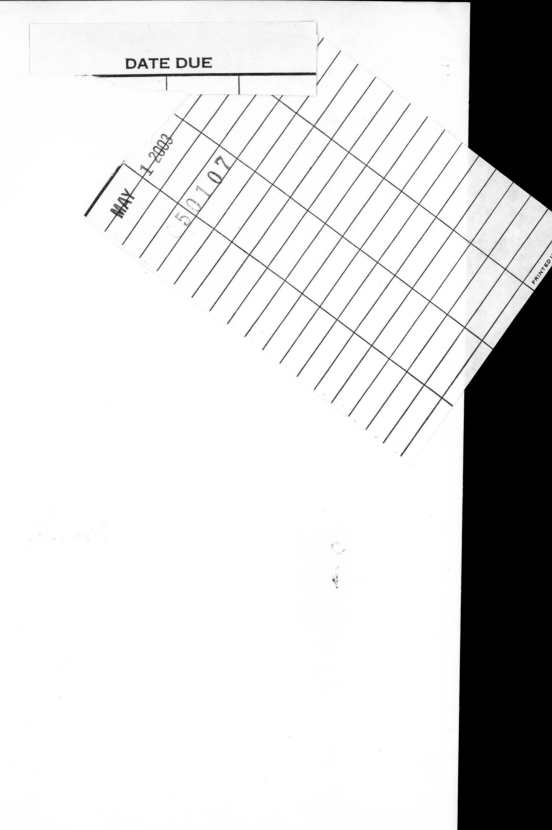